ALL TOGETHER NOW

CW00410465

THE BEATLES COMPLETE

Wise Publications
part of The Music Sales Group
London / New York / Paris / Sydney / Copenhagen / Berlin / Madrid / Tokyo

Published by

Wise Publications
14-15 Berners Street, London W1T 3LJ, UK

Exclusive Distributors:

Music Sales Limited
Distribution Centre, Newmarket Road,
Bury St Edmunds, Suffolk IP33 3YB, UK

Music Sales Pty Limited
20 Resolution Drive,
Caringbah, NSW 2229, Australia

Order No. NO91311
ISBN 978-1-84938-221-2

Music arranged by Frank Booth
Music processed by MSS Studios
Cover designed by Liz Barrand

Printed in the EU

www.musicsales.com

A Day In The Life 201
A Hard Day's Night 64
Across The Universe 268
All I've Got To Do 12
All My Loving 14
All Together Now 271
All You Need Is Love 409
And I Love Her 70
And Your Bird Can Sing 184
Another Girl 122
Any Time At All 67
Ask Me Why 16
Baby You're A Rich Man 218
Baby's In Black 72
Back In The USSR 274
Bad To Me 22
Because 353
Being For The Benefit Of Mr Kite 220
Birthday 276
Blackbird 278
Blue Jay Way 222
Can't Buy Me Love 74
Carry That Weight 354
Come Together 356
Cry Baby Cry 282
Day Tripper 124
Dear Prudence 284
Dig A Pony 394
Dig It 381
Do You Want To Know A Secret? 24
Doctor Robert 186
Don't Bother Me 19
Don't Let Me Down 358
Don't Pass Me By 287
Drive My Car 126
Eight Days A Week 76
Eleanor Rigby 188
Every Little Thing 78
Everybody's Got Something To Hide
Except Me And My Monkey 290
Fixing A Hole 224
Flying 292
For No One 190
For You Blue 397
From A Window 80
From Me To You 26
Get Back 360
Getting Better 227
Girl 128
Give Peace A Chance 361
Glass Onion 294
Golden Slumbers 362
Good Day Sunshine 192
Good Morning, Good Morning 230
Goodbye 364
Goodnight 293
Got To Get You Into My Life 177
Happiness Is A Warm Gun 296
Hello Goodbye 233
Hello Little Girl 28
Help! 130
Helter Skelter 299
Her Majesty 365
Here Comes The Sun 366
Here, There And Everywhere 194
Hey Bulldog 302
Hey Jude 398
Hold Me Tight 60

Honey Pie 304
I Am The Walrus 236
I Call Your Name 30
I Don't Want To See You Again 89
I Don't Want To Spoil The Party 82
' Feel Fine 84
I Me Mine 400
I Need You 132
I Saw Her Standing There 32
I Should Have Known Better 86
I Wanna Be Your Man 88
I Want To Hold Your Hand 34
I Want To Tell You 196
I Want You 368
I Will 310
I'll Be Back 90
I'll Be On My Way 63
I'll Cry Instead 92
I'll Follow The Sun 94
I'll Get You 36
I'll Keep You Satisfied 38
I'm A Loser 96
I'm Down 134
I'm Happy Just To Dance With You 98
I'm In Love 40
I'm Looking Through You 113
I'm Only Sleeping 198
I'm So Tired 312
I've Got A Feeling 402
I've Just Seen A Face 136
If I Fell 100
If I Needed Someone 138
In My Life 140
It Won't Be Long 42
It's All Too Much 307
It's For You 95
It's Only Love 142
Julia 314
Lady Madonna 316
Let It Be 406
Like Dreamers Do 102
Little Child 44
Long Long Long 318
Love Me Do 6
Love Of The Loved 46
Love You To 200
Lovely Rita 242
Lucy In The Sky With Diamonds 244
Maggie Mae 420
Magical Mystery Tour 246
Martha My Dear 320
Maxwell's Silver Hammer 370
Mean Mr Mustard 372
Michelle 144
Misery 48
Mother Nature's Son 323
No Reply 104
Nobody I Know 106
Norwegian Wood 146
Not A Second Time 56
Nowhere Man 148
Ob-La-Di, Ob-La-Da 324
Octopus's Garden 373
Oh! Darling 376
Old Brown Shoe 378
One After 909 412
Only A Northern Song 330
Oo You 216

P.S. I Love You 8
Paperback Writer 204
Penny Lane 239
Piggies 332
Please Please Me 10
Polythene Pam 382
Power To The People 217
Rain 206
Revolution 334
Rocky Raccoon 336
Run For Your Life 150
Savoy Truffle 327
Sexy Sadie 340
Sgt. Pepper's Lonely Hearts Club Band 248
She Came In Through The Bathroom Window 384
She Loves You 50
She Said She Said 208
She's A Woman 107
She's Leaving Home 251
Something 386
Step Inside Love 342
Strawberry Fields Forever 254
Sun King 396
Taxman 210
Tell Me What You See 143
Tell Me Why 108
Thank You Girl 52
That Means A Lot 152
The Ballad Of John And Yoko 414
The Continuing Story Of Bungalow Bill 280
The End 388
The Fool On The Hill 256
The Inner Light 344
The Long And Winding Road 416
The Night Before 154
The Word 156
There's A Place 54
Things We Said Today 110
Think For Yourself 158
This Boy 58
Ticket To Ride 160
Tip Of My Tongue 62
Tomorrow Never Knows 212
Two Of Us 390
Wait 162
We Can Work It Out 164
What Goes On? 166
What You're Doing 112
When I Get Home 116
When I'm Sixty Four 258
While My Guitar Gently Weeps 346
Why Don't We Do It In The Road? 348
Wild Honey Pie 343
With A Little Help From My Friends 261
Within You Without You 264
World Without Love 118
Yellow Submarine 214
Yer Blues 350
Yes It Is 168
Yesterday 170
You Can't Do That 120
You Know My Name (Look Up The Number) 418
You Like Me Too Much 172
You Never Give Me Your Money 392
You Won't See Me 174
You're Going To Lose That Girl 180
You've Got To Hide Your Love Away 182
Your Mother Should Know 266

Love Me Do.

WORDS & MUSIC BY JOHN LENNON & PAUL McCARTNEY.

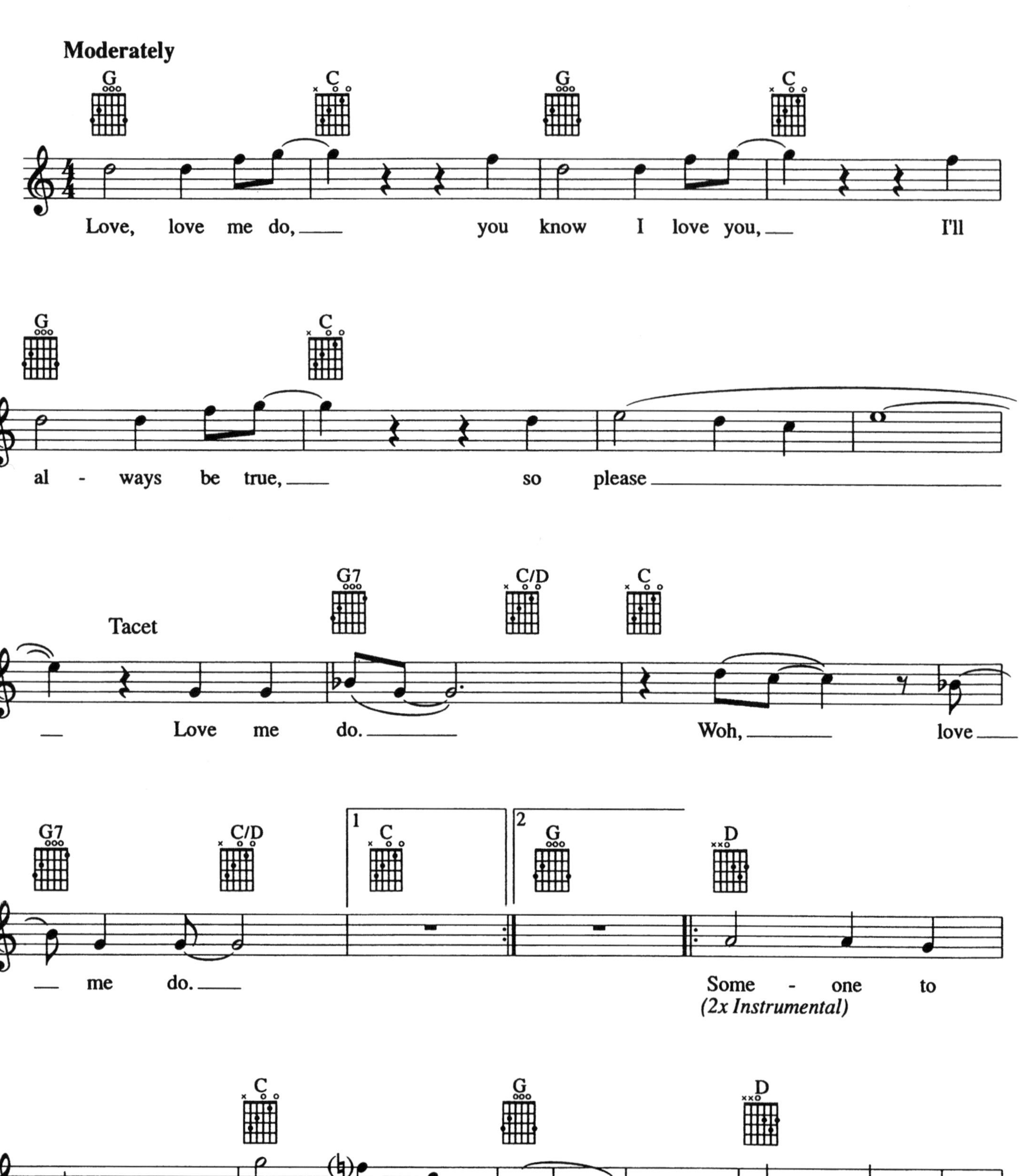
Moderately
G C G C
Love, love me do, you know I love you, I'll
G C
al - ways be true, so please
Tacet
G7 C/D C
Love me do. Woh, love
G7 C/D 1 C 2 G D
me do. Some - one to
(2x Instrumental)
C G D
love, Some - bod - y new. Some - one to

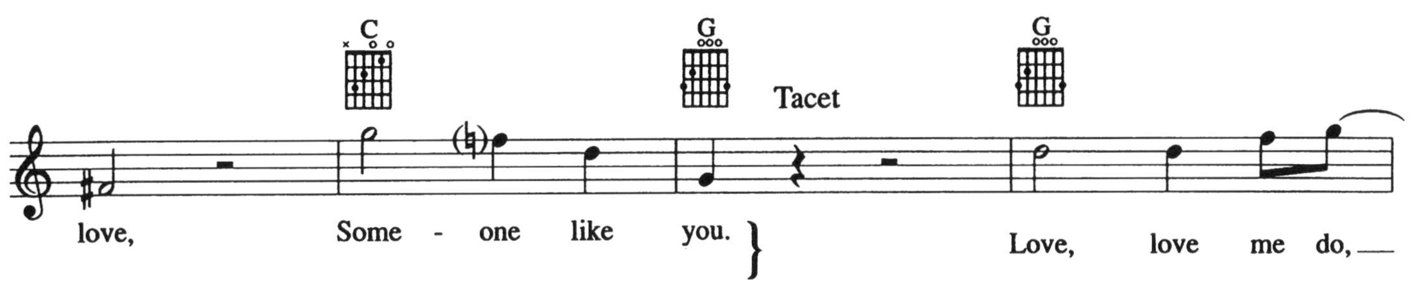
C
G
Tacet
G
love, Some - one like you. }
Love, love me do,

C
G
C
you know I love you,
I'll

G
C
Tacet
al - ways be true, so please
Love me

G7
C/D
C
1
G7
C/D
do. Woh, love me do.

G
2
C
G7
C/D
Repeat and Fade
Woh, love me do.

P.S. I Love You.

Words & Music by John Lennon & Paul McCartney.

Moderately Bright
Em7 C#7 D Em7 C#7 D
As I write this let - ter, send my love to you. Re-
Em7 C#7 D D/A A7 D
- mem - ber that I'll al - ways be in love with you.
Em7 D
Trea - sure these few words 'till we're to - geth - er, Keep
A7 Bm7 A A7 B♭
all my love for - ev - er; P. S. I love you.
C7 D D
you, you, you.
1-3. I'll be com - ing
2. Treas - ure these few
Em7 D A7 Bm7
home a - gain to you, love Un - til the day I do love,
words 'till we're to - geth - er, Keep all my love for - ev - er,

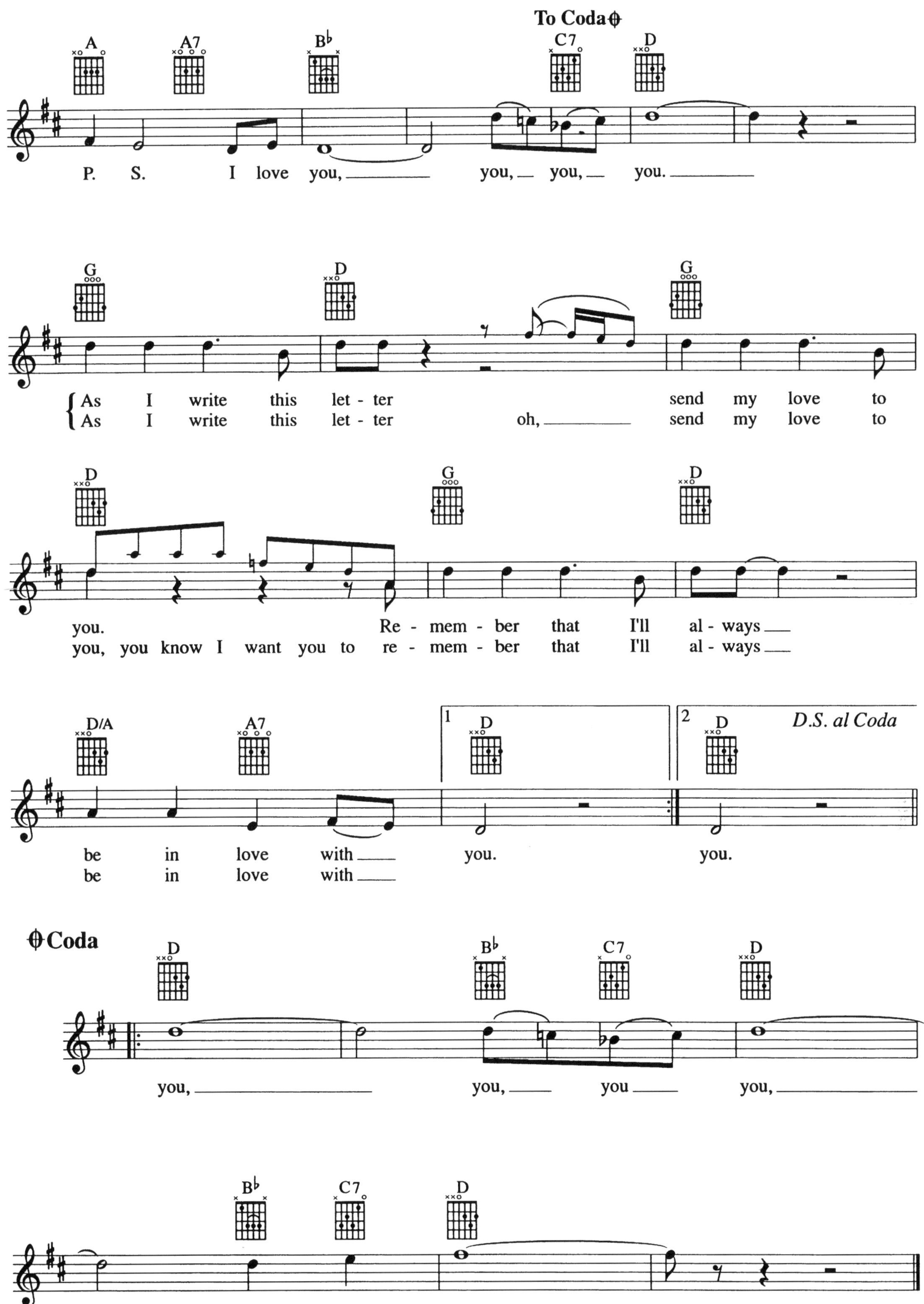
To Coda
A A7 B♭ C7 D
P. S. I love you, you, you, you.
G D G
As I write this let - ter send my love to
As I write this let - ter oh, send my love to
D G D
you. Re - mem - ber that I'll al - ways
you, you know I want you to re - mem - ber that I'll al - ways
D/A A7 D D
D.S. al Coda
be in love with you. you.
be in love with
Coda
D B♭ C7 D
you, you, you you,
B♭ C7 D
I love you.

Please Please Me.

Words & Music by John Lennon & Paul McCartney.

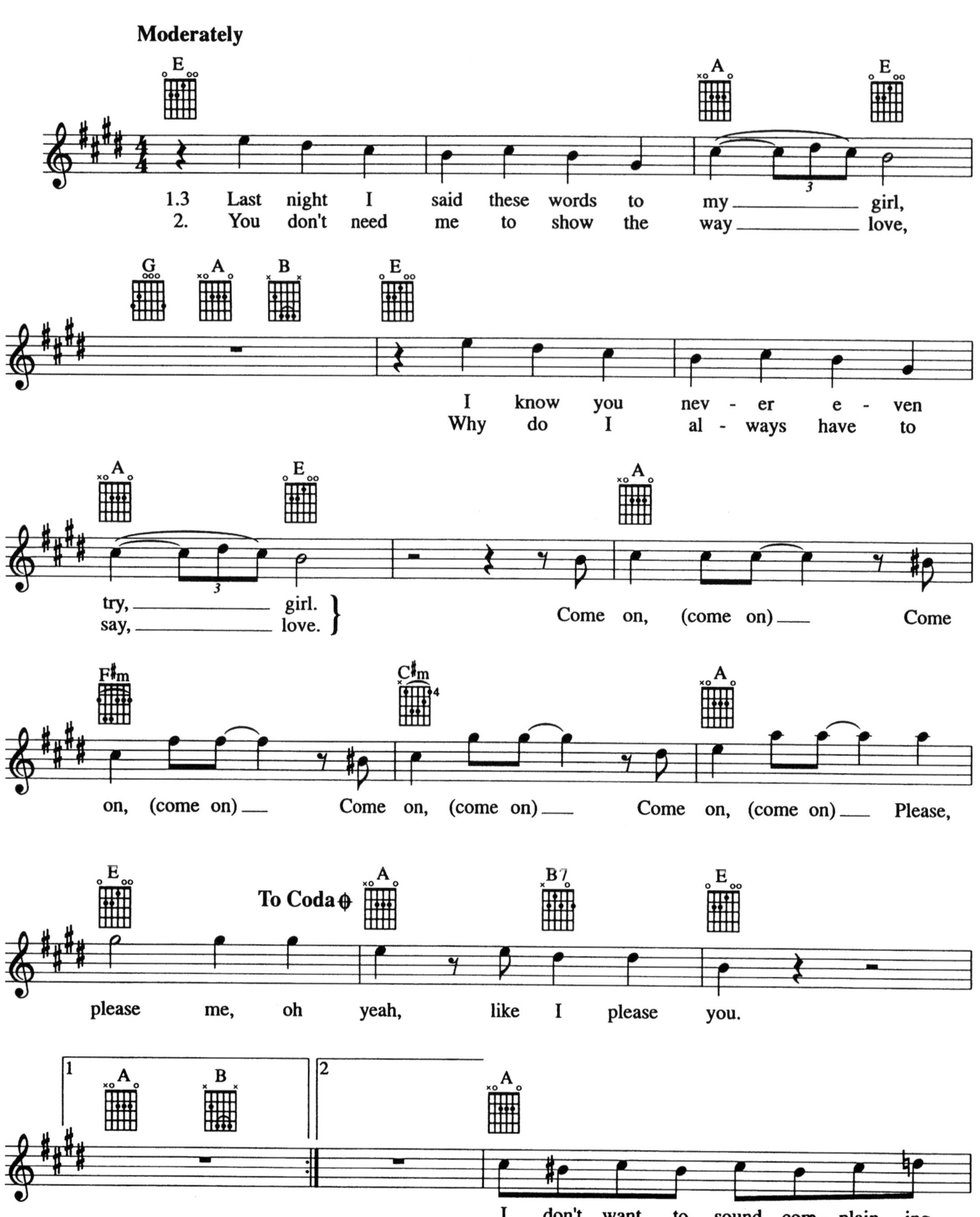
Moderately
E
A
E
1.3 Last night I said these words to my girl,
2. You don't need me to show the way love,
G
A
B
E
I know you never even try, girl.
Why do I always have to say, love.
A
E
A
Come on, (come on) Come on, (come on) Come on, (come on) Come on, (come on) Please,
F♯m
C♯m
A
E
To Coda
A
B7
E
please me, oh yeah, like I please you.
1
A
B
2
A
I don't want to sound com - plain - ing

B7
E
but you know there's al - ways rain in my heart.

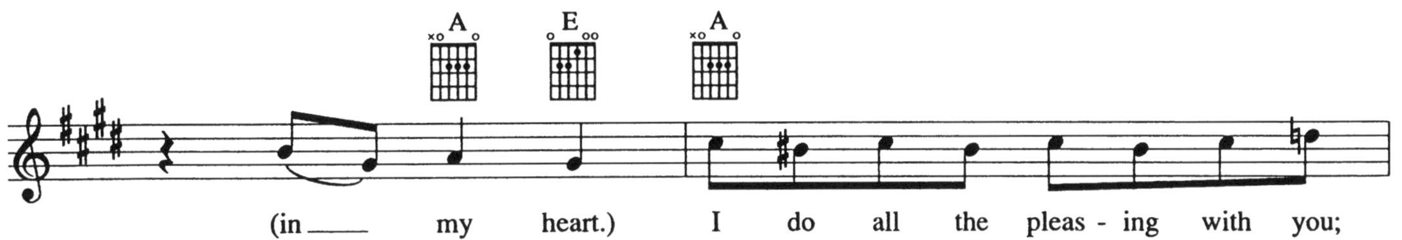
A
E
A
(in my heart.) I do all the pleas - ing with you;

B7
E
It's so hard to reas - on with you. oh

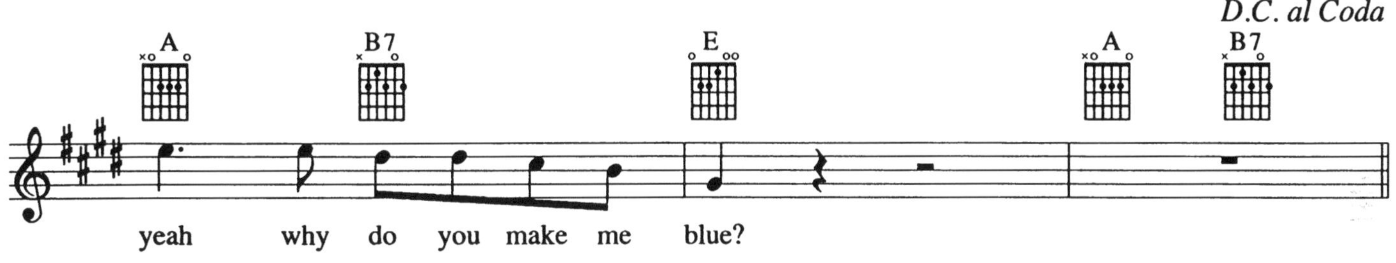
D.C. al Coda
A
B7
E
A
B7
yeah why do you make me blue?

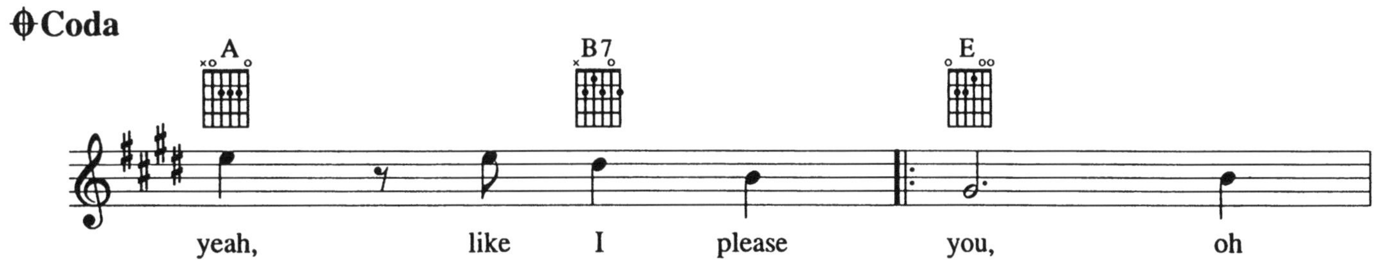
Coda
A
B7
E
yeah, like I please you, oh

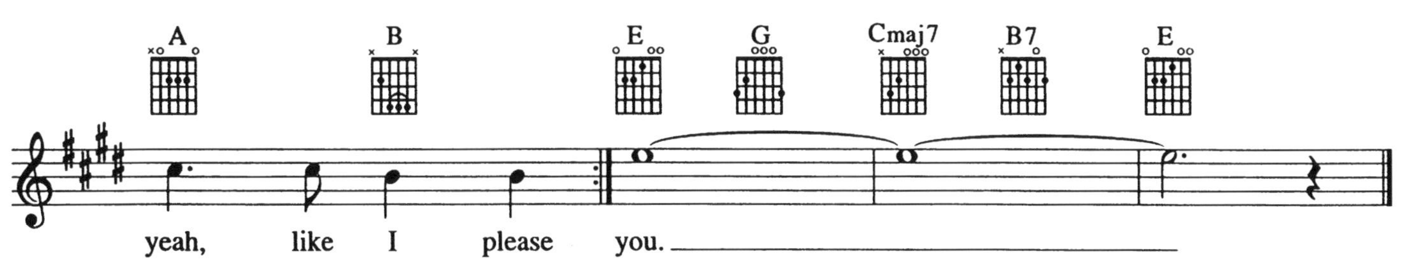
A
B
E
G
Cmaj7
B7
E
yeah, like I please you.

All I've Got To Do.

Words & Music by John Lennon & Paul McCartney.

Moderately
C#m
1. When - ev - er I want you a - round, yeah, All I got - ta do is call you on the phone and you'll come run - ning home, Yeah
I, I wan - na kiss you, yeah, All I got - ta do is whis - per in your ear the words you long to hear And
I, I wan - na kiss you, yeah, All I got - ta do is call you on the phone and you'll come run - ning home, Yeah
E
F#m
Am
1
that's all I got - ta do.
Tacet
2. And when
2.3
I'll be kis - sin' you.
that's all I got - ta do.
And the same goes for

A
C♯m
me when - ev - er you want me at all,
I'll be here, yes I will, when -

A
E
ev - er you call;
You just got - ta call on me,
yeah,
you

A
To Coda
E
D.S. al Coda
Tacet
just got - ta call on me.
3. And when

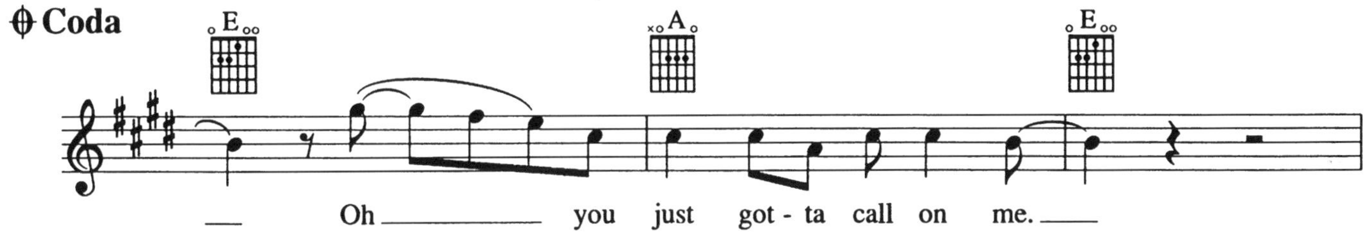
Coda
E
A
E
Oh
you just got - ta call on me.

Tacet
C♯m
E
Mm - mm - mm
mm

C♯m
E
mm
mm.

All My Loving.

Words & Music by John Lennon & Paul McCartney.

Brightly, with a beat
F♯m7 B9 E
1. Close your eyes and I'll kiss you, To - mor - row I'll miss
- tend that I'm kiss - ing, The lips I am miss -
C♯m A F♯m D
you; Re - mem - ber I'll al - ways be true.
- ing And hope that my dreams will come true.
B7 F♯m B7 E
And then while I'm a - way I'll write home ev - 'ry day
C♯m A B7 1 E Tacet
And I'll send all my lov - ing to you. 2. I'll pre -
2 E Tacet C♯m C+
you. All my lov - ing I will send to

E
C♯m
C+
To Coda
you,
All
my
lov - ing
dar - ling, I'll
be true.

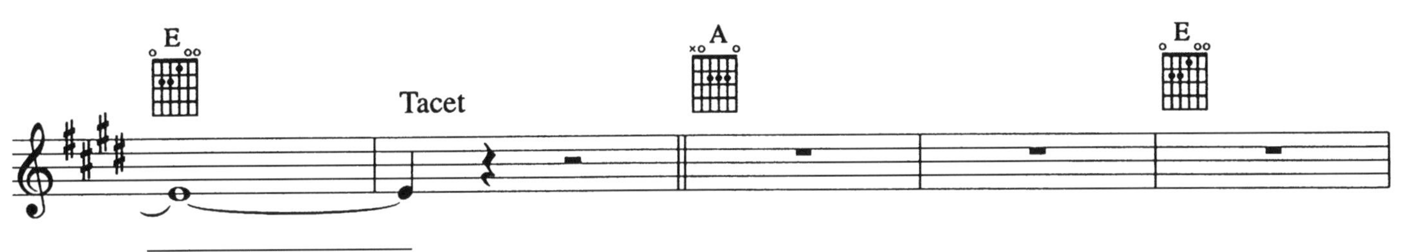
E
Tacet
A
E

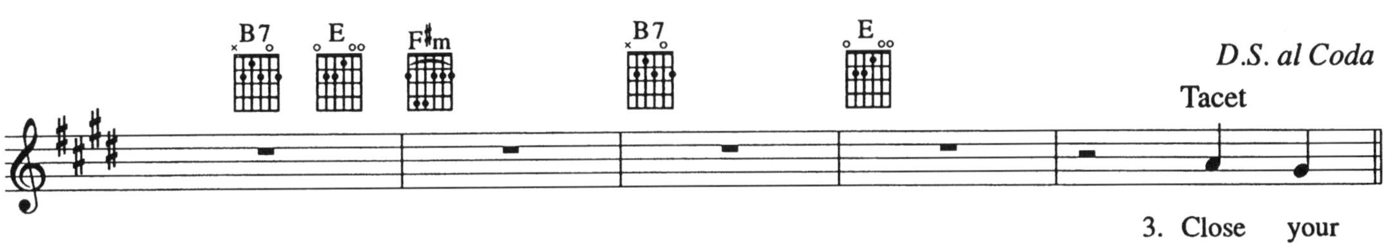
B7
E
F♯m
B7
E
D.S. al Coda
Tacet
3. Close your

Coda

E
C♯m
All
my
lov - ing,

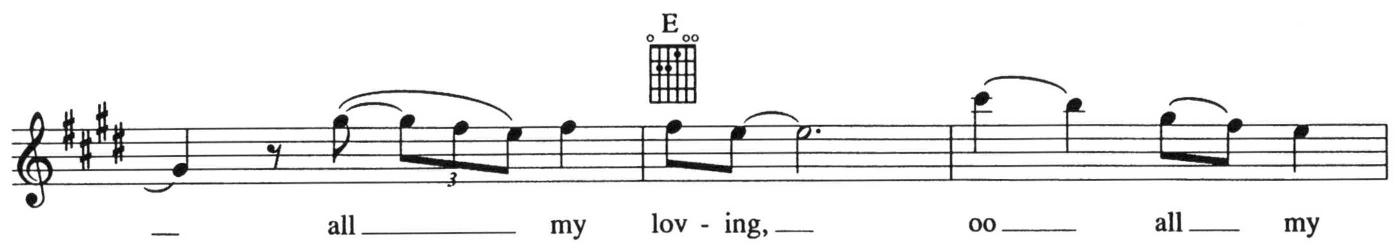
E
all
my
lov - ing,
oo
all
my

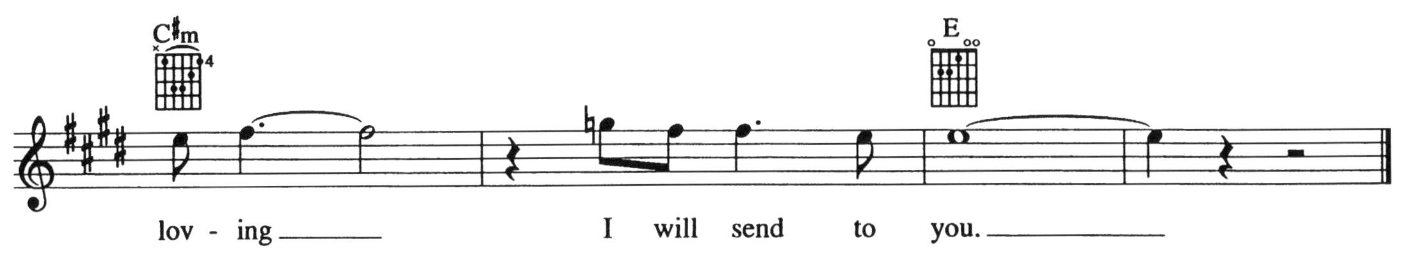
C♯m
E
lov - ing
I will send to you.

Ask Me Why.

Words & Music by John Lennon & Paul McCartney.

Moderately
B♭ E♭ Fm7 Gm7 Fm7
I love you, 'cause you tell me things I
E♭ Fm7 Gm7 Fm7
want to know. And it's true that it real - ly on - ly
E♭ G7 Cm
goes to show That I know that I, I, I, I, Should
A♭m F9 B♭7 E♭ Fm7
To Coda
nev - er, nev - er, nev - er, be blue.
Now you're
Ask me
Gm7 Fm7 E♭
mi - ne, my hap - pi - ness still makes me cry.
Fm7 Gm7 Fm7
And in ti - me, you'll un - der - stand the

E♭
G7
Cm
rea - son why
If I cry,
it's not be - cause I'm sad,
A♭m
E♭
But you're the on - ly love that I've ev - er had.
E♭+
A♭
B♭7
I can't be - lieve
it's hap - pened to
E♭
E♭+
A♭
me,
I can't con - ceive
B♭7
E♭
Tacet
E♭
Fm7
of an - y more
mis - er - y.
Ask me
Gm7
A♭
Gm7
why,
I'll say I love you,
And I'm al - ways think - ing of
A♭maj7
E♭
Fm7
D.S. al Coda
you, oo - oo - oo
I love

Coda
Gm7
A♭
Gm7
why; I'll say I love you, And I'm al - ways think - ing of
A♭maj7
E♭
E♭+
you, oo - oo - oo. I can't be -
A♭
B♭7
E♭
- lieve it's hap - pened to me,
E♭+
A♭
B♭7
I can't con - ceive of an - y more
E♭
Tacet
Fm7
Gm7
mis - er - y. Ask me why, I'll say I
A♭
Gm7
A♭maj7
love you, And I'm al - ways think - ing of you, oo - oo - oo
E♭
A♭maj7
E♭
A♭maj7
E♭
E♭maj7
you, oo - oo - oo you, oo - oo - oo oo.

Don't Bother Me.

Words & Music by George Harrison.

Moderate Rock
Bm
A
Since she's been gone I want no - one to talk to me.
that she would leave me on my own.
G
Em
Bm
It's not the same, but I'm to blame
It's just not right when ev - 'ry night
A
G
Tacet
Em
it's plain to see, So go a - way, leave me a - lone,
I'm all a - lone, I've got no time for you right now,
A
Em
1
don't both - er me. I can't be - lieve
don't both - er me.
2
Em
D
Em
I know I'll nev - er be the same.

D
Em
If I don't get her back a - gain,

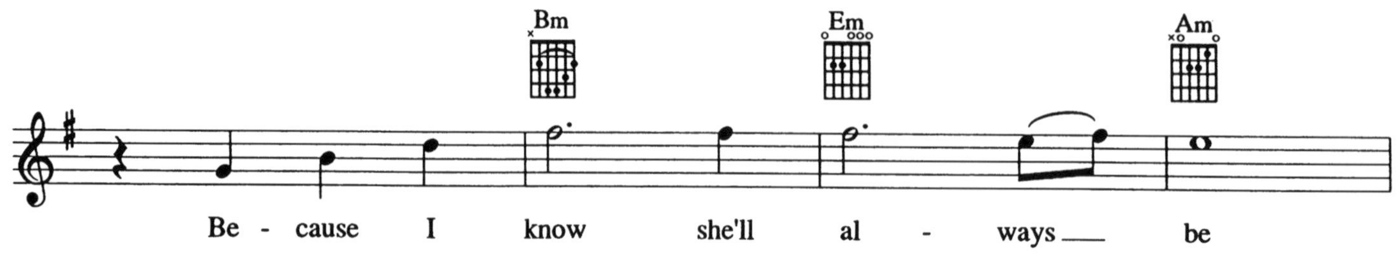
Bm
Em
Am
Be - cause I know she'll al - ways be

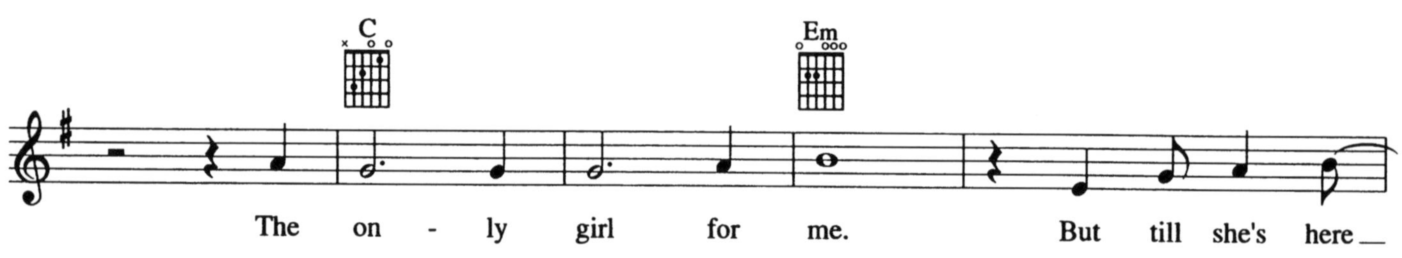
C
Em
The on - ly girl for me. But till she's here

Bm
A
G
please don't come near, just stay a - way,

Em
A
I'll let you know when she's come home. Un - til that

G
Em
A
Tacet
day, don't come a - round, leave me a - lone, don't both - er me.

Em
To Coda
Tacet
Em
A
I've got no time for you right now,

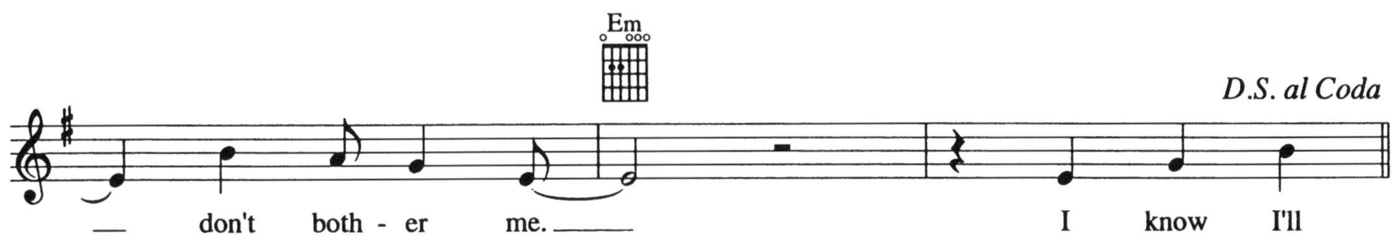
Em
D.S. al Coda
don't both - er me. I know I'll

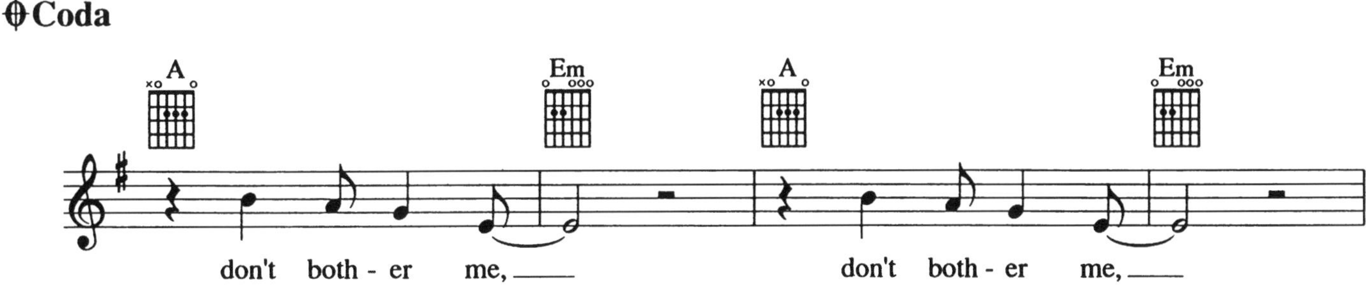
Coda
A
Em
A
Em
don't both - er me, don't both - er me,

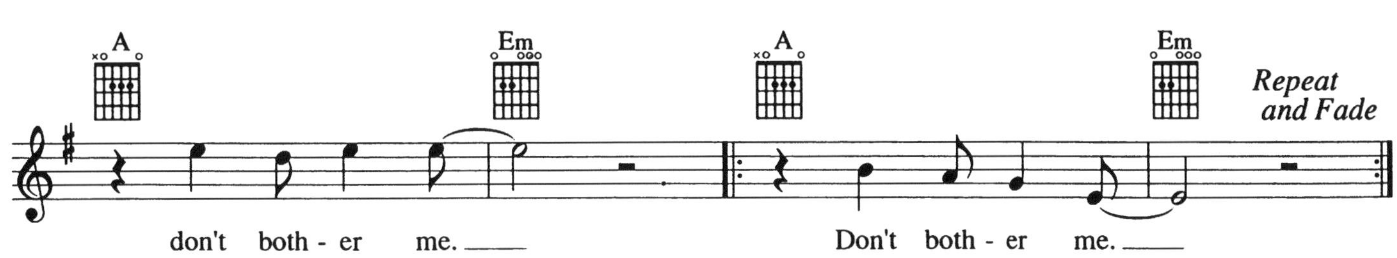
A
Em
A
Em
Repeat and Fade
don't both - er me. Don't both - er me.

Bad To Me.

WORDS & MUSIC BY JOHN LENNON & PAUL McCARTNEY.

Moderately
D F♯m/C♯ Bm
The birds in the sky would be sad and lone - ly if they
leaves in the trees would be soft - ly sigh - in' if they
D F♯m/C♯ Bm
knew that I lost my one and on - ly; They'd be
heard from the breeze that you left me cry - in'; They'd be
G A7 D 1 F♯m A7
sad, don't be bad to me. The
sad, don't be bad to me.
2 D G A7
But I know you won't leave me, 'cause you told me so and
F♯m B7 Em
I've no in - ten - tions of let - ting you go, just as long as you

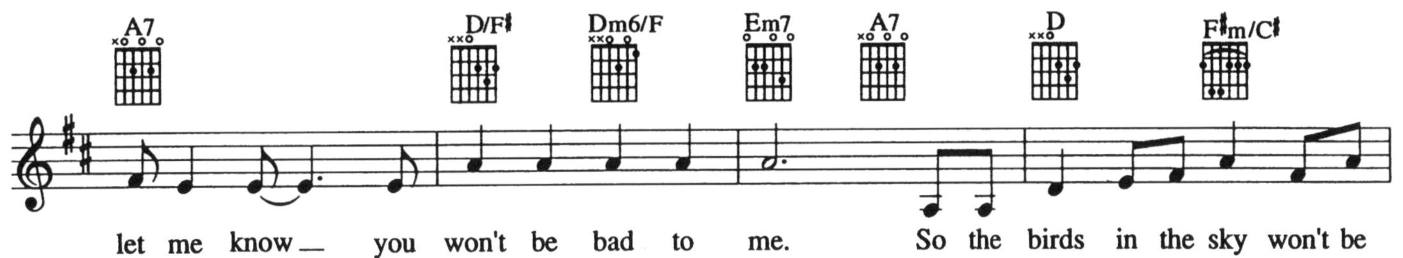
A7
D/F♯
Dm6/F
Em7
A7
D
F♯m/C♯
let me know — you won't be bad to me. So the birds in the sky won't be

Bm
D
F♯m/C♯
Bm
sad and lone - ly 'cos they know that — I got my one and on - ly, they'll be

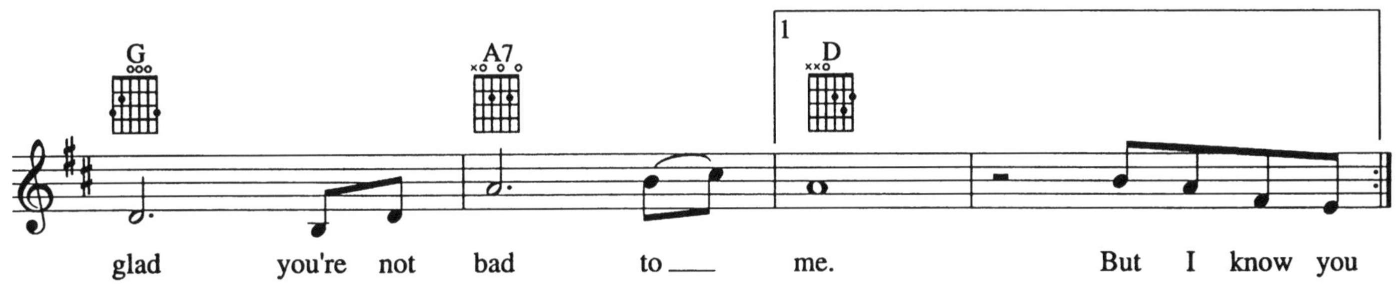
G
A7
1
D
glad you're not bad to — me. But I know you

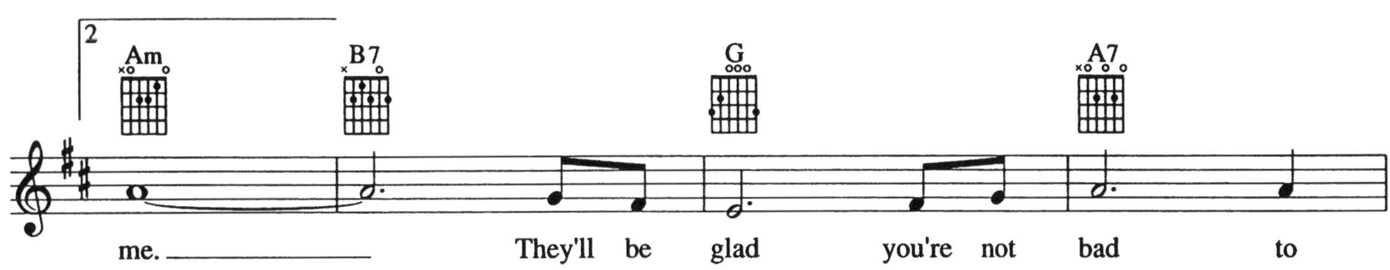
2
Am
B7
G
A7
me. — They'll be glad you're not bad to

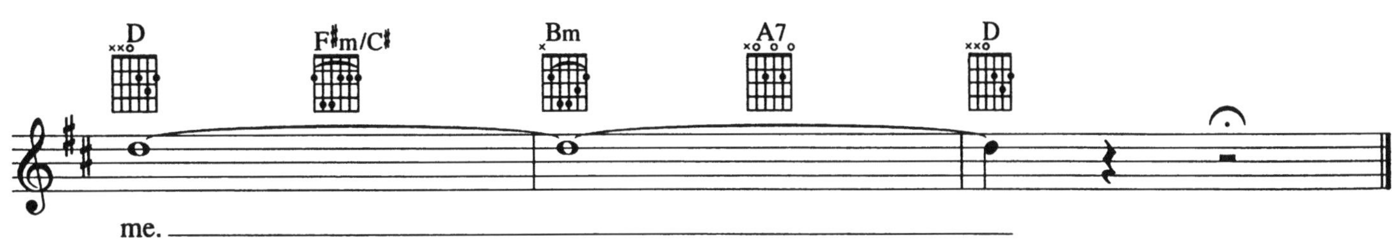
D
F♯m/C♯
Bm
A7
D
me. —

Do You Want To Know A Secret?

Words & Music by John Lennon & Paul McCartney.

Freely
Em Am Em
You'll nev - er know how much I real - ly love you,
G F B7
You'll nev - er know how much I real - ly care.
a tempo (moderately)
E G♯m Gm F♯m B7 E G♯m Gm
Lis - ten, do you want to know a sec - ret?
F♯m B7 E G♯m Gm F♯m7 B7♭9
Do you prom - ise not to tell? Wo, wo,
E G♯m Gm F♯m B7 E G♯m Gm
Clos - er, let me whis - per in your ear,

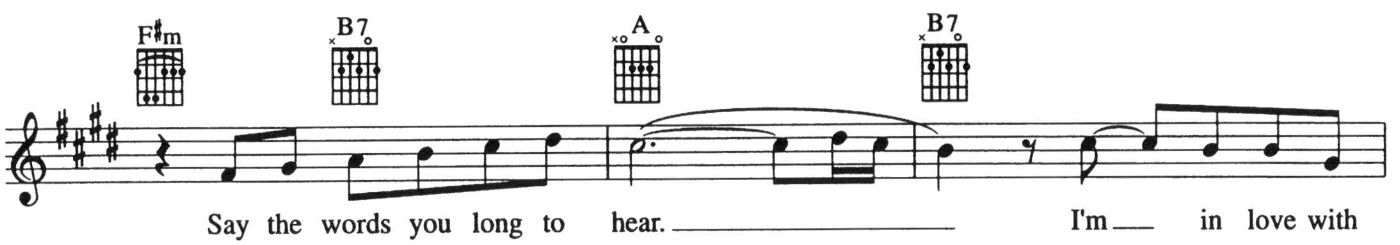
F#m
B7
A
B7
Say the words you long to hear.
I'm in love with

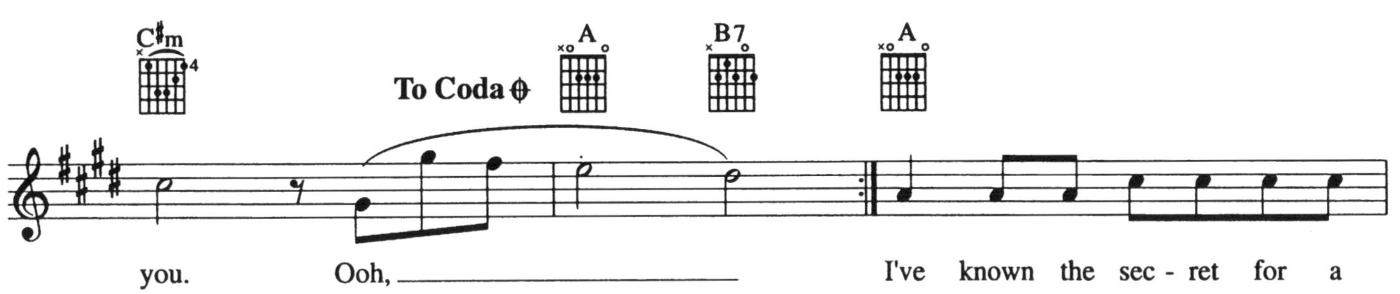
C#m
To Coda
A
B7
A
you. Ooh,
I've known the sec - ret for a

C#m
Bm
A
F#m
C#m
Bm
week or two,
No - bod - y knows,
just we two.

F#m
B7
D.S. al Coda
Coda
A
B7

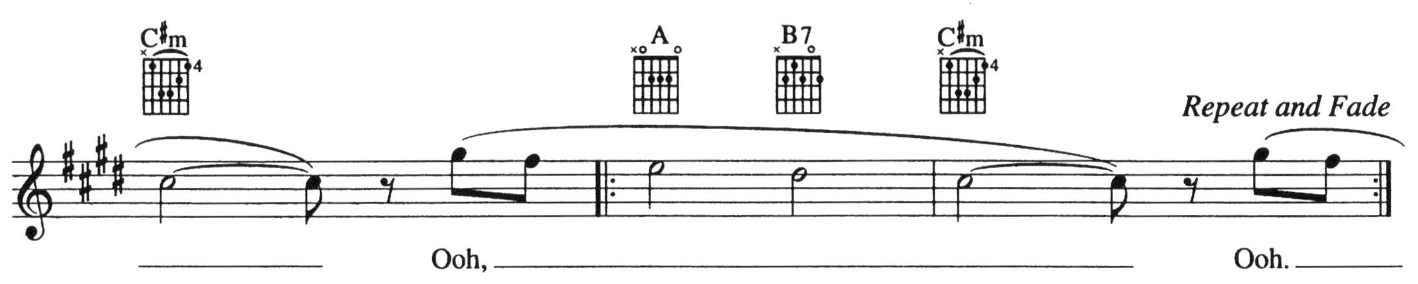
C#m
A
B7
C#m
Repeat and Fade
Ooh,
Ooh.

From Me To You.

Words & Music by John Lennon & Paul McCartney.

Moderately

C Am C

Da da da da da dum dum da, Da da da da da dum dum

Am C Am

da. 1. If there's an - y - thing that you want, If there's
(2) ev - 'ry - thing that you want, Like a

C G F7

an - y - thing I can do,
heart that's oh so true,
Just call on me and I'll

Am C G7 1 C Am

send it a - long with love from me to you. 2. I've got

2
C
Gm7
C7
I've got arms that long to hold you, and

F C7 F Am7 D7
keep you by my side. I've got lips that long to kiss you and

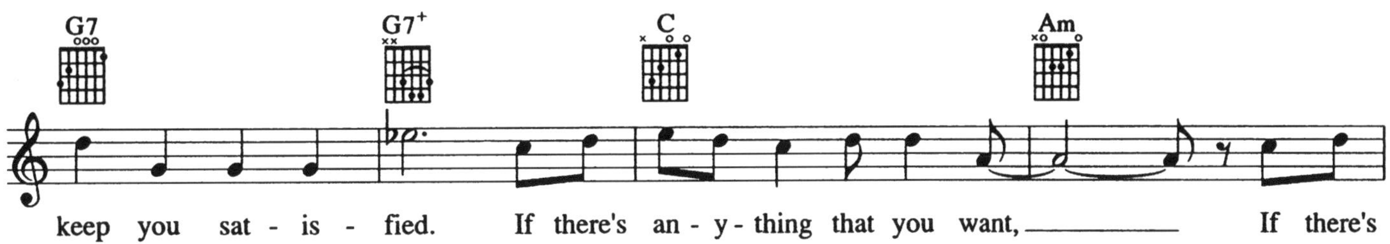
G7 G7+ C Am
keep you sat - is - fied. If there's an - y - thing that you want, If there's

C G F7
an - y - thing I can do, Just call on me and I'll

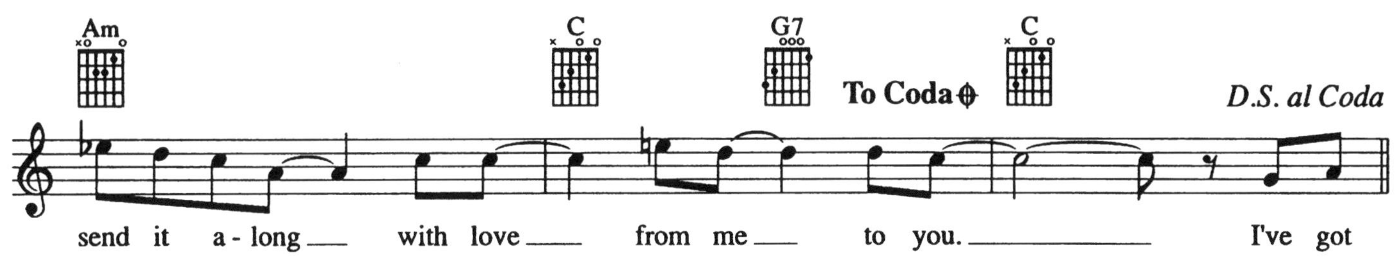
Am C G7 C
To Coda
D.S. al Coda
send it a - long with love from me to you. I've got

Coda
C Am A♭+ C Am
To you, to you, to you.

Hello Little Girl.

Words & Music by John Lennon & Paul McCartney.

Moderately
G Em C D G Em
Hel - lo lit - tle girl, girl.
C D G C D7
1. When I (3) see you ev - 'ry - day I say mm - mm
(2) see you pas - sing by I cry mm - mm
C D7 G G
Hel - lo lit - tle girl. When you're pas - sing on your way I say
Hel - lo lit - tle girl. When I try to catch your eye I cry
C D7 C D7 1 G
mm - mm Hel - lo lit - tle girl. 2. If I
mm - mm Hel - lo lit - tle girl.
2.3. G Em C D7
I send you flow - ers, but, you don't care.
It's not the first time it's hap - pened to me,

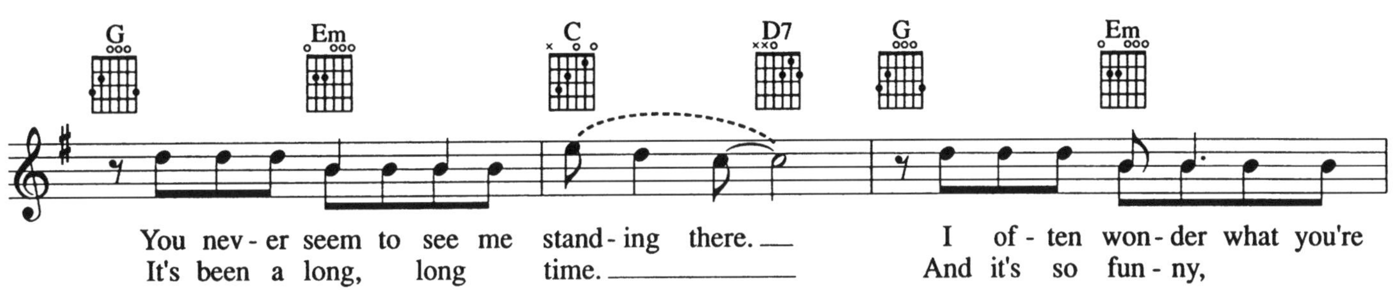
G Em C D7 G Em
You nev - er seem to see me stand - ing there. I of - ten won - der what you're
It's been a long, long time. And it's so fun - ny,

C D7 G Em Am G D7
think - ing of, I hope it's me, love, love, love.
fun - ny to see, That I'm a - bout to lose my mi - mi - mind.
So I

G C D7
hope there'll come a day when you'll say mm - mm.

C D7 To Coda G
D.S. al Coda
You're my lit - tle girl. (3) When I

Coda
G Am7 D7 G
Repeat and Fade
you're my lit - tle girl.

I Call Your Name.

Words & Music by John Lennon & Paul McCartney.

Moderately
E♭7
C7
I call your name, but you're not there,
F7
B♭7
Was I to blame for be - in' un - fair?
E♭7
Oh, I can't sleep at night Since you've been gone,
C7
F7
A♭
I nev - er weep at night, I can't go on.
E♭
E♭7
A♭7
Don't you know I can't take it?
Cm
I don't know who can. I'm not goin' to

F7
C♭
ma - ya - yake it,
I'm not that kind of man.

B♭
E♭7
Oh, I can't sleep at night,
But just the same,

C7
F7
To Coda
I nev - er weep at night,

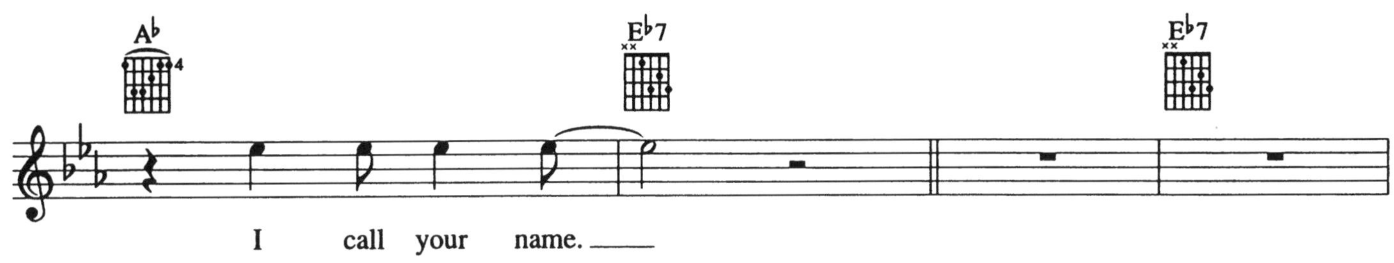
A♭
E♭7
E♭7
I call your name.

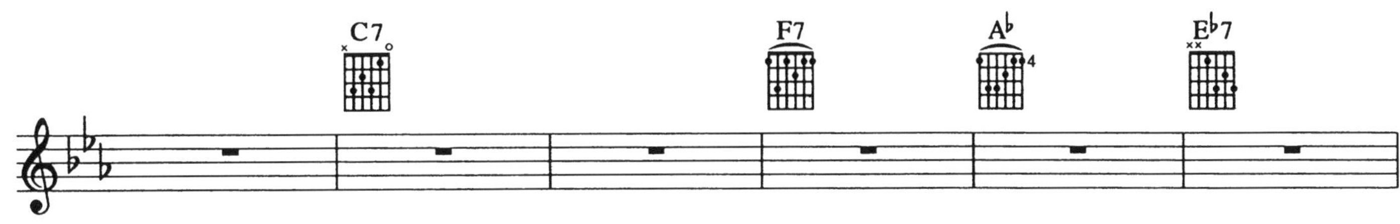
C7
F7
A♭
E♭7

D.S. al Coda
Don't you know I can't
Coda
A♭
E♭
Repeat and Fade
I call your name.

I Saw Her Standing There.

Words & Music by John Lennon & Paul McCartney.

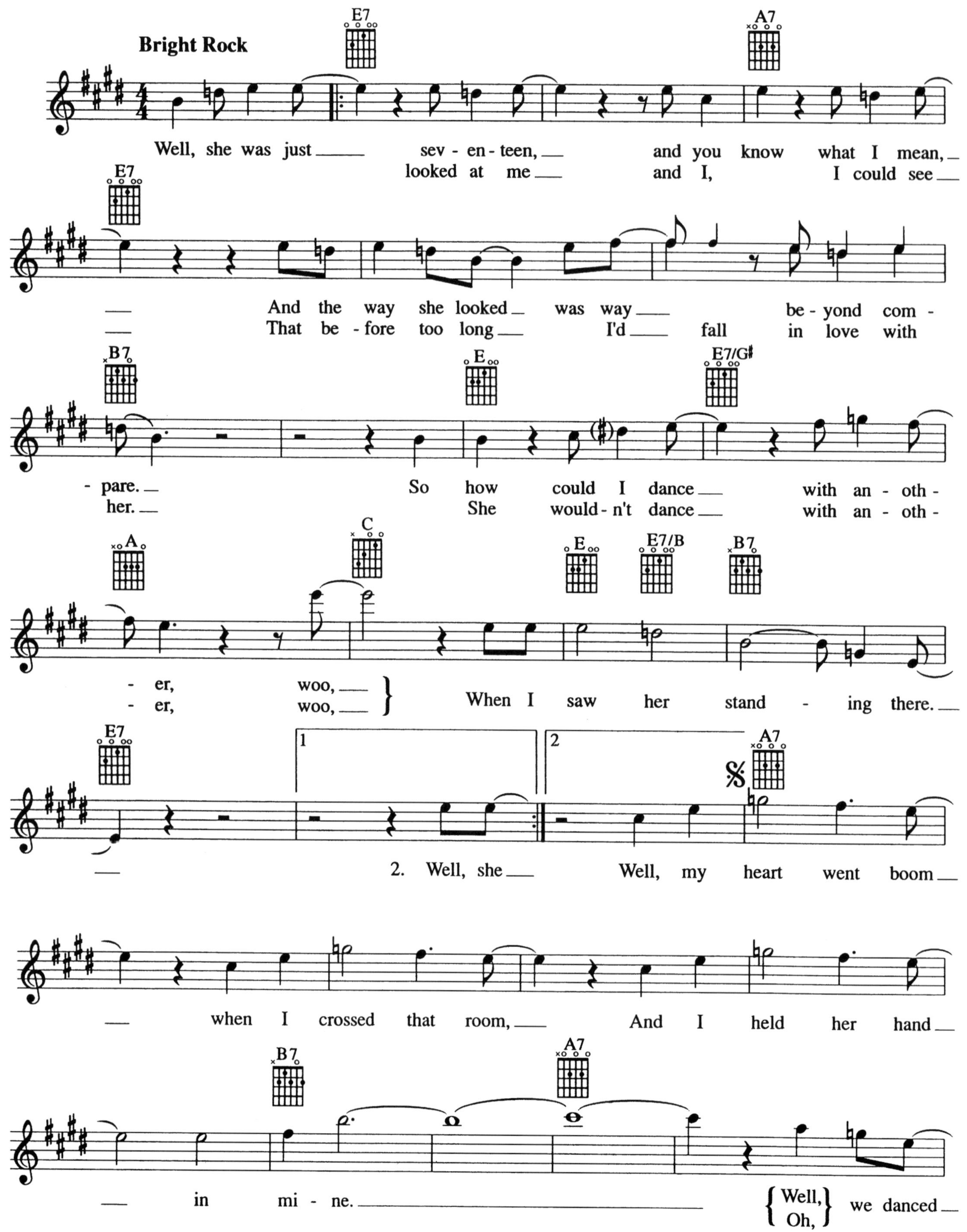
Bright Rock
E7
A7
Well, she was just sev - en - teen, and you know what I mean,
looked at me and I, I could see
E7
And the way she looked was way be - yond com -
That be - fore too long I'd fall in love with
B7
E
E7/G♯
- pare. So how could I dance with an - oth -
her. She would - n't dance with an - oth -
A
C
E
E7/B
B7
- er, woo,
- er, woo,
When I saw her stand - ing there.
E7
1
2
A7
2. Well, she
Well, my heart went boom
when I crossed that room, And I held her hand
B7
A7
in mi - ne.
Well, we danced
Oh,

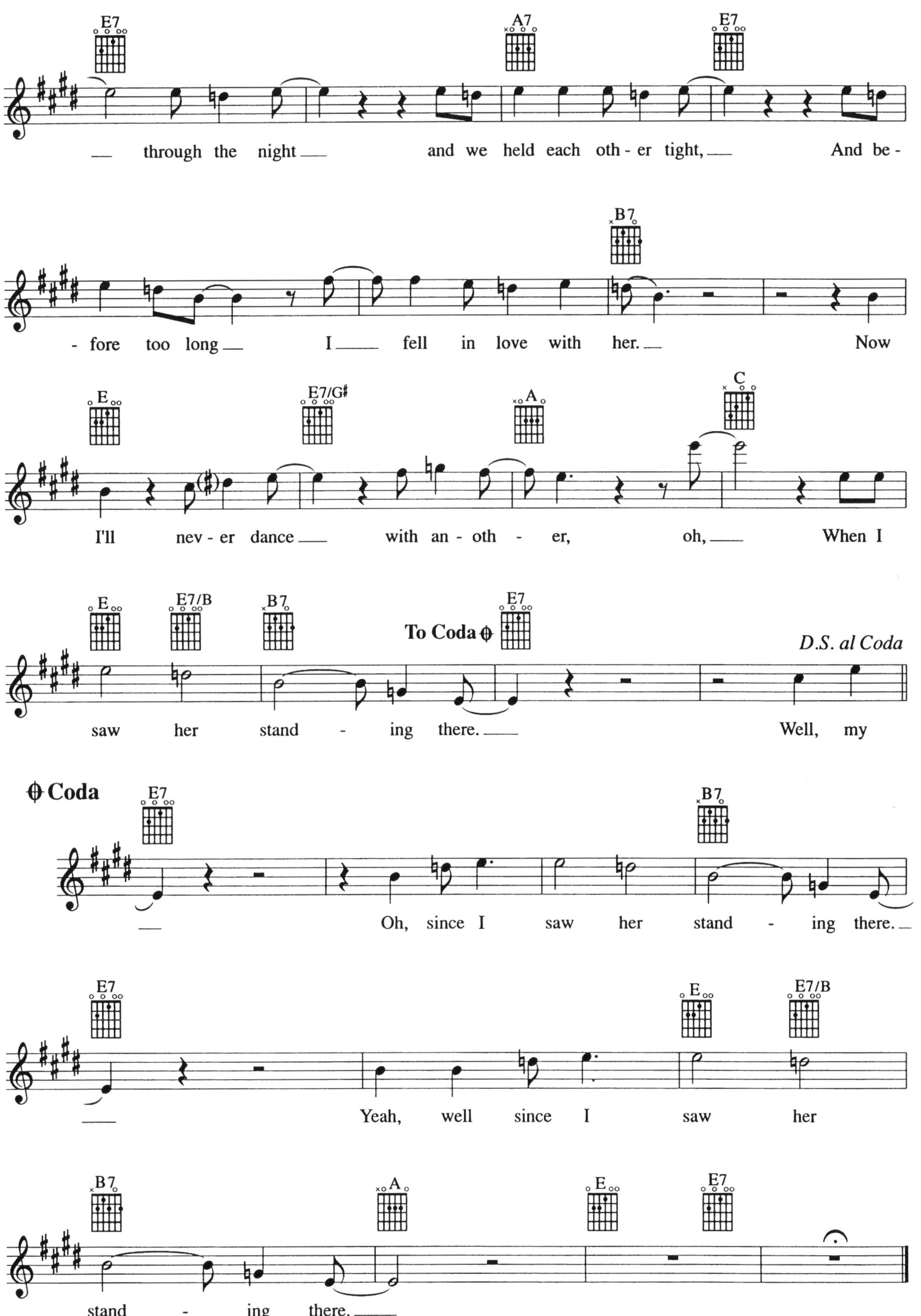
E7
A7
E7
— through the night — and we held each oth - er tight, — And be -
B7
- fore too long — I — fell in love with her. — Now
E
E7/G♯
A
C
I'll nev - er dance — with an - oth - er, oh, — When I
E
E7/B
B7
To Coda
E7
D.S. al Coda
saw her stand - ing there. — Well, my
Coda
E7
B7
— Oh, since I saw her stand - ing there. —
E7
E
E7/B
— Yeah, well since I saw her
B7
A
E
E7
stand - ing there. —

I Want To Hold Your Hand.

WORDS & MUSIC BY JOHN LENNON & PAUL MCCARTNEY.

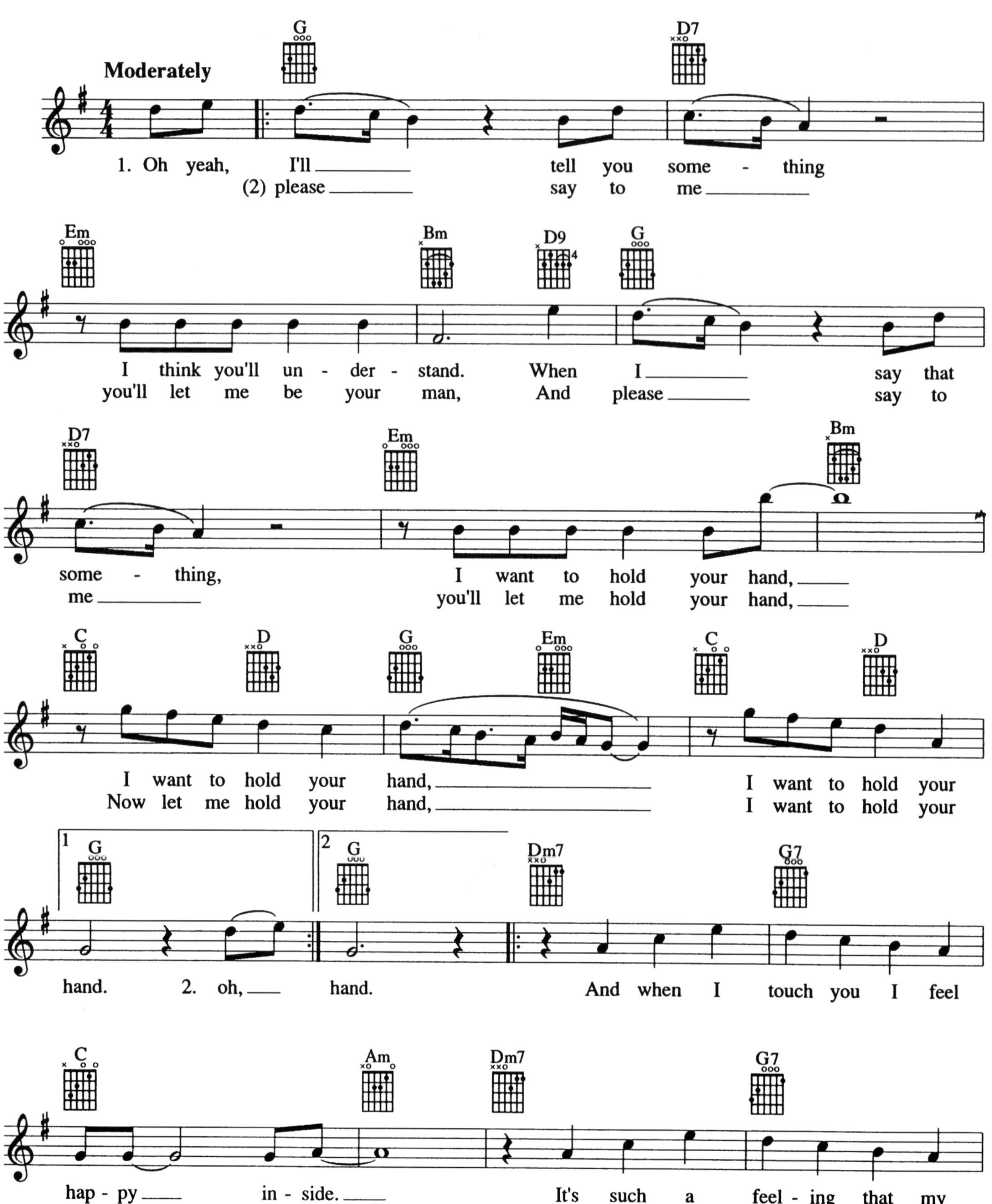
Moderately
G D7
1. Oh yeah, I'll tell you some - thing
(2) please say to me
Em Bm D9 G
I think you'll un - der - stand. When I say that
you'll let me be your man, And please say to
D7 Em Bm
some - thing, I want to hold your hand,
me you'll let me hold your hand,
C D G Em C D
I want to hold your hand, I want to hold your
Now let me hold your hand, I want to hold your
1 G 2 G Dm7 G7
hand. 2. oh, hand. And when I touch you I feel
C Am Dm7 G7
hap - py in - side. It's such a feel - ing that my

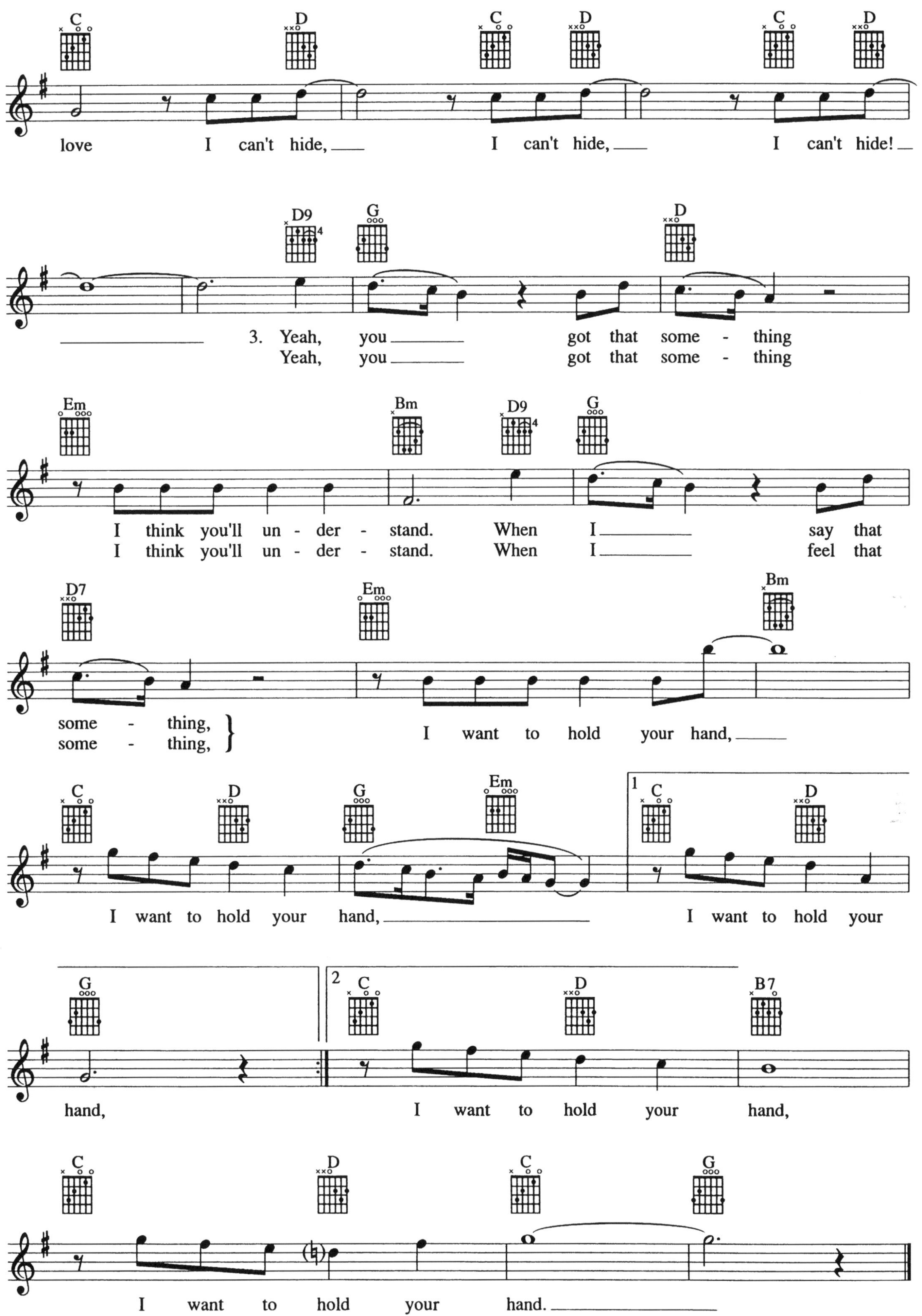
C D C D C D
love I can't hide, I can't hide, I can't hide!
D9 G D
3. Yeah, you got that some - thing
Yeah, you got that some - thing
Em Bm D9 G
I think you'll un - der - stand. When I say that
I think you'll un - der - stand. When I feel that
D7 Em Bm
some - thing,
some - thing,
I want to hold your hand,
C D G Em
I want to hold your hand,
1 C D
I want to hold your
G
hand,
2 C D B7
I want to hold your hand,
C D C G
I want to hold your hand.

I'll Get You.

Words & Music by John Lennon & Paul McCartney.

Moderately
C G C G
Oh yeah, oh yeah, oh yeah, oh yeah. 1. Im -
C F
(3) - ag - ine I'm in love with you, it's eas - y 'cause I
(2) think a - bout you night and day, I need you, and it's
G C Am
know; I've im - ag - ined I'm in love with you
true; When I think a - bout you, I can say, I'm
F G C
Man - y, man - y, man - y times be - fore. It's not like me to pre -
nev - er, nev - er, nev - er, nev - er blue. So I'm tell - ing you, my
Gm7 C Am
- tend, But I'll get you, I'll get you in the end; Yes, I
friend, That I'll get you, I'll get you in the end; Yes, I

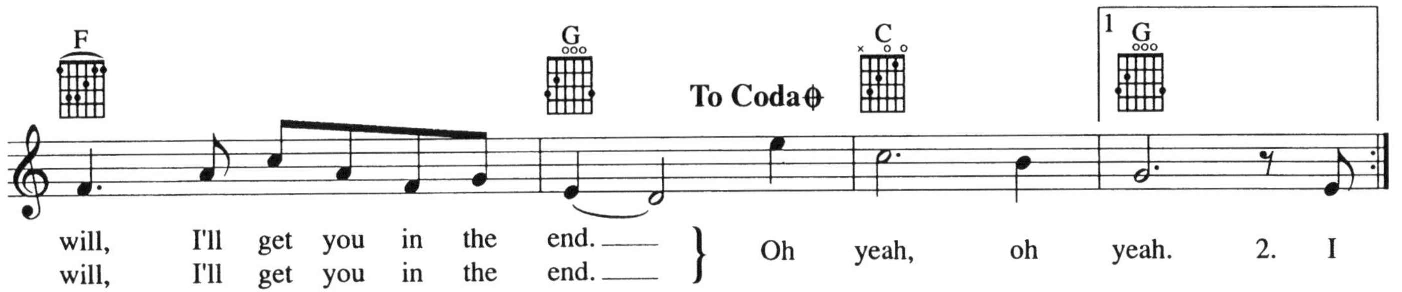
F
G
To Coda
C
1
G
will, I'll get you in the end.
will, I'll get you in the end.
Oh yeah, oh yeah. 2. I

2
G
F
yeah. Well, there's gon - na be a time, When I'm

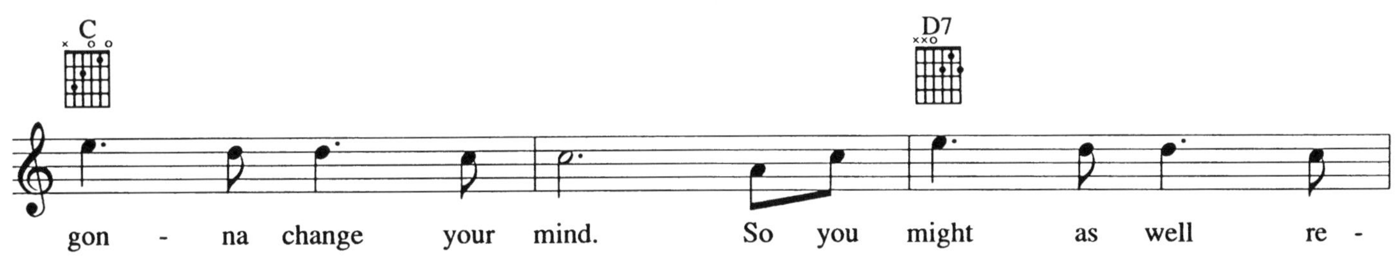
C
D7
gon - na change your mind. So you might as well re -

G
D.S. al Coda
Coda
C
- sign your - self to me. oh yeah. 3. Im -
yeah, oh

G
C
G
C
yeah, oh yeah, oh yeah, oh yeah!

I'll Keep You Satisfied.

Words & Music by John Lennon & Paul McCartney.

Moderately
F♯m7 B7 E
You don't need an - y - bod - y to hold you, Here I
(2) need an - y - bod - y to kiss you, Ev - 'ry
F♯m7 B7 E E/D
stand with my arms o - pen wide; Give me love and re - mem - ber what I
day I'll be here by your side; Don't go 'way, I'm a - fraid that I might
A/C♯ Am/C E B13 1 E
told you, I'll keep you sat - is - fied. 2. You don't
miss you, I'll keep you sat - is -
2 E B
- fied. You can al - ways get a sim - ple thing like
E B/D♯ C♯m B A
love an - y time; But it's dif - f'rent with a boy like me and a

F#m7
B7
F#m7
B7
love like mine. So be - lieve ev - 'ry - thing that I told

E
F#m7
B7
E
you; And a - gree that with me by your side; you don't
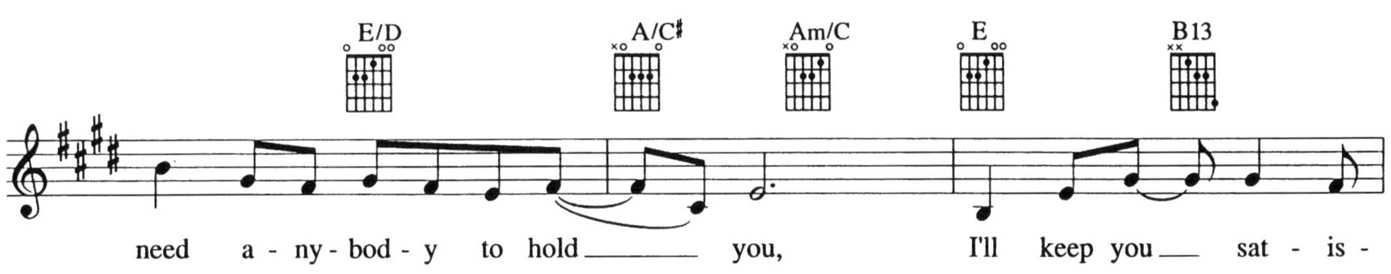
E/D
A/C#
Am/C
E
B13
need a - ny - bod - y to hold you, I'll keep you sat - is -
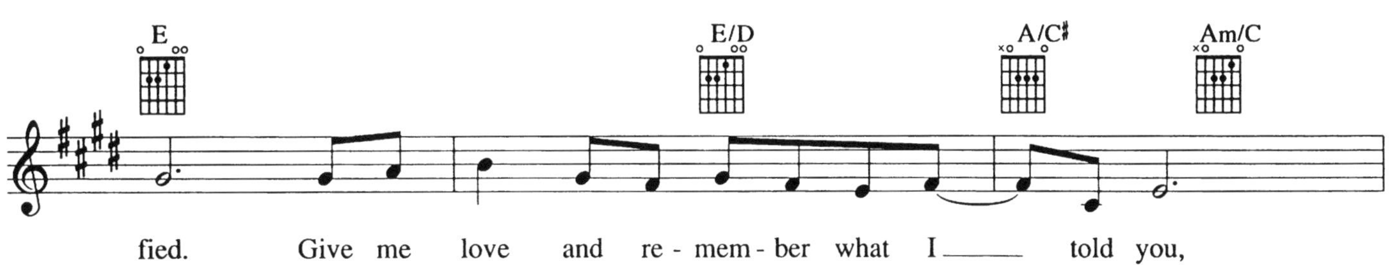
E
E/D
A/C#
Am/C
fied. Give me love and re - mem - ber what I told you,
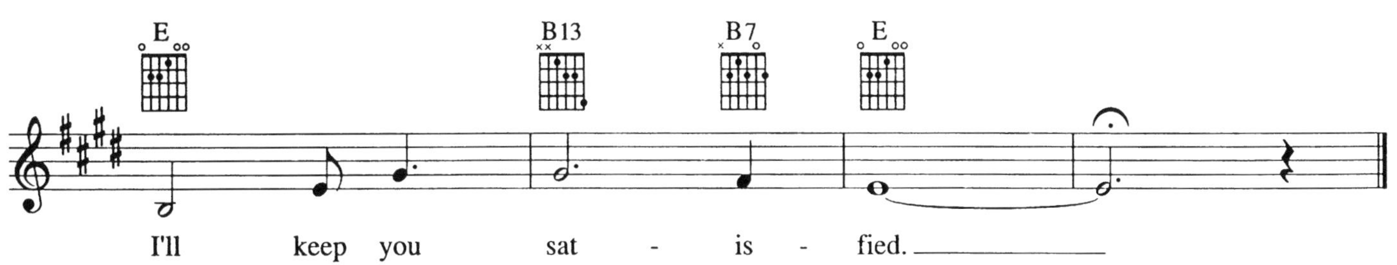
E
B13
B7
E
I'll keep you sat - is - fied.

I'm In Love.

Words & Music by John Lennon & Paul McCartney.

Moderately
Am
A♭+
I've got some - thing to tell you, I'm in love; I've been

C/G
D7/F♯
F
long - ing to tell you I'm in love. You'll be - lieve me when I tell you

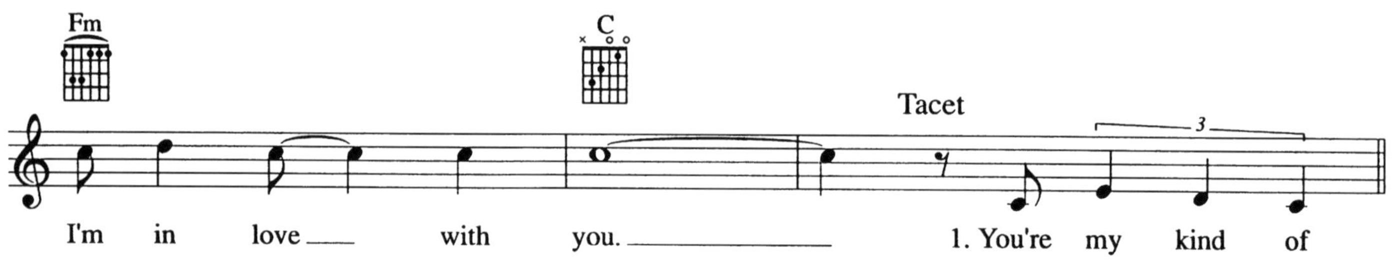
Fm
C
Tacet
I'm in love with you. 1. You're my kind of

Am
A♭+
F
girl, you make me feel proud;
2.3. sleep think - ing of you,

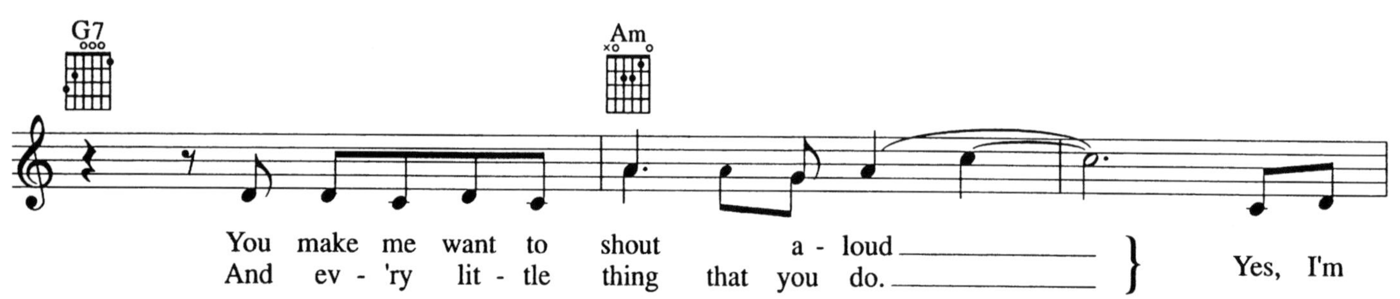
G7
Am
You make me want to shout a - loud
And ev - 'ry lit - tle thing that you do.
Yes, I'm

F
G7
To Coda
C
1
Tacet
3
tell - ing all my friends
I'm in love.
2. Ev - 'ry night I can't

2 C6
F
Oh yes, I'm sit - tin' on top of the world,
I'm in

E7
Am
love with a won - der - ful girl,
And I nev - er felt so good be -

Dm7
G7
Dm7
G7
3
3
3
- fore.
If this is love, give me more, more, more, more.

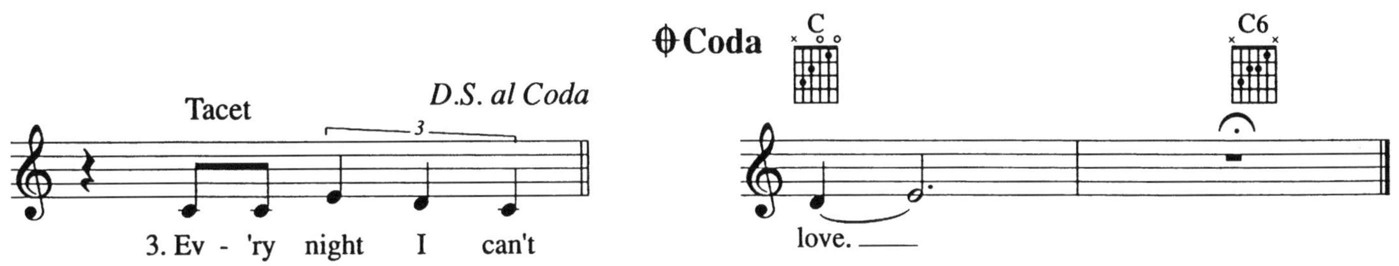
Tacet
D.S. al Coda
3
3. Ev - 'ry night I can't
Coda
C
C6
love.

It Won't Be Long.

WORDS & MUSIC BY JOHN LENNON & PAUL MCCARTNEY.

Brightly
Bm
D
It won't be long, yeah, yeah, yeah, It won't be long, yeah, yeah,

Bm
G
G♯°
D
yeah. It won't be long, yeah, till I be-long to you.

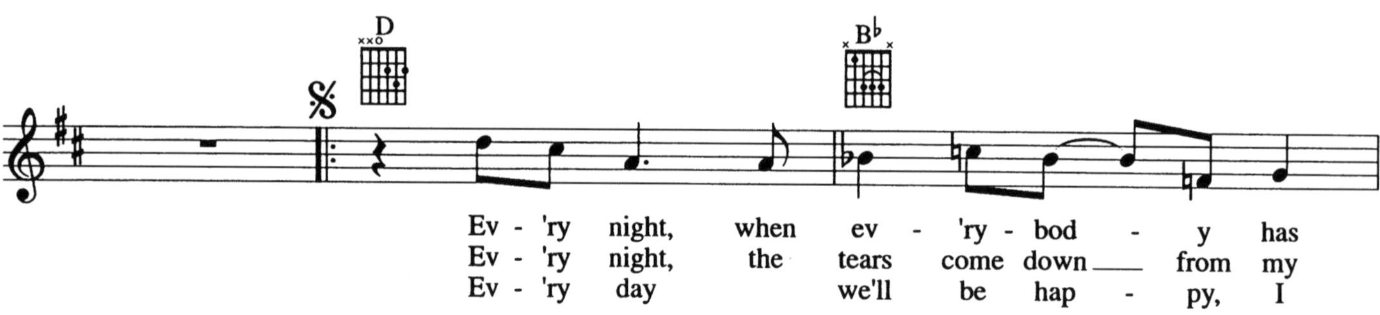
D
B♭
Ev-'ry night, when ev-'ry-bod-y has
Ev-'ry night, the tears come down from my
Ev-'ry day we'll be hap-py, I

D
B♭
fun, Here am I sit-ting all on my
eyes, Ev-'ry day I've done noth-ing but
know. Now I know that you won't leave me no

D
Bm
own.
cry.
more.
It won't be long, yeah, yeah, yeah, It won't be

D
Bm
To Coda
long, yeah, yeah, yeah. It won't be long, yeah, till

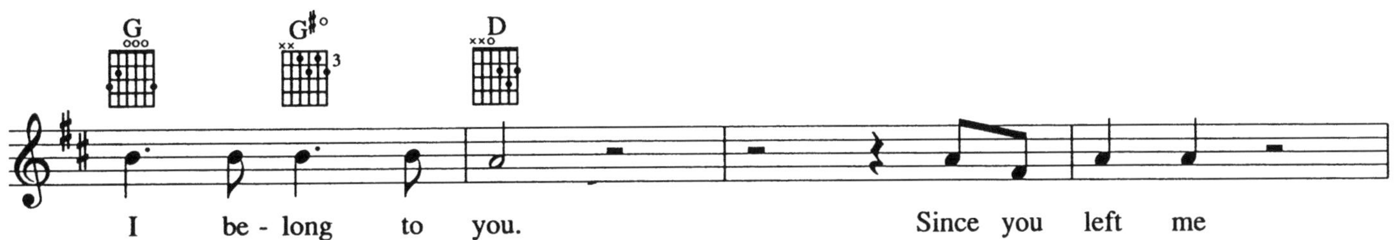
G
G♯°
D
I be - long to you. Since you left me

C♯+
Am6/C
B7
I'm so a - lone. Now you're com - ing, you're com - ing on home.

G
A
A7
I'll be good like I know I should, you're com - ing

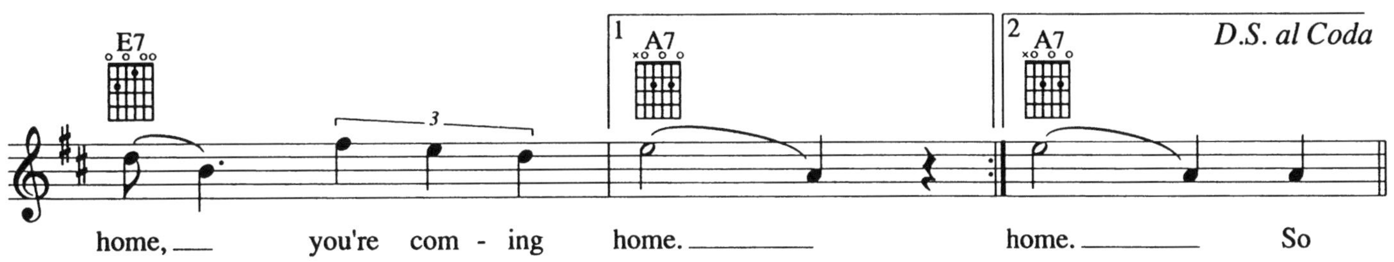
E7
1 A7
2 A7
D.S. al Coda
home, you're com - ing home. home. So

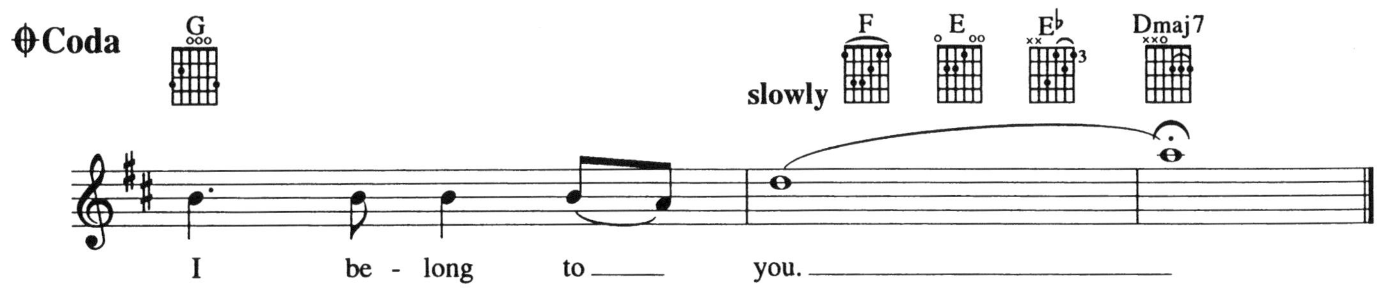
Coda
G
slowly
F
E
E♭
Dmaj7
I be - long to you.

Little Child.

Words & Music by John Lennon & Paul McCartney.

Moderately
E♭7
Lit - tle child, Lit - tle child, Lit - tle child,
E♭ A♭ E♭7 B♭7
won't you dance with me? I'm so sad and
A♭ 1 F7 B♭7
lone - ly, Ba - by take a chance with me. Lit - tle child,
2 F7 B♭7 E♭ E♭
Ba - by take a chance with me. If you want some - one to make you
by my side you're the
B♭ E♭
feel so fine then we'll have some fun when you're
on - ly one, don't you run and hide, just come

E♭7
F
mine, all mine. So, come on, come on, come
on, come on. Yeah, come on, come on, come
B♭
E♭7
on.
on.
Lit - tle child, lit - tle child,
E♭
A♭
E♭7
lit - tle child, won't you dance with me?
B♭7
A♭
F7
B♭7
To Coda
I'm so sad and lone - ly, Ba - by take a chance with me.
E♭
F♯°
B♭7
D.S. al Coda
When you're
Coda
E♭
C7
oh, yeah,
F7
B♭7
E♭
C7
Repeat and Fade
Ba - by take a chance with me. oh, yeah.

Love Of The Loved.

Words & Music by John Lennon & Paul McCartney.

Moderately
C
Em
E♭
1.3. Each time I look in - to your eyes, I see that there,
2. Some day they'll see that from the start, my place has been
Fm
C
A♭7
G7
there heav - en lies, And as I look, I see the love of the
deep in your heart, And in your heart, I see the love of the
C
1 G7
2 B♭7
loved.
loved.
Though I've
E♭
Gm
said it all be - fore, I will say it more and more, now that
A♭
G7
E♭
I'm real - ly sure you love me. And I know that from to - day, I'll see

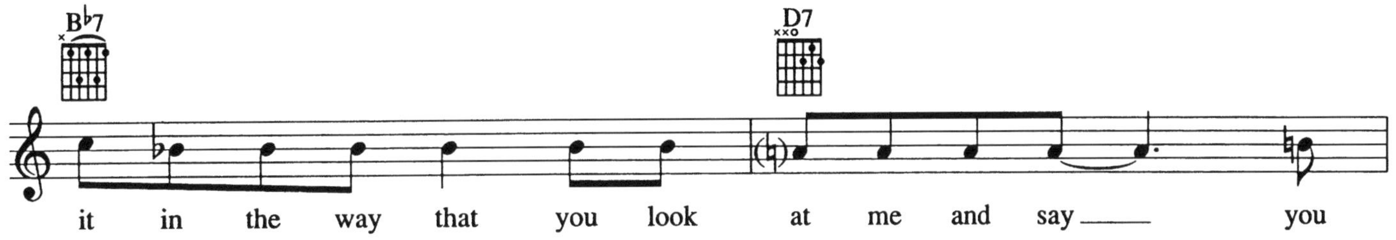
B♭7
D7
it in the way that you look at me and say you

G7
C
Em
love me. So let it rain, what do I care,

E♭
Fm
C
Deep in your heart, I'll still be there. And when I'm there,

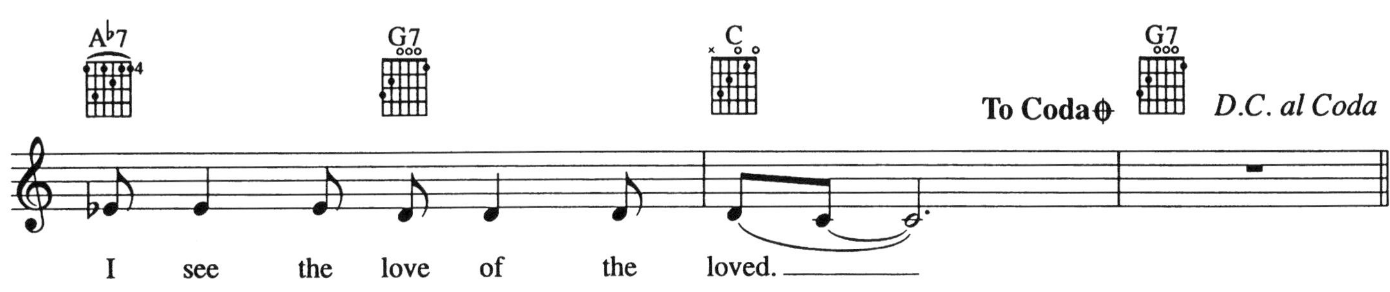
A♭7
G7
C
To Coda
G7
D.C. al Coda
I see the love of the loved.

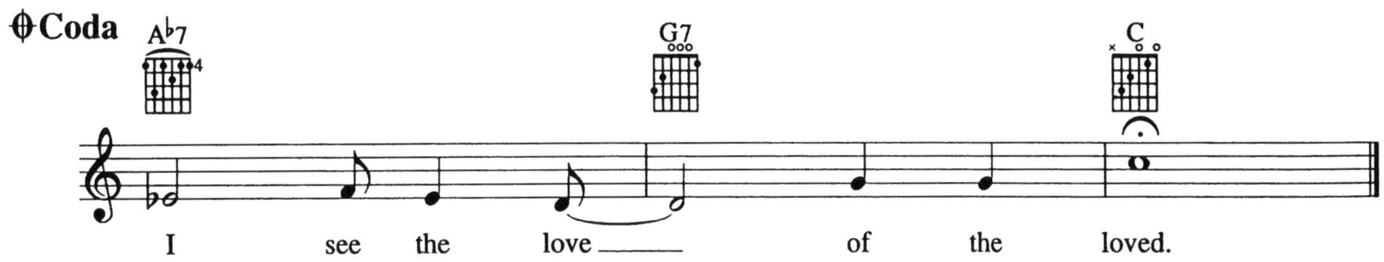
Coda
A♭7
G7
C
I see the love of the loved.

Misery.

WORDS & MUSIC BY JOHN LENNON & PAUL MCCARTNEY.

Freely
F
G
3
The world is treat - ing me bad,

Moderately, with a beat
C
Am
G
C
F
mis - er - y.
I'm the kind of guy who

C
F
3
nev - er used to cry;
The world is treat - ing me

G
C
Am
C
bad,
mis - er - y.
I've lost her now for

F
C
F
sure;
I won't see her no more.
It's gon - na be a

G
C
Am
drag, mis - er - y.
I'll re - mem - ber
C
Am
all the lit - tle things we've done.
1. Can't she see she'll
2. She'll re - mem - ber
G
G7
C
al - ways be the on - ly one, on - ly one.
and she'll miss her on - ly one, lone - ly one.
Send her back to
F
C
F
me 'cause ev - 'ry - one can see
With - out her I will
G
1
C
2
C
be in mis - er - y.
mis - er - y.
Am
C
Am
Repeat and Fade
Oh, in mis - er - y.
Ooh, my

She Loves You.

Words & Music by John Lennon & Paul McCartney.

Moderately
Em
A7
She loves you, yeh, yeh, yeh. She loves you, yeh,
C
G6
yeh, yeh. She loves you, yeh, yeh, yeh, yeh. 1. You
G
Em
Bm
think you've lost your love? Well, I saw her yes - ter -
(2) said you hurt her so, She al - most lost her
(3) know it's up to you, I think it's on - ly
D
G
Em
Bm
- day. It's you she's think - ing of And she told me what to
mind, and now she says she knows You're not the hurt - ing
fair, Pride can hurt you too, A - pol - o - gize to
D
G6
say: She says she
kind. She says she
her. Be - cause she
loves you and you know that can't be
Em
Cm6
bad. Yes, she loves you and you
1 D7
2 D7
know you should be glad. 2. She Oo!

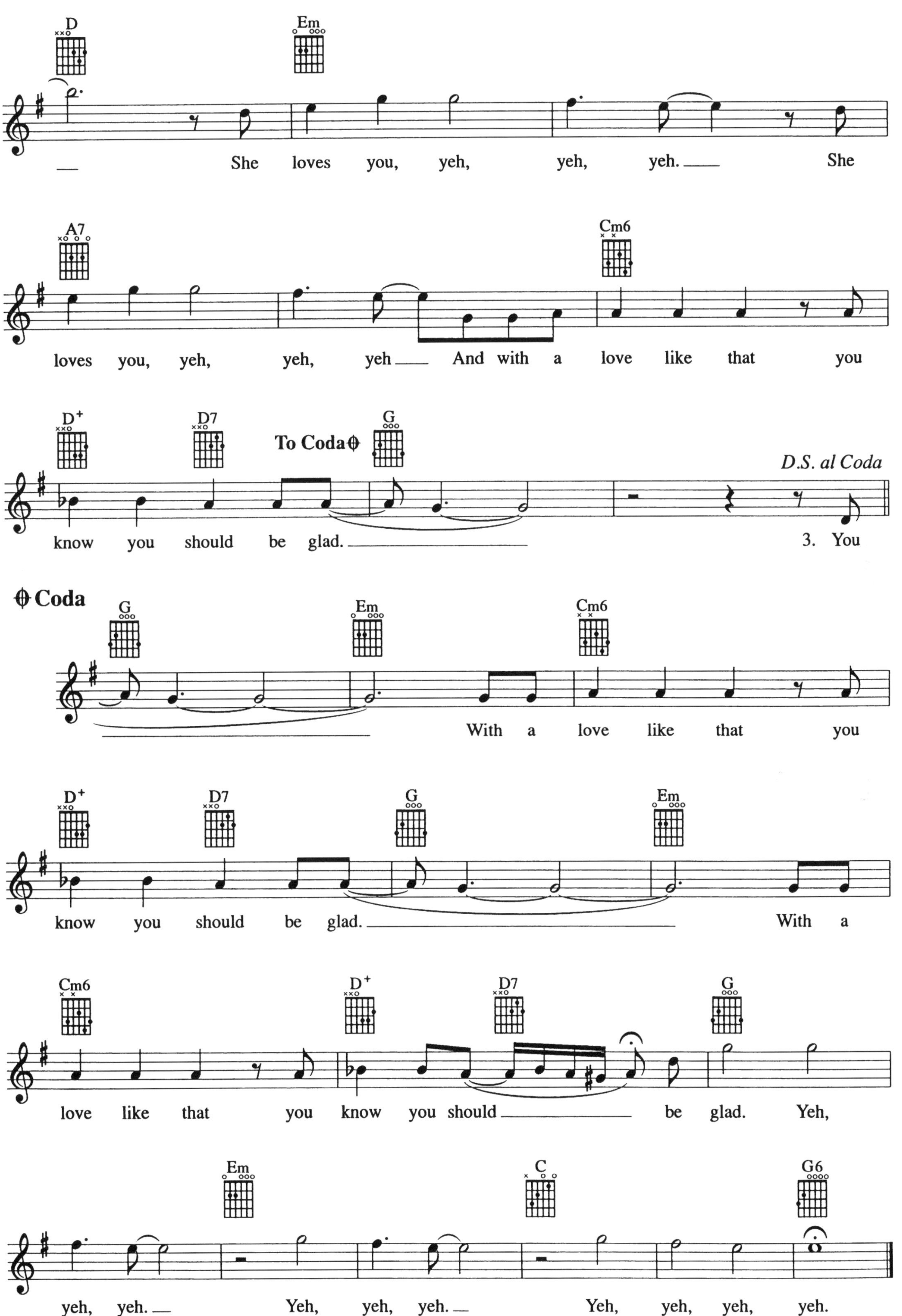
D
Em
She loves you, yeh, yeh, yeh. She
A7
Cm6
loves you, yeh, yeh, yeh And with a love like that you
D+
D7
To Coda
G
D.S. al Coda
know you should be glad. 3. You
Coda
G
Em
Cm6
With a love like that you
D+
D7
G
Em
know you should be glad. With a
Cm6
D+
D7
G
love like that you know you should be glad. Yeh,
Em
C
G6
yeh, yeh. Yeh, yeh, yeh. Yeh, yeh, yeh, yeh.

Thank You Girl.

WORDS & MUSIC BY JOHN LENNON & PAUL McCARTNEY.

Moderately bright
A G A G D G
Oh! Oh! You've been good to
I could tell the
D G D A D G
me you make me glad when I was blue,
world a thing or two a - bout our love,
D G D G D A
And e - ter - nal - ly I'll al - ways be in love with
I know, lit - tle girl, on - ly a fool would doubt our
D G A G
To Coda
you.
love.
And all I got - ta do is thank you, girl;
1 A
thank you, girl.
2 A
thank you, girl.
Bm
Thank you, girl, for

D
A7
lov - in' me the way that you do. (way that you do)

Em
A
D
That's the kind of love that is too good to be true. And

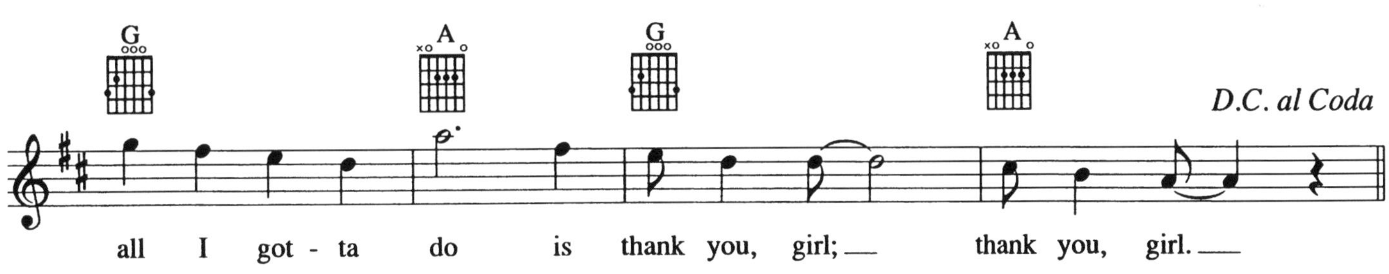
G
A
G
A
D.C. al Coda
all I got - ta do is thank you, girl; thank you, girl.

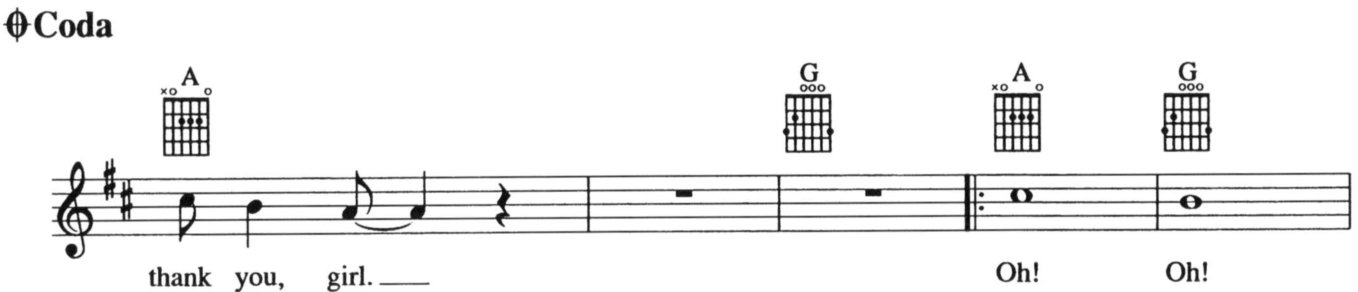
Coda
A
G
A
G
thank you, girl. Oh! Oh!

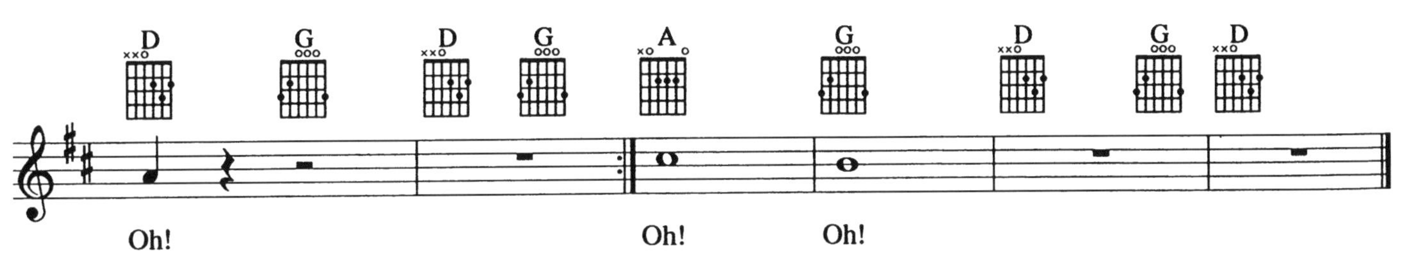
D
G
D
G
A
G
D
G
D
Oh! Oh! Oh!

There's A Place.

Words & Music by John Lennon & Paul McCartney.

Moderately bright
F
B♭
C/B♭
There
there's a place where I can
go when I feel low, When I feel blue.
Dm
C
C7
Am
And it's my mind, And there's no
Fmaj7
time When I'm a - lone.
To Coda
Tacet
I I think of you and things you

F
B♭
C
F
Dm
do go round my head, The things you've
C
B♭
C
said, like "I love on - ly you."
Dm
G7
In my mind there's no sor - row.
F
Am
Dm
Don't you know that it's so? There'll be no sad to -
G7
F
Am
Dm
Tacet
- mor - row. Don't you know that it's so? There
D.S. al Coda
C7
Coda
C7
F
B♭
C7
Repeat and Fade
for there's a
There's a place. Oh, there's a

Not A Second Time.

Words & Music by John Lennon & Paul McCartney.

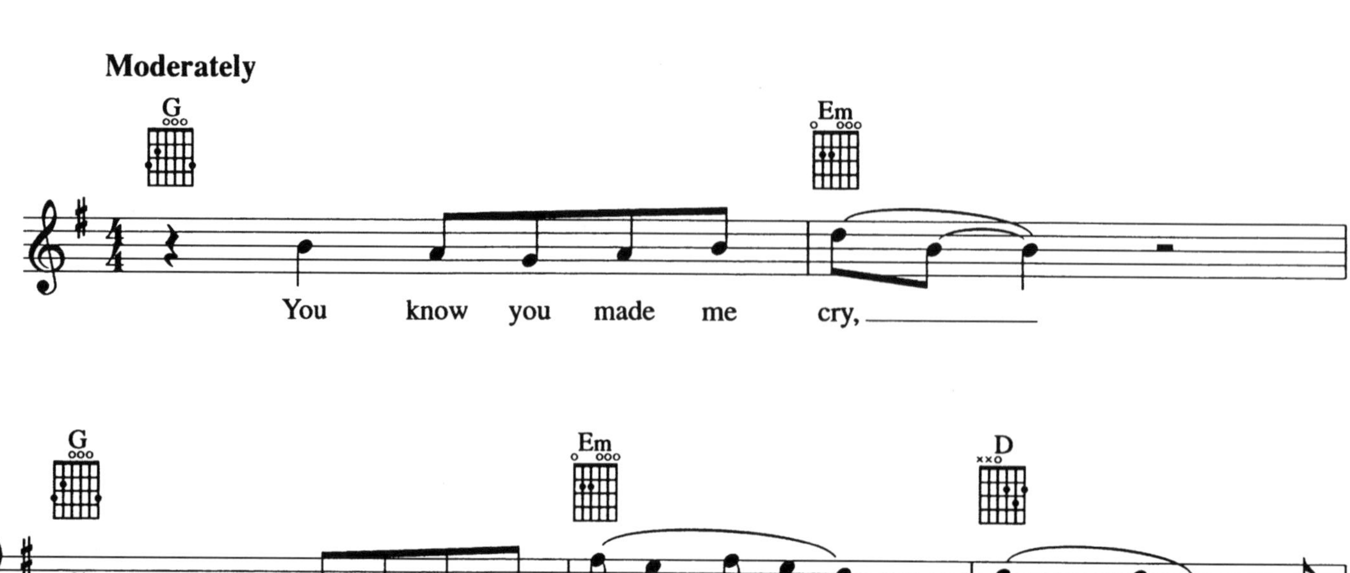
Moderately
G
Em
You know you made me cry,

G
Em
D
I see no use in won-d'rin' why
I cried
for

G
D
G
you.
you,
yeah.
And now you've changed your

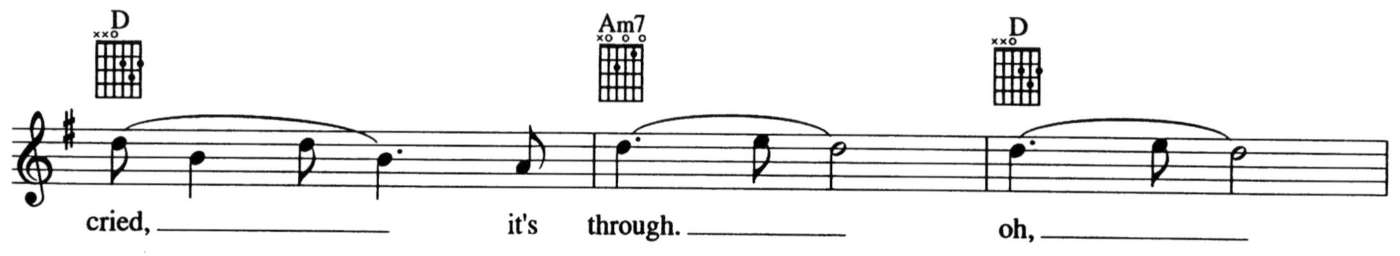
Em
G
Em
mind
I see no reas-on to change mine;
I

D
Am7
D
cried, it's through. oh,

Am7
Bm
G
You're giv - ing me the same old line, I'm won - d'ring

Em
Am7
why. You hurt me then, you're back a - gain;

Bm
D7
Em
To Coda
D.C. al Coda
No, no, no, not a sec - ond time!

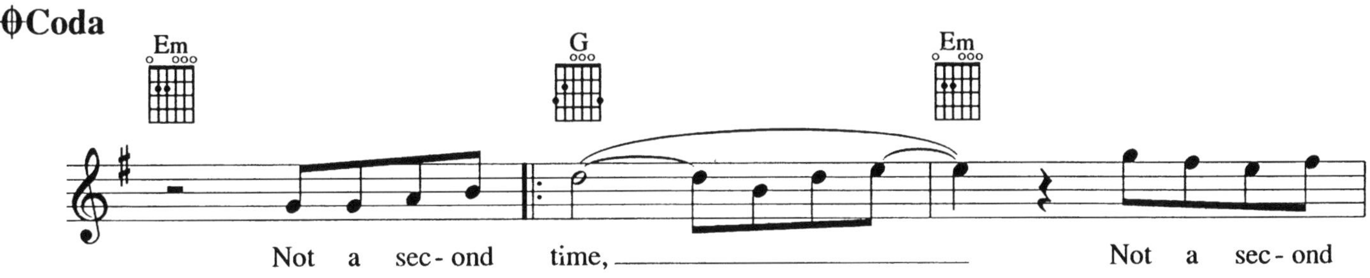
Coda
Em
G
Em
Not a sec - ond time, Not a sec - ond

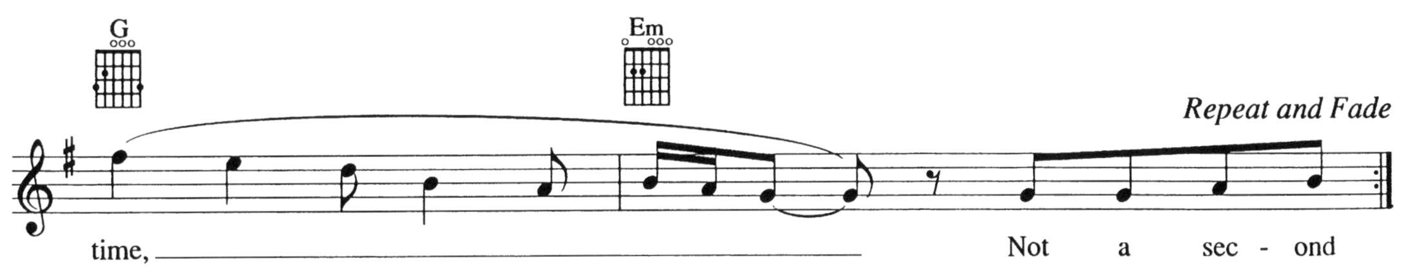
G
Em
Repeat and Fade
time, Not a sec - ond

This Boy.

Words & Music by John Lennon & Paul McCartney.

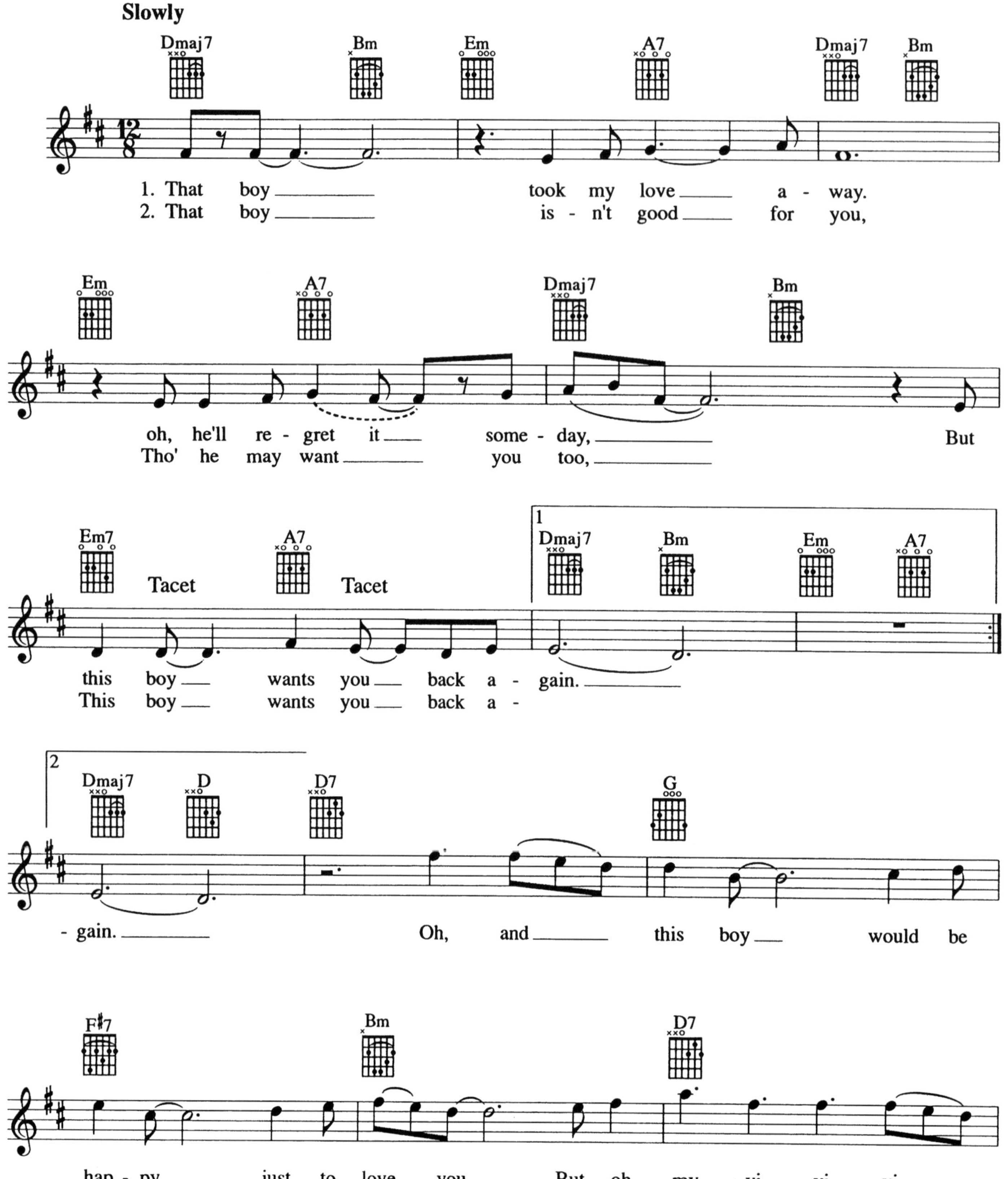
Slowly
Dmaj7
Bm
Em
A7
Dmaj7
Bm
1. That boy took my love a - way.
2. That boy is - n't good for you,
Em
A7
Dmaj7
Bm
oh, he'll re - gret it some - day, But
Tho' he may want you too,
Em7
Tacet
A7
Tacet
1
Dmaj7
Bm
Em
A7
this boy wants you back a - gain.
This boy wants you back a -
2
Dmaj7
D
D7
G
- gain. Oh, and this boy would be
F♯7
Bm
D7
hap - py just to love you, But, oh my - yi - yi - yi

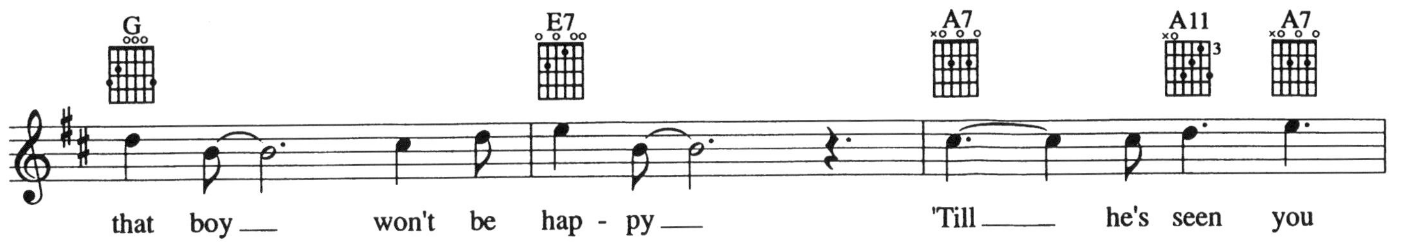
G
E7
A7
A11
A7
that boy won't be hap - py 'Till he's seen you

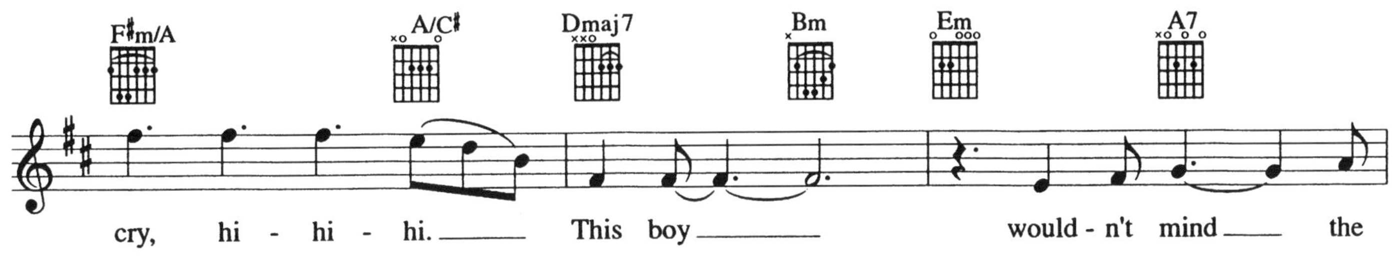
F♯m/A
A/C♯
Dmaj7
Bm
Em
A7
cry, hi - hi - hi. This boy would - n't mind the

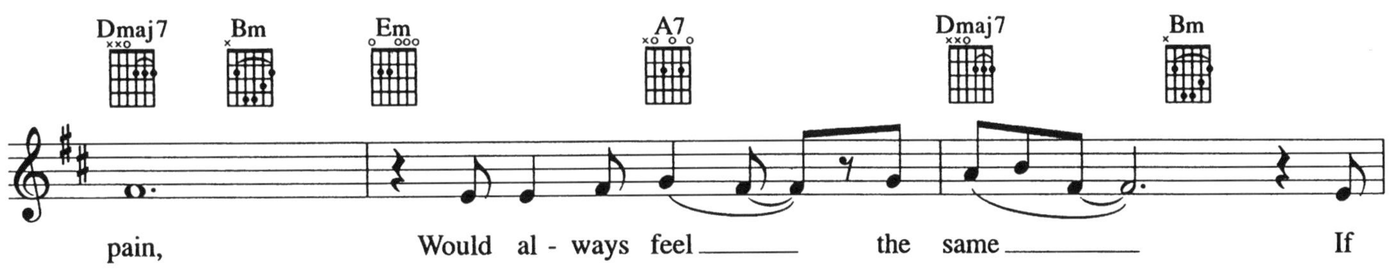
Dmaj7
Bm
Em
A7
Dmaj7
Bm
pain, Would al - ways feel the same If

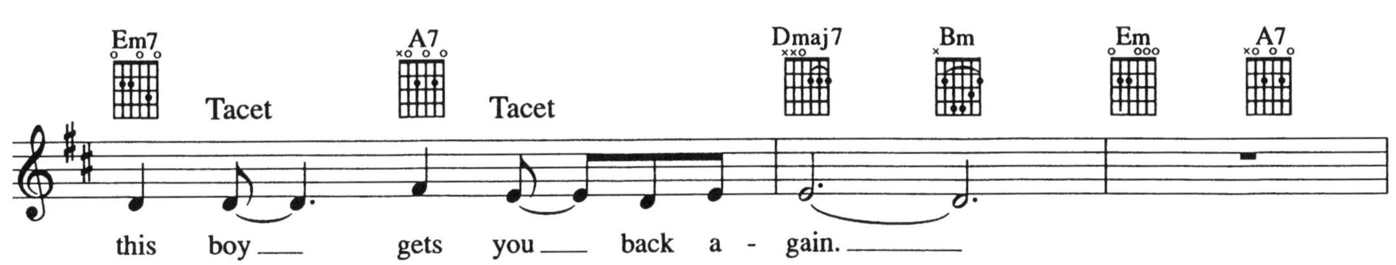
Em7
Tacet
A7
Tacet
Dmaj7
Bm
Em
A7
this boy gets you back a - gain.

Repeat and Fade

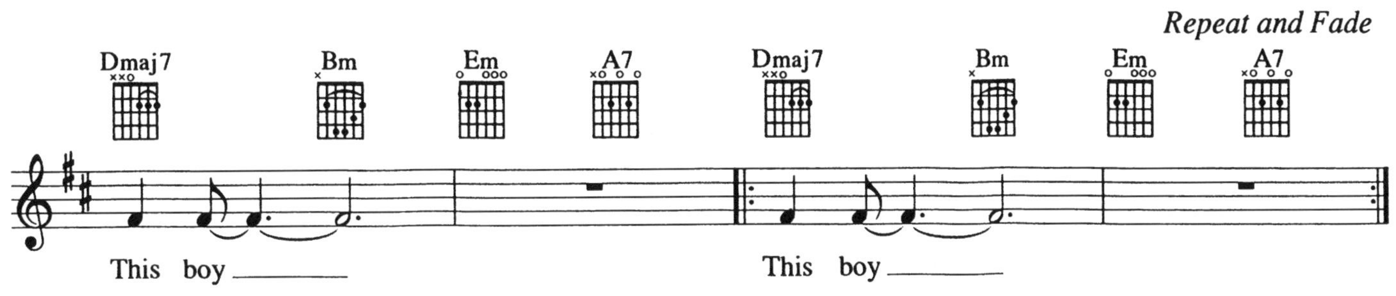
Dmaj7
Bm
Em
A7
Dmaj7
Bm
Em
A7
This boy This boy

Hold Me Tight.

WORDS & MUSIC BY JOHN LENNON & PAUL McCARTNEY.

Moderately
F C F B♭
It feels so right now, Hold me tight
Hold me tight
G7 C7 F
Tell me I'm the on - ly one, And then I might
Let me go on lov - ing you, To - night, to - night,
B♭ G7 C7
Nev - er be the lone - ly one.
Mak - ing love to on - ly you.
So
F F7 B♭ B♭m
hold me tight, To - night, to - night, It's
F B♭m F 1 C
you, you, you, you.
2 A♭ F A♭ F
Don't know What it means to hold you tight;

B♭ Gm G
Be - ing here a - lone to - night with you, It
C7 F B♭ G7
feels so right { Now hold me tight Tell me I'm the
So hold me tight Let me go on
C7 F B♭
on - ly one, and then I might
lov - ing you, to - night, to - night,
G7 C7 F
Nev - er be the lone - ly one. } So hold me tight
Mak - ing love to on - ly you.
F7 B♭ B♭m F
to - night, to - night, It's you,
B♭m F 1 A♭
you, you, you, Don't
2 A♭ G♭ F A♭ G♭ F
hoo hoo, you, hoo hoo.

Tip Of My Tongue.

Words & Music by John Lennon & Paul McCartney.

Moderately
F
1. When I want to speak to you, it some - times takes a
2. When the skies are not so blue, there's noth - ing left for
3. Soon e - nough my time will come, and af - ter all is
week or two to think of things I want to say to
me to do, just think of some - thing new to say to
said and done, I'll mar - ry you and we will live as
C7 Gm7 C° C7 F B♭ C7 To Coda F
you. But words just stay on the tip of my tongue.
you. But words just stay on the tip of my tongue.
one. With no more words on the tip of my
1 C7 Gm7 C7 2 C7 Gm7 C7 B♭ B♭m F
Peo - ple say I'm lone - ly; on - ly
B♭ B♭m F B♭ B♭m
you know that's not true. You know I'm wait - ing
D.C. al Coda
F G7 C7 Gm7 C° C7
for a chance to prove my love to you.
Coda
F C7 F
tongue no more; No words on the tip of my tongue.

I'll Be On My Way.

Words & Music by John Lennon & Paul McCartney.

Moderately
G D G
1. The sun is fad - ing a - way, That's the end of the
2. They were right, I was wrong; True love did - n't last
C G D7 G C To Coda
day, long, As the June - light turns to moon - light, I'll be on my
G G D G
way. Just one kiss, then I'll go, Don't hide the tears that don't
C G D7 G C
show. As the June - light turns to moon - light, I'll be on my
G A7 D A7
way. To where the winds don't blow, and gold - en riv - ers
D.S. al Coda
D E7 A7 D7
flow, This way will I go.
Coda
G
way.

A Hard Day's Night.

Words & Music by John Lennon & Paul McCartney.

Moderately, with a beat
G
C (add 9)
G
1. It's been a (3) hard day's night and I've been
(2) work all day to get you
F
G
C (add 9)
work - ing like a dog. It's been a hard day's night
mon - ey to buy you things. And it's worth it just to hear you say
G
F
G
I should be sleep - ing like a log. But when I
You're gon - na give me ev - 'ry - thing. So why I
C
D
get home to you, I find the thing that you do will make me
love to come home 'Cause when I get you a - lone you know I'll
G
C9
To Coda
1
G
2
G
feel al - right. (2) You know I When I'm home
be O. K.

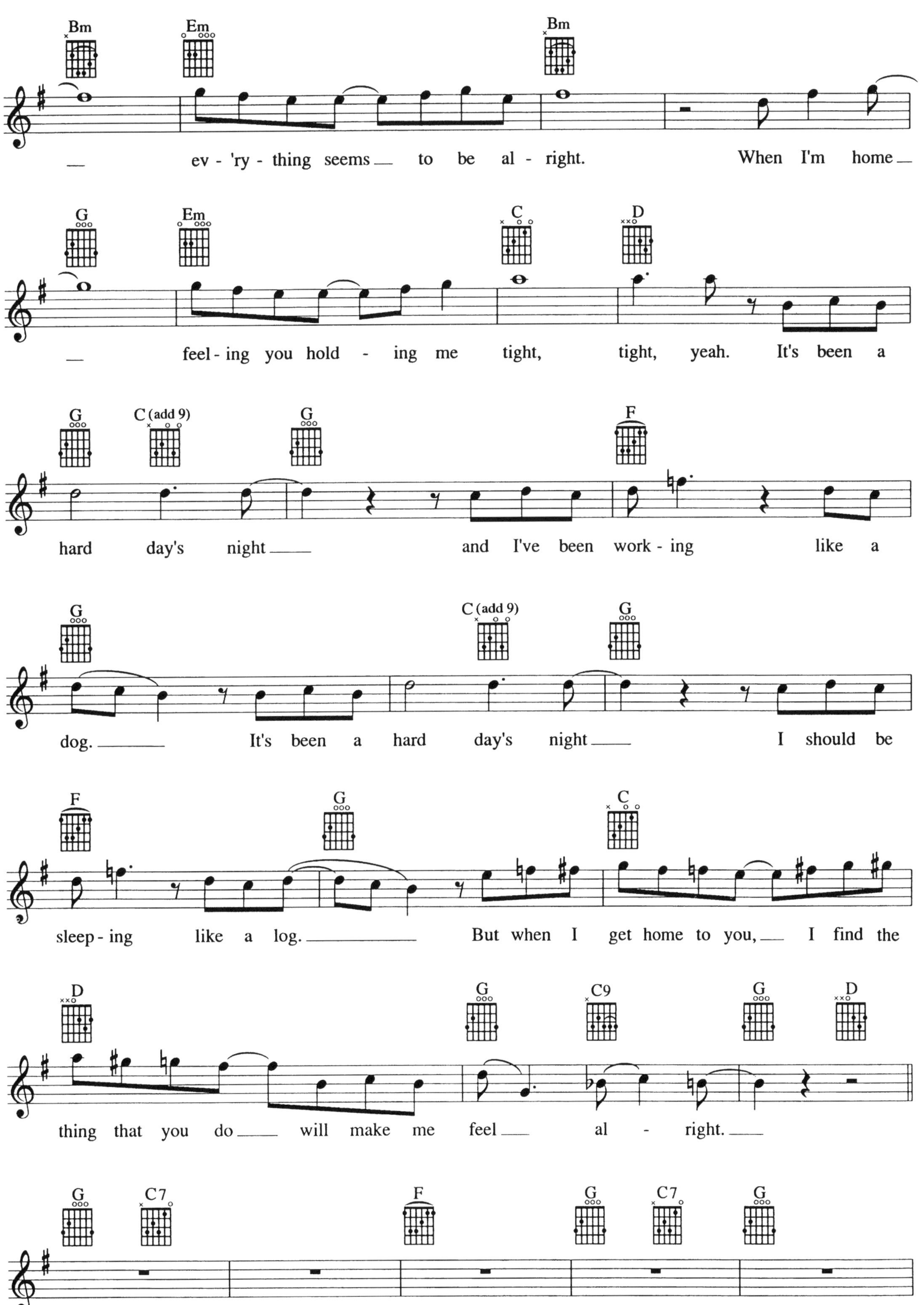
Bm
Em
Bm
ev - 'ry - thing seems to be al - right. When I'm home
G
Em
C
D
feel - ing you hold - ing me tight, tight, yeah. It's been a
G
C (add 9)
G
F
hard day's night and I've been work - ing like a
G
C (add 9)
G
dog. It's been a hard day's night I should be
F
G
C
sleep - ing like a log. But when I get home to you, I find the
D
G
C9
G
D
thing that you do will make me feel al - right.
G
C7
F
G
C7
G

F
G
C
So why I love to come home 'Cause when I

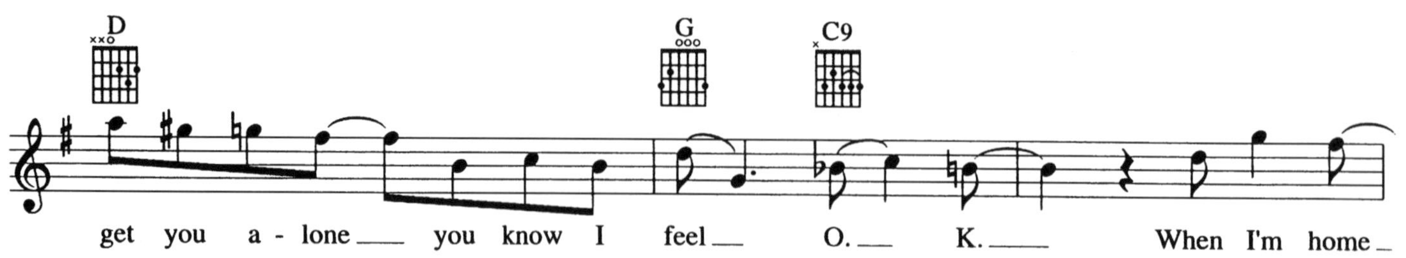
D
G
C9
get you a - lone you know I feel O. K. When I'm home

Bm
Em
Bm
G
ev - 'ry - thing seems to be al - right. When I'm home

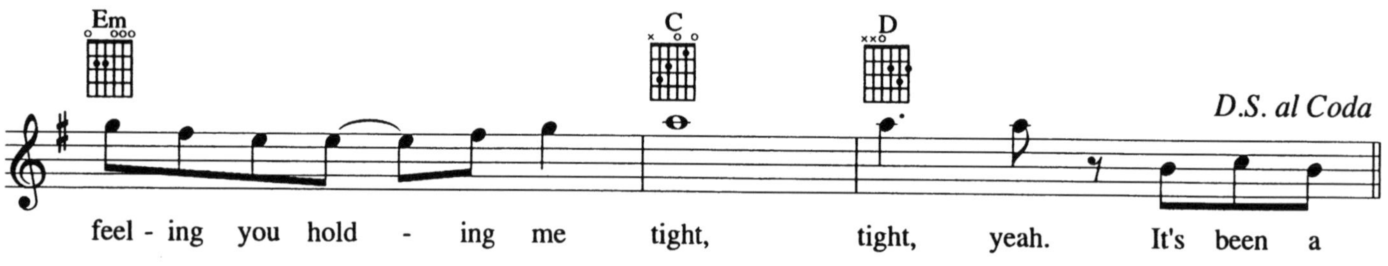
Em
C
D
D.S. al Coda
feel - ing you hold - ing me tight, tight, yeah. It's been a

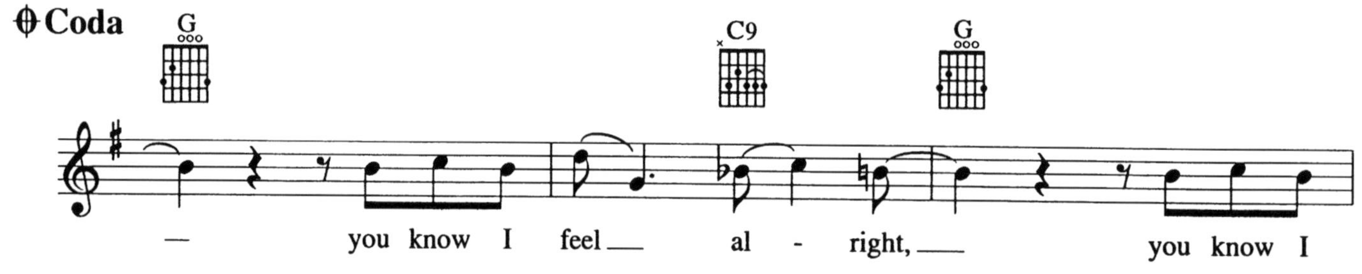
Coda
G
C9
G
you know I feel al - right, you know I

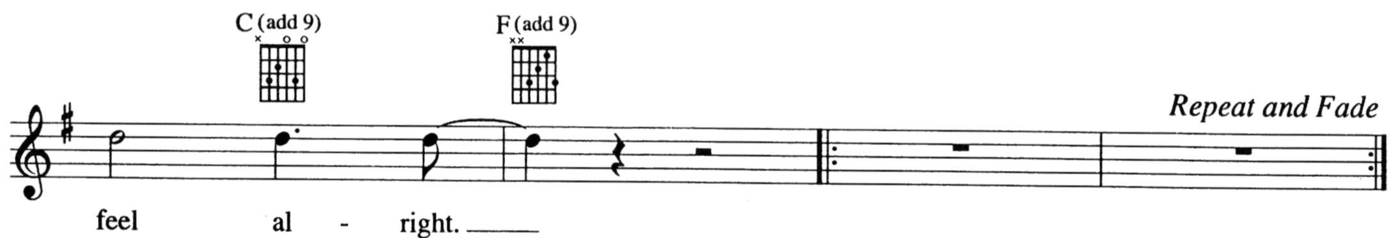
C (add 9)
F (add 9)
Repeat and Fade
feel al - right.

Any Time At All.

Words & Music by John Lennon & Paul McCartney.

With a beat
Bm
D
An - y - time at all,
an - y - time at
A
Bm
all,
An - y - time at all,
all you got - ta do is
G
A7
D
To Coda
call,
and I'll be there.
1. If you need some -
2. If the sun has
F♯m/C♯
Bm
Gm/B♭
- bod - y to love
just look in - to my eyes;
fad - ed a - way
I'll try to make it shine;
D/A
A/C♯
D
I'll be there to make you feel right. If you're feel - ing
There is noth - in' I won't do. When you need a

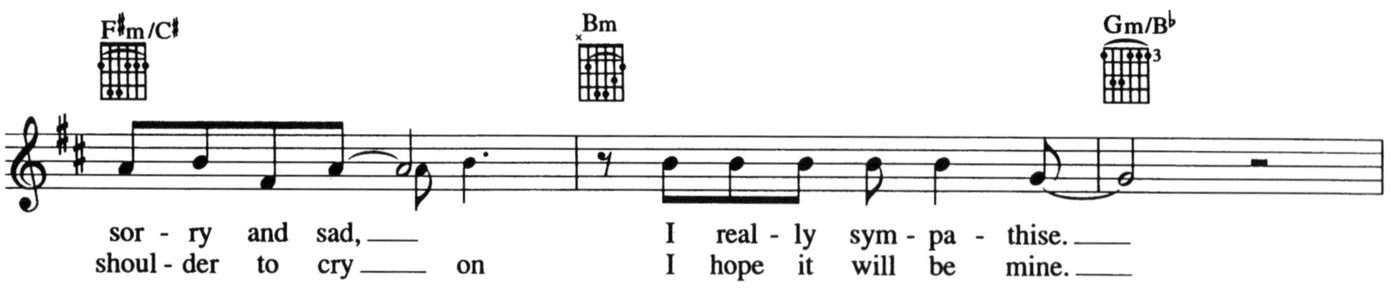
F♯m/C♯
Bm
Gm/B♭
sor - ry and sad, I real - ly sym - pa - thise.
shoul - der to cry on I hope it will be mine.

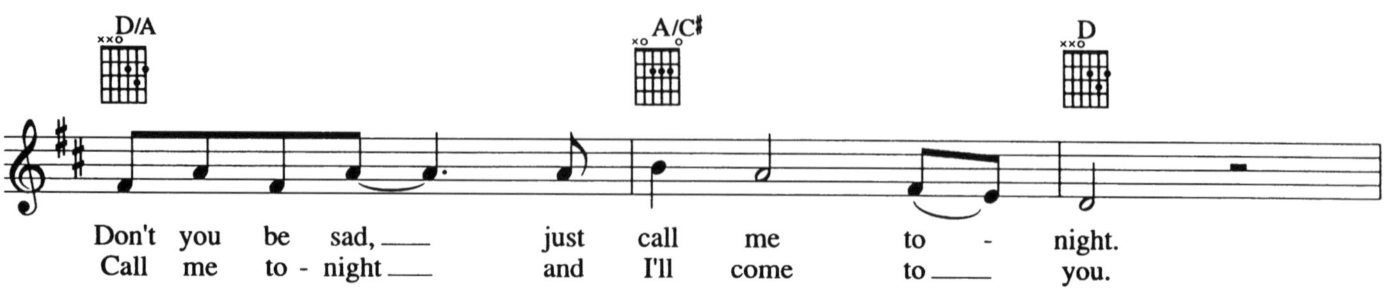
D/A
A/C♯
D
Don't you be sad, just call me to - night.
Call me to - night and I'll come to you.

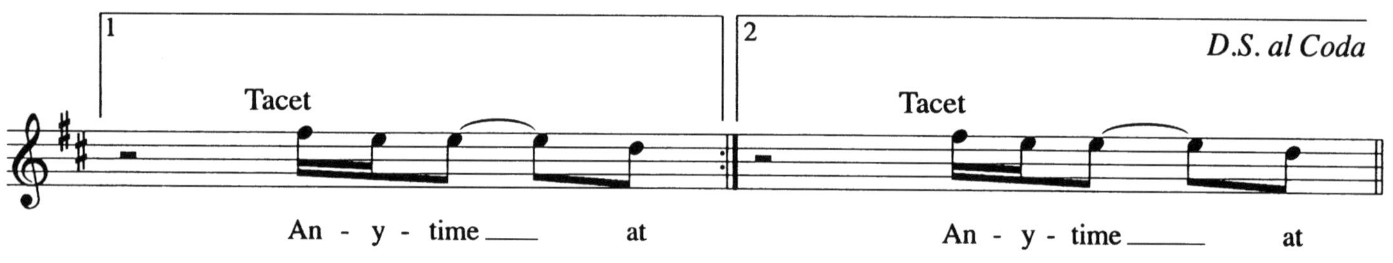
1
Tacet
An - y - time at
2
D.S. al Coda
Tacet
An - y - time at

Coda

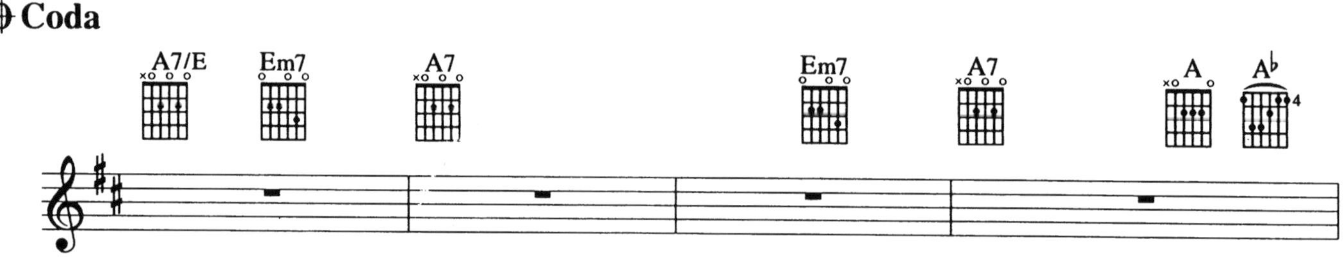
A7/E
Em7
A7
Em7
A7
A
A♭

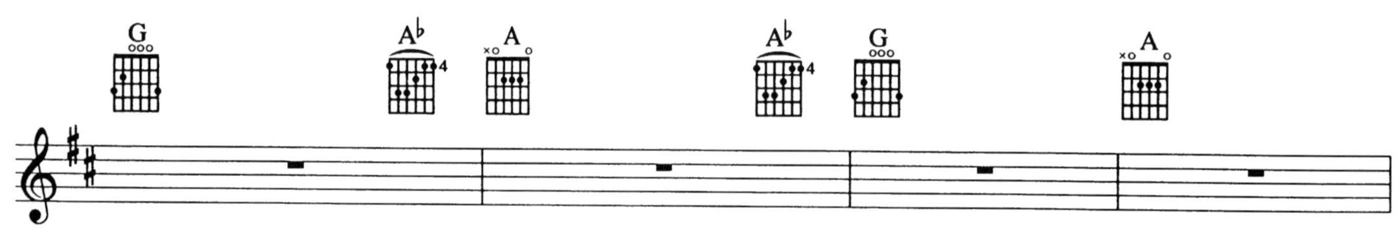
G
A♭
A
A♭
G
A

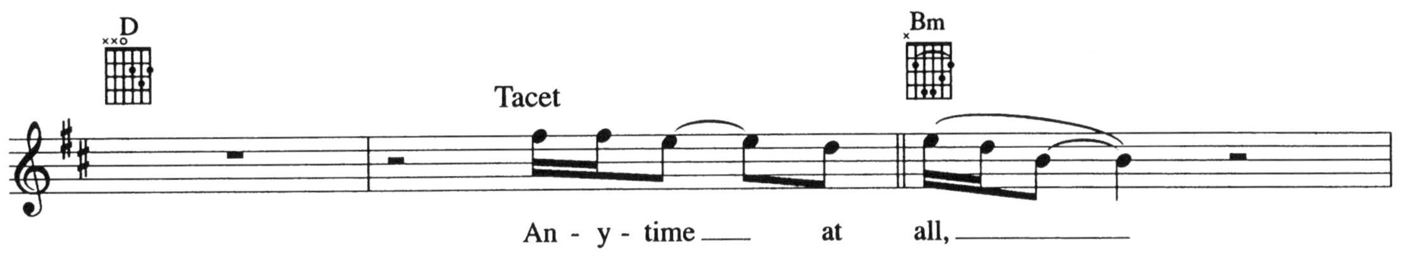
D
Tacet
Bm
An - y - time at all,

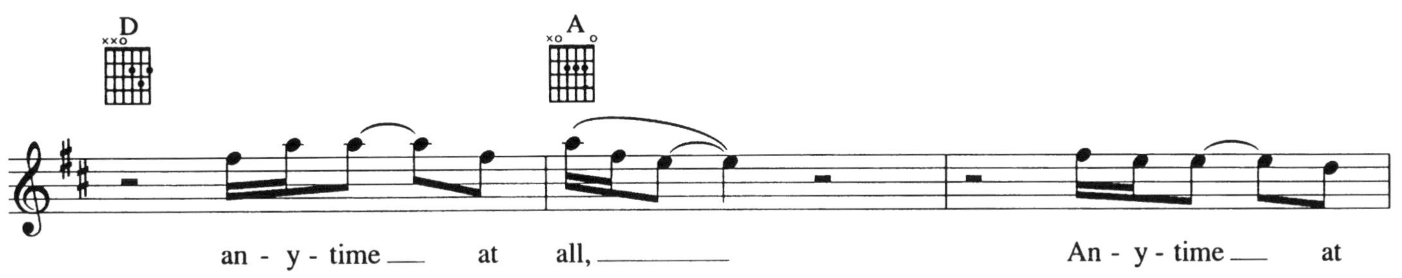
D
A
an - y - time at all,
An - y - time at

Bm
G
A7
all, all you got - ta do is call, and I'll be

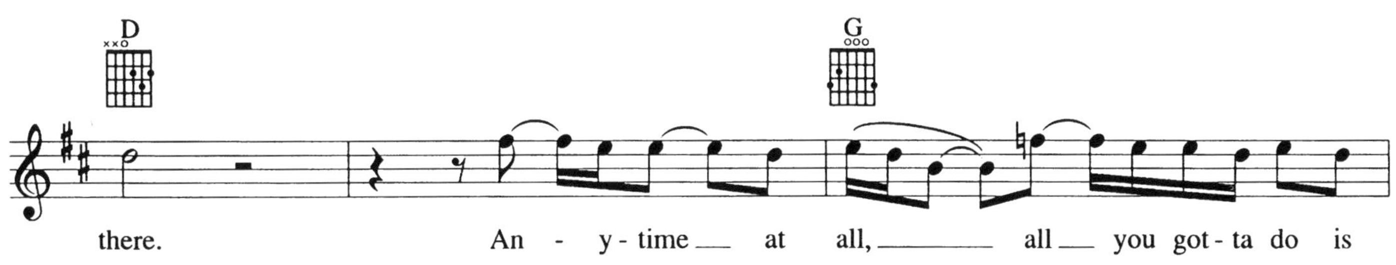
D
G
there. An - y - time at all, all you got - ta do is

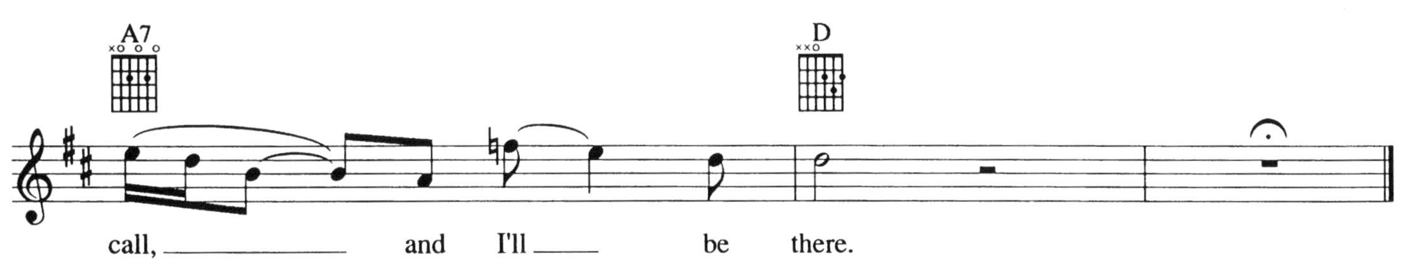
A7
D
call, and I'll be there.

And I Love Her.

Words & Music by John Lennon & Paul McCartney.

Moderately
F♯m
C♯m
1. I give her all my love,
2. She gives me ev - 'ry - thing
3. Bright are the stars that shine,
F♯m
C♯m
F♯m
that's all I do. And if you saw
and ten - der - ly. The kiss my lov -
dark is the sky. I know this love
C♯m
A
B7
my love you'd love her too. I love
- er brings she brings to me. And I love
of mine will nev - er die. And I love
E6
To Coda
1
2
C♯m
her.
her.
her.
A love like ours
B
C♯m
G♯m
C♯m
could nev - er die As long as I

G♯m
B
D.C. al Coda
Coda
have you near me.
Gm
Dm
Gm
1. Bright are the stars that shine, dark is the sky.
2. (Instrumental solo)
Dm
Gm
Dm
I know this love of mine
B♭
C
1
F
will nev - er die. And I love
2
F
Gm
her.
F6
Gm
D

Baby's In Black.

Words & Music by John Lennon & Paul McCartney.

Slowly, with a strong beat
A E7 D7 E7
Oh dear, what can I do? Ba-by's in black and I'm feel-ing blue. Tell me
A D A E A
oh, what can I do? 1,3. She thinks of him and
2. I think of her but
A7 D A E7
To Coda
so she dress-es in black, And though he'll nev-er come back, she's dressed in
she thinks on-ly of him, And though it's on-ly a whim, she thinks of
1 A 2 A F♯m7 B7
black. him Oh, how long will it take
D E7 A E7
'till she sees the mis-take she has made? Dear what can I do?

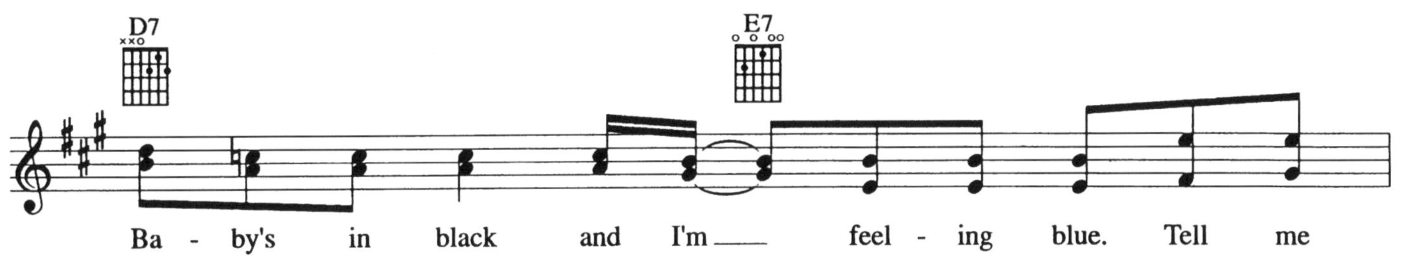
D7
E7
Ba - by's in black and I'm feel - ing blue. Tell me

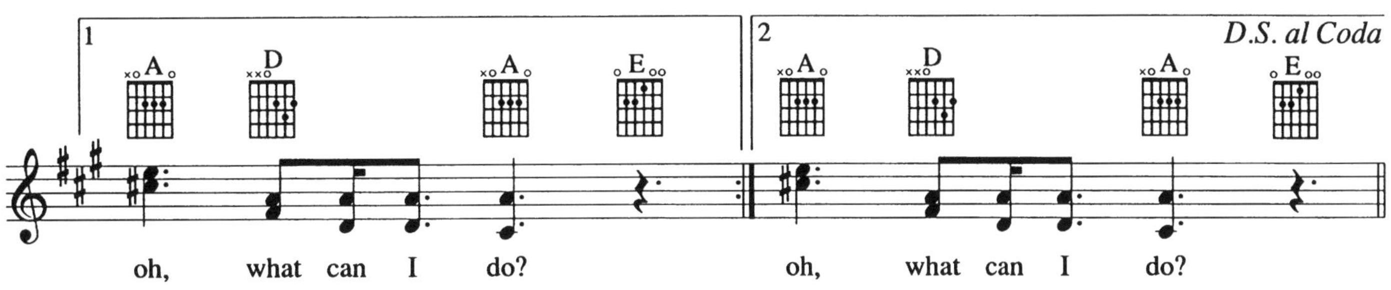
1
2
D.S. al Coda
A
D
A
E
oh, what can I do?
oh, what can I do?

Coda
A
A
E7
black
Oh dear, what can I do?

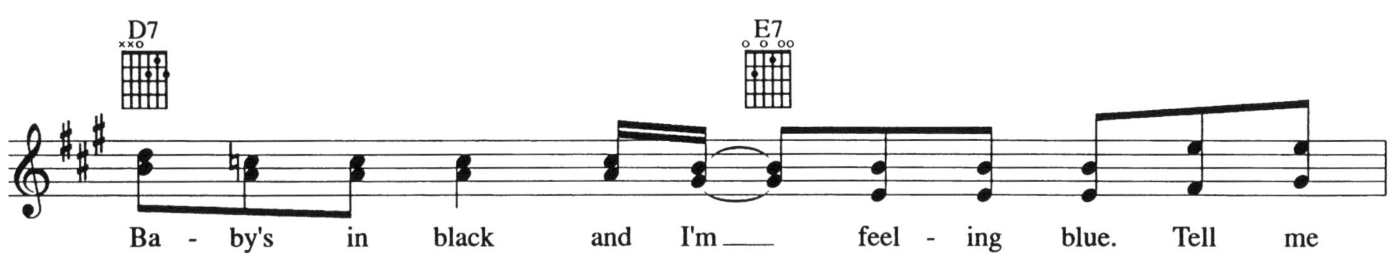
D7
E7
Ba - by's in black and I'm feel - ing blue. Tell me

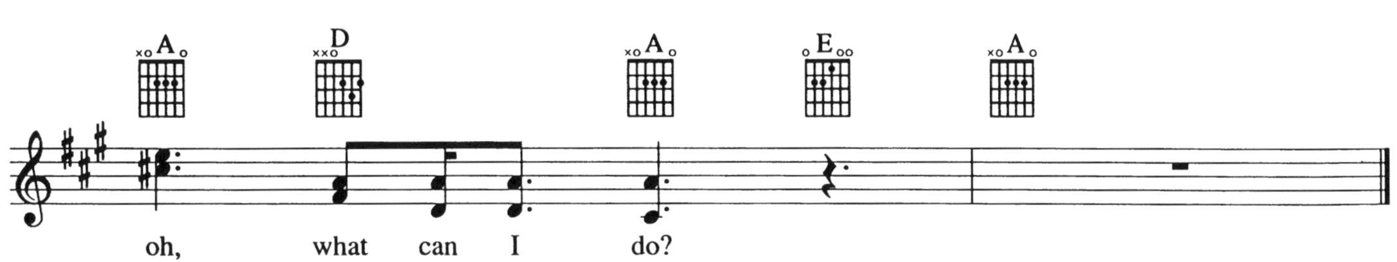
A
D
A
E
A
oh, what can I do?

Can't Buy Me Love.

Words & Music by John Lennon & Paul McCartney.

Moderately
Em Am Em
Can't buy me love, oh, love, oh,
Am Dm7 G13 C
can't buy me love, oh.
1. I'll buy you a dia - mond ring,
2. give you all I've got
3. Instrumental
my friend if it makes you feel all right,
to give if you say you love me too,
F7
I'll get you an - y - thing,
I may not have a lot
C
my friend, if it makes you feel all - right
to give, But what I've got I'll give to you,
G
'Cause
For
I don't care too
F7 Tacet F7
much for mon - ey, for mon - ey can't buy me love.
1 C
2. I'll
2,3 C
Can't buy me love,
vocal 3x
Em Am C
oh, ev - 'ry - bod - y tells me so. Can't buy me love,

Em
Am
Dm7
G
C
oh, no no no no! Say you don't need no dia -

F7
- mond rings and I'll be sat - is - fied, Tell me that you want the kind

C
G
of things that mon - ey just can't buy. I don't care too

F7
To Coda
F7
C
Tacet
D.S. al Coda
much for mon - ey, mon - ey can't buy me love.

Coda
F7
C
Em
Am
mon - ey can't buy me love. Can't buy me love love

Em
Am
Dm7
G13
C
can't buy me love.

Eight Days A Week.

Words & Music by John Lennon & Paul McCartney.

Moderately
D
E7
G
D
1. Ooh I need your love, babe, guess you know it's true.
2. Love you ev - 'ry day, girl, al - ways on my mind.
E7
G
D
Hope you need my love, babe, just like I need you.
One thing I can say, girl, love you all the time.
Bm
G
Bm
E7
Hold me, love me, Hold me, love me. I
D
E7
G
D
ain't got noth - in' but love, girl, eight days a week.
A(no 3rd)
Bm
Eight days a week, I love you.
3
E
G
A
Eight days a week, is not e - nough to show I care.

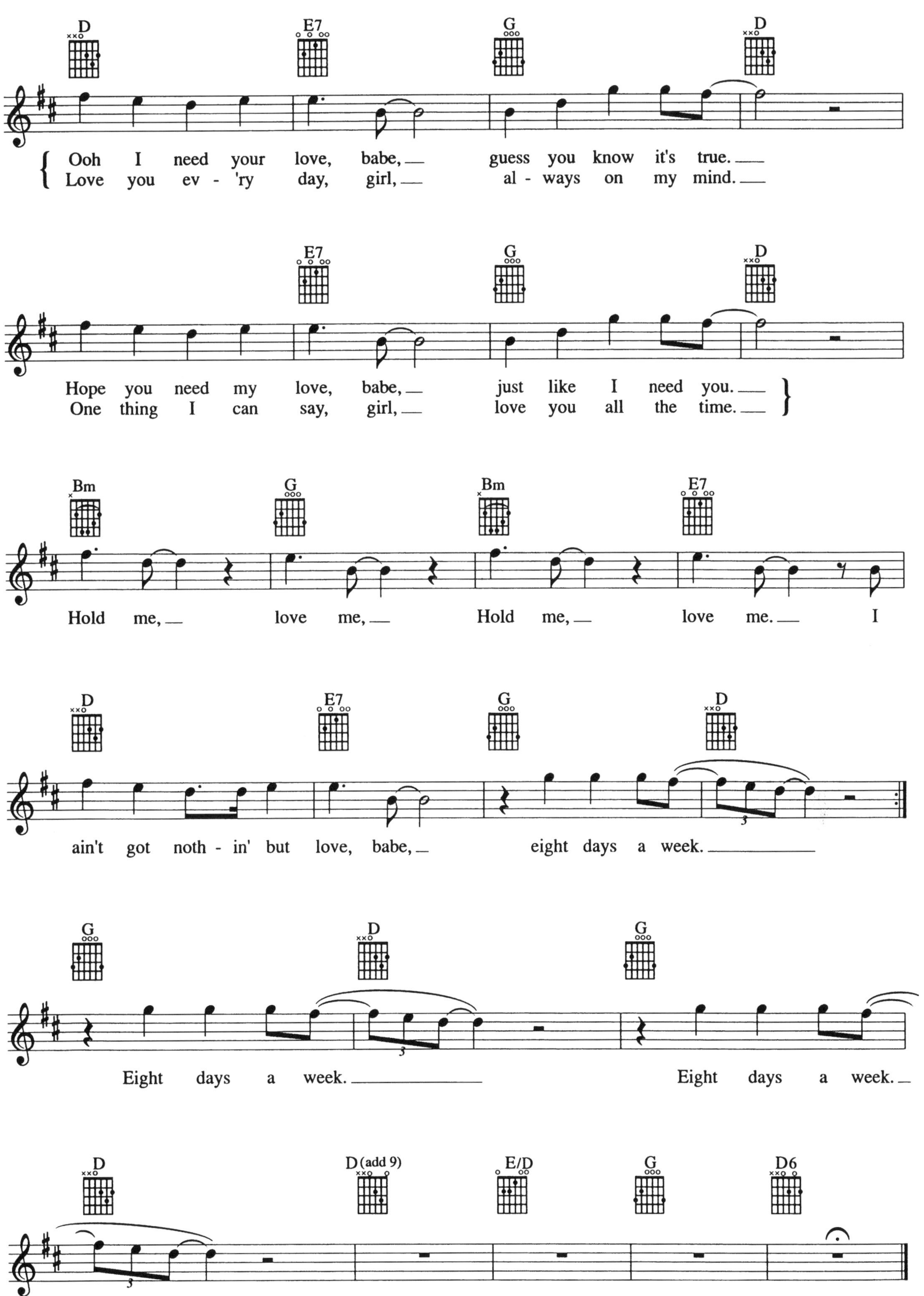
D E7 G D
Ooh I need your love, babe, guess you know it's true.
Love you ev - 'ry day, girl, al - ways on my mind.
E7 G D
Hope you need my love, babe, just like I need you.
One thing I can say, girl, love you all the time.
Bm G Bm E7
Hold me, love me, Hold me, love me. I
D E7 G D
ain't got noth - in' but love, babe, eight days a week.
G D G
Eight days a week. Eight days a week.
D D (add 9) E/D G D6
3

Every Little Thing.

Words & Music by John Lennon & Paul McCartney.

Moderately
A
D
E
A
When I'm walk - ing be - side her, peo - ple tell me I'm
I re - mem - ber the first time, I was lone - ly with -
G
D
Bm
Bm/A
E/G♯
A
3
luck - y. Yes, I know I'm a luck - y guy.
- out her. Yes, I'm think - ing a - bout her now.
A
G
A
Ev - 'ry lit - tle thing she does, she does for me, yeah.
G
A
And you know the things she does, she does for me, ooh.
A
D
E
A
When I'm with her I'm hap - py Just to know that she
There is one thing I'm sure of, I will love her for -

G
D
Bm
Bm/A
E/G♯
A
3
loves __ me.
Yes, I know that she loves me now. __
-ev - er.
For I know love will nev - er die. __

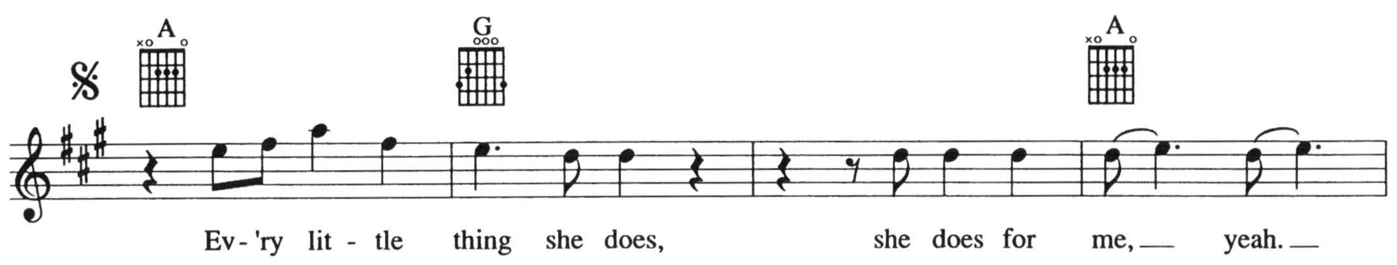
A
G
A
Ev-'ry lit - tle thing she does, she does for me, __ yeah. __

G
A
To Coda
And you know the things she does, she does for me, __ ooh. __

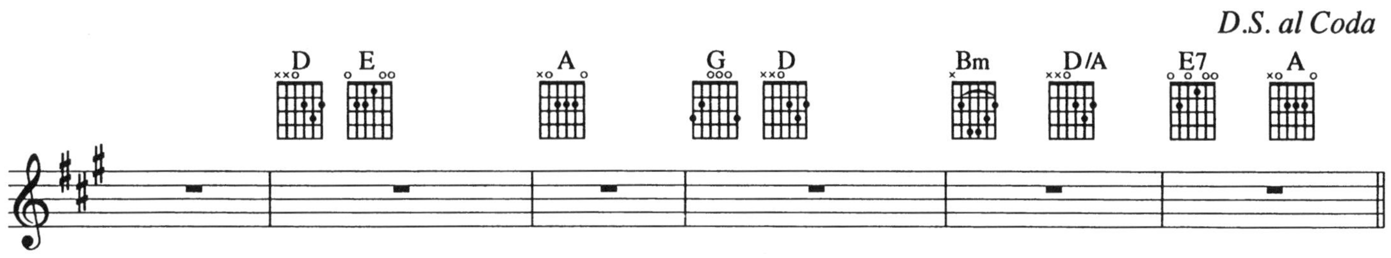
D.S. al Coda
D
E
A
G
D
Bm
D/A
E7
A

Coda
A
E7
A
E7
Repeat and Fade
Ev - 'ry lit - tle thing. __ Ev - 'ry lit - tle

From A Window.

Words & Music by John Lennon & Paul McCartney.

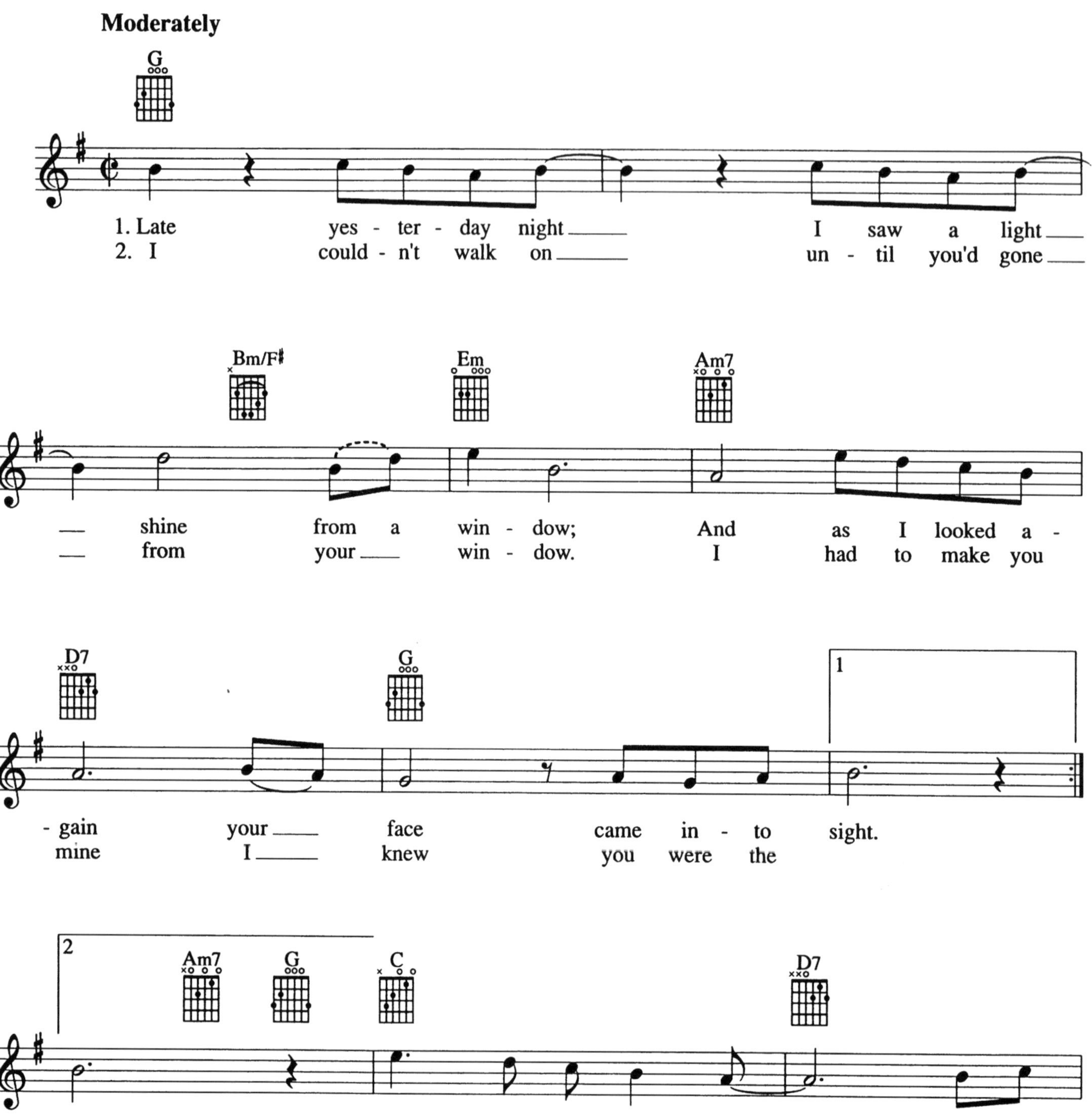
Moderately
G
1. Late yes - ter - day night I saw a light
2. I could - n't walk on un - til you'd gone
Bm/F♯ Em Am7
shine from a win - dow; And as I looked a -
from your win - dow. I had to make you
D7 G
- gain your face came in - to sight.
mine I knew you were the
1
2
Am7 G C D7
one. Oh, I would be glad just to

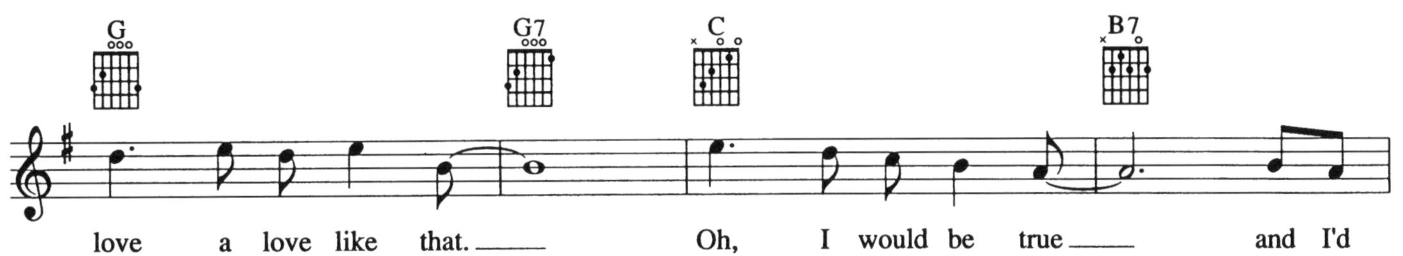
G
G7
C
B7
love a love like that.
Oh, I would be true and I'd

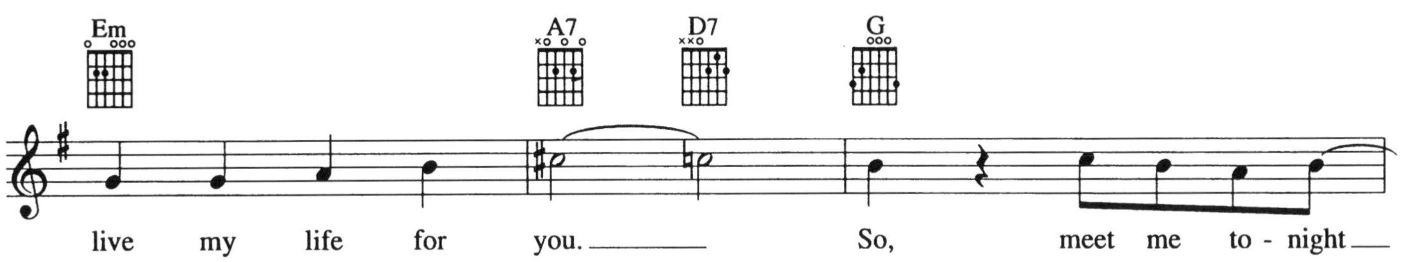
Em
A7
D7
G
live my life for you.
So, meet me to - night

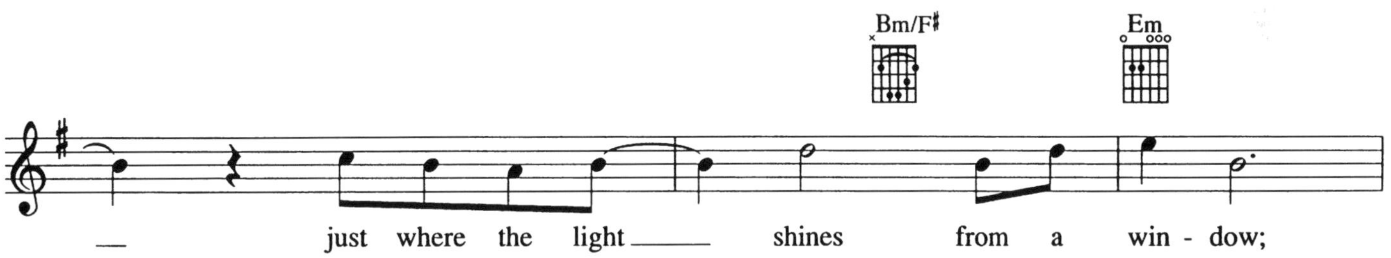
Bm/F♯
Em
just where the light shines from a win - dow;

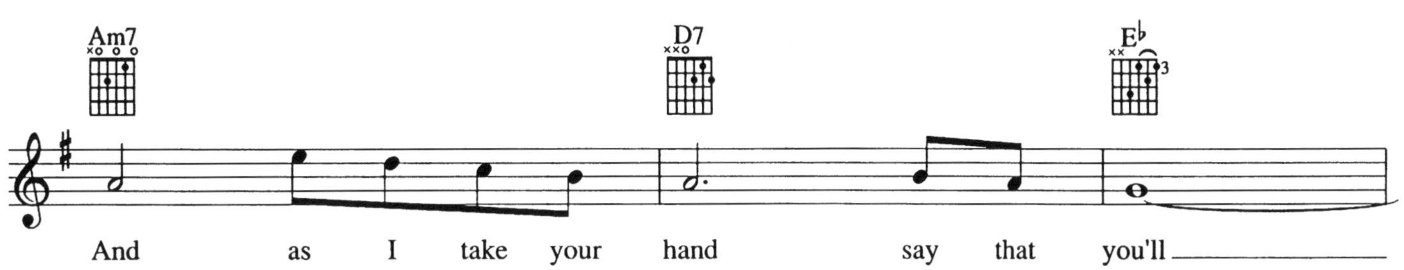
Am7
D7
E♭
And as I take your hand say that you'll

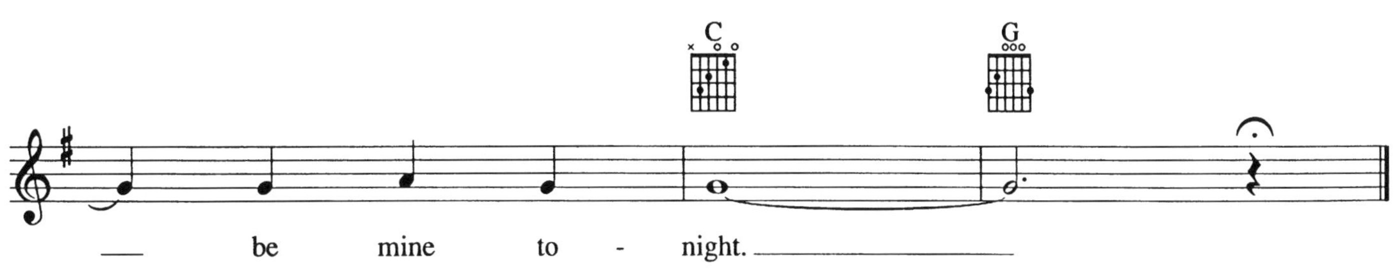
C
G
be mine to - night.

I Don't Want To Spoil The Party.

Words & Music by John Lennon & Paul McCartney.

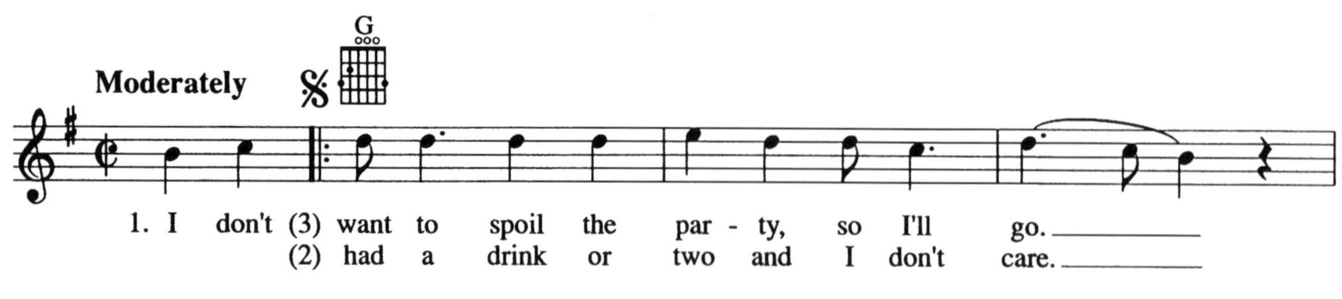
Moderately
G
1. I don't (3) want to spoil the par - ty, so I'll go.
(2) had a drink or two and I don't care.

D
I would hate my dis - ap - point - ment to show.
There's no fun in what I do if she's not there.

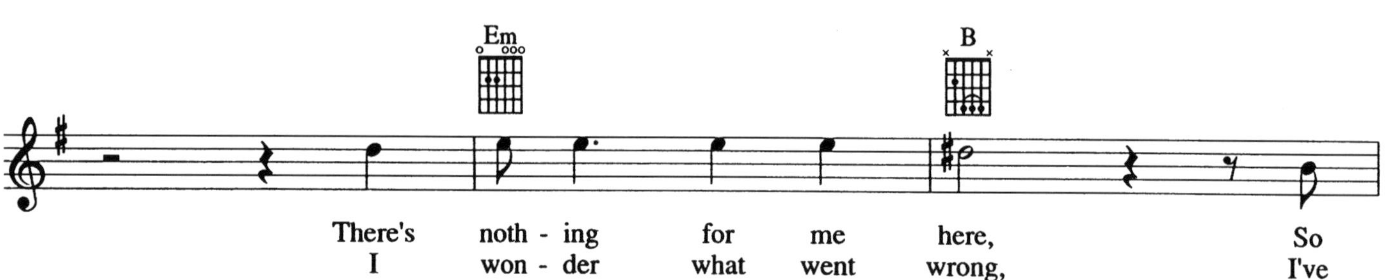
Em
B
There's noth - ing for me here, So
I won - der what went wrong, I've

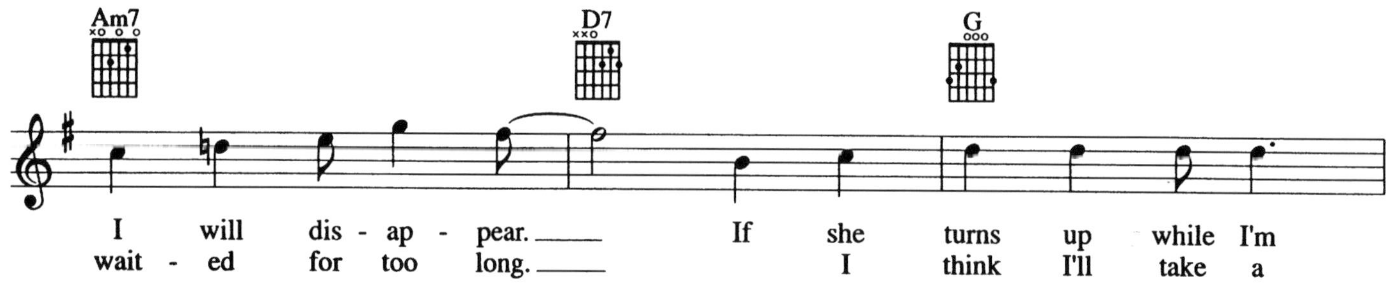
Am7
D7
G
I will dis - ap - pear. If she turns up while I'm
wait - ed for too long. I think I'll take a

F
G
To Coda
1
gone please let me know. 2. I've
walk and look for her.

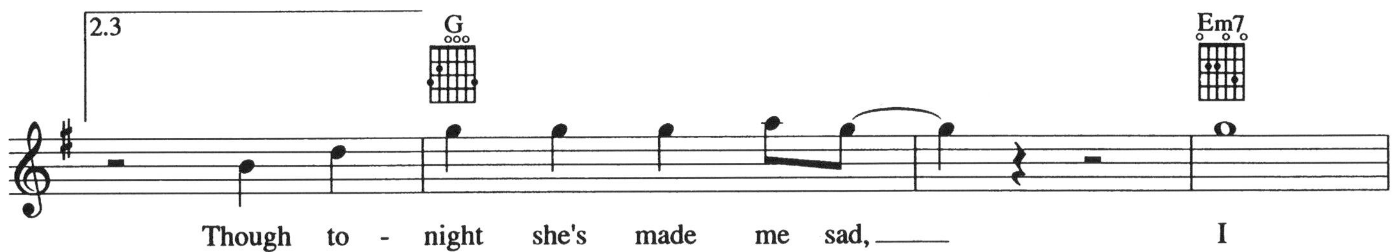
2.3
G
Em7
Though to - night she's made me sad, I

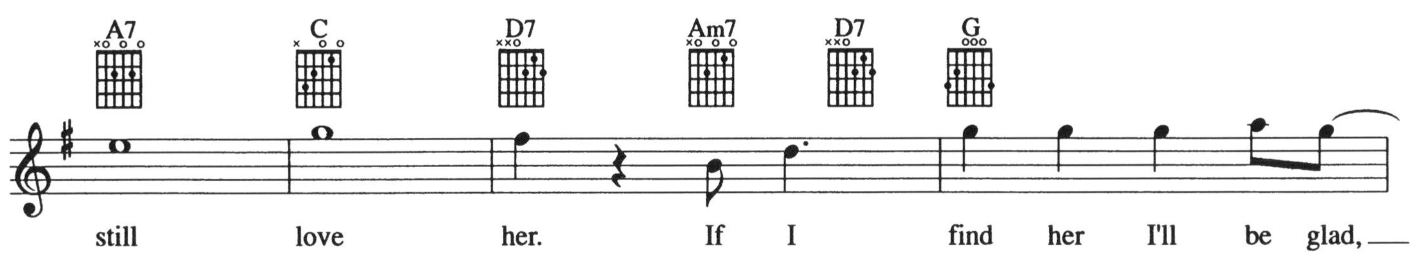
A7 C D7 Am7 D7 G
still love her. If I find her I'll be glad,

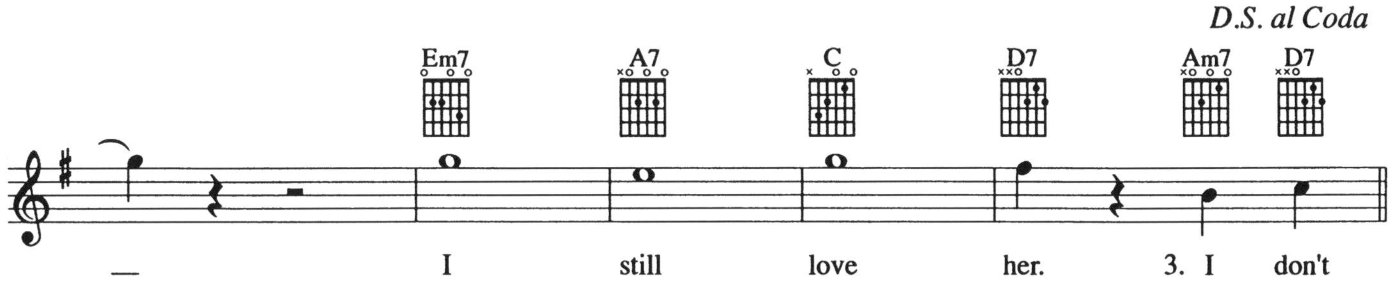
D.S. al Coda
Em7 A7 C D7 Am7 D7
I still love her. 3. I don't

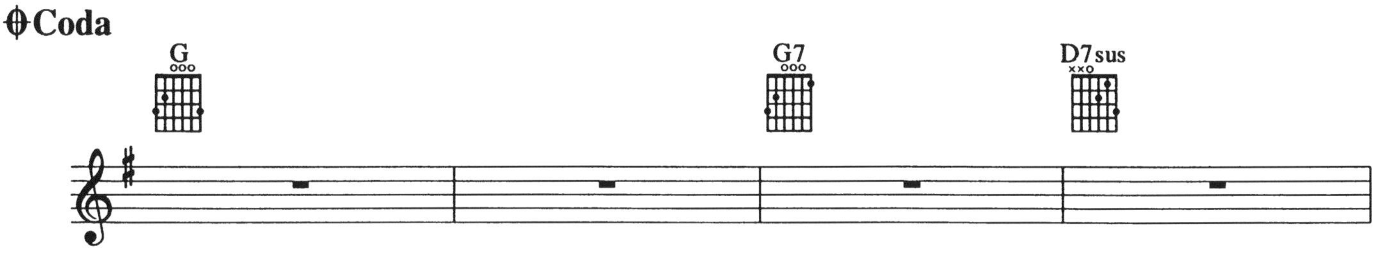
Coda
G G7 D7sus

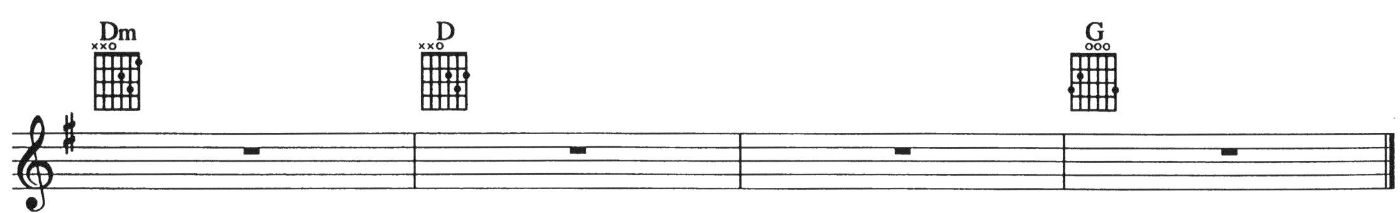
Dm D G

I Feel Fine.

Words & Music by John Lennon & Paul McCartney.

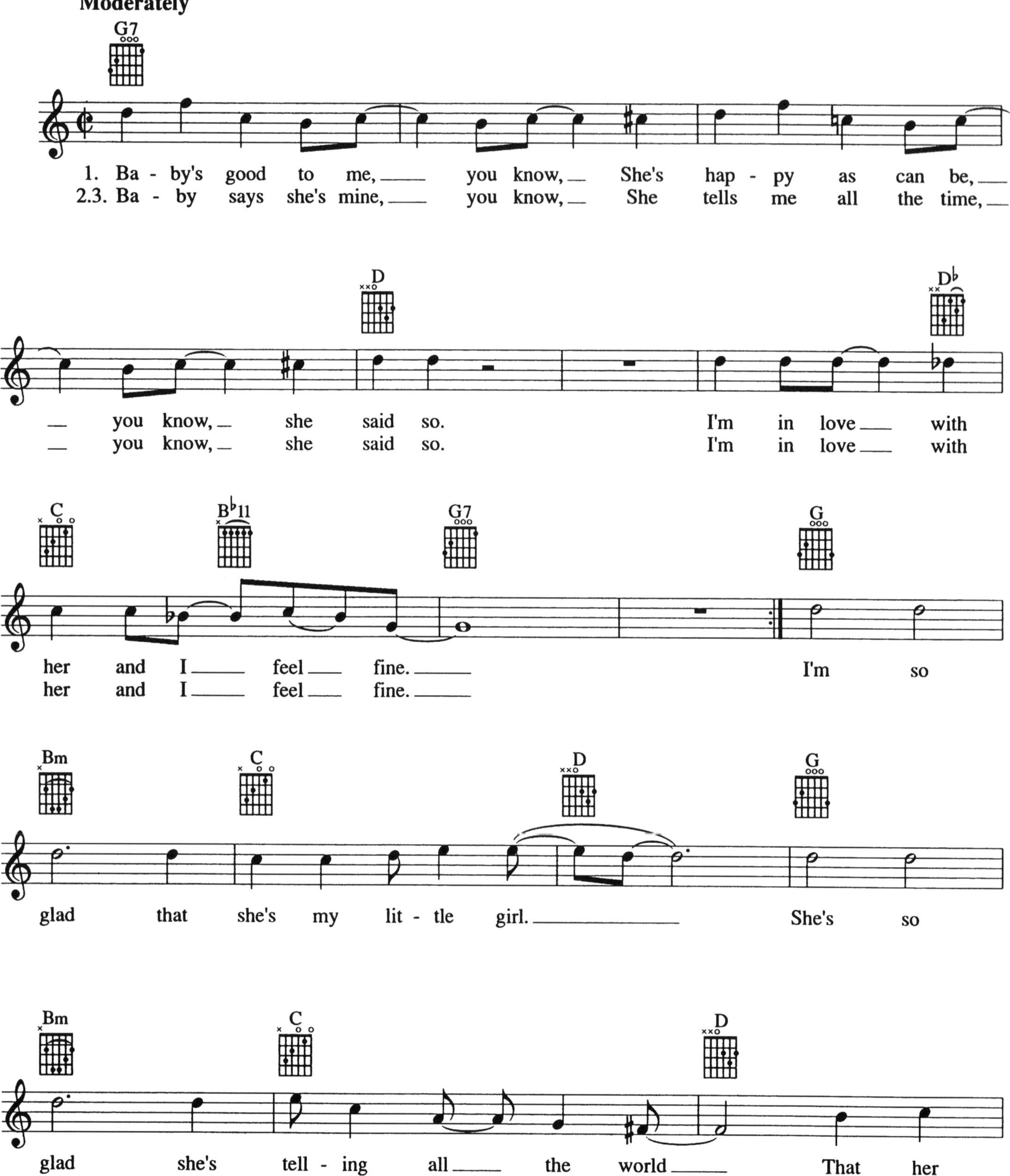
Moderately
G7
1. Ba - by's good to me, you know, She's hap - py as can be,
2.3. Ba - by says she's mine, you know, She tells me all the time,
D
you know, she said so.
you know, she said so.
D♭
I'm in love with
I'm in love with
C
B♭11
G7
her and I feel fine.
her and I feel fine.
G
I'm so
Bm
C
D
G
glad that she's my lit - tle girl.
She's so
Bm
C
D
glad she's tell - ing all the world
That her

G7
ba - by buys her things, ___ you know, ___ he buys her dia - mond rings ___

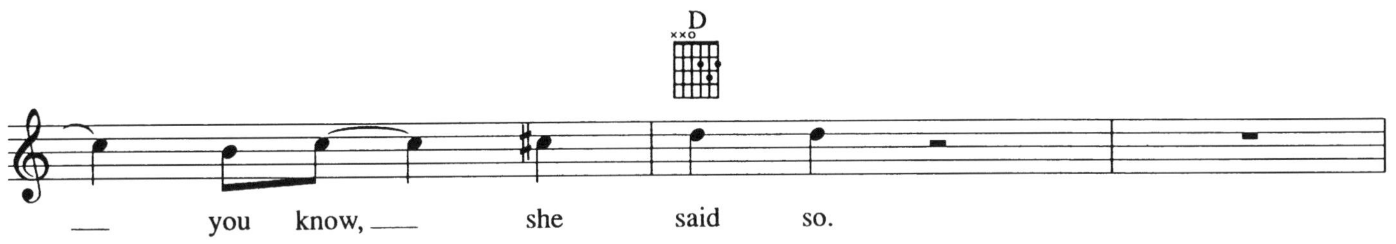
D
___ you know, ___ she said so.

D♭
C
B♭11
To Coda
G7
D.C. al Coda
She's in love ___ with me and I ___ feel ___ fine. ___

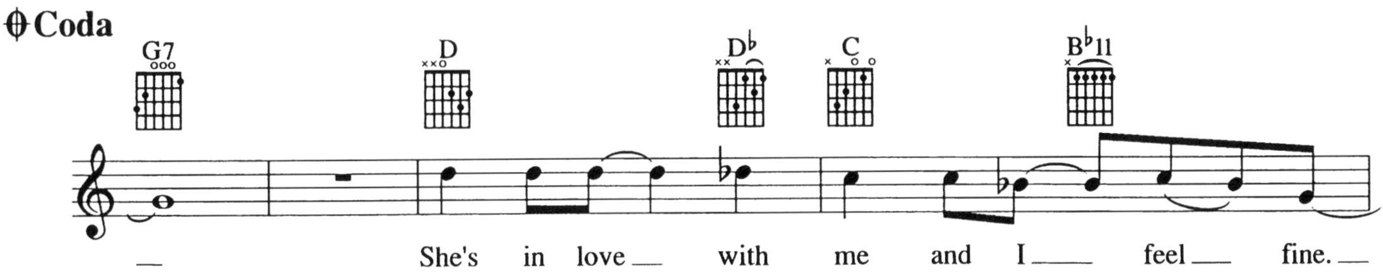
Coda
G7
D
D♭
C
B♭11
___ She's in love ___ with me and I ___ feel ___ fine. ___

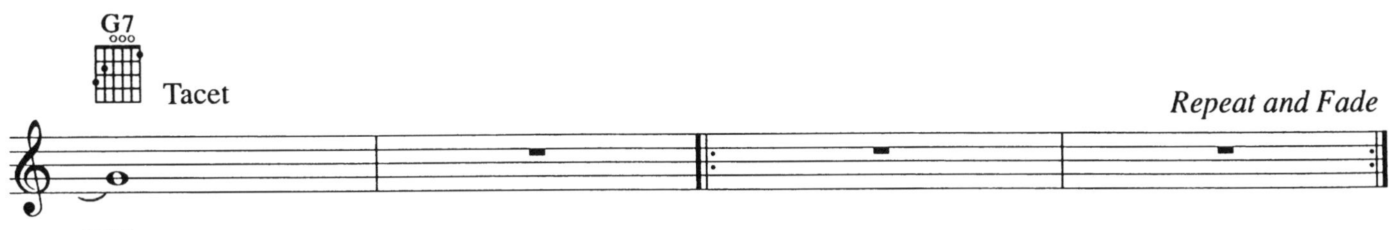
G7
Tacet
Repeat and Fade

I Should Have Known Better.

Words & Music by John Lennon & Paul McCartney.

Moderately
G D G D G D
1. I should have known better with a girl like you,
2.3. I never realized what a kiss could be,
G D G D Em
That I would love ev-'ry-thing that you do; And I do,
This could only happen to me; Can't you see?
1 C D G D
hey, hey, hey, And I do.
G D
Wo wo
2 C B
Can't you see?
Em C G B
That when I tell you that I love you, oh!
Em C G
You're gon-na say you love me too, hoo hoo hoo

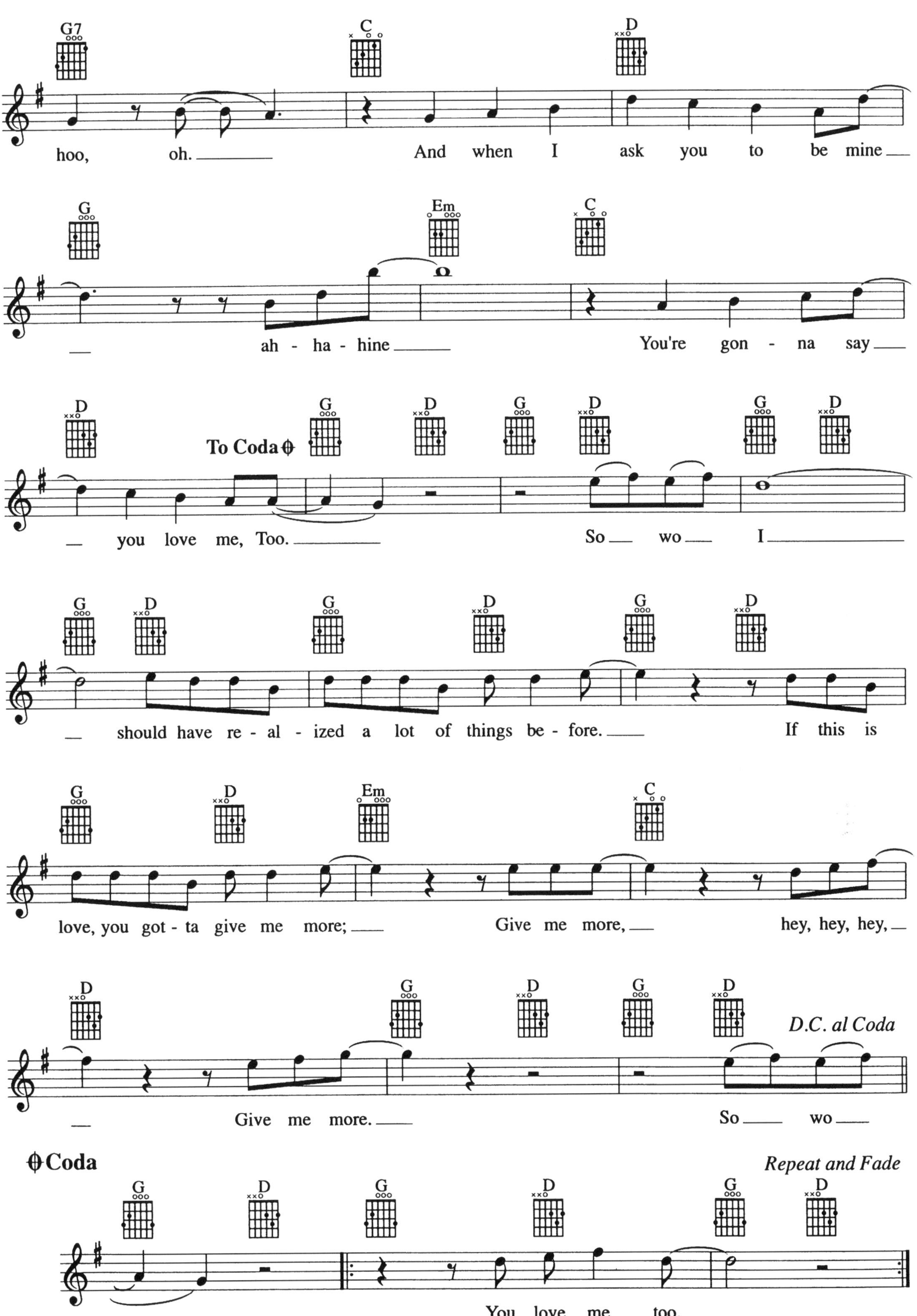
G7 C D
hoo, oh. And when I ask you to be mine
G Em C
ah - ha - hine You're gon - na say
D To Coda G D G D G D
you love me, Too. So wo I
G D G D G D
should have re - al - ized a lot of things be - fore. If this is
G D Em C
love, you got - ta give me more; Give me more, hey, hey, hey,
D G D G D D.C. al Coda
Give me more. So wo
Coda Repeat and Fade
G D G D G D
You love me too.

I Wanna Be Your Man.

Words & Music by John Lennon & Paul McCartney.

Moderately
E♭7
1.3. I wan-na be your lov-er, ba-by, I wan-na be your man.
2. Tell me that you love me, ba-by, Let me un-der-stand.
I wan-na be your lov-er, ba-by, I wan-na be your man.
Tell me that you love me, ba-by, I wan-na be your man.
Love you like no oth-er, ba-by, Like no oth-er can.
I wan-na be your lov-er, ba-by, I wan-na be your man.
Love you like no oth-er, ba-by, Like no oth-er can.
I wan-na be your lov-er, ba-by, I wan-na be your man.
Tacet
F7
B♭7
E♭
I wan-na be your man,
I wan-na be your man,
C7
F7
B♭7
E♭7
I wan-na be your man,
I wan-na be your man.
1.2
3
E♭7
Repeat and Fade
I wan-na be your man.

I Don't Want To See You Again.

Words & Music by John Lennon & Paul McCartney.

Moderately
F
Am
B♭m
C7
3
1. I hear that love is planned. How can I un - der - stand
2. Why do I cry at night? Some - thing wrong could be right.
when some - one says to me I don't want to see you a - gain?
I hear you say to me I don't want to see you a -
1
2
F/A
B♭
- gain As you turned your back on me, you hid the light of
Dm
Gm
A7
G7
day. I did - n't have to play at be - ing brok - en heart - ed.
I know that lat - er on af - ter love's been and gone,
I'll still hear some - one say I don't want to see you a - gain.

I'll Be Back.

Words & Music by John Lennon & Paul McCartney.

Moderately
Gm
B♭/F
F
E♭
1. You know if you break my heart I'll go, But I'll be back again.
2. You could find better things to do, than to break my heart again.
D7
G
'Cause I told you once before goodbye, But I came back again.
This time I will try to show that I'm not trying to pretend.
Em7
Em
Am
I love you so oh, I'm the one who wants you.
I wanna go, But I hate to leave you.
C
Yes, I'm the one who wants you, oh ho, oh ho. oh
You know I hate to leave you, oh ho, oh ho. oh
You could find better things to do than to
You, If you break my heart, I'll go; but

D7
G
To Coda
Gm
break my heart a - gain.
I'll be back a - gain.
This time I will

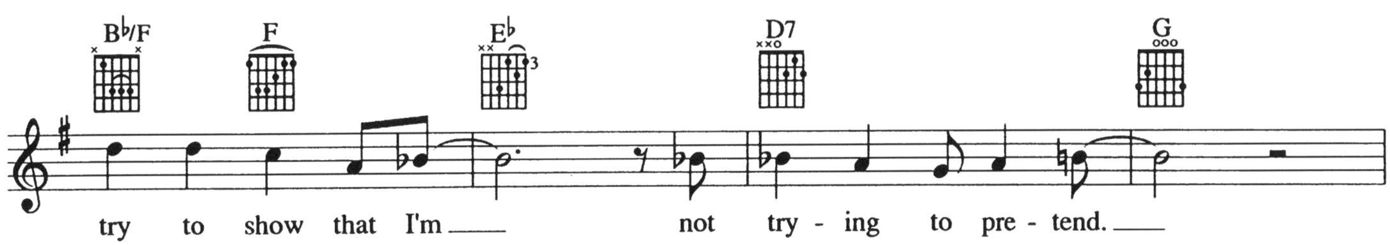
B♭/F
F
E♭
D7
G
try to show that I'm not try - ing to pre - tend.

Am7
Bm
I thought that you would re - al - ize

Em
A7
That if I ran a - way from you, that you would want me too, But

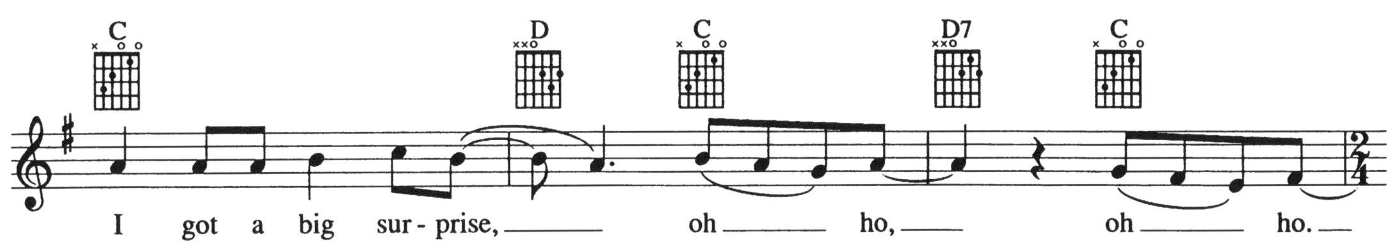
C
D
C
D7
C
I got a big sur - prise, oh ho, oh ho.

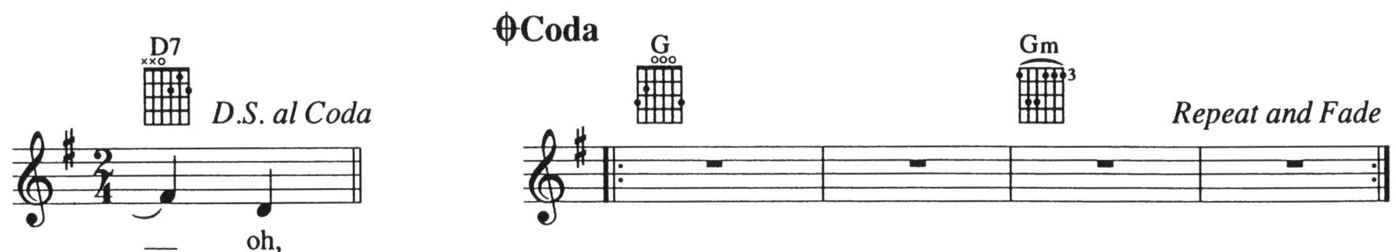
D7
D.S. al Coda
Coda
G
Gm
Repeat and Fade
oh,

I'll Cry Instead.

Words & Music by John Lennon & Paul McCartney.

Bright Tempo
G D11 G D11
I've got ev - 'ry reas - on on earth to be mad,
(2) chip on my shoul - der that's big - ger than my feet,
G D11 G D11 G D11 G
'Cause I've just lost the on - ly girl I had;
I can't talk to peo - ple that I meet;
D7 C7
And if I could get my way, I'd
If I could see you now, I'd
G
get my - self locked up to - day, But I can't, So I'll cry
try to make you say it some - how, But I can't, So I'll cry
D7 G D11 1 G D11 2 G Cmaj7
in - stead. 2. I've got a Don't want to
in - stead.
Bm A
cry when there's peo - ple there, I get shy when they start to stare,

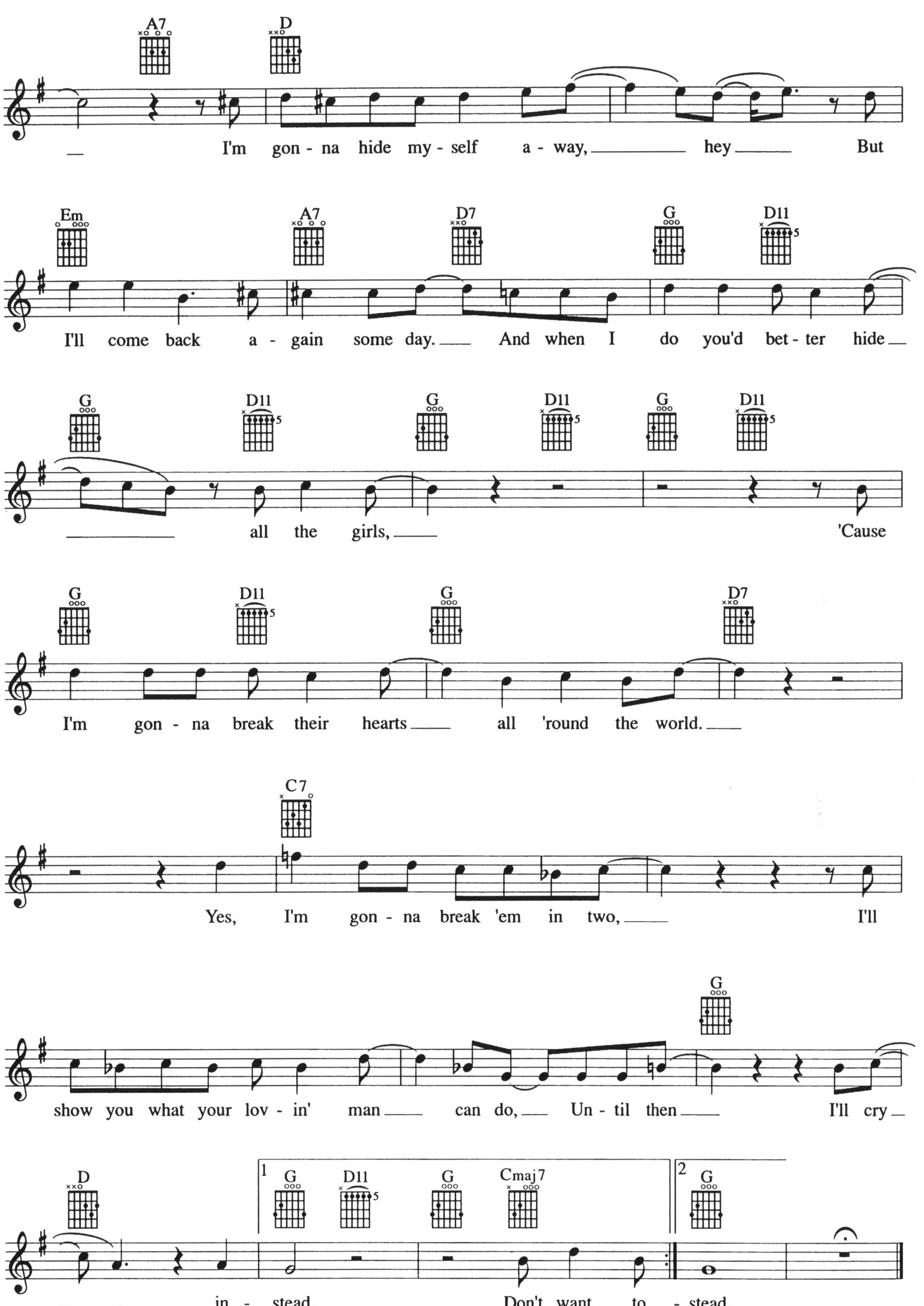
A7 D
— I'm gon - na hide my - self a - way, — hey — But
Em A7 D7 G D11
I'll come back a - gain some day. — And when I do you'd bet - ter hide —
G D11 G D11 G D11
— all the girls, — 'Cause
G D11 G D7
I'm gon - na break their hearts — all 'round the world. —
C7
Yes, I'm gon - na break 'em in two, — I'll
G
show you what your lov - in' man — can do, — Un - til then — I'll cry —
D 1 G D11 G Cmaj7 2 G
— in - stead. Don't want to - stead.

I'll Follow The Sun.

Words & Music by John Lennon & Paul McCartney.

Moderately
G F7 C D7
1. One day you'll look to see I've gone, For to-
2. Some-day you'll know I was the one, But to-
3. Instrumental Yeah, to-
C Em/B D7 G7 C Dm7/G F C
-mor-row may rain, so I'll fol-low the sun.
-mor-row may rain, so I'll fol-low the
-mor-row may rain, so I'll fol-low the
C C7 Dm7 Fm
sun. And now the time has come, And so, my love, I must go.
C C7 Dm7 Fm
And though I lose a friend in the end you will know.
C Dm7 G F7
Oh, One day you'll find
C D7 C Em/B
that I have gone, But to-mor-row may rain. So
D7 G7 C Dm7/G F C F C
I'll fol-low the sun.

It's For You.

Words & Music by John Lennon & Paul McCartney.

Moderately
Dm Dm7 G/D Gm/D F B♭ E♭
1. I'd say some day I'm bound to give my heart a -
(2) you love, true love Seems to be all I'm think - ing
(3) love comes, love shows, I give my heart and no - one
A♭ Gm Gm7 To Coda C9 1 Tacet 2 Tacet
- way, when I do 2. It's for it's for
of, but it's true,
knows that I do;
F Gm Am Gm F Gm6/B♭ A7 Dm
you. They said that love was a lie,
So I just tell them they're right;
G Gm6
Told me that I Should nev - er try to find Some - bod - y who'd be
Who wants a fight? Tell them I quite a - gree; No - bod - y'd love
Dm Gm/D 1 A7 2 A7
kind, Kind to on - ly me. you. 3. And
me. Then I look at
Coda C9 Tacet F B♭ Dm
It's for you.

I'm A Loser.

Words & Music by John Lennon & Paul McCartney.

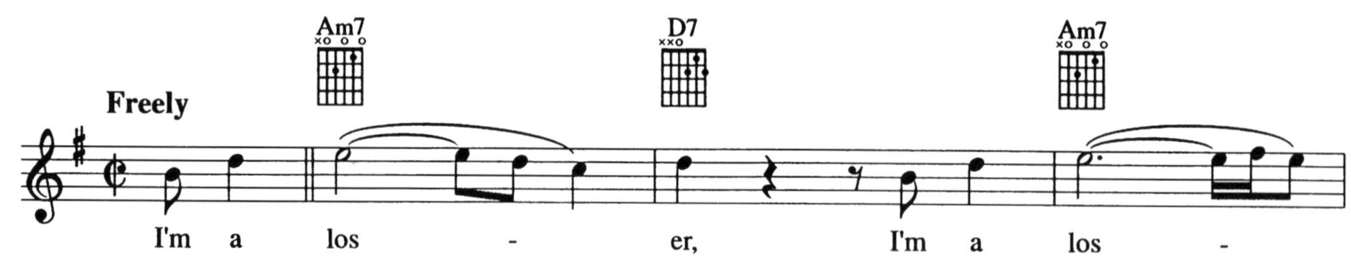
Freely
Am7
D7
Am7
I'm a los - er, I'm a los -

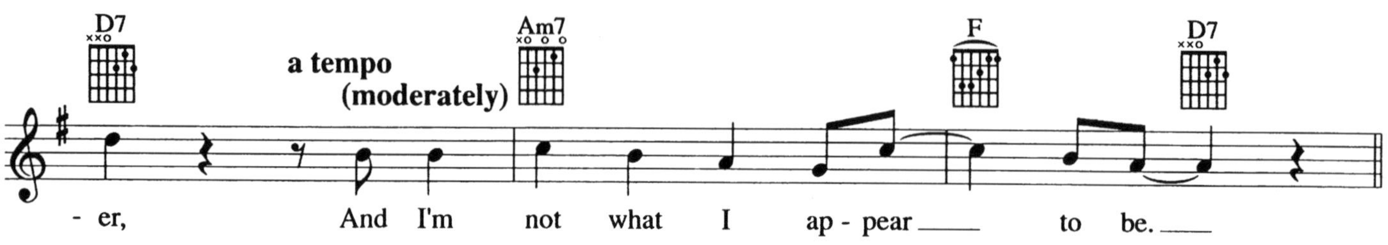
D7
a tempo
(moderately)
Am7
F
D7
- er, And I'm not what I ap - pear to be.

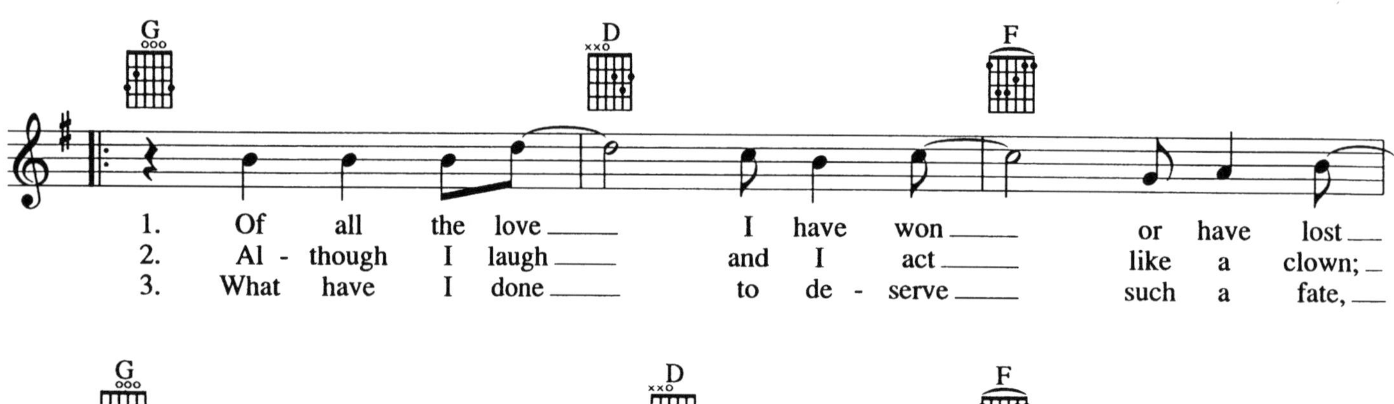
G
D
F
1. Of all the love I have won or have lost
2. Al - though I laugh and I act like a clown;
3. What have I done to de - serve such a fate,

G
D
F
There is one love I should nev - er have crossed.
Be - neath this mask I am wear - ing a frown.
I re - a - lize I have left it too late.

G
D
She was a girl in a mil -
My tears are fal - ling like rain
And so it's true pride comes be -

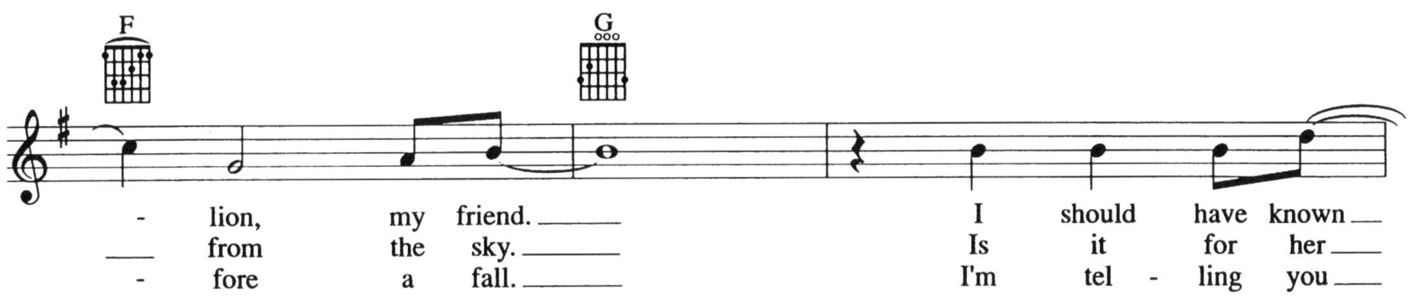
F
G
- lion, my friend.
I should have known
from the sky.
Is it for her
- fore a fall.
I'm tel - ling you

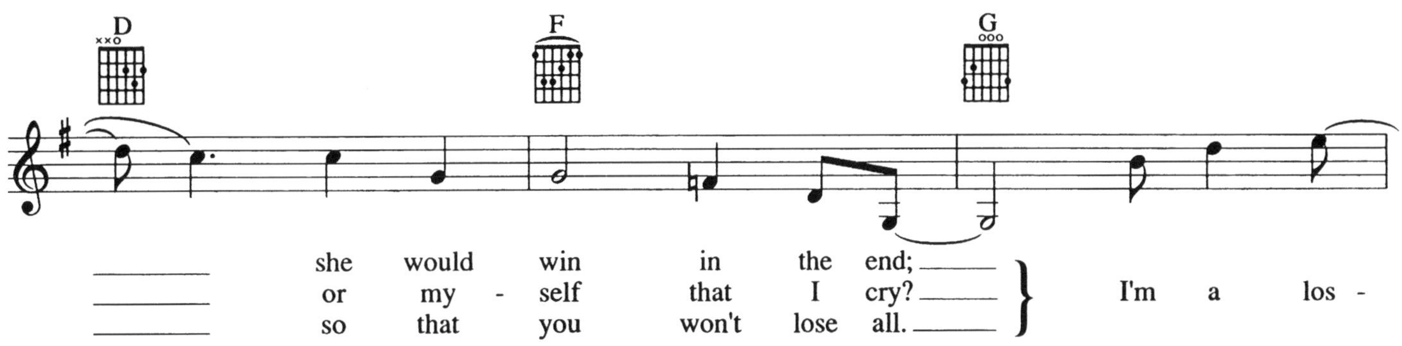
D
F
G
she would win in the end;
or my - self that I cry?
so that you won't lose all.
I'm a los -

Am7
D7
Am7
- er,
And I lost
some - one who's near

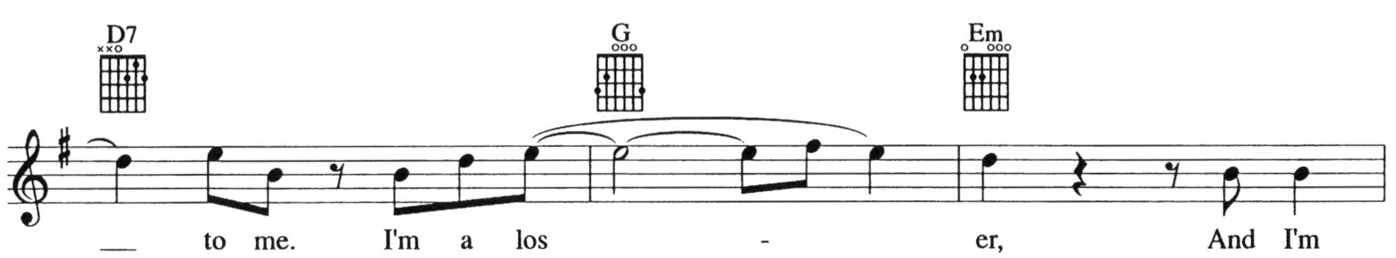
D7
G
Em
to me. I'm a los - er,
And I'm

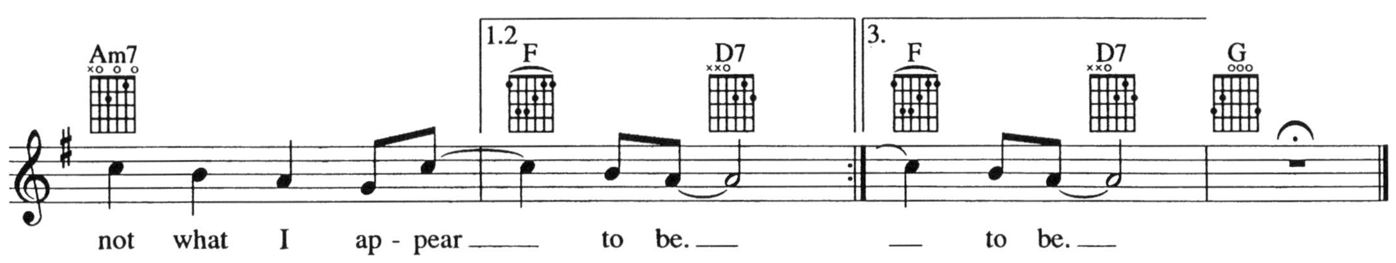
Am7
1.2
F
D7
3.
F
D7
G
not what I ap - pear to be.
to be.

I'm Happy Just To Dance With You.

Words & Music by John Lennon & Paul McCartney.

Moderately
Cm
Fm
G7
Be - fore this dance is through, I think I'll love you too; I'm so
A♭
B♭7
E♭
B♭7
E♭
Gm
hap - py when you dance with me. 1. I don't want to kiss or hold your hand,
(2) need to hug or hold you tight,
Fm7
B♭7
E♭
Gm
Fm7
B♭7
If it's fun - ny, try and un - der - stand. There is
I just wan - na dance with you all night. In this
A♭
E♭
Cm7
real - ly noth - ing else I'd rath - er do,
world there's noth - ing I would rath - er do,
'Cause I'm
A♭
B♭+
1
E♭
B♭7
2
E♭
hap - py just to dance with you. 2. I don't you. Just to
Cm
Fm
G
Cm
dance with you, is ev - 'ry - thing I

Fm G Cm Fm G7
need. Be - fore this dance is through, I think I'll love you too; I'm so
A♭ B♭7 E♭ Gm7
hap - py when you dance with me. 3. If some - bod - y tries to take my place,
Fm7 B♭7 E♭ Gm7 Fm7 B♭7
Let's pre - tend we just can't see his face. In this
A♭ E♭ Cm7
world there's noth - ing I would rath - er do
'Cause I'm
I've dis -
A♭ B♭+ 1 E♭
hap - py just to dance with you. Just to
- cov - ered I'm in love with
2 Cm Fm G A♭ B♭+
you. 'Cause I'm hap - py just to dance with
Cm Fm7 G7 A♭6 B♭7 E♭6
you, oh, oh, oh, oh, oh!

If I Fell.

Words & Music by John Lennon & Paul McCartney.

Moderately
E♭m7
D
If I fell in love with you would you prom - ise to be true and

D♭
B♭m
E♭m
help me un - der - stand? 'Cause I've been in love be - fore and I

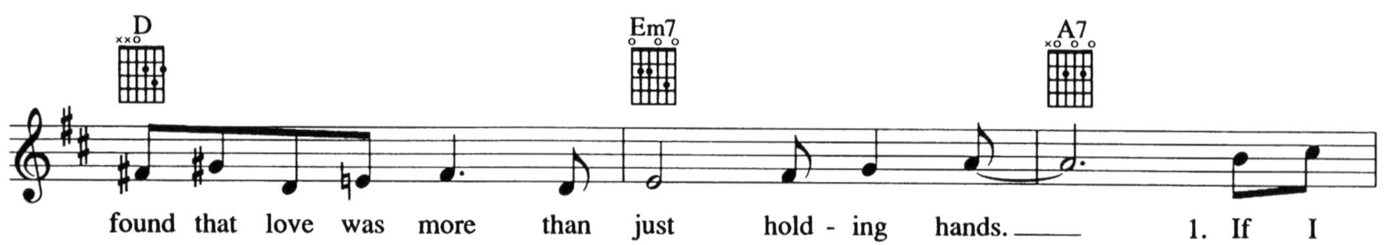
D
Em7
A7
found that love was more than just hold - ing hands. 1. If I

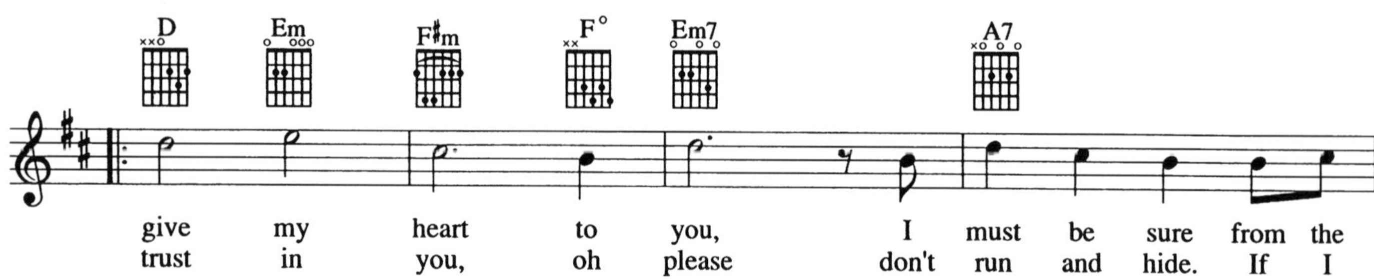
D
Em
F♯m
F°
Em7
A7
give my heart to you, I must be sure from the
trust in you, oh please don't run and hide. If I

D
Em
F♯m
F°
Em7
A7
ver - y start that you would love me more than
love you too, oh please don't hurt my pride like

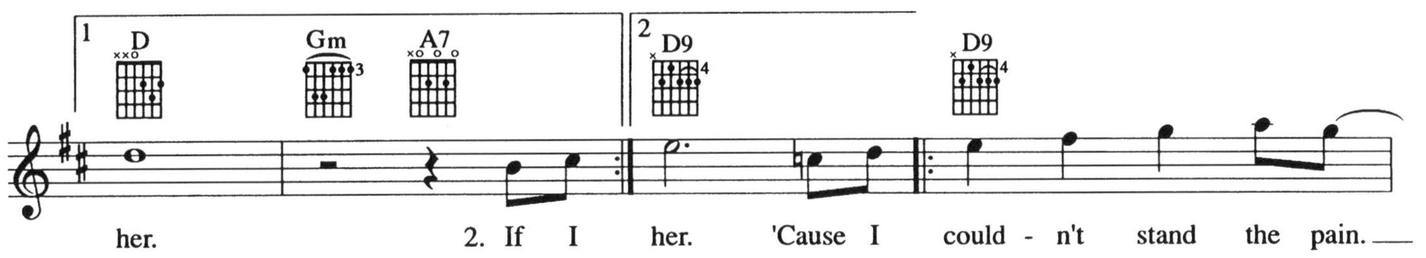
1
D
Gm
A7
2
D9
D9
her.
2. If I
her.
'Cause I
could - n't stand the pain.

G
Gm
D
And I
would be sad if our new love was in

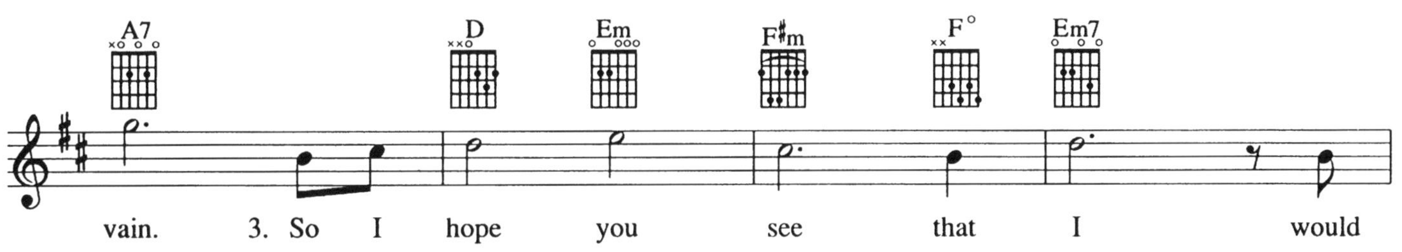
A7
D
Em
F♯m
F°
Em7
vain.
3. So I hope you see that I would

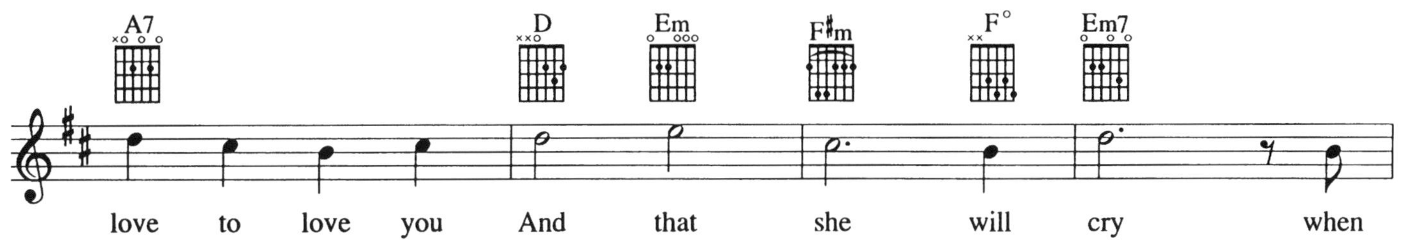
A7
D
Em
F♯m
F°
Em7
love to love you And that she will cry when

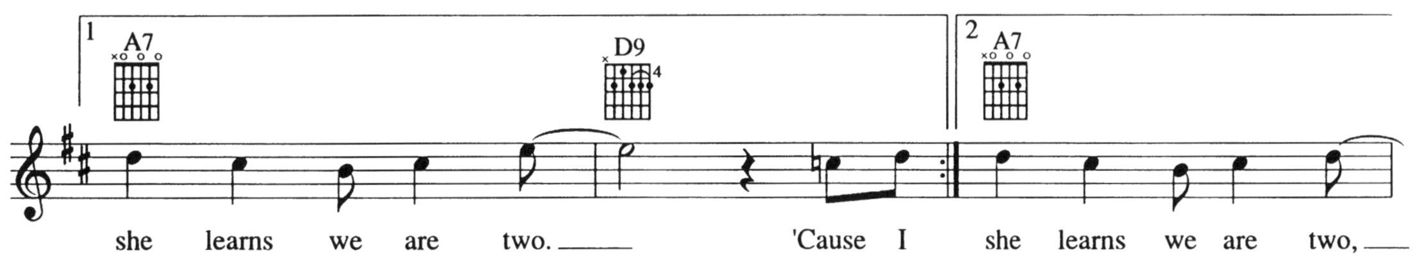
1
A7
D9
2
A7
she learns we are two.
'Cause I
she learns we are two,

D
Gm
D
Gm
D
If I fell in love with you.

Like Dreamers Do.

Words & Music by John Lennon & Paul McCartney.

Moderately
F
Dm
3
3
1. Dreams, I saw a girl in my dreams,
2. You, You came just one dream a - go,

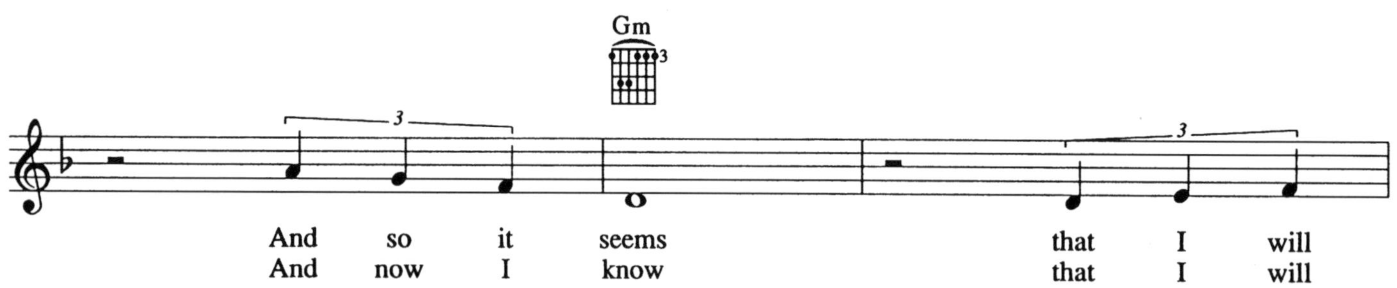
Gm
3
3
3
And so it seems that I will
And now I know that I will

C7
F
3
3
love her. Oh you, you are the girl in my
love you. Oh I know when you first said "hel -

Dm
Gm
3
3
3
dreams, And so it seems that I will
- lo," That's how I know that I will

C7
F
love you.
love you.
And I yi yi yi yi wait - ed for your

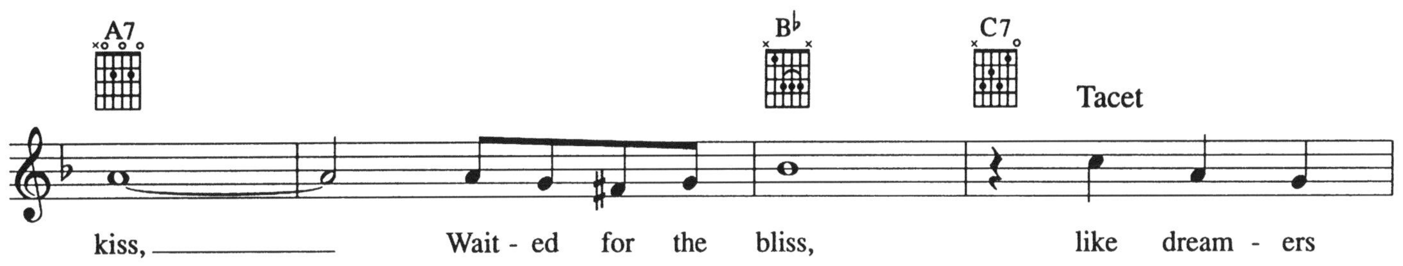
A7
B♭
C7
Tacet
kiss, Wait - ed for the bliss, like dream - ers

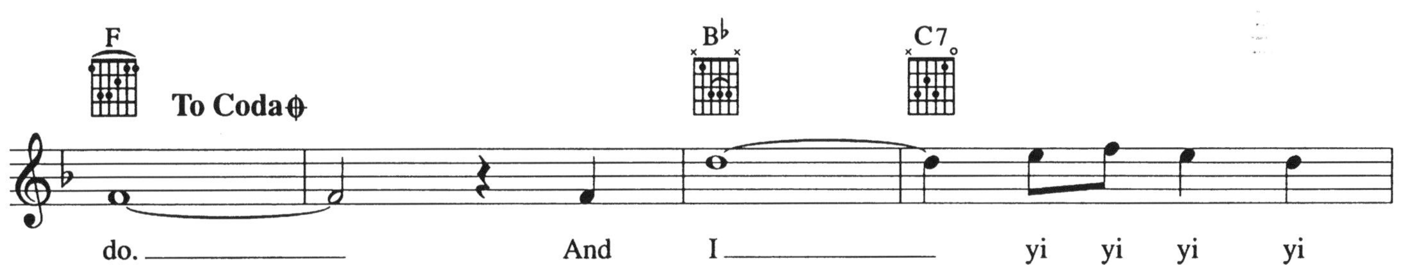
F
To Coda
B♭
C7
do. And I yi yi yi yi

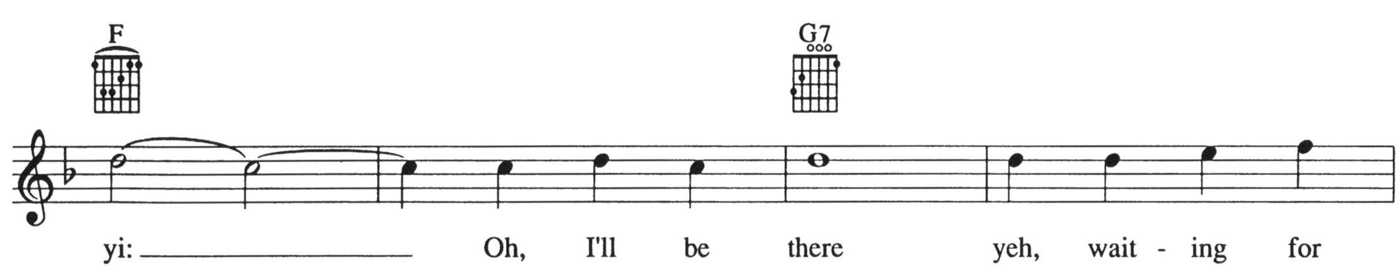
F
G7
yi: Oh, I'll be there yeh, wait - ing for

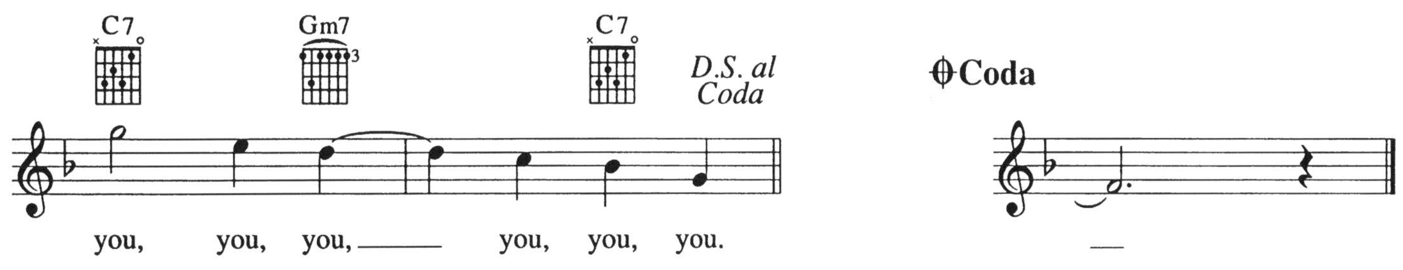
C7
Gm7
C7
D.S. al Coda
Coda
you, you, you, you, you, you.

No Reply.

Words & Music by John Lennon & Paul McCartney.

Moderately
F
G7
1. This hap - pened once be - fore when I came to your door, no re -
(2.3) phone, they said you were not home, that's a

C
F
- ply. They said it was - n't you, but I saw you peep
lie. 'Cause I know where you've been, and I saw you walk

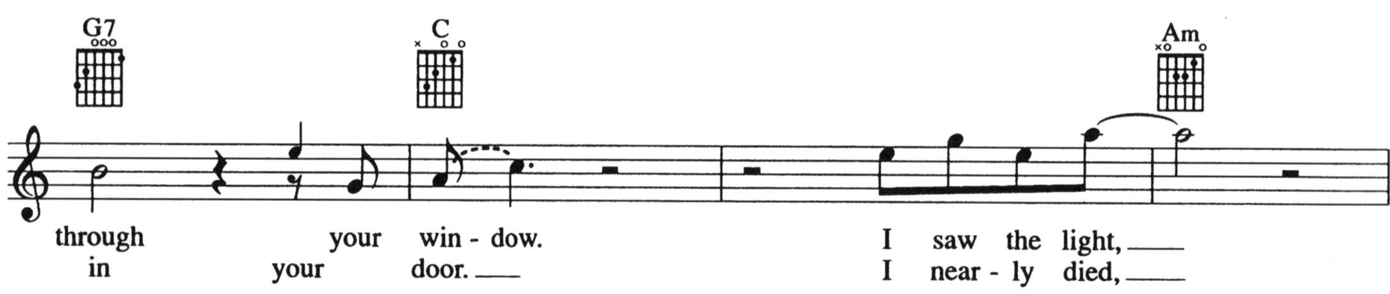
G7
C
Am
through your win - dow. I saw the light,
in your door. I near - ly died,

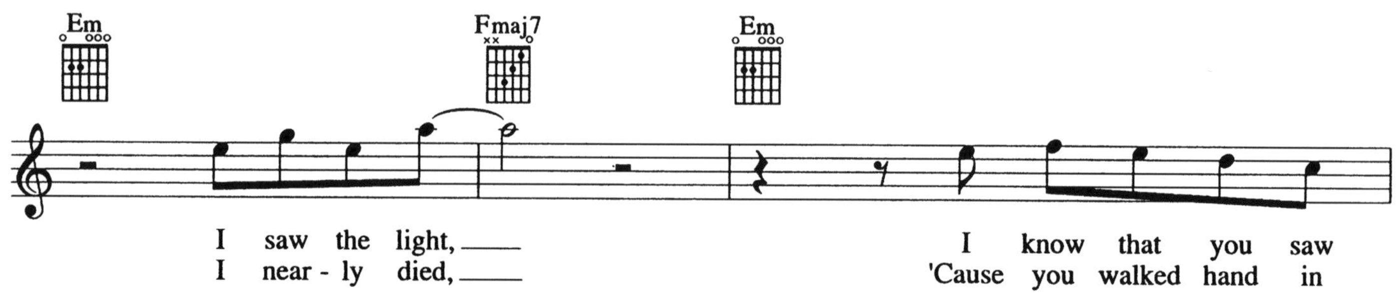
Em
Fmaj7
Em
I saw the light, I know that you saw
I near - ly died, 'Cause you walked hand in

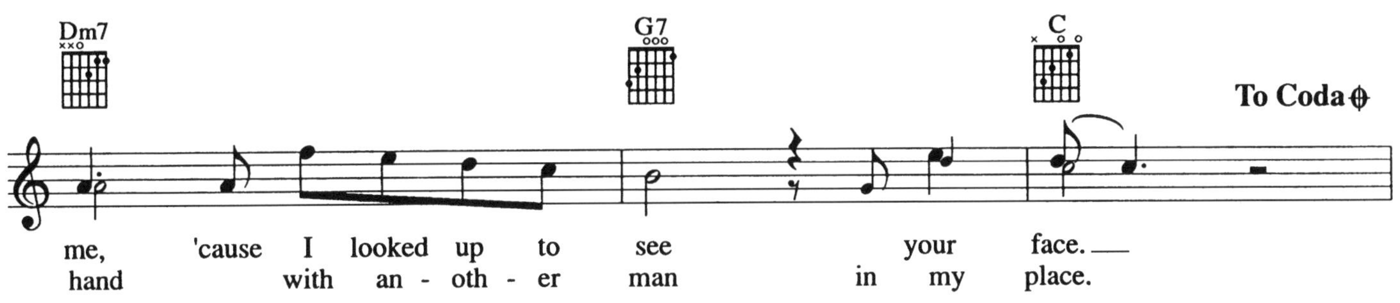
Dm7
G7
C
To Coda
me, 'cause I looked up to see your face.
hand with an - oth - er man in my place.

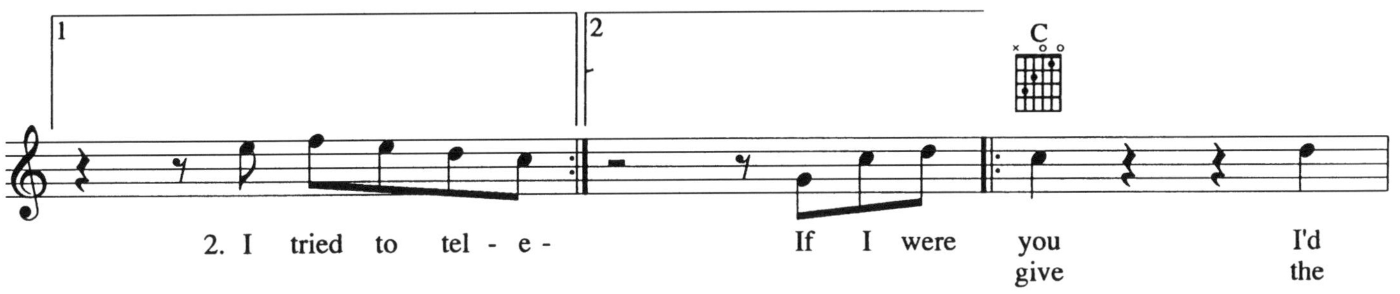
1
2
C
2. I tried to tel - e -
If I were you I'd
give the

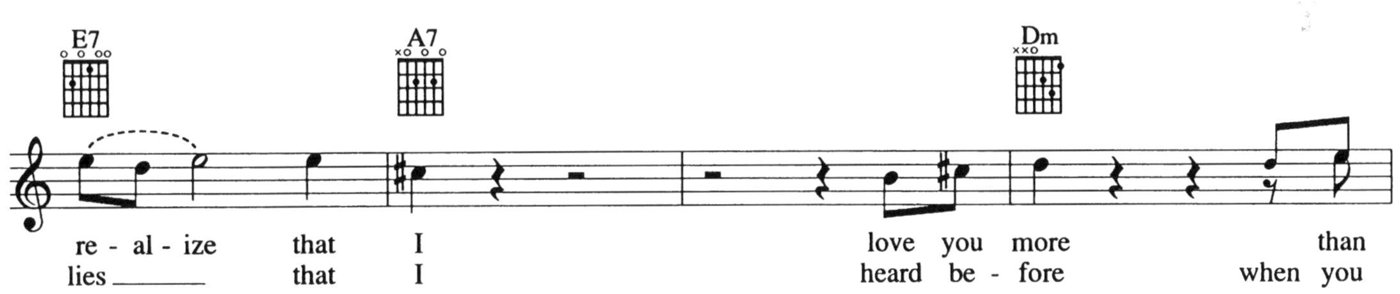
E7
A7
Dm
re - al - ize that I love you more than
lies that I heard be - fore when you

F
C
1
2
D.S. al Coda
an - y oth - er guy. And I'll for - 3. I tried to tel - e -
gave me no re - ply.

Coda
C
Am
Em
Fmaj7
C6 (add 9)
No re - ply, No re - ply.

Nobody I Know.

Words & Music by John Lennon & Paul McCartney.

Moderately
C
Dm7
G7
1.3. No - bod - y I know could love me more than you.
2. Ev - 'ry - where I go the sun comes shin - ing through.
B♭
D7
You can give me so much love it seems un - true.
Ev - 'ry - one I know is sure it shines for you.
Lis - ten to the bird who
Ev - en in my dreams I
Em
Am
A♭
sings it to the tree and then when you've heard him see if you a - gree.
look in - to your eyes, sud - den - ly it seems I've found a par - a - dise.
No - bod - y I know could love you more than me.
Ev - 'ry - where I go the sun comes shin - ing through.
To Coda
Bm7♭5
E7
It means so much to be a part of a heart of a won - der - ful
one. When oth - er lov - ers are gone, we'll live on;
Tacet
Dm7sus
We'll live on.
D.C. al Coda
Coda

She's A Woman.

Words & Music by John Lennon & Paul McCartney.

Steady 2 beat
G7 C7 G7
1.3.4. My love don't give me pres - ents, I know that
2. She don't give boys the eye. She hates to
C7 G7 C7
she's no peas - ant. On - ly ev - er has to give me
see me cry. She is hap - py just to hear me
G7 C7
love for ev - er and for - ev - er; My love don't give me pres - ents.
say that I will nev - er leave her; She don't give boys the eye.
G7 D7 C7
Turn me on when I get lone - ly, Peo - ple tell me
She will nev - er make me jeal - ous, Gives me all her
G7 C7 G7 1 D7 2.3 G7
that she's on - ly fool - in', I know she is - n't
time as well as lov - in', Don't ask me why.
Bm E7 Bm
She's a wom - an who un - der - stands; She's a wom - an who
C D7 4 G7
Repeat and Fade
loves her man. She's a wom - an, She's a wom -

Tell Me Why.

Words & Music by John Lennon & Paul McCartney.

Moderately
B♭ Gm7 Cm7
Tell me why you cried, And why you
F7 Cm7 F7 B♭ Gm7 Cm7 F13
lied to me. Tell me
B♭ Gm7 Cm7
why you cried, And why you
F7 Cm7 F7 B♭ To Coda Cm7 F7
lied to me.
1. Well, I
2. If it's
B♭ Gm7
gave you ev - 'ry - thing I had, But you
some - thing that I've said or done, Tell me
Cm7 F7
left me sit - ting on my own. Did you
what, and I'll a - pol - o - gize. If you

B♭
Gm7
have to treat me oh, so bad?
All I
don't, I real - ly can't go on
Hold - ing
Cm7
1 F7 F13
2 F7 F13
D.S. al Coda
do is hang my head and moan.
Tell me
Tell me
back these tears in my eyes.
Coda
B♭7
E♭7
Well, I beg you on my bend - ed knees,
If you'll
F7
on - ly lis - ten to my pleas,
Is there
Gm
Cm
Cm7
an - y - thing I can do?
'Cause I real - ly can't stand it, I'm
F7
Cm7
F7
B♭
so in love with you.

Things We Said Today.

Words & Music by John Lennon & Paul McCartney.

Moderately fast
Am Em7 Am Em7 Am Em7 Am Em7
You say you will love me if I have to go.
You say you'll be mine, girl, 'til the end of time.
Am Em7 Am Em7 Am Em7 Am
You'll be think-ing of me, Some-how I will know.
These days, such a kind girl, seems so hard to find.
C C9 F
Some-day when I'm lone - ly wish-ing you weren't so
Some-day when we're dream - ing deep in love, not a
B♭ Am Em7 Am Em7
far a - way, Then I will re - mem - ber
lot to say, Then we will re - mem - ber
Am Em7 1 Am 2 A A
Things we said to - day.
Things we said to - day.
Me, I'm just the luck -
D7 B7 E7
- y kind, Love to hear you say that love is love.

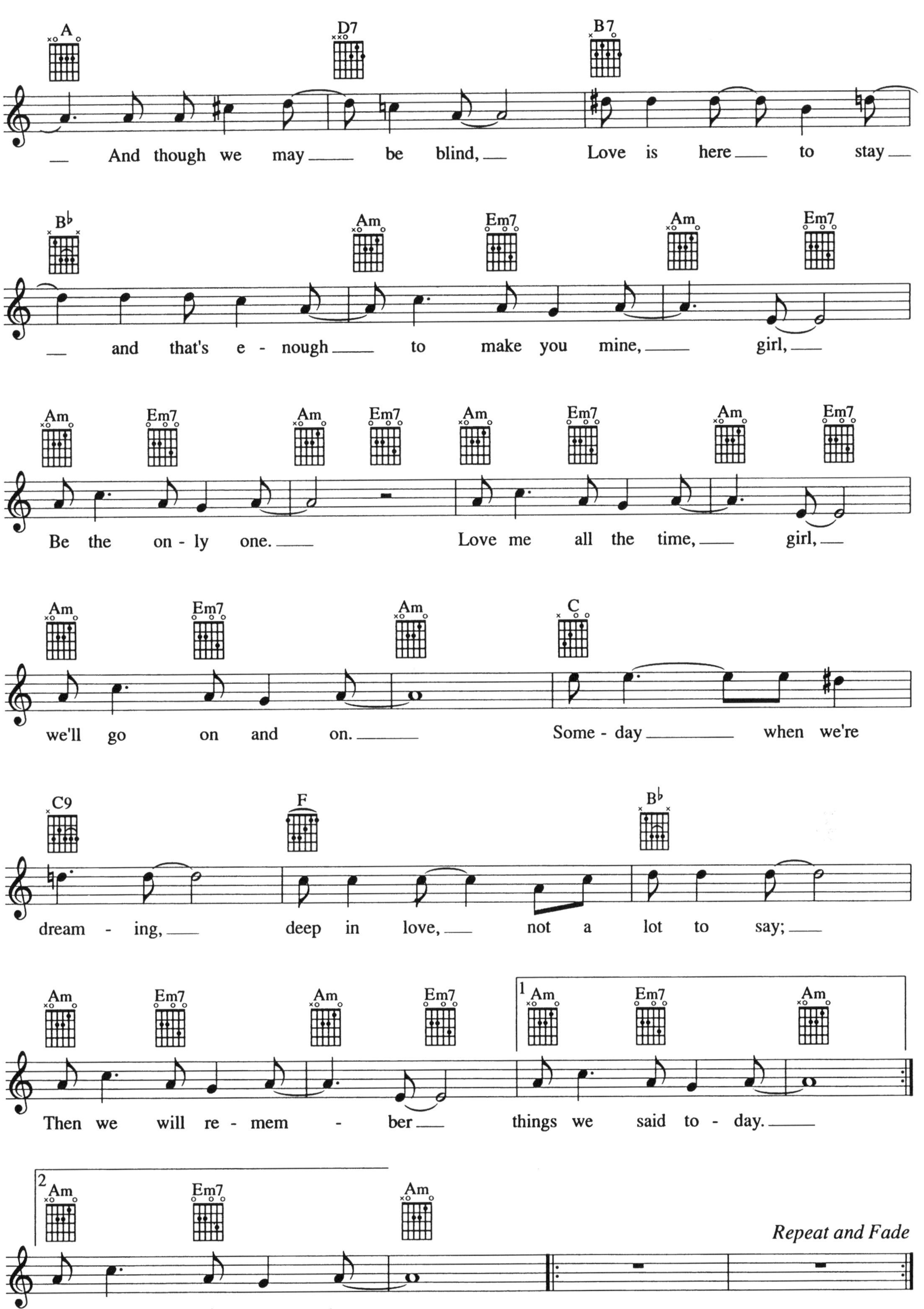
A D7 B7
And though we may be blind, Love is here to stay
Bb Am Em7 Am Em7
and that's e - nough to make you mine, girl,
Am Em7 Am Em7 Am Em7 Am Em7
Be the on - ly one. Love me all the time, girl,
Am Em7 Am C
we'll go on and on. Some - day when we're
C9 F Bb
dream - ing, deep in love, not a lot to say;
Am Em7 Am Em7 1 Am Em7 Am
Then we will re - mem - ber things we said to - day.
2 Am Em7 Am
things we said to - day.
Repeat and Fade

What You're Doing.

Words & Music by John Lennon & Paul McCartney.

Moderately
F
B♭7
F
1. Look what you're do - ing, I'm feel - ing
2. You got me run - ning and there's no
3. Please stop your ly - ing, you got me
B♭7
Dm7
B♭7
blue and lone - ly, Would it be too much to ask of you what you're
fun in it. Why should it be so much to ask of you what you're
cry - ing girl. Why should it be so much to ask of you what you're
To Coda
1
F
B♭
2
F
do - ing to me? me?
do - ing to
do - ing to
B♭
Dm7
B♭
I've been wait - ing here for you, Won - d'ring what you're
Dm7
G7
gon - na do. And should you need a
C7
D.C. al Coda
love that's true, it's me.
Coda
F
B♭7
F
me, What you're do - ing to me?

I'm Looking Through You.

Words & Music by John Lennon & Paul McCartney.

Steady 2 beat
B♭ E♭ Cm7 Gm F
1. I'm look - ing through you, where did you go?
2. Your lips are mov - ing, I can - not hear.
B♭ E♭ Cm7 Gm F
I thought I knew you, What did I know?
Your voice is sooth - ing, but the words aren't clear.
Gm F Cm B♭ E♭ F
You don't look dif - f'rent, but you have changed;
You don't sound dif - f'rent, I've learned the game;
B♭ E♭ Cm7 E♭7
I'm look - ing through you, you're not the same.

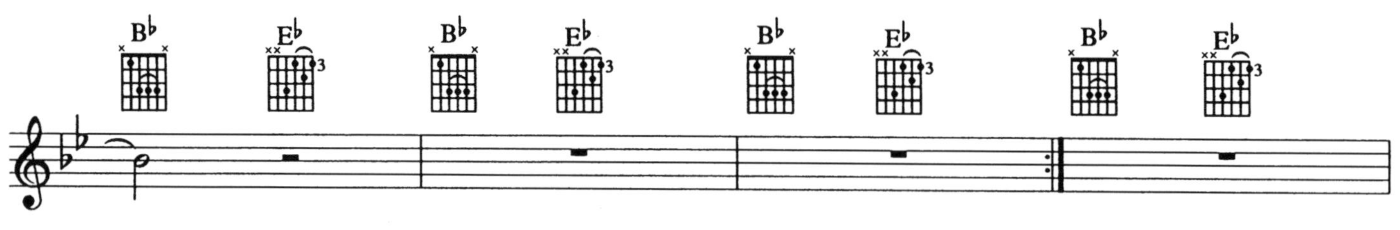
B♭
E♭
B♭
E♭
B♭
E♭
B♭
E♭

E♭
B♭
Why, tell me why did you not treat me right?

E♭
Fsus
F
Love has a nas - ty hab - it of dis - ap - pear - ing o - ver - night.

B♭
E♭
Cm7
Gm
F
3. You're think - ing of me, the same old way;
4. I'm look - ing through you, where did you go?

B♭
E♭
Cm7
Gm
F
You were a - bove me, but not to - day.
I thought I knew you, what did I know?

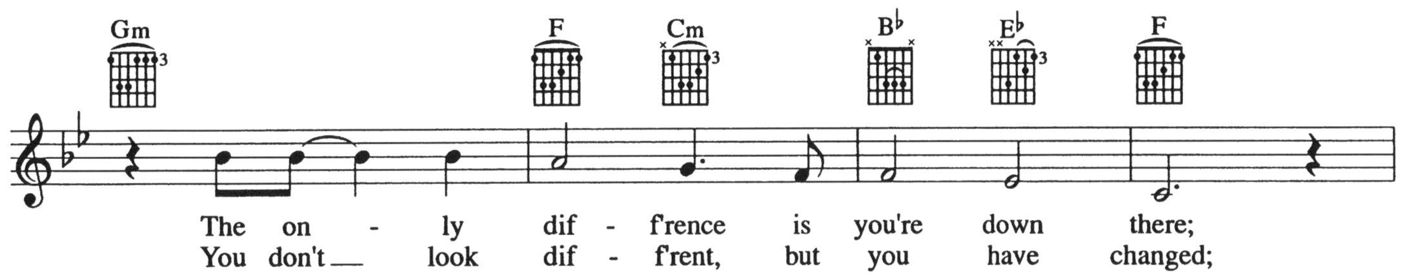
Gm F Cm B♭ E♭ F
The on - ly dif - f'rence is you're down there;
You don't look dif - f'rent, but you have changed;
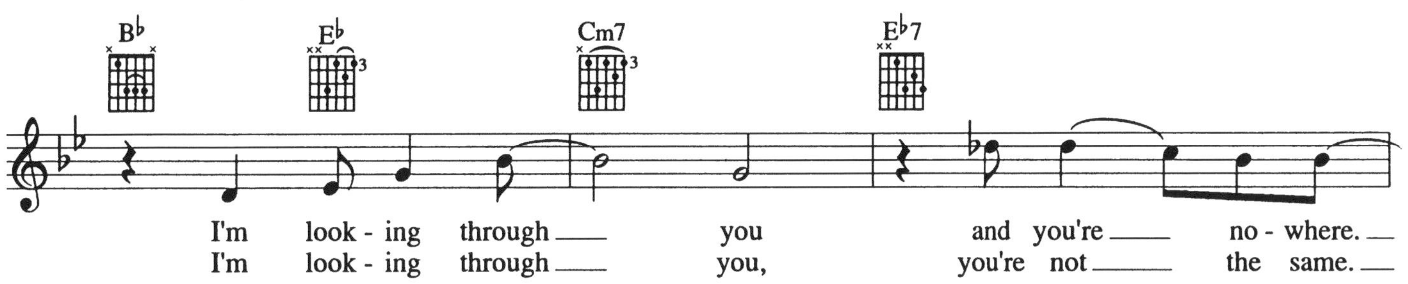
B♭ E♭ Cm7 E♭7
I'm look - ing through you and you're no - where.
I'm look - ing through you, you're not the same.
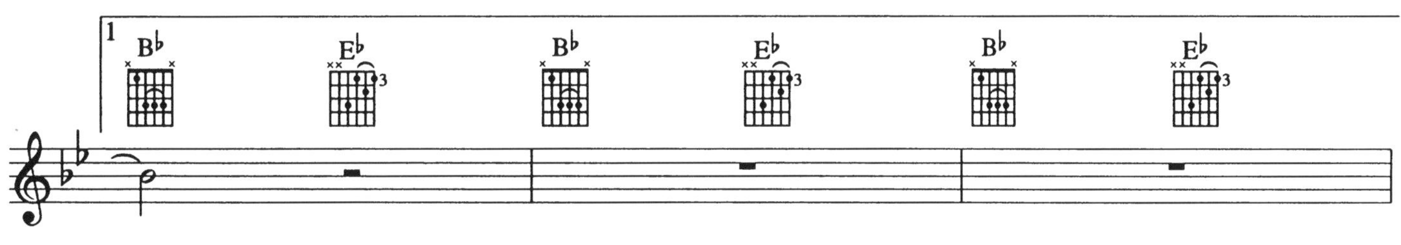
1
B♭ E♭ B♭ E♭ B♭ E♭

B♭ E♭ 2 B♭ E♭ B♭ E♭
Yeah! Well, ba - by you've changed.

Repeat and Fade
B♭ E♭ B♭ E♭ B♭ E♭
Ah, I'm look - ing through you.

When I Get Home.

Words & Music by John Lennon & Paul McCartney.

Moderately
E
Tacet
E
Whoa ho Whoa ho
A7
D7
Tacet
I got a whole lot of things to tell her, when I get home.
Em
D7
G7
1. Come on I'm on my
(2) on if you
(3) on let me
C7
G7
way, 'Cos I'm a - gon - na see my ba - by to -
please, I've got no time for triv - i - al - i -
through, I've got so man - y things I've got to
C7
G7
- day; I've got a whole lot of things I've got - ta
- ties; I've got a girl who's wait - ing home for
do; I've got no bus' - ness be - ing here with
C7
D7
Tacet
E
say, to her.
me, to - night.
you, this way.
Whoa ho

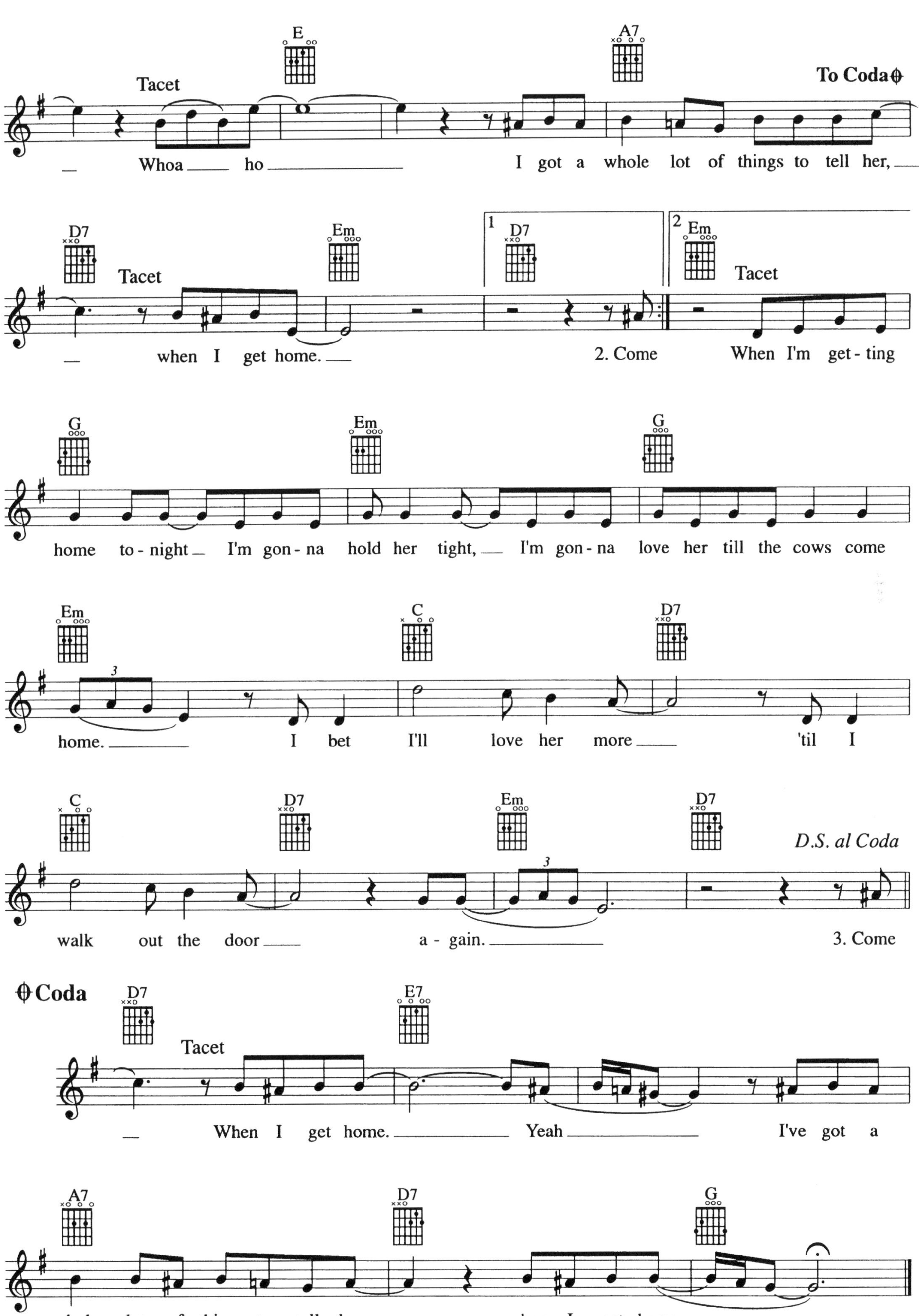
E
A7
To Coda
Tacet
Whoa ho I got a whole lot of things to tell her,
D7
Em
1 D7
2 Em
Tacet
when I get home.
2. Come
When I'm get-ting
G
Em
G
home to-night I'm gon-na hold her tight, I'm gon-na love her till the cows come
Em
C
D7
3
home. I bet I'll love her more 'til I
C
D7
Em
D7
D.S. al Coda
walk out the door a-gain.
3. Come
Coda
D7
E7
Tacet
When I get home. Yeah I've got a
A7
D7
G
whole lot of things to tell her when I get home.

World Without Love.

Words & Music by John Lennon & Paul McCartney.

Moderately
E♭
G7
Cm
1. Please lock me a - way and don't al - low the
2. Birds sing out of tune and rain - drops hide the
(3) then, lock me a - way and don't al - low the
E♭
A♭6
day. Here in - side where I hide with my
moon. I'm O. K. here I'll stay with my
day. Here in - side where I hide with my
E♭
Fm7
lone - li - ness
lone - li - ness
lone - li - ness
I don't care what they say, I won't
B♭7
To Coda
E♭
C♭
B♭7
E♭
stay in a world with - out love.
love.

E♭7
A♭m
So I wait and in a while

E♭
A♭m
I will see my true love smile.
She may come, I

Fm7
C♭
B♭7
D.C. al Coda
know not when;
When she does I'll know 3. So ba - by, un - til

Coda

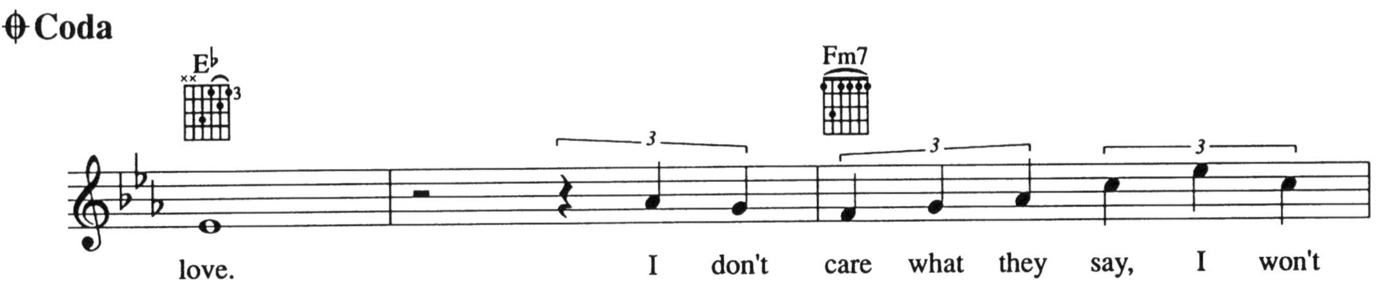
E♭
Fm7
love.
I don't care what they say, I won't

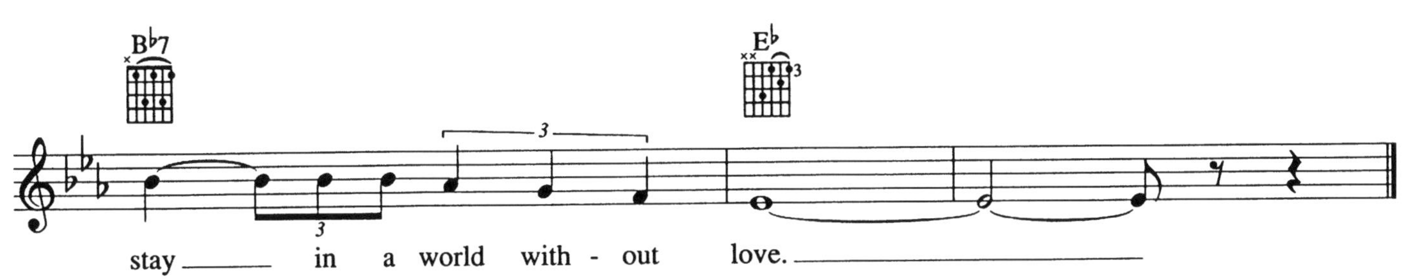
B♭7
E♭
stay in a world with - out love.

You Can't Do That.

Words & Music by John Lennon & Paul McCartney.

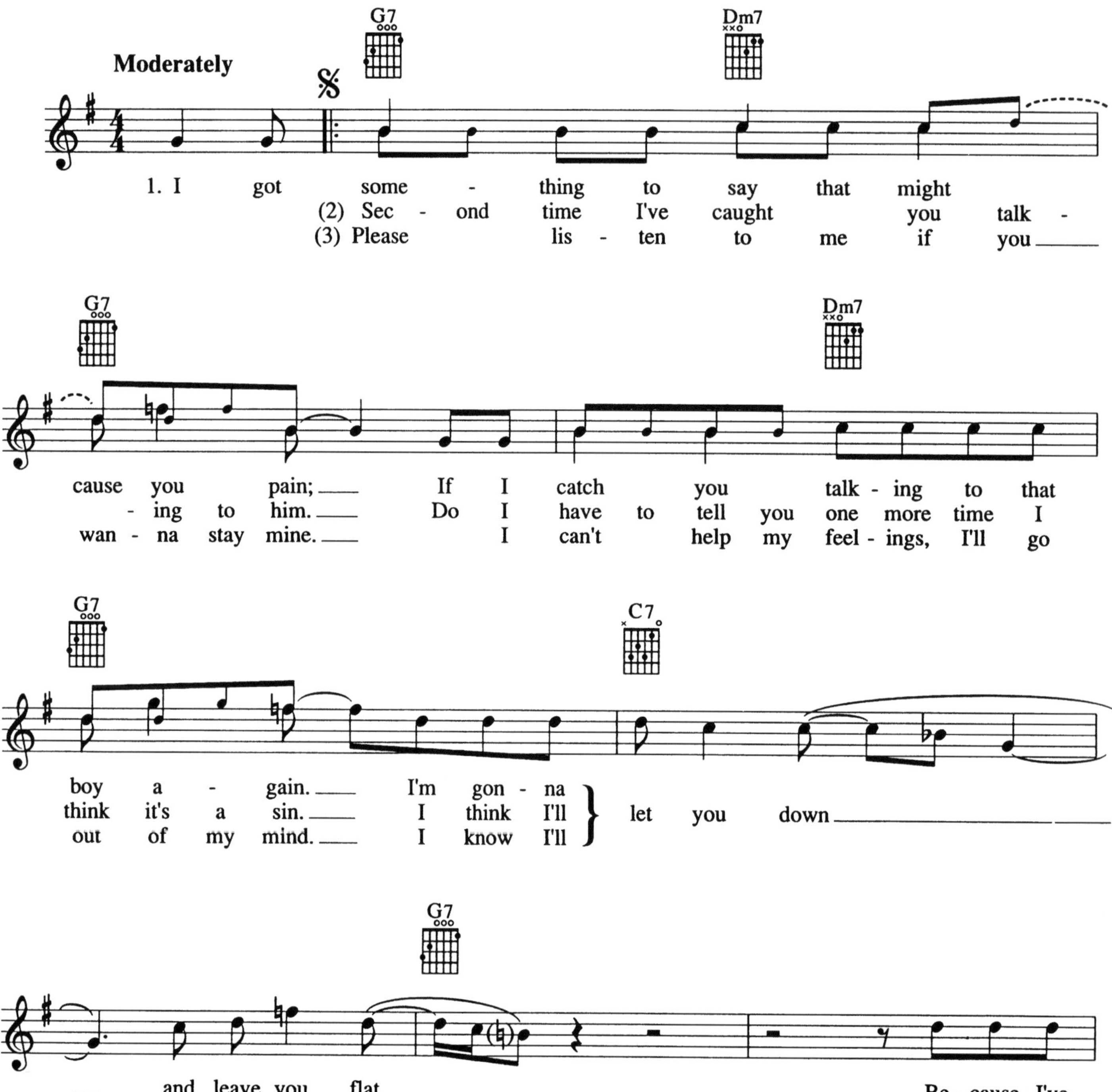
Moderately
G7
Dm7
C7
1. I got some - thing to say that might cause you pain; If I catch you talk - ing to that boy a - gain. I'm gon - na
(2) Sec - ond time I've caught you talk - ing to him. Do I have to tell you one more time I think it's a sin. I think I'll
(3) Please lis - ten to me if you wan - na stay mine. I can't help my feel - ings, I'll go out of my mind. I know I'll
let you down and leave you flat, Be - cause I've

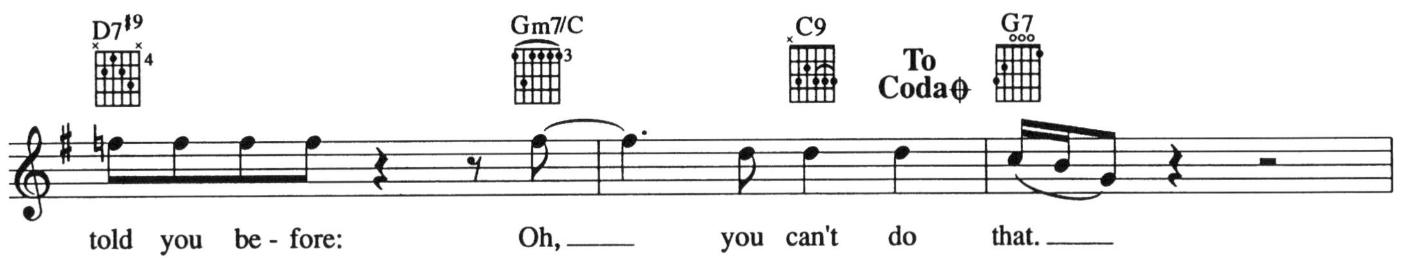
D7♭9
Gm7/C
C9
To Coda
G7
told you be - fore: Oh, you can't do that.

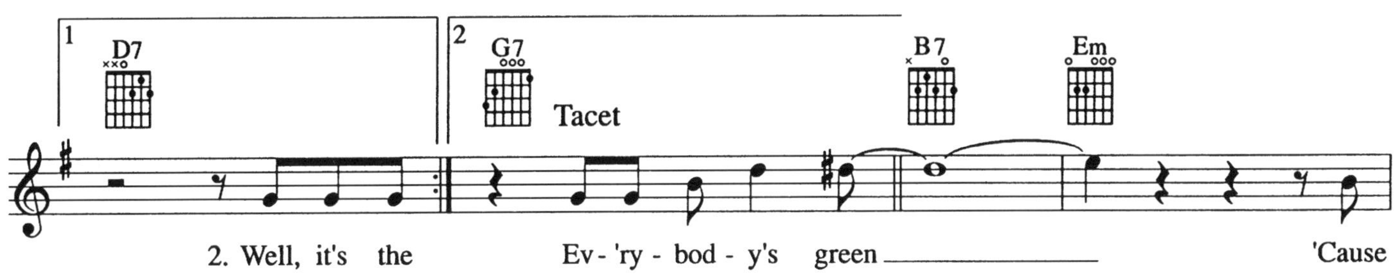
1
D7
2
G7
Tacet
B7
Em
2. Well, it's the Ev - 'ry - bod - y's green 'Cause

Am
B7
Em
B7
Em
I'm the one who won your love. But if it's seen you're

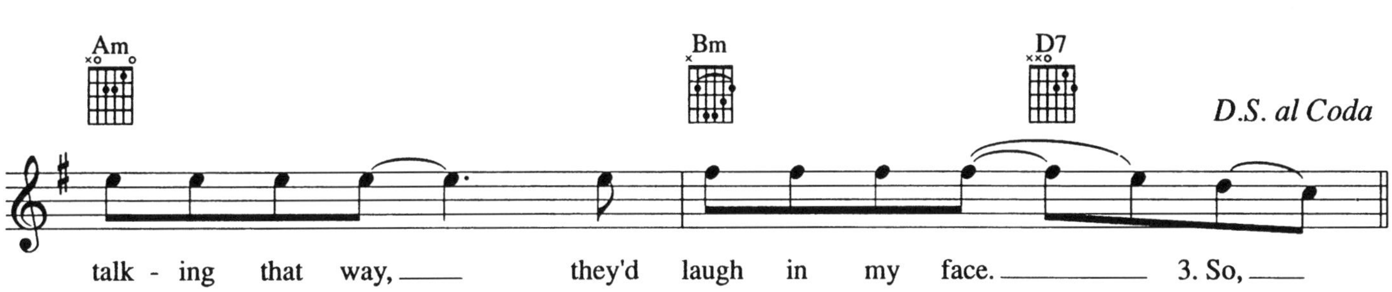
Am
Bm
D7
D.S. al Coda
talk - ing that way, they'd laugh in my face. 3. So,

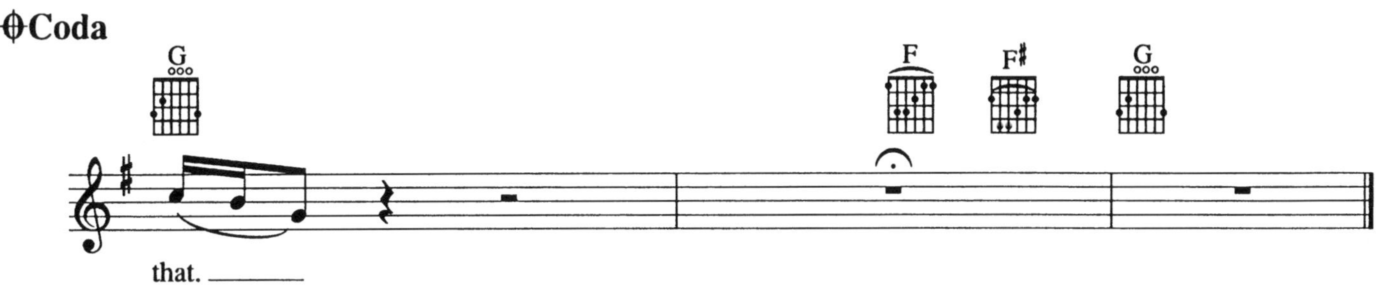
Coda
G
F
F♯
G
that.

Another Girl.

Words & Music by John Lennon & Paul McCartney.

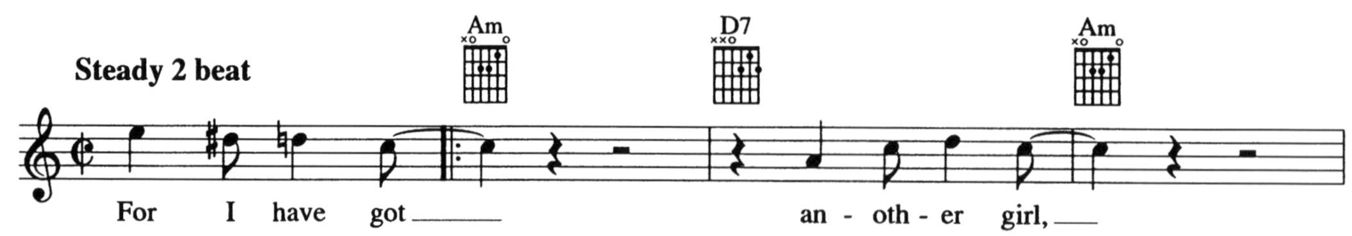
Steady 2 beat
Am D7 Am
For I have got ___ an - oth - er girl, ___

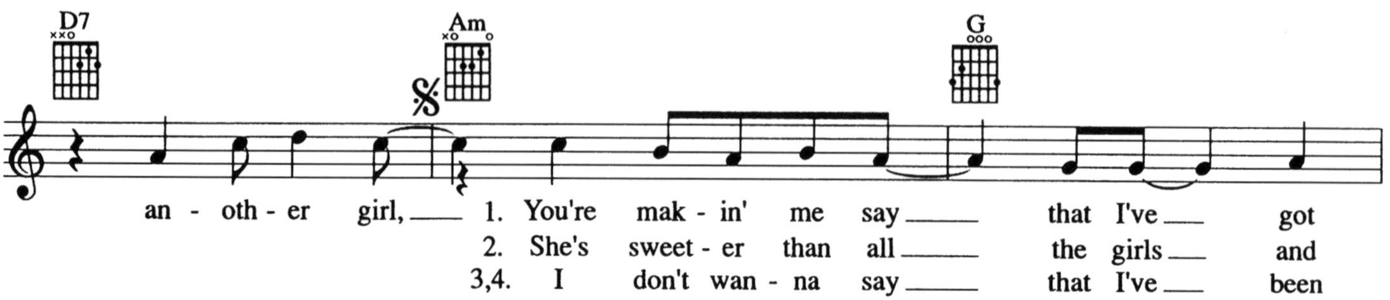
D7 Am G
an - oth - er girl, ___ 1. You're mak - in' me say ___ that I've ___ got
2. She's sweet - er than all ___ the girls ___ and
3,4. I don't wan - na say ___ that I've ___ been

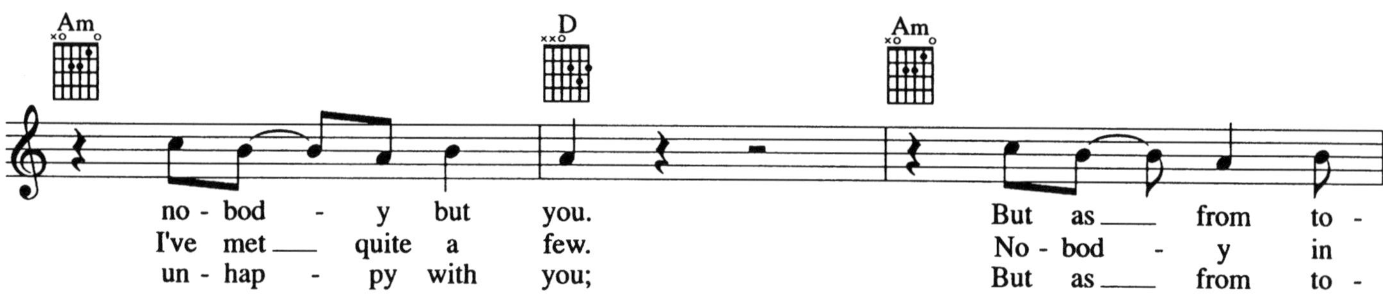
Am D Am
no - bod - y but you. But as ___ from to -
I've met ___ quite a few. No - bod - y in
un - hap - py with you; But as ___ from to -

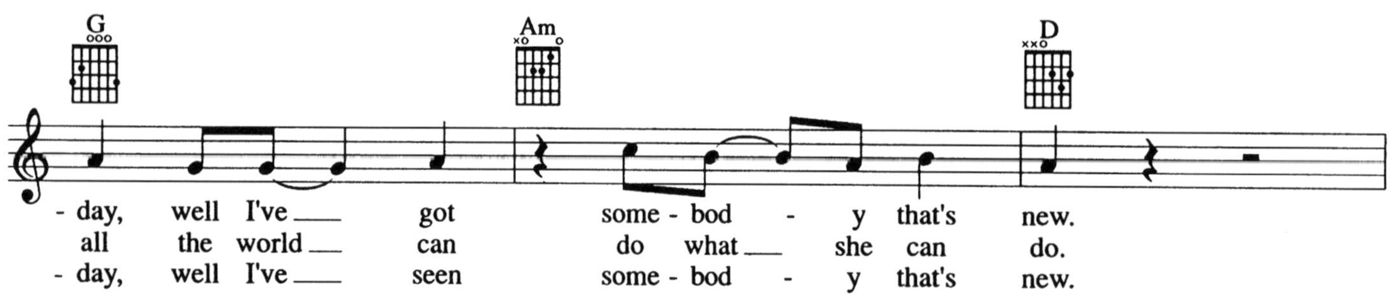
G Am D
- day, well I've ___ got some - bod - y that's new.
all the world ___ can do what ___ she can do.
- day, well I've ___ seen some - bod - y that's new.

D7
I ain't ___ no fool, and I ___ don't take what I ___ don't
And so I'm tell - ing you, ___ This time you'd bet - ter
I ain't no fool, and I ___ don't take what I ___ don't

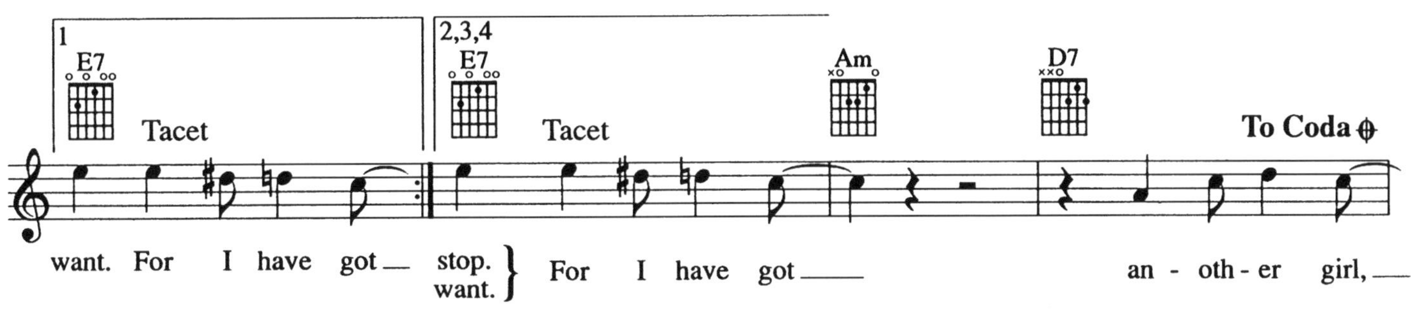
1
E7
Tacet
2,3,4
E7
Tacet
Am
D7
To Coda
want. For I have got stop. want. For I have got an - oth - er girl,
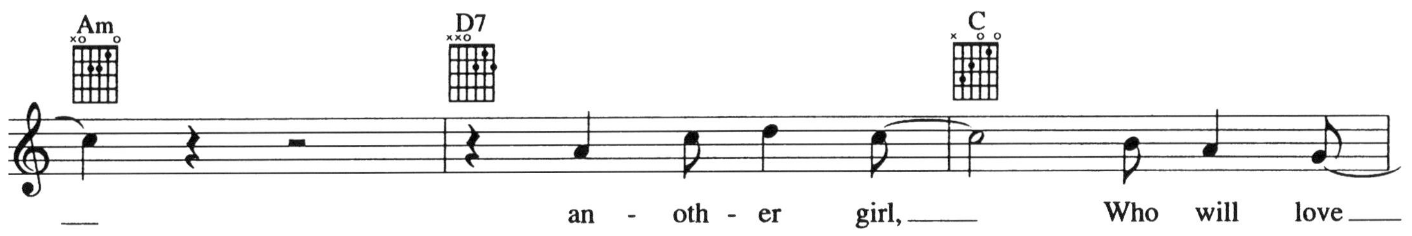
Am
D7
C
an - oth - er girl, Who will love
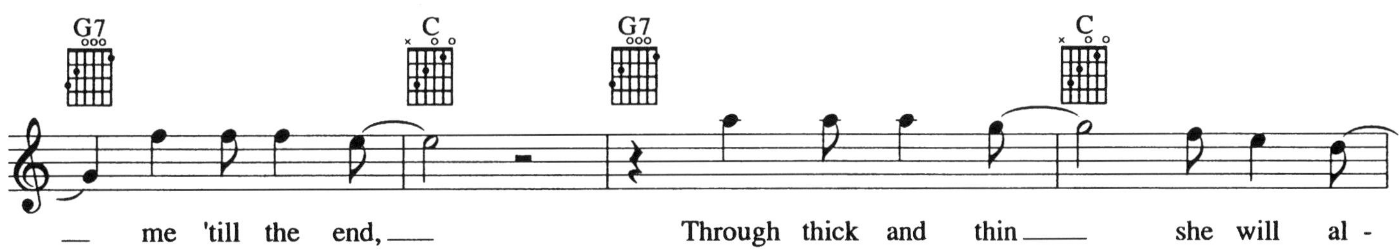
G7
C
G7
C
me 'till the end, Through thick and thin she will al -
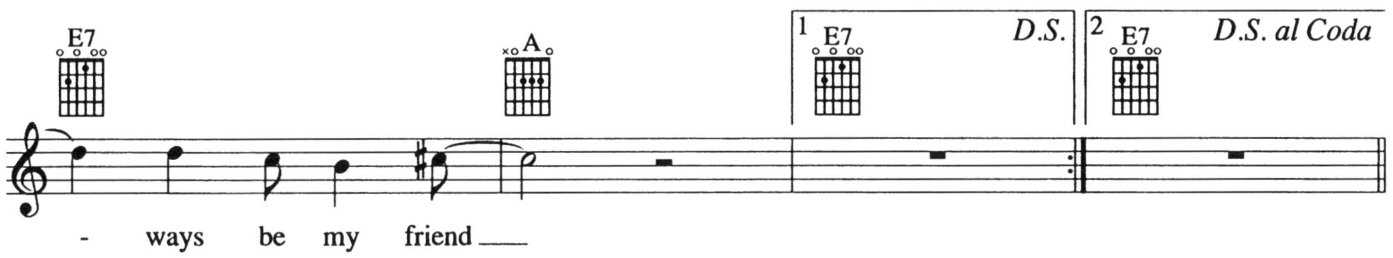
E7
A
1 E7
D.S.
2 E7
D.S. al Coda
- ways be my friend

Coda
Am
D7
Am
an - oth - er girl,
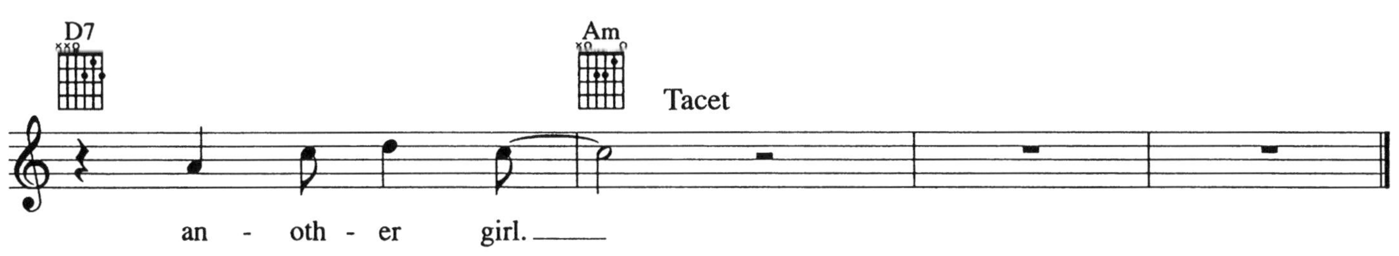
D7
Am
Tacet
an - oth - er girl.

Day Tripper.

WORDS & MUSIC BY JOHN LENNON & PAUL MCCARTNEY.

Moderate Rock

N.C.

Guitar

E♭

Got a good rea - son for tak - ing the eas - y way out, —
She's a big teas - er, She took me half — the way there. —
Tried — to please — her, She on - ly played — one night stands. —

A♭ E♭

— Got a good rea - son for tak - ing the eas - y way out, —
— She's a big teas - er, She took me half — the way there, —
— Tried — to please — her, She on - ly played — one night stands, —

F

— now. She was a Day — Trip - per,
— now. She was a Day — Trip - per,
— now. She was a Day — Trip - per,

A♭7

One - way tick - et, yeah; —
One - way tick - et, yeah; —
Sun - day driv - er, yeah; —
It took me so —

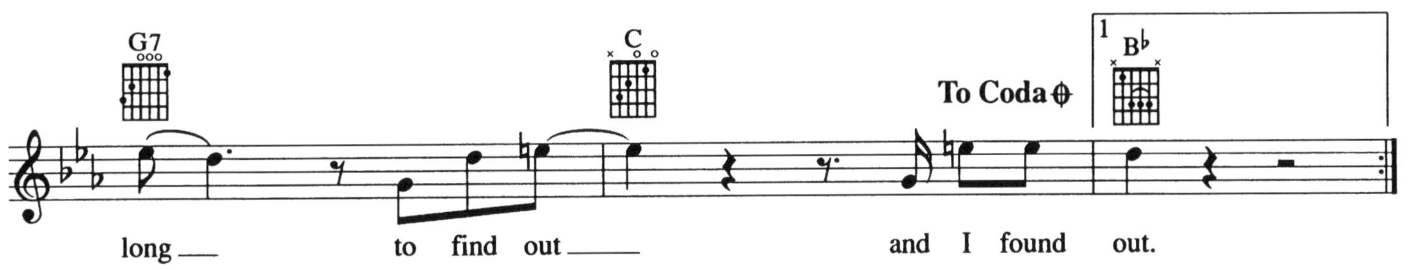
G7
C
To Coda
1
B♭
long
to find out
and I found out.

2
B♭
N.C.
Guitar
etc.
4
out.

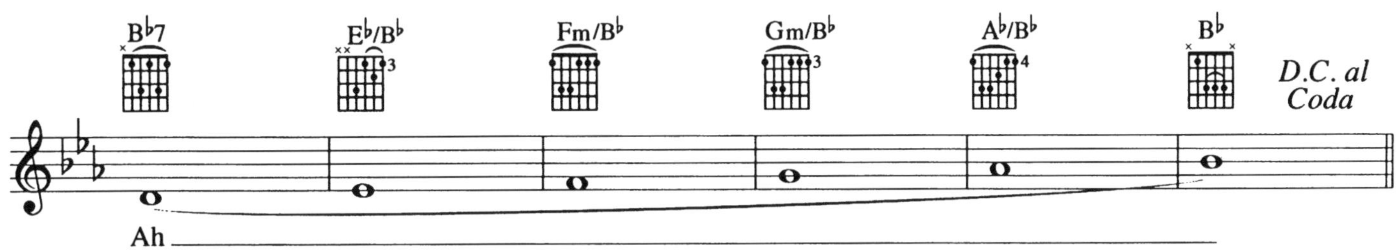
B♭7
E♭/B♭
Fm/B♭
Gm/B♭
A♭/B♭
B♭
D.C. al Coda
Ah

Coda

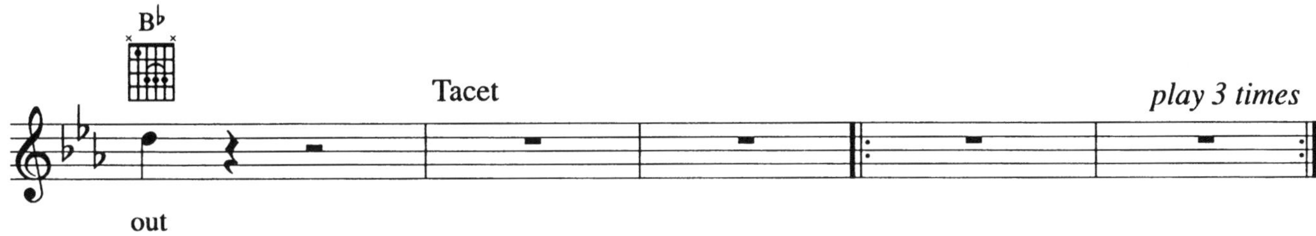
B♭
Tacet
play 3 times
out

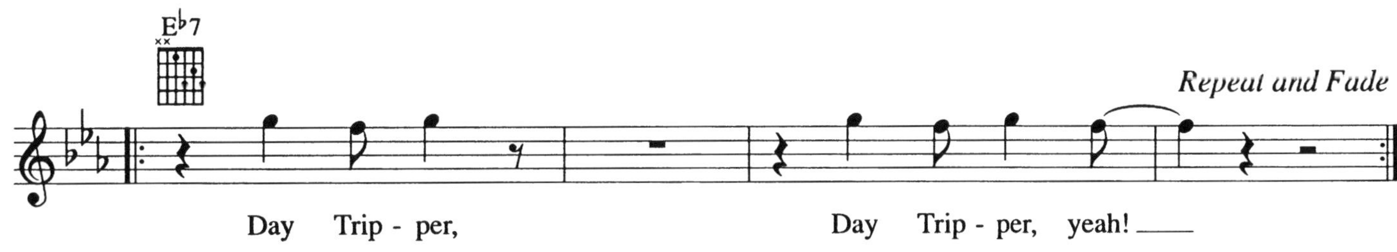
E♭7
Repeat and Fade
Day Trip - per,
Day Trip - per, yeah!

Drive My Car.

Words & Music by John Lennon & Paul McCartney.

Moderately, with a beat
D7
G
1. Asked a girl what she want - ed to be,
2. I told the girl that my pros - pects were good,
3. I told that girl I could start right a - way,
D7
G
She said "Ba - by, can't you see?
And she said "Ba - by, it's un - der - stood.
And she said "Lis - ten babe, I got some - thing to say:
D7
G
I wan - na be fam - ous, a star of the screen, But
Work - ing for pea - nuts is all ver - y fine, But
I got no car and it's break - ing my heart, But
Dm7/A
you can do some - thing in be - tween."
I can show you a bet - ter time."
I found a driv - er and that's a start."
Bm
G7
Bm
"Ba - by, you can drive my car,
Yes, I'm gon - na be a star;

G7
Bm
E7♭9
Am
To Coda
Baby, you can drive my car, and maybe I'll love
D
G
1
A
2
A
Tacet
you."
Beep, beep, mm beep, beep. Yeah.
D7
G
D7
G
D7
G
Dm7/A
Bm
G7
"Baby, you can drive my car,
Bm
G7
Bm
Yes, I'm gonna be a star; Baby, you can drive my car,
E7♭9
Am
D
G
A
D.C. al Coda
(verse 3)
and maybe I'll love you."
Coda
Repeat and Fade
D
G
A
D
G
you." Beep, beep, mm beep beep. Yeah.

Girl.

Words & Music by John Lennon & Paul McCartney.

Moderately
Cm G7 Cm
1. Is there an - y - bod - y goin' to lis - ten to my sto - ry
think of all the times I tried so hard to leave her
told when she was young that pain would lead to plea - sure?
Fm E♭ G7
all a - bout the girl who came to stay? She's the
She will turn to me and start to cry. And she
Did she un - der - stand it when they said That a
Cm G7 Cm
kind of girl you want so much it makes you sor - ry,
prom - is - es the earth to me and I be - lieve her,
man must break his back to earn his day of lei - sure?
Fm Cm
To Coda
Still, you don't re - gret a sin - gle day.
Af - ter all this time I don't know why.
Will she still be - lieve it when he's dead?
Ah
E♭ Gm/D Fm/C B♭7 E♭ Gm/D
Girl, Girl, Girl.

1
Fm/C
B♭7
2. When I
2
Fm/C
B♭7
Fm/C
She's the kind of girl who puts you
C
down when friends are there, you feel a fool.
Fm/C
C
Fm/C
When you say she's looking good, she acts as if it's understood, she's
C
Fm/C
cool, ooh, ooh, ooh,
A♭/C
E♭
Gm/D
Girl,
Fm/C
B♭7
E♭
Gm/D
Girl, Girl,
Fm/C
B♭7
D.S. al Coda
3. Was she
Coda
E♭
Gm/D
Fm/C
B♭7
E♭
Gm/D
Girl,
Girl.
Fm/C
B♭7
Cm
G7
Cm
Fm
E♭
G7
Repeat & Fade

Help!

Words & Music by John Lennon & Paul McCartney.

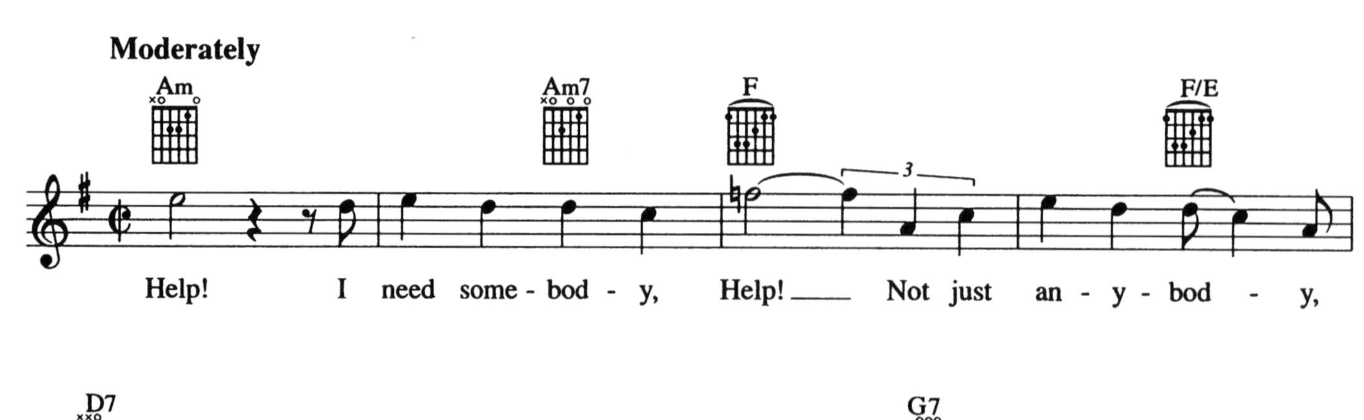
Moderately
Am
Am7
F
F/E
3
Help! I need some - bod - y, Help! Not just an - y - bod - y,

D7
G7
Tacet
Help! You know I need some - one, Help!

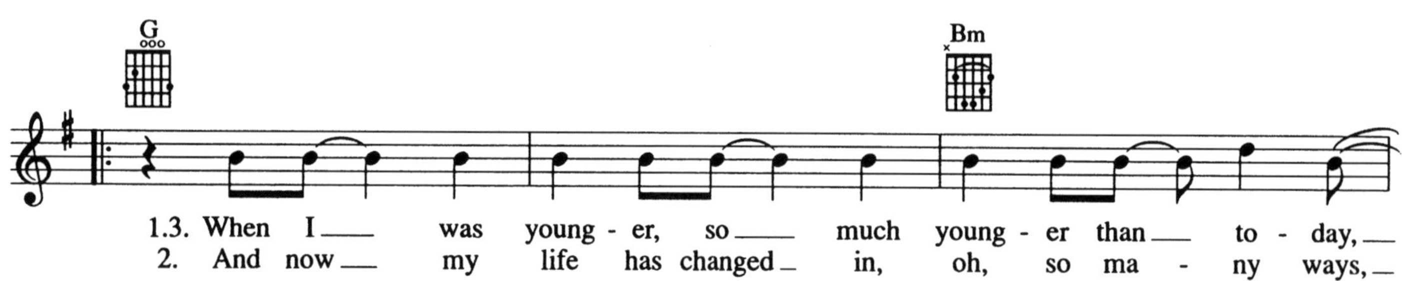
G
Bm
1.3. When I was young - er, so much young - er than to - day,
2. And now my life has changed in, oh, so ma - ny ways,

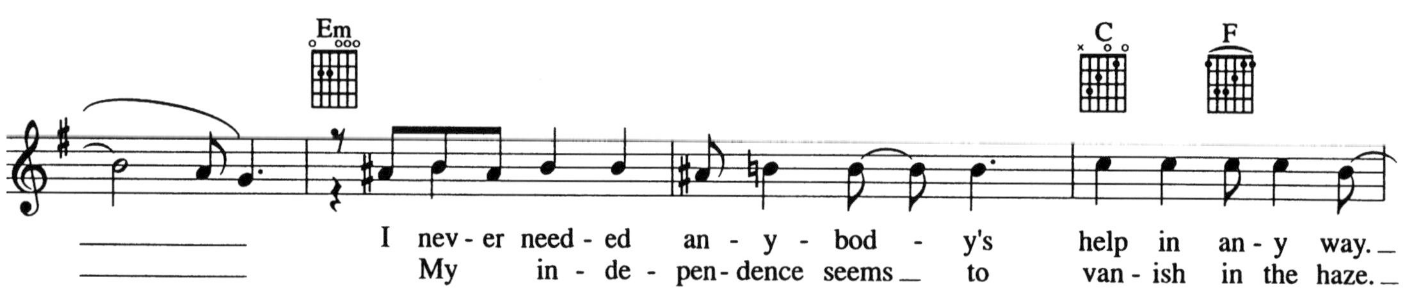
Em
C
F
I nev - er need - ed an - y - bod - y's help in an - y way.
My in - de - pen - dence seems to van - ish in the haze.

G
Bm
But now these days are gone, I'm not so self - as - sured,
But ev - 'ry now and then I feel so in - se - cure,

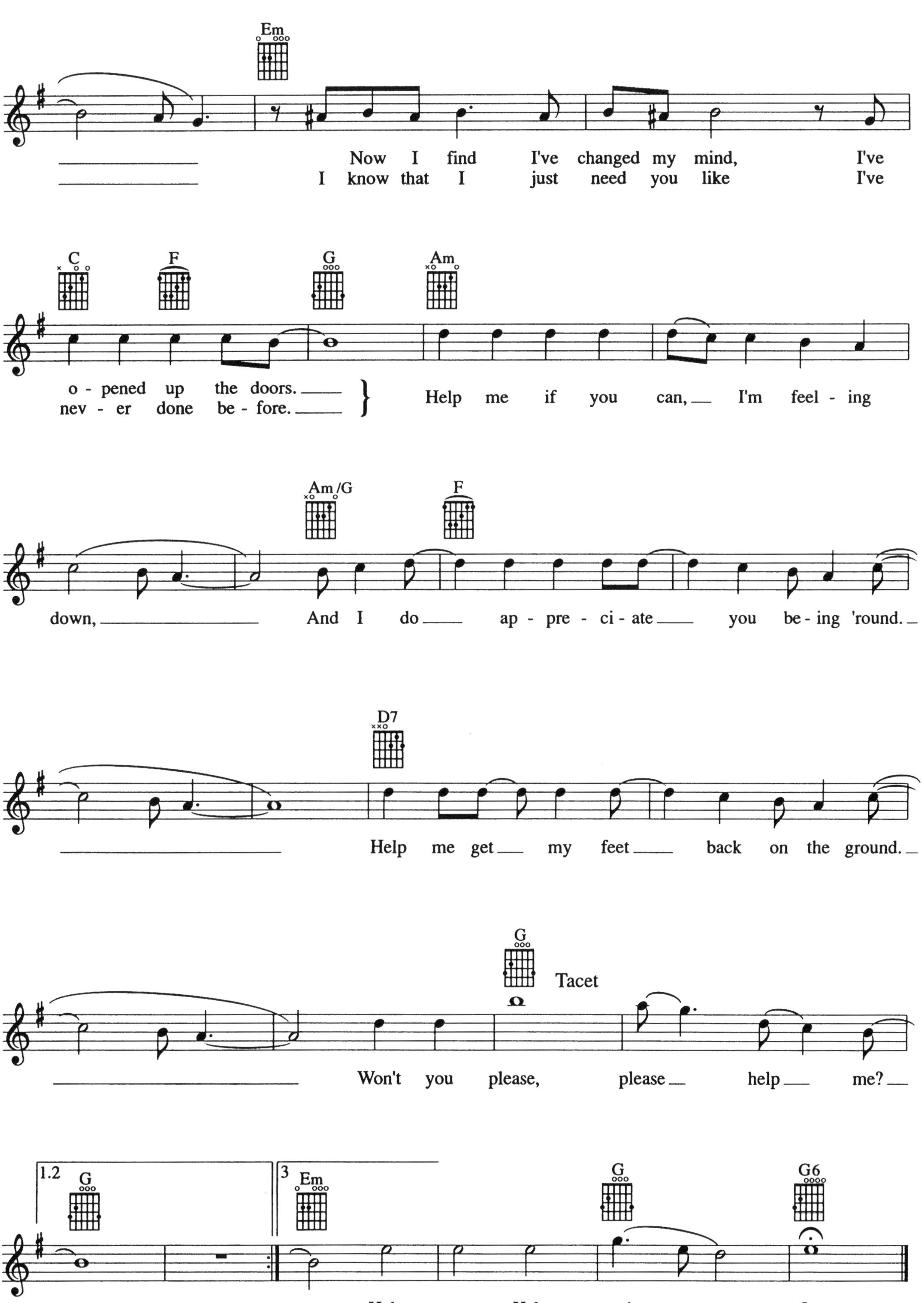
Em
Now I find I've changed my mind, I've
I know that I just need you like I've
C F G Am
o - pened up the doors.
nev - er done be - fore.
Help me if you can, I'm feel - ing
Am/G F
down, And I do ap - pre - ci - ate you be - ing 'round.
D7
Help me get my feet back on the ground.
G
Tacet
Won't you please, please help me?
1.2 G
3 Em
G G6
Help me, Help me! Oo

I Need You.

Words & Music by George Harrison.

Moderately
G
C
G
1. You don't re - a - lize how much I need you,
2. Said you had a thing or two to tell me.
3. Please re - mem - ber how I feel a - bout you,

C
Love you all the time and nev - er leave
How was I to know you would up - set
I could nev - er real - ly live with - out

G
Gsus
G
Em
you. Please come on back to me.
me? I did - n't re - a - lize
you; So, come on back and see

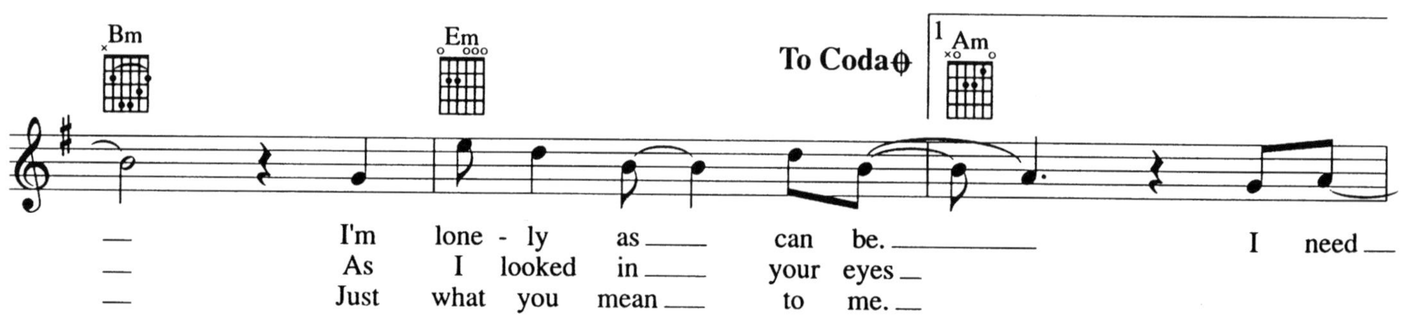
Bm
Em
To Coda
1
Am
I'm lone - ly as can be. I need
As I looked in your eyes
Just what you mean to me.

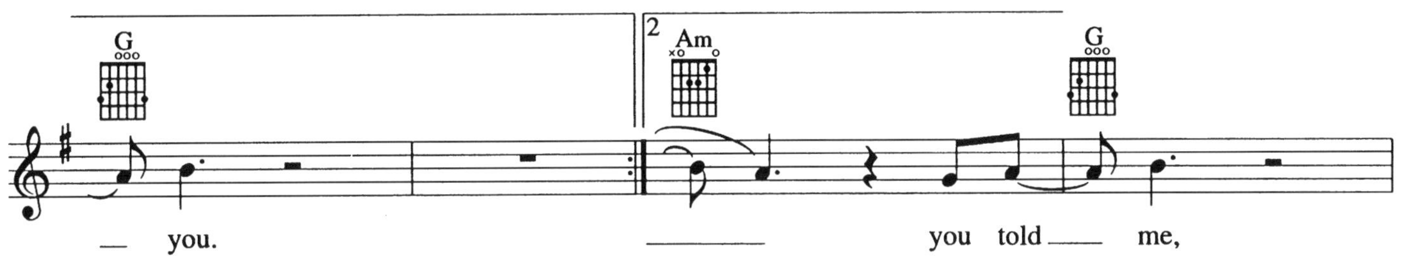
G
2
Am
G
you.
you told me,
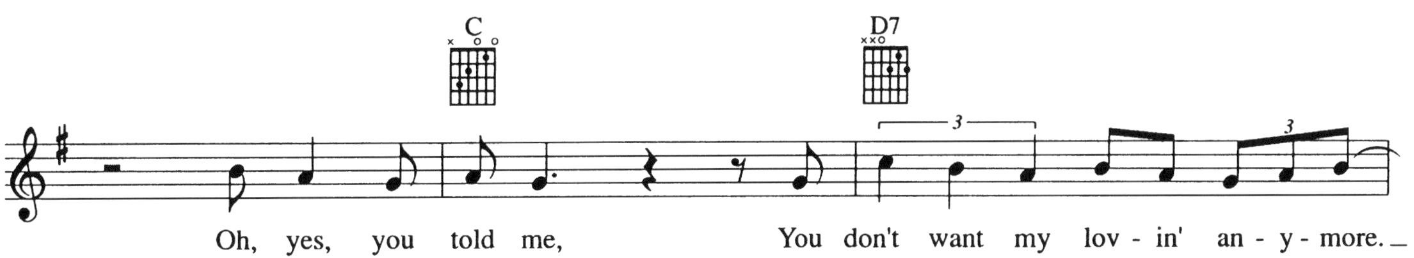
C
D7
Oh, yes, you told me,
You don't want my lov - in' an - y - more.

G
C
D7
That's when it hurt me
And feel - ing like this I
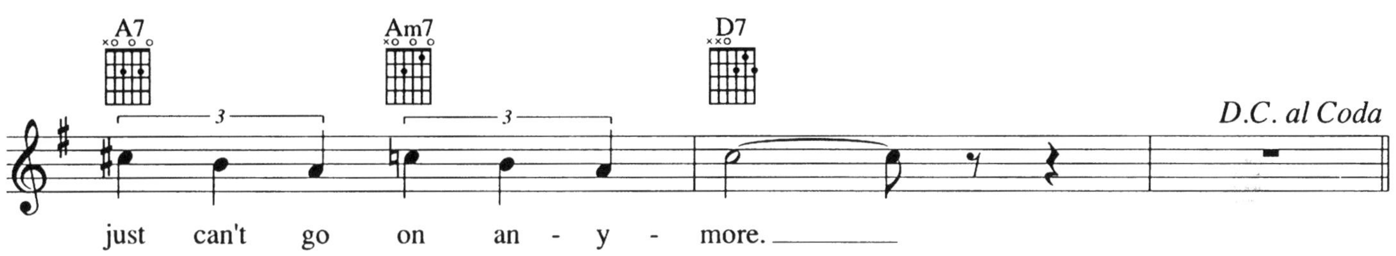
A7
Am7
D7
D.C. al Coda
just can't go on an - y - more.

Coda
Am
G
Em
I need you,
I need you,
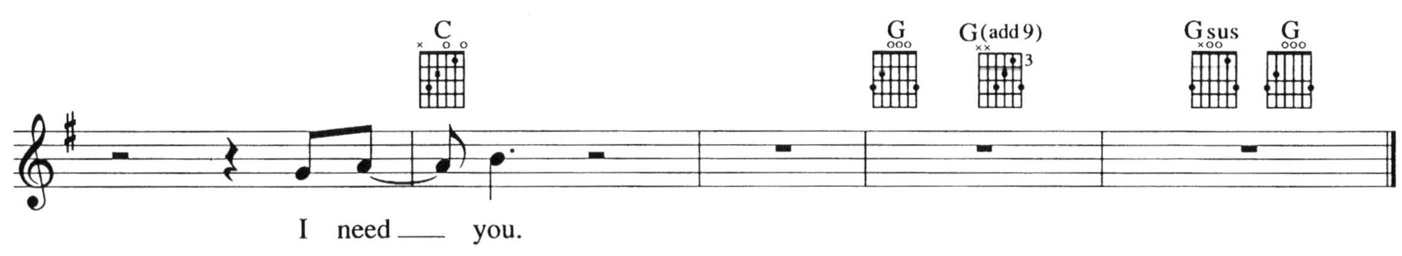
C
G
G(add 9)
Gsus
G
I need you.

I'm Down.

Words & Music by John Lennon & Paul McCartney.

Bright 4
F
Tacet
1. You tell lies think - in' I can't see.
2. Man buys ring, wo - man throws it a - way.
3. We're all a - lone and there's no - bod - y else.
F
Tacet
You can't cry, 'cause you're laugh - in' at me.
Same old thing hap - pens ev - er - y day.
She'll still moan, "Keep your hands to your - self!"
I'm down.
B♭7
F7
(I'm real - ly down) I'm down. (Down on the ground)
B♭7
I'm down. (I'm real - ly down)
C7
F
Tacet
How can you laugh when you know I'm down?

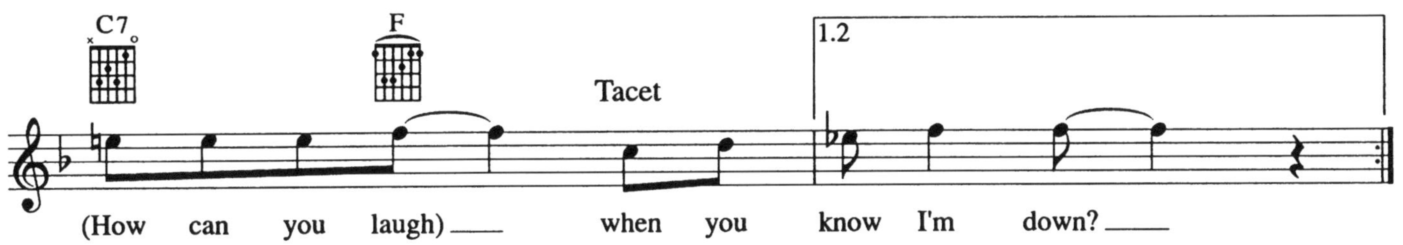
C7
F
Tacet
1.2
(How can you laugh) when you know I'm down?

3
F7
know I'm down? (I'm real - ly down) I guess I'm down

(I'm real - ly down) I'm down on the

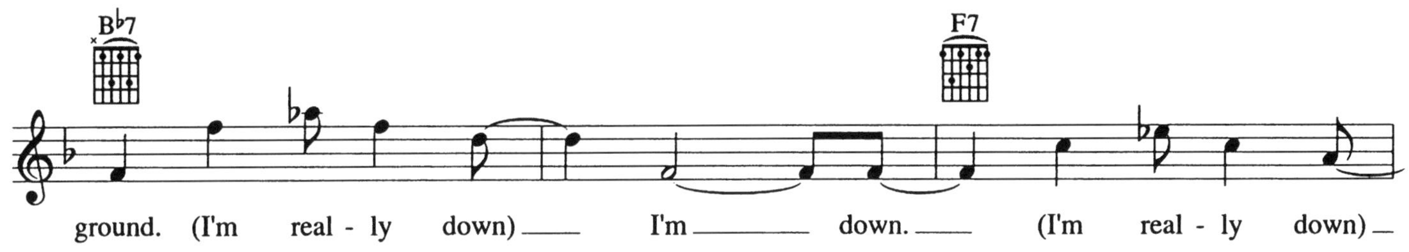
B♭7
F7
ground. (I'm real - ly down) I'm down. (I'm real - ly down)

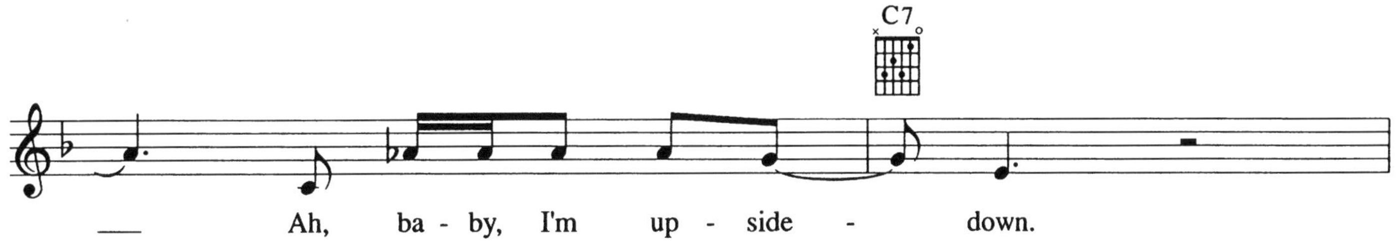
C7
Ah, ba - by, I'm up - side - down.

B♭7
F7
Repeat and Fade
Oh yeah, yeah, yeah, yeah, yeah. I'm down.

I've Just Seen A Face.

Words & Music by John Lennon & Paul McCartney.

Brightly, in 2

G
I've just seen a face I can't for - get the time or place where we just

Em
met. She's just the girl for me and I want all the world to see we've

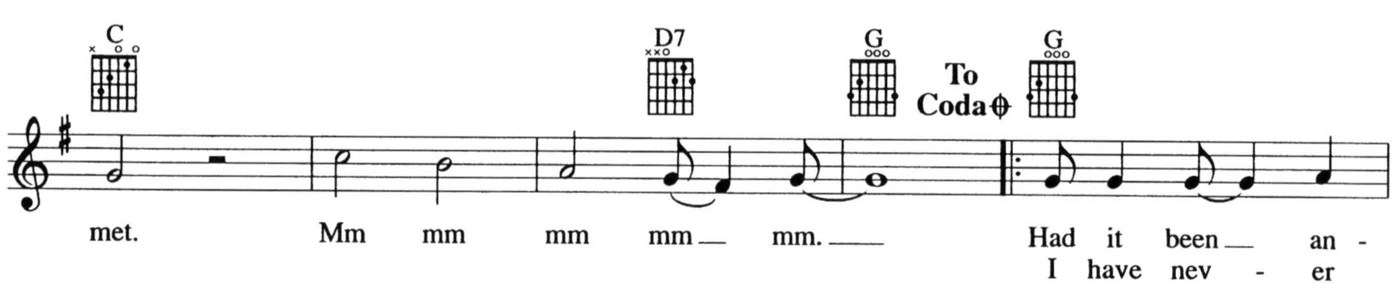
C
D7
G
To Coda
G
met. Mm mm mm mm mm.
Had it been an -
I have nev - er

- oth - er day I might have looked the oth - er way and
known the like of this I've been a - lone and I have

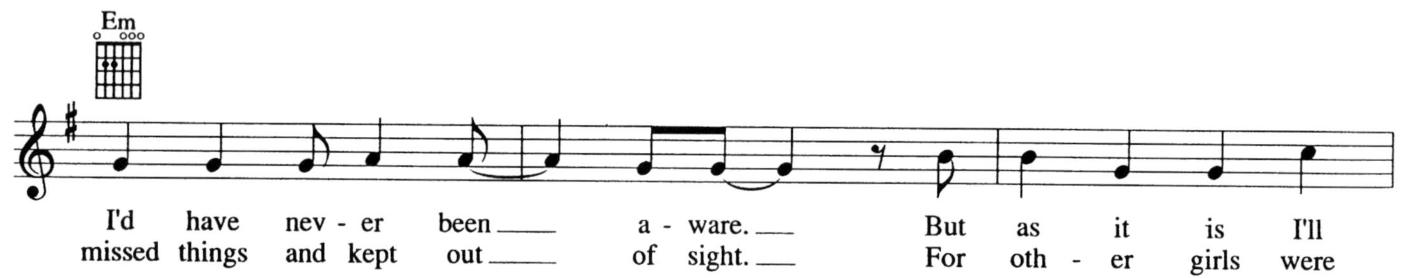
Em
I'd have nev - er been a - ware. But as it is I'll
missed things and kept out of sight. For oth - er girls were

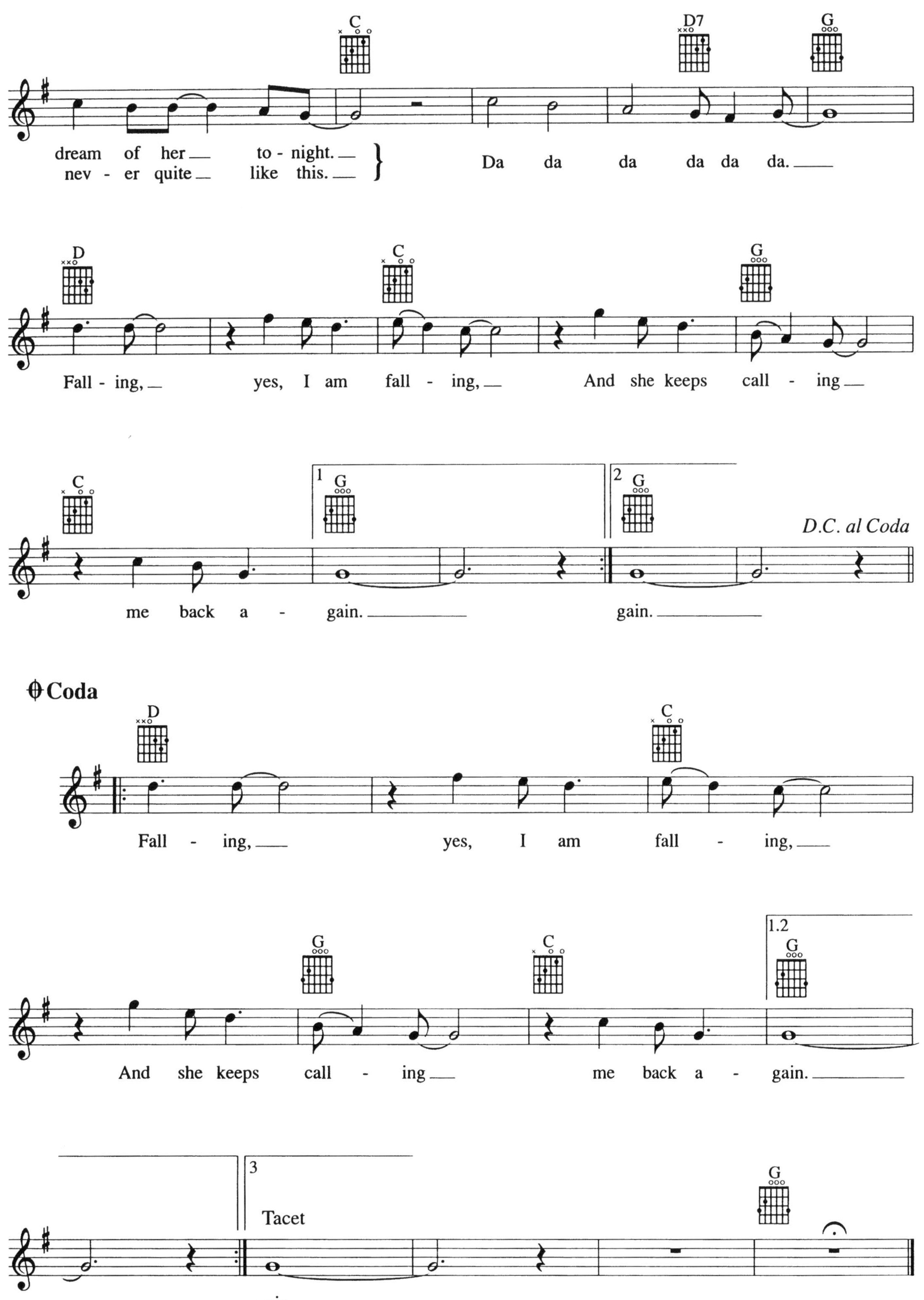
C
D7
G
dream of her to - night.
nev - er quite like this.
Da da da da da da.
D
C
G
Fall - ing, yes, I am fall - ing, And she keeps call - ing
C
1 G
2 G
D.C. al Coda
me back a - gain. gain.
Coda
D
C
Fall - ing, yes, I am fall - ing,
G
C
1.2 G
And she keeps call - ing me back a - gain.
3
Tacet
G
- gain.

If I Needed Someone.

Words & Music by George Harrison.

Moderately
A♭
If I need - ed some - one to love, You're the one that I'd be think - ing of,
If I had some more time to spend, Then I guess I'd be with you, my friend.
G♭/A♭
If I need - ed some - one.
If I need - ed some - one.
A♭
E♭m
F7
Had you come some oth - er day, then
it might not have been like this,
B♭m
E♭m
But you see now I'm too much in love.
F7
B♭m
E♭
A♭
Carve your num - ber on

my wall and may - be you will get a call from me,

G♭/A♭
A♭
To Coda
If I need - ed some - one.

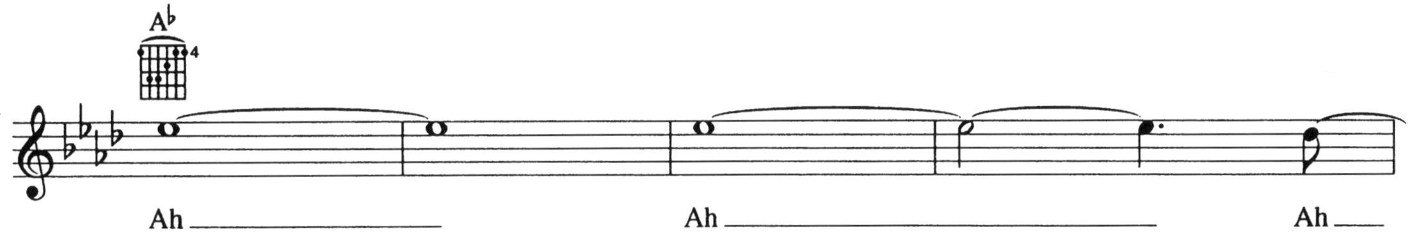
A♭
Ah
Ah
Ah

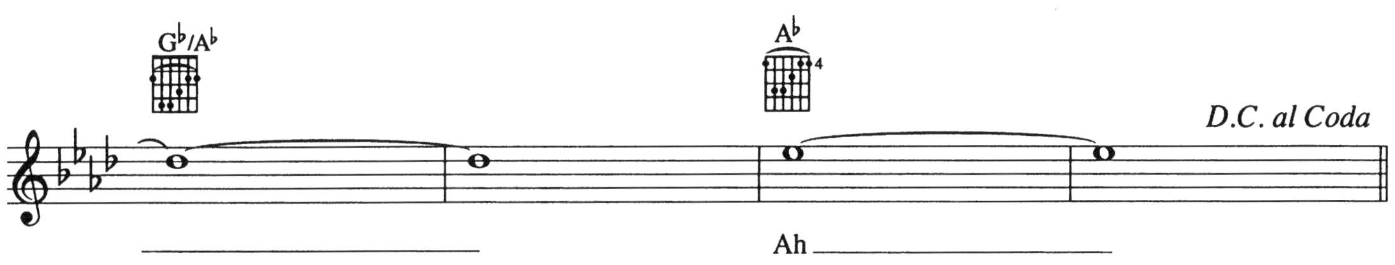
G♭/A♭
A♭
D.C. al Coda
Ah

Coda

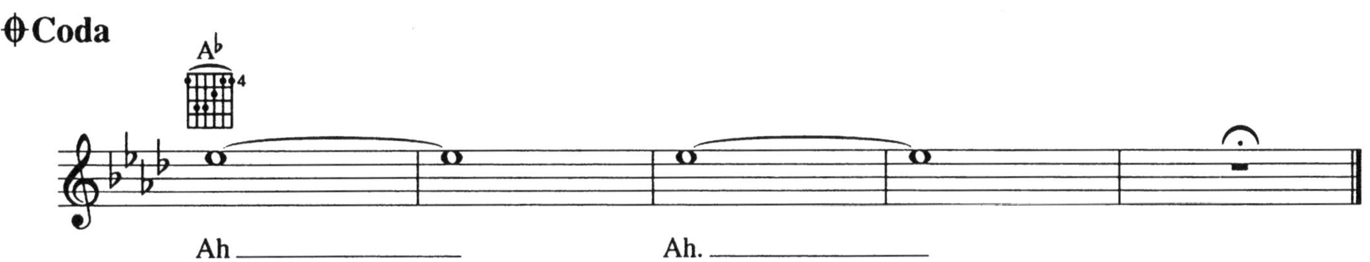
A♭
Ah
Ah.

In My Life.

Words & Music by John Lennon & Paul McCartney.

Moderately
A
F♯m7/A
A7
There are plac - es I'll re - mem - ber all my
But of all these friends and lov - ers there is
D
Dm
A
life, though some have changed. Some for - ev - er, not for
no one com - pares with you. And these mem - 'ries lose their
F♯m7/A
A7
D
Dm
A
bet - ter; Some have gone and some re - main. All these
mean - ing When I think of love as some - thing new. Tho' I
F♯m7
D
(1) plac - es had their mo - ments with
(2,3) know I'll nev - er lose af - fec - tion for
G
A
lov - ers and friends I still can re - call, Some are
peo - ple and things that went be - fore, I

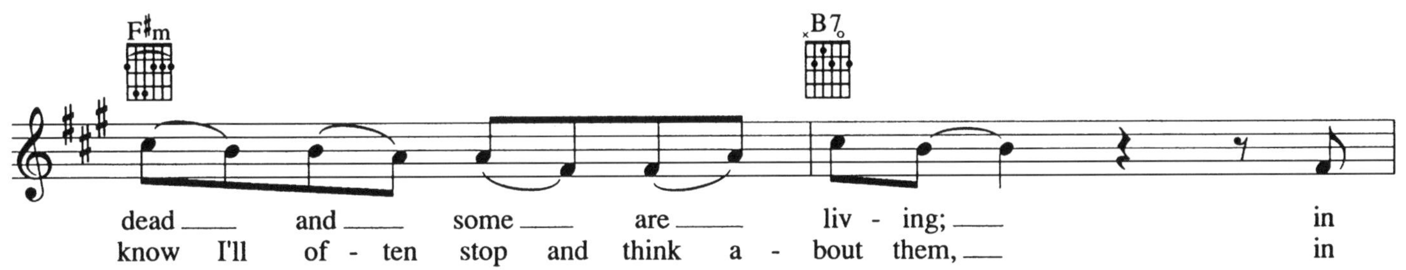
F♯m
B7
dead and some are liv - ing; in
know I'll of - ten stop and think a - bout them, in

Dm
A
To Coda
A
E
my life I've loved them all.
my life I love you more.

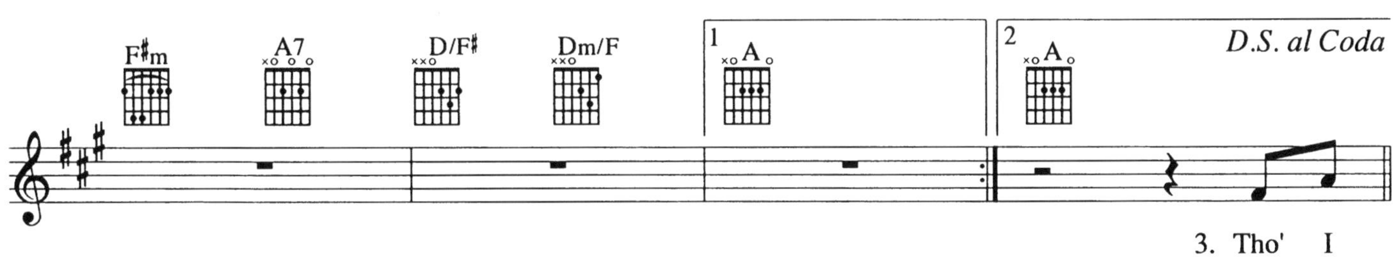
F♯m
A7
D/F♯
Dm/F
1
A
2
A
D.S. al Coda
3. Tho' I

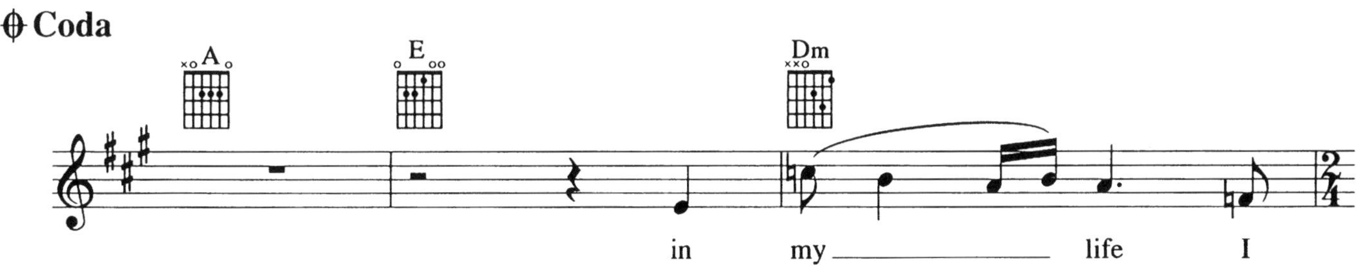
Coda
A
E
Dm
in my life I

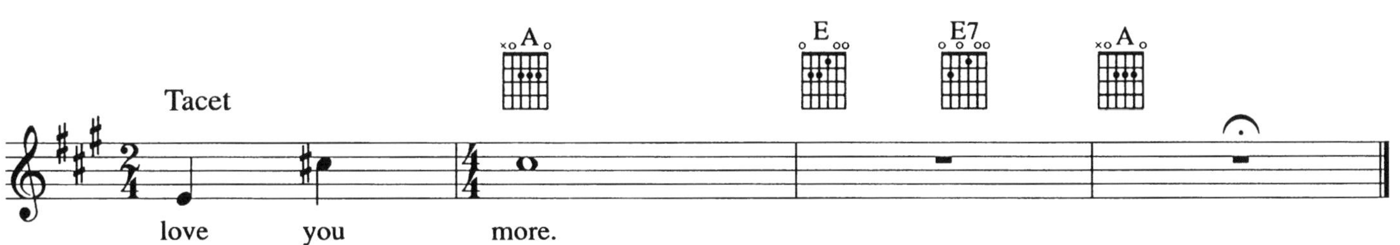
Tacet
A
E
E7
A
love you more.

It's Only Love.

Words & Music by John Lennon & Paul McCartney.

Moderately
C Em/B B♭ F G7sus G7 G+
I get high when I see you go by. My oh my!
Is it right that you and I should fight ev - 'ry night?
C Em/B B♭ F G7sus G7 G+
when you sigh, my my in - side just flies, but - ter - flies.
Just the sight of you makes night - time bright, ver - y bright.
F G C Am
Why am I so shy when I'm be - side you?
Have - n't I the right to make it up, girl?
It's on - ly
B♭ G7 C
love and that is all, why should I feel the way I do?
Am B♭ G7 F
It's on - ly love and that is all, But it's so hard lov - ing
1 G7
you.
2 G7 F G7
you. Yes, it's so hard lov - ing you, lov - ing
C Am C Am C Am C
you.

Tell Me What You See.

Words & Music by John Lennon & Paul McCartney.

Moderately
G C D7 G C
1. If you let __ me take __ your heart, __ I will prove __ to you; __
2. Big and black __ the clouds __ may be, __ Time will pass __ a - way. __
3. Lis - ten to __ me one __ more time, __ How can I __ get through? __
G G C D7 G C D7 C
We will nev - er be __ a - part, __ if I'm part __ of you. __
If you put __ your trust __ in me, __ I'll make bright __ your day. __
Can't you try __ to see __ that I'm __ try - in' to __ get you. __
G C G C
O - pen up __ your eyes __ now, __ tell me what __ you see. __
Look in - to __ these eyes __ now, __ tell me what __ you see. __
O - pen up __ your eyes __ now, __ tell me what __ you see. __
G C G C
It is no __ sur - prise __ now, __ What you see __ is me. __
Don't you re - a - lize, __ now, __ What you see __ is me. __
It is no __ sur - prise __ now, __ What you see __ is me. __
1 G 2 G Dm/G C
Tell me what you see. __
Tacet 3 G Dm/G C G
Mm mm mm mm mm.

Michelle.

Words & Music by John Lennon & Paul McCartney.

Moderately
F B♭m7 E♭ D°
Mi - chelle, ma belle, These are words that go to - geth - er
C B° C F B♭m7
well, my Mi - chelle. Mi - chelle, ma belle,
Mi - chelle, ma belle,
E♭ D° C B° C
sont les mots qui vont très bien en - semble, très bien en - semble. I
sont les mots qui vont très bien en - semble, très bien en - semble. I
Fm A♭7sus D♭
love you, I love you, I love you; That's all I want to say.
need to, I need to, I need to; I need to make you see.
C7sus Fm C+
Un - til I find a way, I will say the on - ly
Oh, what you mean to me un - til I do, I'm
Fm7 Fm6 D♭maj7/F 1 C 2 C
words I know that you'll un - der - stand. mean.
hop - ing you will know what I

F
B♭m7
E♭
D°
C
B°
I love you.
C
Fm
I want you, I want you, I want you,
A♭7sus
D♭
C7sus
I think you know by now, I'll get to you some-
Fm
C+
Fm7
Fm6
D♭maj7/F
-how. Un-til I do, I'm tell-ing you, so you'll un-der-
C
F
B♭m7
E♭
D°
-stand: Mi-chelle, ma belle, sont les mots qui vont très bien en-
C
B°
C
Fm
C7
-semble, très bien en-semble. And I will say the on-ly words
Fm7
Fm6
D♭/F
C
F
I know that you'll un-der-stand, my Mi-chelle.
B♭m7
E♭
D°
C
B°
C
F
Repeat and Fade

Norwegian Wood.

Words & Music by John Lennon & Paul McCartney.

Moderately
G Dm7 C
I once had a girl, or should I say she once had
(Instrumental)
G G
me; She showed me her room, Is - n't it good
Dm7 C G Gm
Nor - we - gian Wood? 1. She asked me to stay and she
2. She told me she worked in the
C
told me to sit an - y - where, So
morn - ing and start - ed to laugh, I
Gm
I looked a - round and I no - ticed there was - n't a
told her I did - n't and crawled off to sleep in the

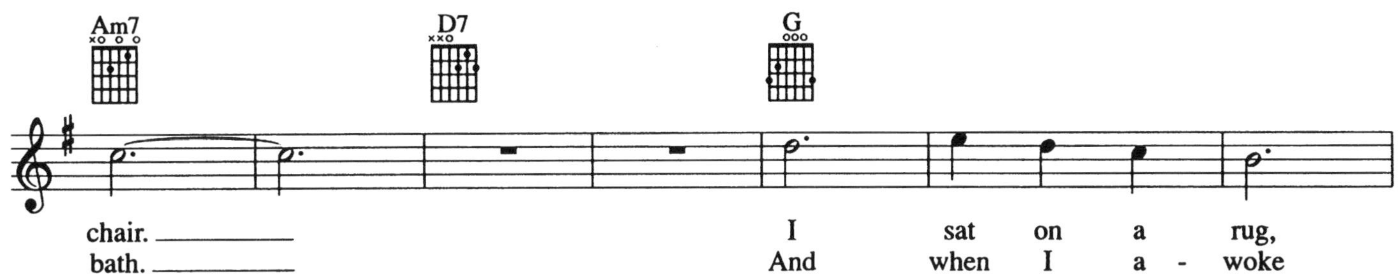
Am7
D7
G
chair.
I sat on a rug,
bath.
And when I a - woke

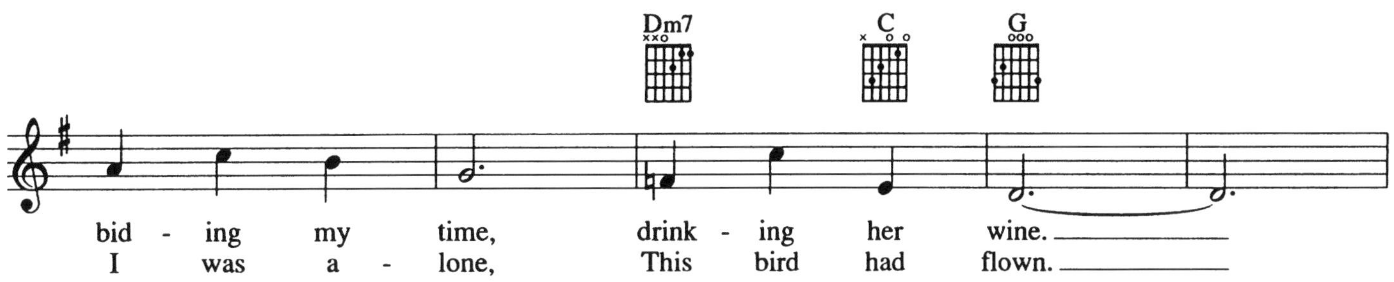
Dm7
C
G
bid - ing my time, drink - ing her wine.
I was a - lone, This bird had flown.

G
Dm7
C
We talked un - til two and then she said "It's time for
So I lit a fire, is - n't it good Nor - we - gian

1
G
2
G
bed".
Wood.

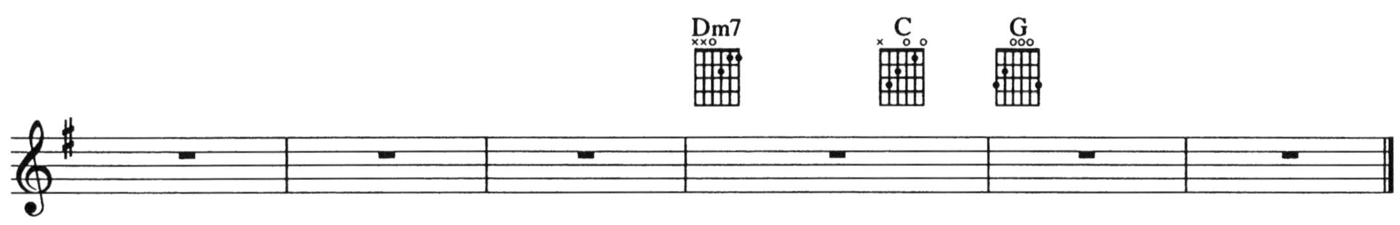
Dm7
C
G

Nowhere Man.

WORDS & MUSIC BY JOHN LENNON & PAUL McCARTNEY.

Moderately
E♭ B♭ A♭ E♭
He's a real no - where man, sit - ting in his no - where land,
A♭ A♭m E♭ E♭7
Mak - ing all his no - where plans for no - bod - y.
E♭ B♭ A♭
Does - n't have a point of view, knows not where he's
He's as blind as he can be, just sees what he
E♭ A♭ A♭m E♭
go - ing to, is - n't he a bit like you and me?
wants to see, no - where man, can you see me at all?
Gm A♭
No - where man, please lis - ten: You don't know
No - where man, don't wor - ry: Take your time,
please lis - ten: You don't know
Gm A♭ Gm
what you're miss - ing. No - where man, The
don't hur - ry. Leave it all 'Till
what you're miss - ing. No - where man, The

Fm7
B♭
world is at your com - mand.
some - bod - y else lends you a hand.
world is at your com - mand.
E♭
B♭
A♭
(Instrumental)
Does - n't have a point of view, knows not where he's
He's a real no - where man, sit - ting in his
E♭
To Coda
A♭
A♭m
go - ing to
no - where land,
Is - n't he a bit like you and
1
E♭
2
E♭
D.S. al Coda
me?
me?
No - where man,
Coda
A♭
A♭m
E♭
Mak - ing all his no - where plans for no - bod - y,
A♭
A♭m
E♭
Mak - ing all his no - where plans for no - bod - y.

Run For Your Life.

Words & Music by John Lennon & Paul McCartney.

Moderately
D
Well, I'd rath - er see you dead lit - tle girl, than to
(2) know that I'm a wick - ed guy, and I was
(3) Let this be a ser - mon; I mean
Bm
D
be with an - oth - er man. You'd bet - ter keep your head
born with a jeal - ous mind. And I can't spend my whole
ev - 'ry - thing I said. Ba - by, I'm de - ter -
Bm
lit - tle girl, or I won't know where I am.
life try - in' just to make you toe the line.
- mined and I'd rath - er see you dead.
You'd bet - ter
E
Bm
run for your life if you can, lit - tle girl. Hide your head in the sand

E
Bm
G
F#7
— lit - tle girl, — Catch you with an - oth - er man, — that's the end -

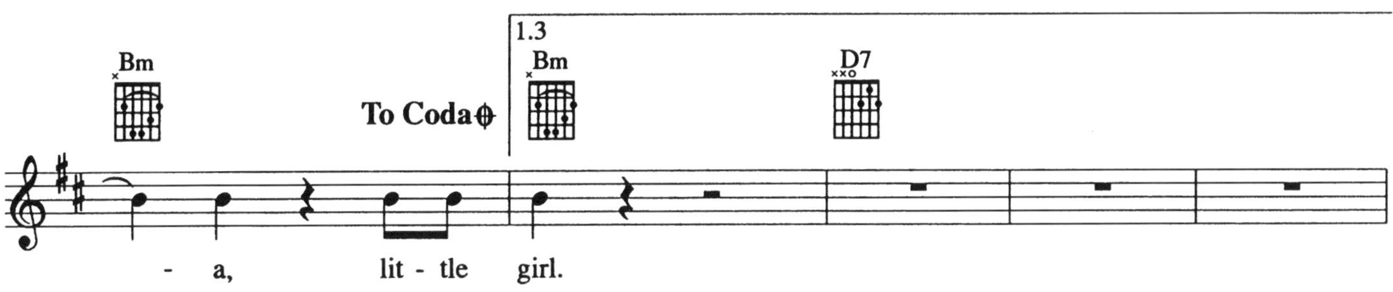
Bm
To Coda
1.3
Bm
D7
- a, lit - tle girl.

2
D7
2. Well, you girl.
3. I'd

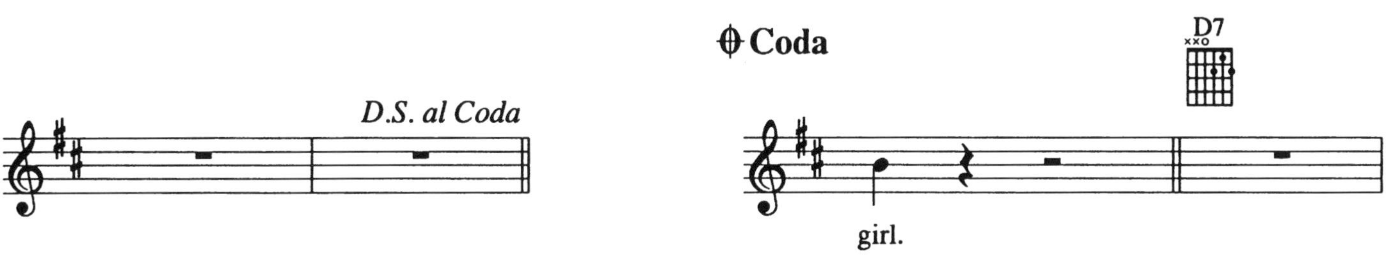
D.S. al Coda
Coda
D7
girl.

Repeat and Fade
No, no, no. —

That Means A Lot.

Words & Music by John Lennon & Paul McCartney.

Moderately
E♭sus9
A♭m6/E♭
E♭add9
A (1.3) friend says that your love won't mean a lot,
(2) friend says that a love is nev - er true,
E♭
D♭/E♭
D♭7/E♭
and you know that your love is all you've
and you know that this could ap - ply to
Fm7
B♭7
G♭
A♭m7
D♭7
got. At times things are so bad and at
you. A touch can mean so much when it's
G♭
Fm7
B♭7
E♭
To Coda
times they are not.
all you've got.
But when she says she loves
A♭
B♭7
E♭
1
2
E♭
B♭7
you that means a lot.
2. A mm love

Cm
A♭m
can be deep in - side, love can be su - i - cide, can't you
E♭
B♭7
Cm
Gm7
D.S. al Coda
see you can't hide what you feel when it's real 3. A
Coda
A♭
B♭7
Cm
F7♭5
you that means a lot. Can't you see
E♭
A♭/B♭
B♭7
Cm
when she says she loves you that means a lot.
F7♭5
E♭
A♭/B♭
B♭7
Can't you see when she says she loves you that means a
E♭
A♭/B♭
Emaj7
E♭
lot.

The Night Before.

Words & Music by John Lennon & Paul McCartney.

Moderately
B♭ A♭ E♭
1. We said our good - byes,
2. Were you tell - ing lies?
(The
F7 B♭ A♭ E♭
night be - fore)
Love was in your eyes,
Was I so un - wise?
(The
F7 Gm E♭m
night be - fore)
1. Now to - day I find
2.3. When I held you near
Gm E♭m B♭
You have changed your mind.
You were so sin - cere.
Treat me like you did
E♭7 B♭
the night be - fore.
1 D♭ E♭
2.3
Fm7 B♭7 E♭
Last night is the night I will re - mem - ber you by;

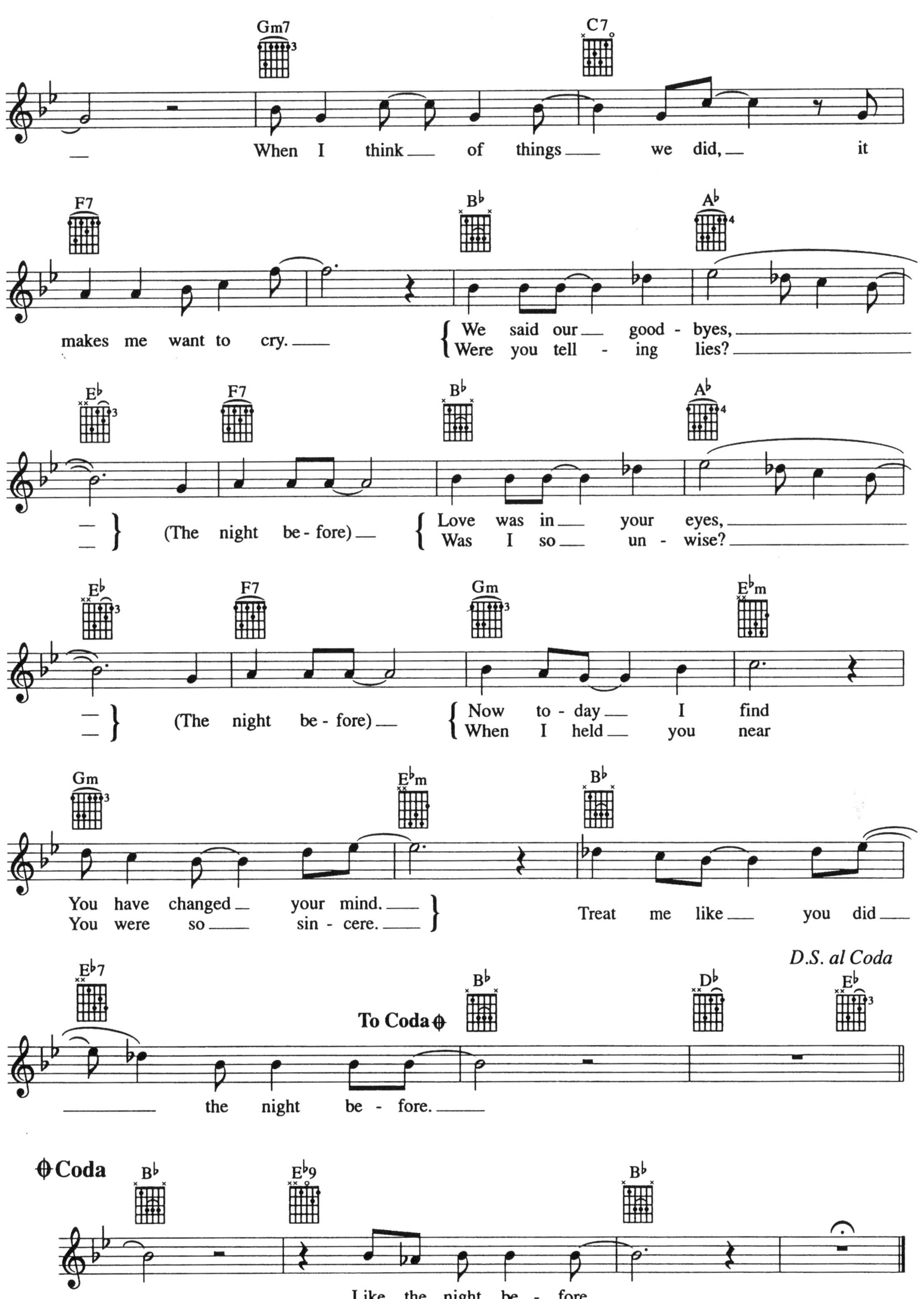
Gm7
C7
When I think of things we did, it
F7
B♭
A♭
makes me want to cry.
We said our good - byes,
Were you tell - ing lies?
E♭
F7
B♭
A♭
(The night be - fore)
Love was in your eyes,
Was I so un - wise?
E♭
F7
Gm
E♭m
(The night be - fore)
Now to - day I find
When I held you near
Gm
E♭m
B♭
You have changed your mind.
You were so sin - cere.
Treat me like you did
D.S. al Coda
E♭7
To Coda
B♭
D♭
E♭
the night be - fore.
Coda
B♭
E♭9
B♭
Like the night be - fore.

The Word.

Words & Music by John Lennon & Paul McCartney.

Moderately, with a beat
G7
Say the 1.3. word and you'll be free, say the word and be like
2. word and you'll be free, spread the word and be like
4. word a chance to say that the word is just the
C9
me. Say the word I'm think - ing of, have you
me. Spread the word I'm think - ing of, have you
way. It's the word I'm think - ing of, And the
G7
Am7
D
heard? the word is "love."
heard? the word is "love."
on - ly word is "love."
It's so fine, it's
Gm7
C
G7
1.2.3
G
sun - shine, it's the word "love."
1. In the be - gin - ning I
2. Ev - 'ry - where I go I
3. Now that I know what I

F
B♭
mis - un - der - stood,
hear it said,
feel must be right,
But now I've got it, the
In the good and the bad books that
I mean to show ev - 'ry -

C
4
G7
word is good.
I have read.
-bod - y the light.
2. Spread the
3. Say the
4. Give the
"love."
Say the word

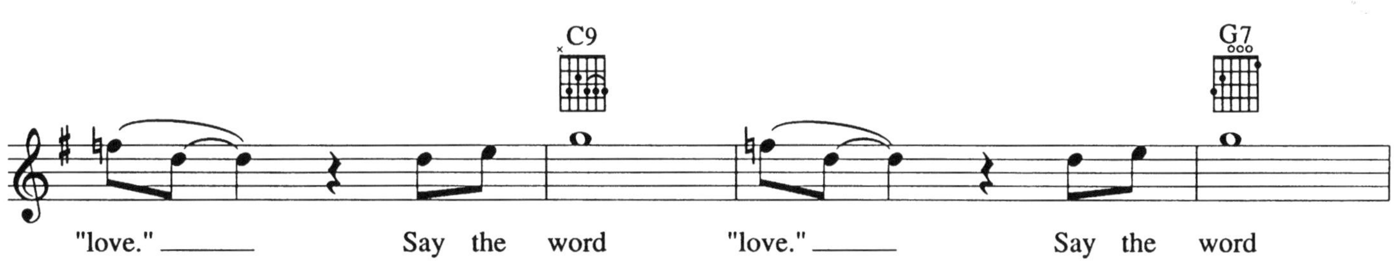
C9
G7
"love."
Say the word
"love."
Say the word

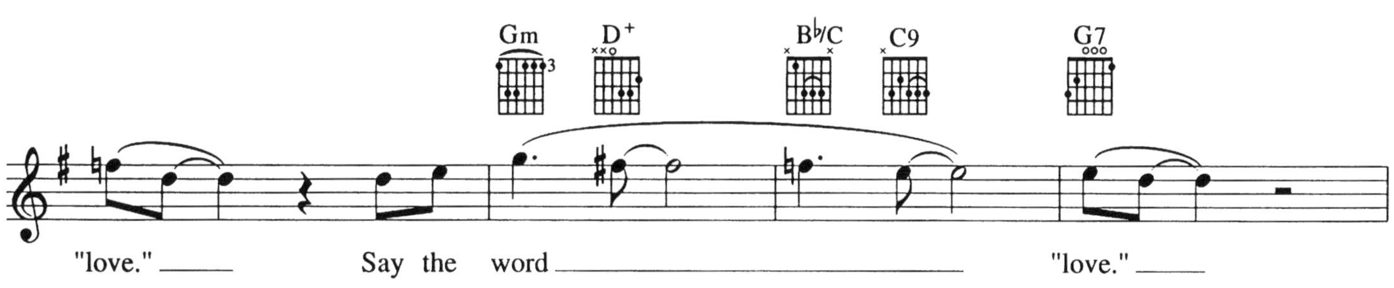
Gm
D+
B♭/C
C9
G7
"love."
Say the word
"love."

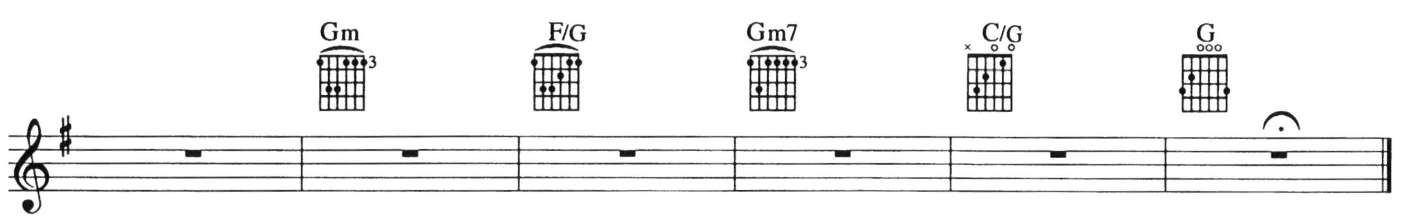
Gm
F/G
Gm7
C/G
G

Think For Yourself.

Words & Music by George Harrison.

Moderately
Am
Dm
B♭
1. I've got a word or two to say a - bout the things that you do.
2. I left you far be - hind the ru - ins of the life that you had in mind.
3. Al - though your mind's o - paque, try think - ing more if just for your own sake.
C
G
Am
Dm
B♭
You're tell - ing all those lies a - bout the good things that we can have if we close our eyes.
And though you still can't see, I know your mind's made up, you're gon - na cause more mis - er - y.
The fu - ture still looks good, and you've got time to rec - ti - fy all the things that you should.
C
G
Am

C7
G7
Do what you want to do, and go where you're go - ing to,

E♭/B♭
D7
To Coda
Think for your - self, 'cause I won't be there with

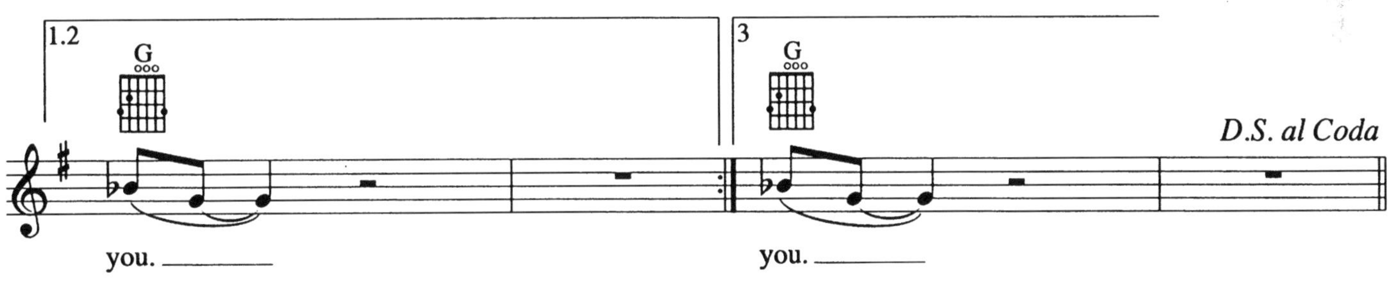
1.2
G
3
G
D.S. al Coda
you. you.

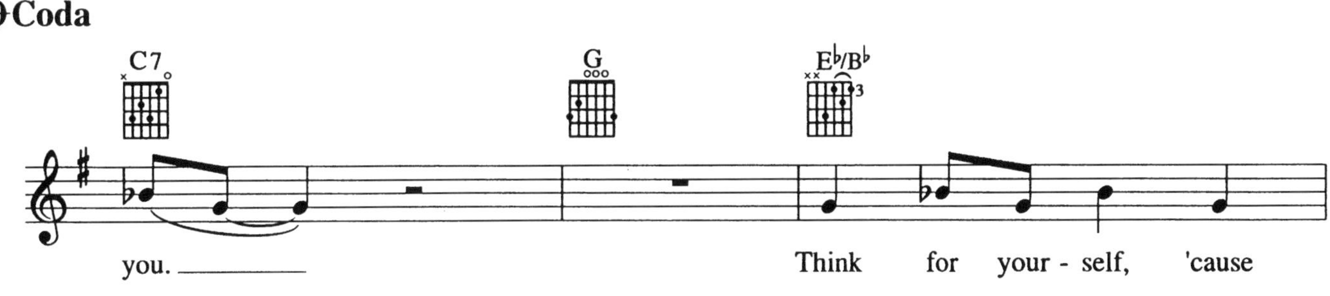
Coda
C7
G
E♭/B♭
you. Think for your - self, 'cause

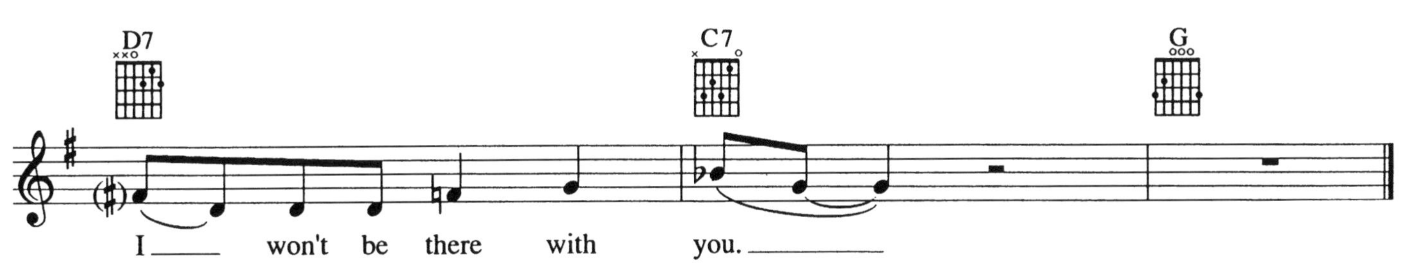
D7
C7
G
I won't be there with you.

Ticket To Ride.

Words & Music by John Lennon & Paul McCartney.

Moderate rock tempo
G
I think I'm gon - na be sad. I think it's to - day,
(2) said that liv - ing with me is bring - ing her down,
yeh! The girl that's driv - ing me mad
yeh! For she would nev - er be free
Am7
D7
Em
is go - ing a - way.
when I was a - round.
She's got a tick - et to ride,
C7
Em
F
Em
She's got a tick - et to ri - hi - hide,
She's got a tick - et to ride,
D7
1
G
but she don't care.
2. She
2
G
C7
I don't know why she's rid - in' so high,
She ought to think right; She ought to do right by

D
C7
me. Be - fore she gets to say - ing good - bye
She ought to
think twice, She ought to do right by me.
D
1. I
2. She
G
think I'm gon - na be sad.
said that liv - ing with me
I think it's to - day,
is bring - ing her down,
yeh!
yeh!
The girl that's driv - ing me mad
For she would nev - er be free
Am7
D7
is go - ing a - way.
when I was a - round.
Yeh!
Yeh.
Oh,
Em
C7
Em
She's got a tick - et to ride,
She's got a tick - et to ri -
F
Em
D7
- hi - hide,
She's got a tick - et to ride,
but she don't care.
1
G
I
2
G
Repeat and Fade
My ba - by don't care.

Wait.

Words & Music by John Lennon & Paul McCartney.

Moderately
Gm7 C/G Cm/G Gm
It's been a long time, now I'm
heart breaks, don't wait,
D7 Gm Gm7 C/G
com - ing back home. I've been a - way now,
turn me a - way. And if your heart's strong,
Cm/G Gm D7 Gm B♭ E♭maj7
oh, how I've been a - lone.
hold on, I won't de - lay.
Wait 'til I
B♭ E♭maj7 B♭ E♭maj7 B♭ D7
come back to your side, we'll for - get the tears we cried;
1 Gm
But if your
2 Gm Cm
I feel as though you ought to
F B♭ Gm
know that I've been good, as good as I can be. And if you
Cm F B♭
do, I'll trust in you and know that you will wait for
3

Gm D7 Gm7 C/G Cm/G Gm
me. It's been a long time, now I'm
But if your heart breaks, don't wait,
D7 Gm Gm7 C/G Cm/G Gm
com - ing back home. I've been a - way now, oh, how
turn me a - way. And if your heart's strong, hold on,
D7 Gm B♭ E♭maj7 B♭ E♭maj7
I've been a - lone.
I won't de - lay.
Wait 'til I come back to your side,
B♭ E♭maj7 B♭ D7 Gm
we'll for - get the tears we cried; I feel as
Gm Gm7 C/G Cm/G Gm
It's been a long time, now I'm
D7 Gm Gm7 C/G
com - ing back home, I've been a - way now,
Cm/G Gm D7 Gm
oh how I've been a - lone.

We Can Work It Out.

Words & Music by John Lennon & Paul McCartney.

Moderately
B♭ B♭sus B♭ B♭sus
Try to see it my way, do I have to keep on talk - ing
Think of what you're say - ing, you can get it wrong and still you
A♭add 9 B♭ B♭ B♭sus B♭
till I can't go on? While you see it your way,
think that it's all right. Think of what I'm say - ing,
B♭sus A♭add 9 B♭
run a risk of know - ing that our love may soon be gone.
we can work it out and get it straight, or say good - night.
E♭ B♭ E♭ Fsus F Gm
We can work it out, We can work it out. Life is ver - y short
Gm/F E♭ D7sus D
and there's no time for fuss - ing and
Gm Gm/F E♭maj7 Gm/D Gm
fight - ing, my friend. I have al - ways thought

Gm/F
E♭
D7sus
D
that it's a crime
So I will
Gm
Gm/F
E♭maj7
Gm/D
B♭
B♭sus
B♭
ask you once a - gain.
Try to see it my way,
B♭sus
A♭add 9
B♭
on - ly time will tell if I am right or I am wrong.
B♭
B♭sus
B♭
B♭sus
While you see it your way,
there's a chance that we might fall a -
A♭add 9
B♭
E♭
B♭
- part be - fore too long.
We can work it out,
E♭
Fsus
F
B♭
E♭/B♭
B♭
We can work it out.

What Goes On?

Words & Music by John Lennon, Paul McCartney & Richard Starkey.

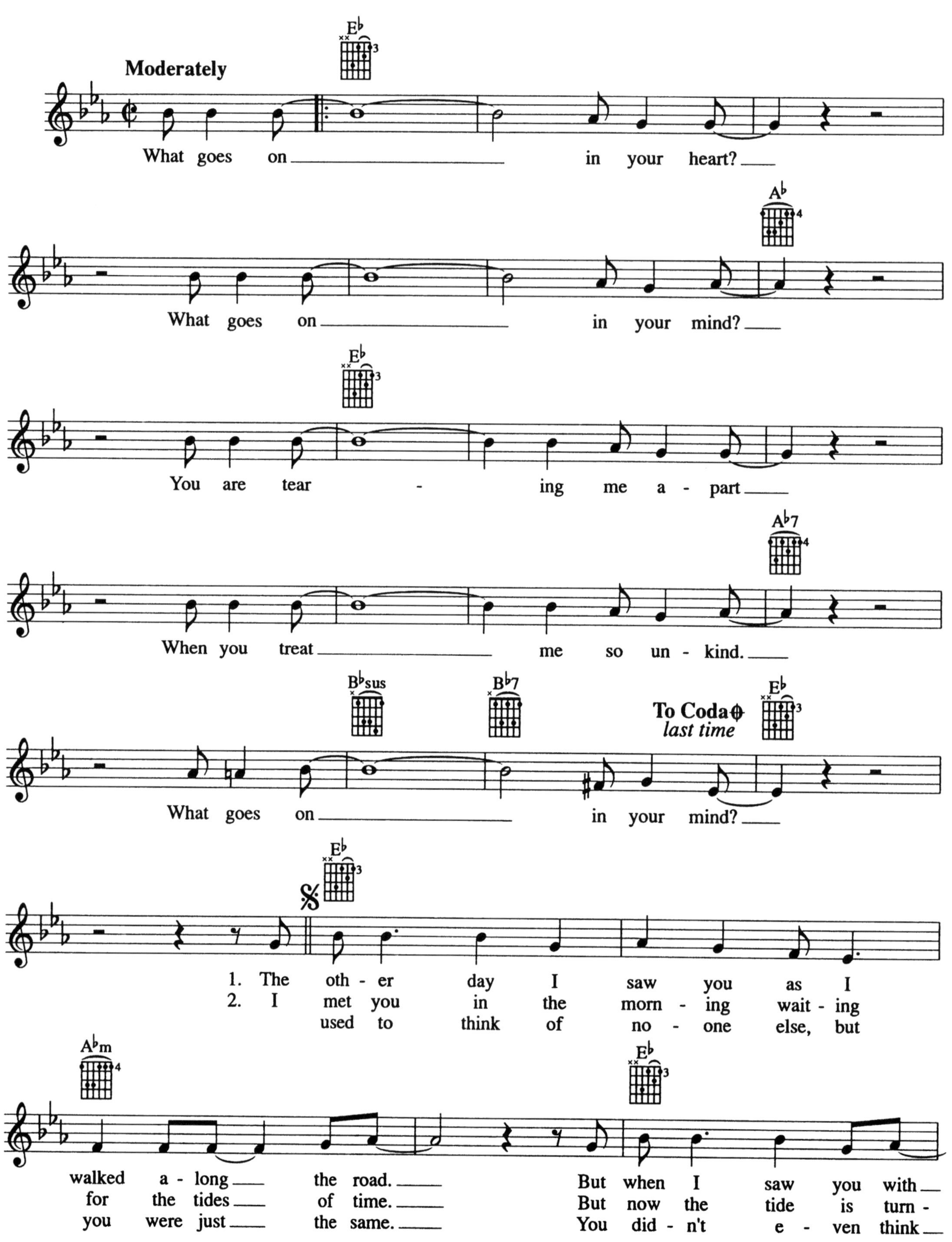
Moderately
E♭
What goes on in your heart?
A♭
What goes on in your mind?
E♭
You are tear - ing me a - part
A♭7
When you treat me so un - kind.
B♭sus
B♭7
To Coda last time
E♭
What goes on in your mind?
E♭
1. The oth - er day I saw you as I
2. I met you in the morn - ing wait - ing
used to think of no - one else, but
A♭m
E♭
walked a - long the road. But when I saw you with
for the tides of time. But now the tide is turn -
you were just the same. You did - n't e - ven think

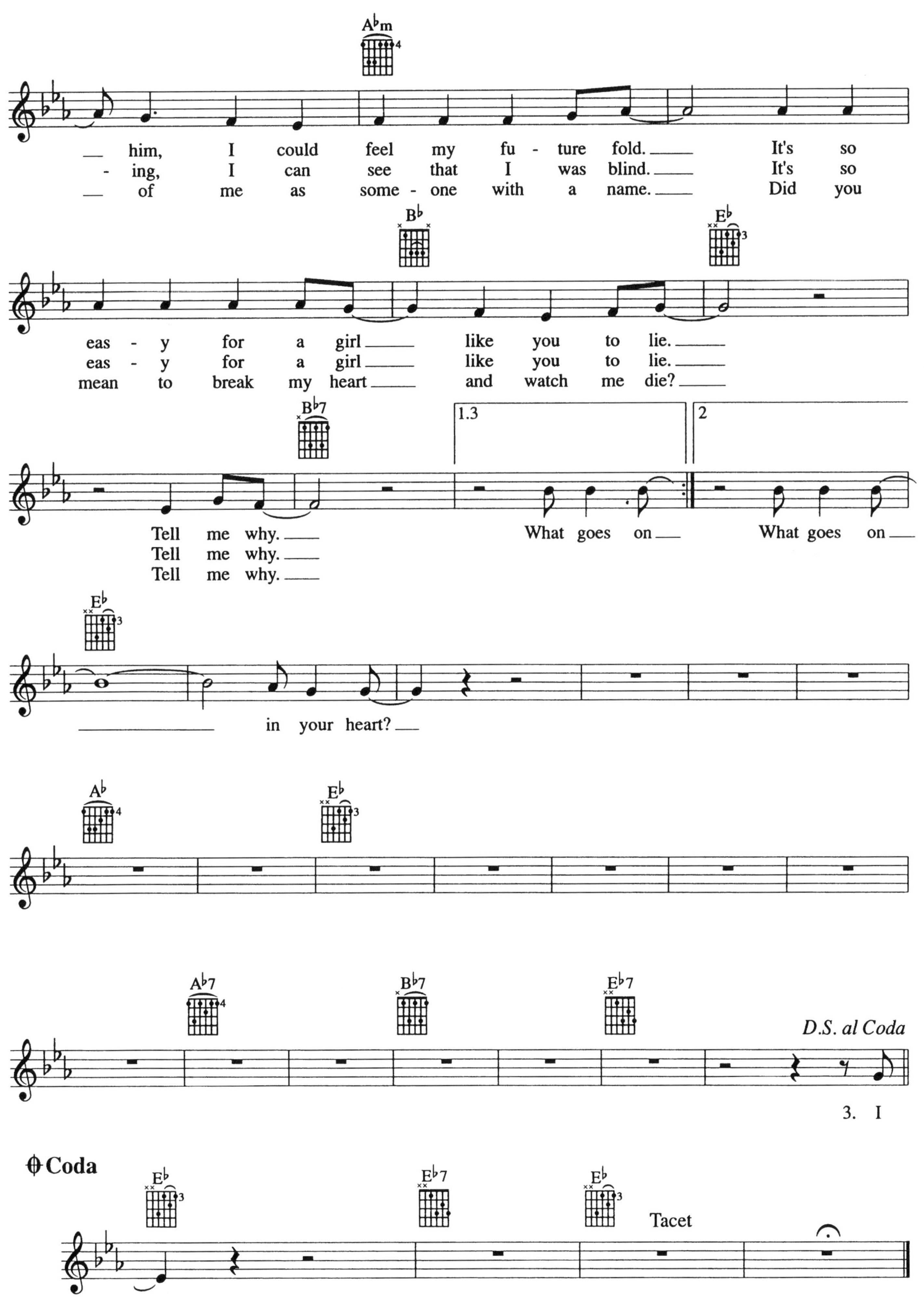
A♭m
him, I could feel my fu - ture fold. It's so
ing, I can see that I was blind. It's so
of me as some - one with a name. Did you
B♭
E♭
eas - y for a girl like you to lie.
eas - y for a girl like you to lie.
mean to break my heart and watch me die?
B♭7
1.3
2
Tell me why. What goes on What goes on
Tell me why.
Tell me why.
E♭
in your heart?
A♭
E♭
A♭7
B♭7
E♭7
D.S. al Coda
3. I
Coda
E♭
E♭7
E♭
Tacet

Yes It Is.

Words & Music by John Lennon & Paul McCartney.

Moderately
E♭ A♭ Fm7 B♭7
1. If you wear red ___ to - night, re -
2. Scar - let were the clothes ___ she wore,
E♭ A♭ D♭6 B♭7 E♭ Cm
- mem - ber what I said ___ to - night; For red is the col - our that my
Ev - 'ry - bod - y knows ___ I'm sure; I would re - mem - ber all the
A♭ D♭ Cm E♭
ba - by wore ___ and what's more ___ it's true, yes, it is.
things we planned, ___ un - der - stand, ___ it's
Cm E♭ E♭7
true, yes, it is, it's true, yes, it is.
B♭m7 E♭7 A♭ Fm
I could be hap - py ___ with you by my side, ___

B♭m7
E♭7
Cm
Cm/B♭
If I could for-get her,
but it's my pride, yes, it is, yes it is
oh, yes it

F7
B♭7
E♭
A♭
Fm7
B♭7
is, yeah
Please don't wear red
to-night,

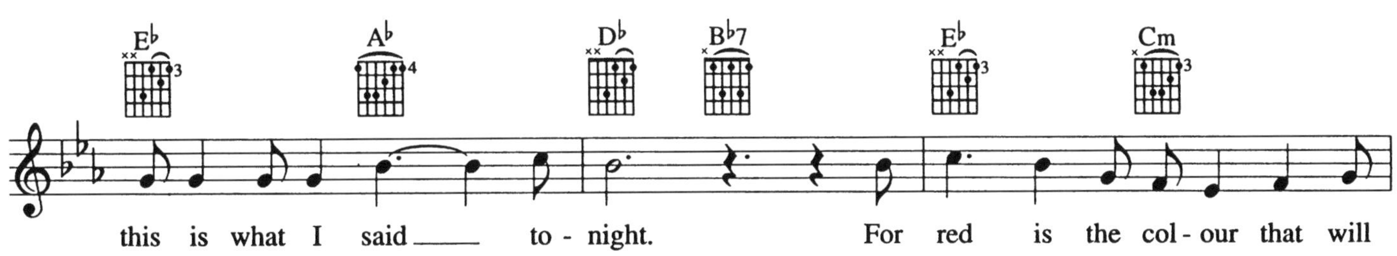
E♭
A♭
D♭
B♭7
E♭
Cm
this is what I said
to-night.
For red is the col-our that will

A♭
D♭
Cm
E♭
make it blue,
in spite of you,
it's true.
yes, it is, it's

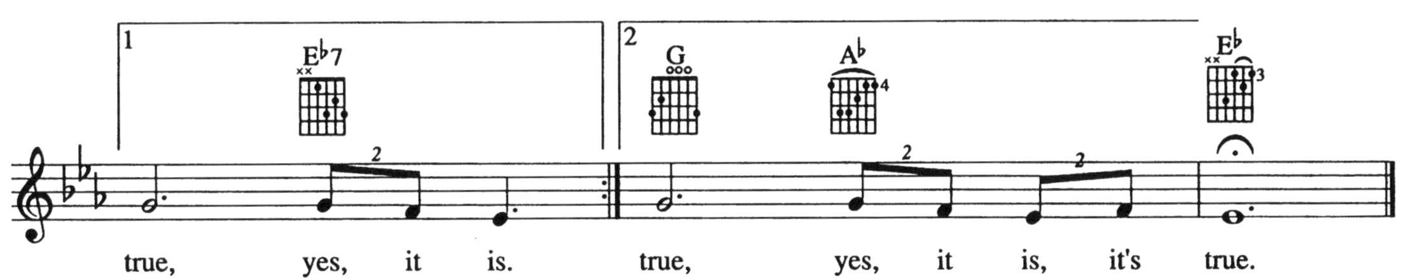
E♭7
G
A♭
E♭
true, yes, it is.
true, yes, it is, it's true.

Yesterday.

WORDS & MUSIC BY JOHN LENNON & PAUL McCARTNEY.

Moderately, with expression
F Em7 A7
1. Yes - ter - day, all my trou - bles seemed so
2. Sud - den - ly, I'm not half the man I
Dm Dm/C B♭ C7
far a - way, Now it looks as though they're
used to be, There's a shad - ow hang - ing
B♭/F F C/E Dm7 G7 B♭ F
here to stay, Oh I be - lieve in yes - ter - day.
o - ver me, Oh yes - ter - day came sud - den - ly.
G/A A7 Dm C B♭maj7 Dm/A Gm C7
Why she had to go I don't know, she would - n't say.
F G/A A7 Dm C B♭maj7 Dm/A
I said some - thing wrong, now I

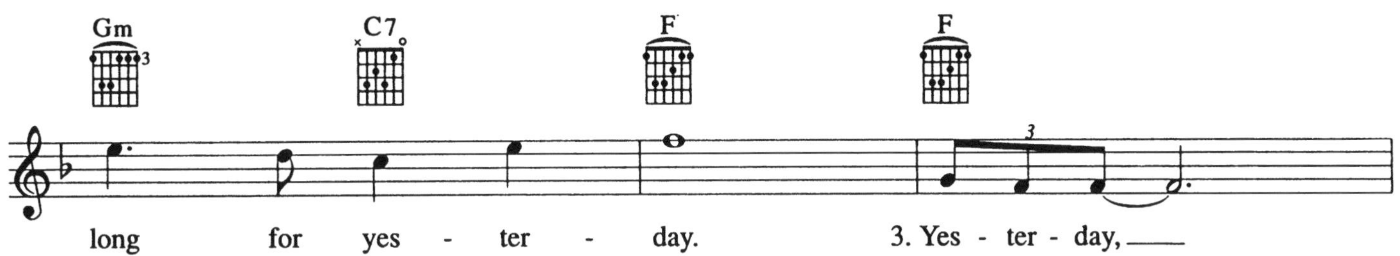
Gm
C7
F
F
long for yes - ter - day.
3. Yes - ter - day,

Em7
A7
Dm
Dm/C
love was such an eas - y game to play.

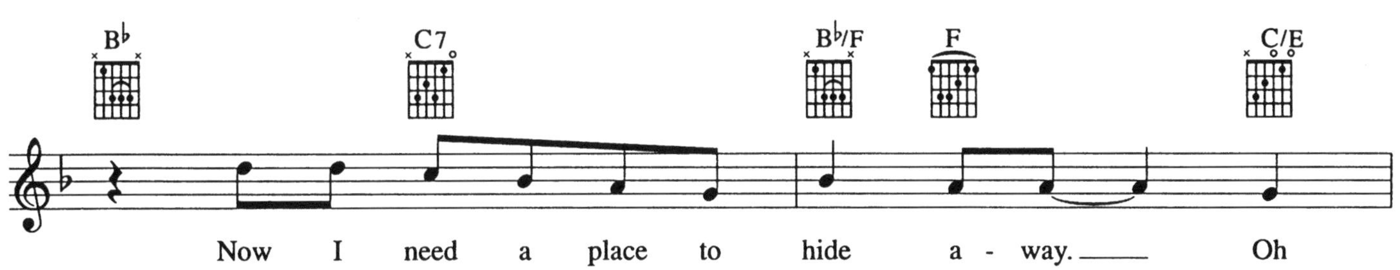
B♭
C7
B♭/F
F
C/E
Now I need a place to hide a - way.
Oh

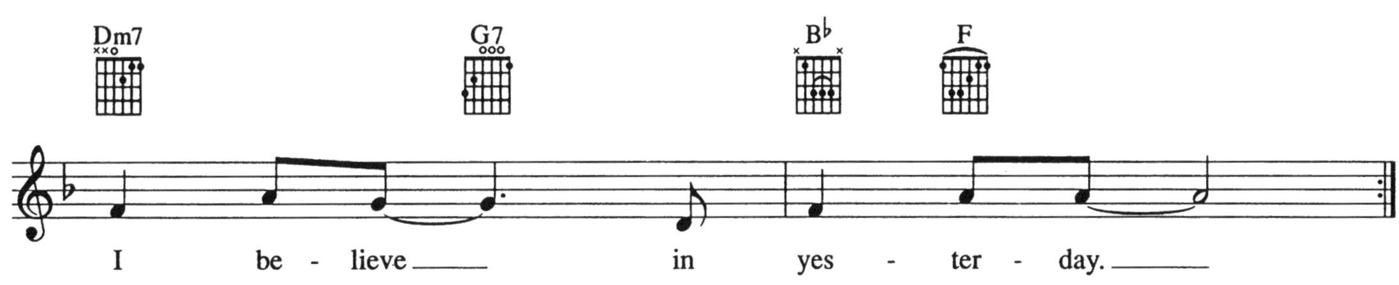
Dm7
G7
B♭
F
I be - lieve in yes - ter - day.

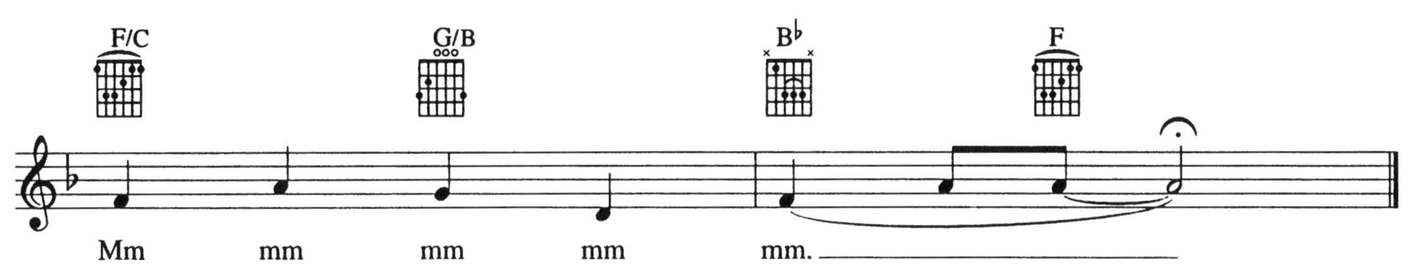
F/C
G/B
B♭
F
Mm mm mm mm mm.

You Like Me Too Much.

Words & Music by George Harrison.

Moderately
Am
Though you've gone a - way this morn - ing, you'll be back
(2) tried be - fore to leave me but you have -
3. I will fol - low you and bring you back
C G Am
a - gain to - night, Tell - ing me there'll be no next
n't got the nerve to walk out and make me lone -
where you be - long, 'cause I could - n't real - ly stand
C G
time if I just don't treat you right, You'll
ly which is all that I de - serve. You'll
it, I'll ad - mit that I was wrong. I
Bm Bm7 D7
nev - er leave me and you know it's true,
nev - er leave me and you know it's true,
would - n't let you leave me 'cause it's true,
G7 C
To Coda
'Cause you like me too much and I like you.
'Cause you like me too much and I like you.
'Cause you like me too much and I like you.

1
D
G/D
D
G/D
2
D7
2. You've

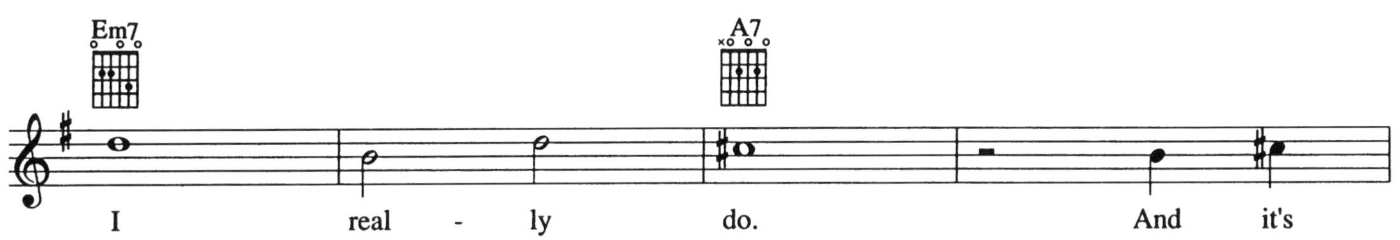
Em7
A7
I real - ly do.
And it's

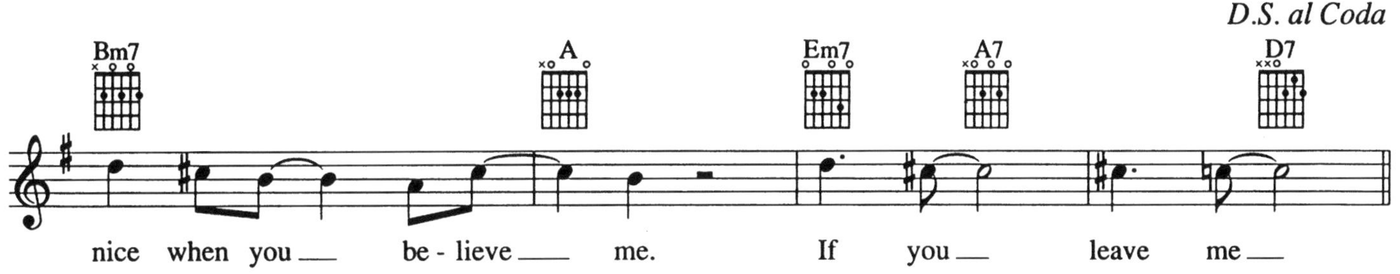
D.S. al Coda
Bm7
A
Em7
A7
D7
nice when you be - lieve me.
If you leave me

Coda
D
D7
G7
'Cause you like me too much

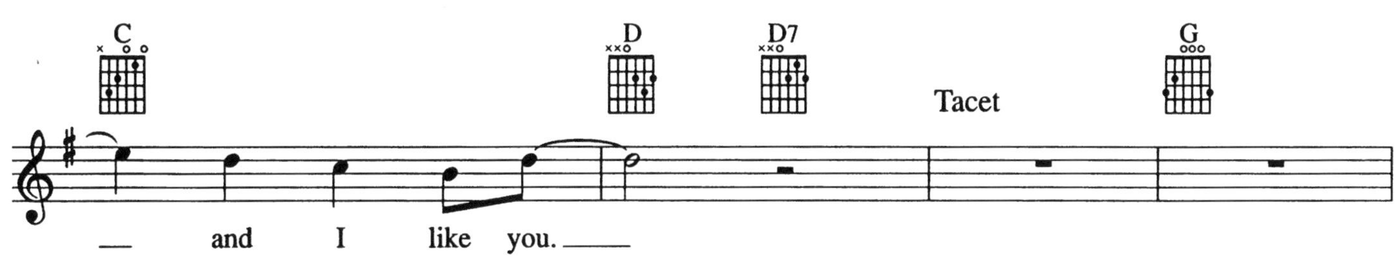
C
D
D7
Tacet
G
and I like you.

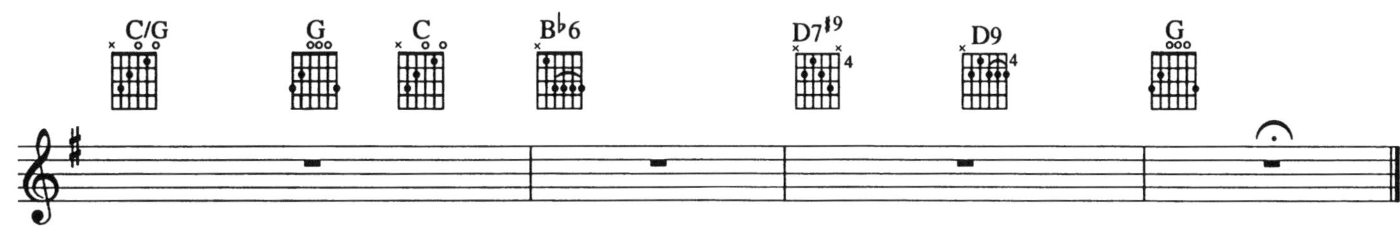
C/G
G
C
B♭6
D7♯9
D9
G

You Won't See Me.

Words & Music by John Lennon & Paul McCartney.

Moderately, with a beat
F G Bb F G Bb F F7 Bb Bbm F G Bb F C7 D° F Bb F
1. When I call you up, your line's engaged. I have had enough. So act your age. We have lost the time that was so hard to find; And I will lose my mind if you won't see me, you won't see me.
(2) why you should want to hide. But I can't get through. My hands are tied. I won't want to stay, I don't have much to say; But I can turn away and you won't see me, you won't see me.

1
C7
D°
F
2
C7
D°
F
Gm
2. I don't know
Time af - ter time
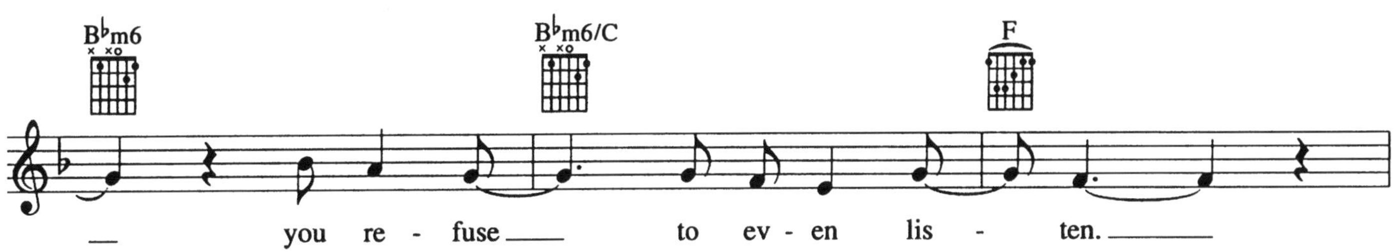
B♭m6
B♭m6/C
F
you re - fuse to ev - en lis - ten.

G7
C7sus
I would - n't mind if I knew what I was mis -

C7
F
G
- sing. 3. Though the days are few, they're filled

B♭
F
with tears; And since I lost you

G
B♭
F
it feels like years. Yes, it seems

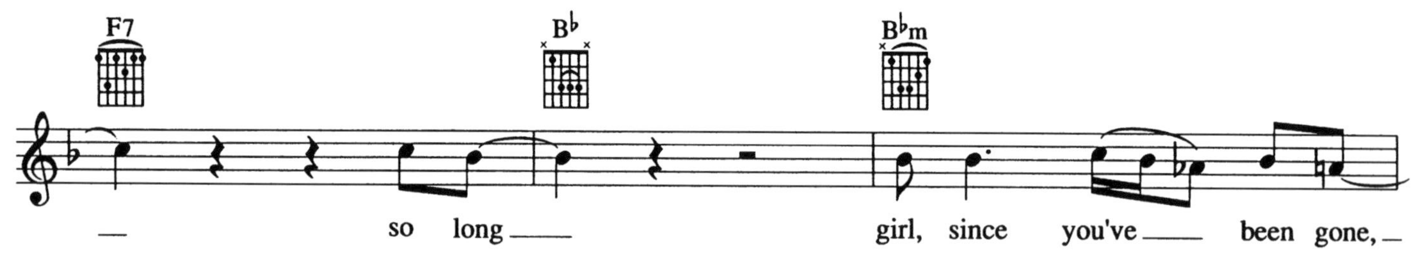
F7
B♭
B♭m
so long
girl, since you've been gone,

F
G
And I just can't go on
if

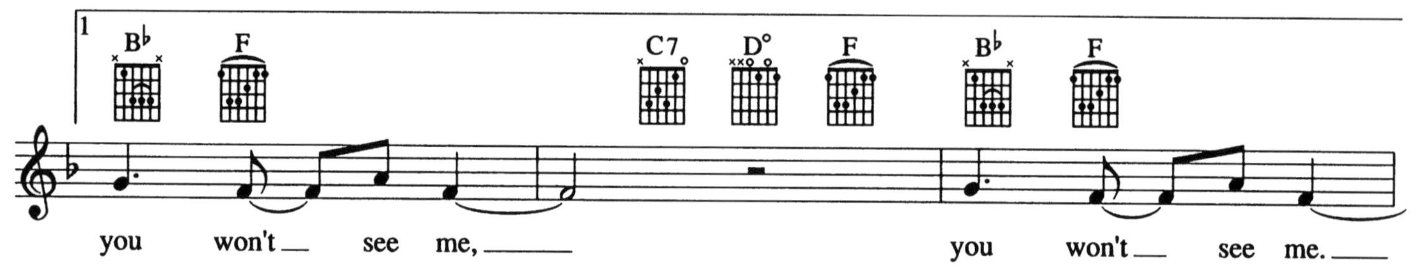
1
B♭
F
C7
D°
F
B♭
F
you won't see me,
you won't see me.

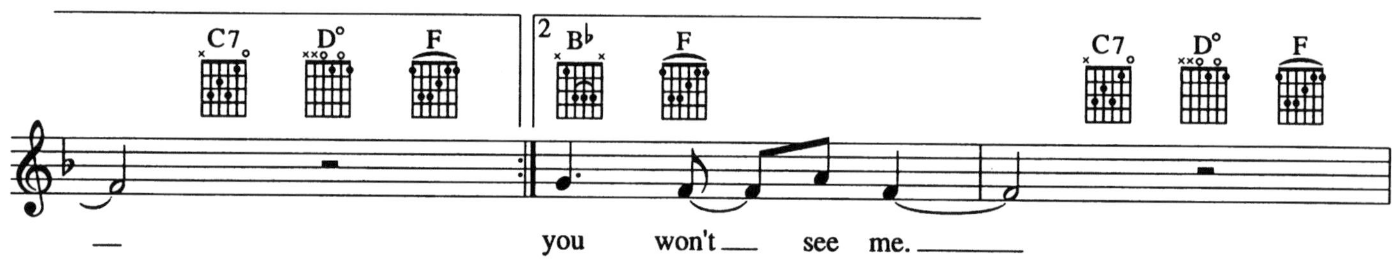
C7
D°
F
2
B♭
F
C7
D°
F
you won't see me.

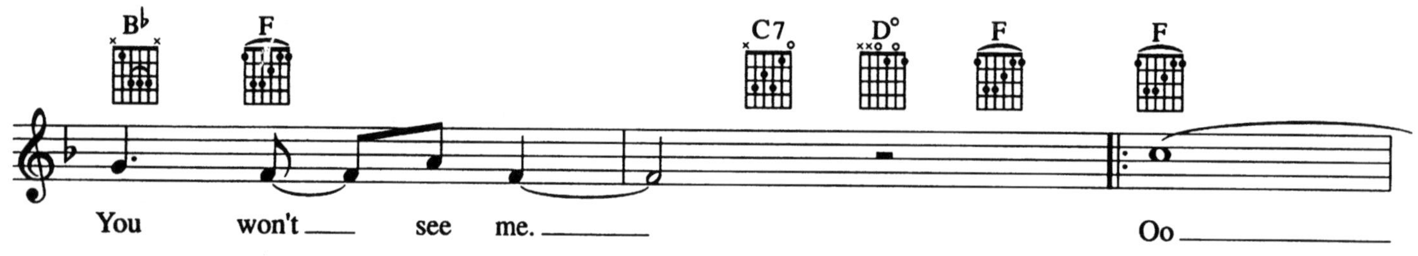
B♭
F
C7
D°
F
F
You won't see me.
Oo

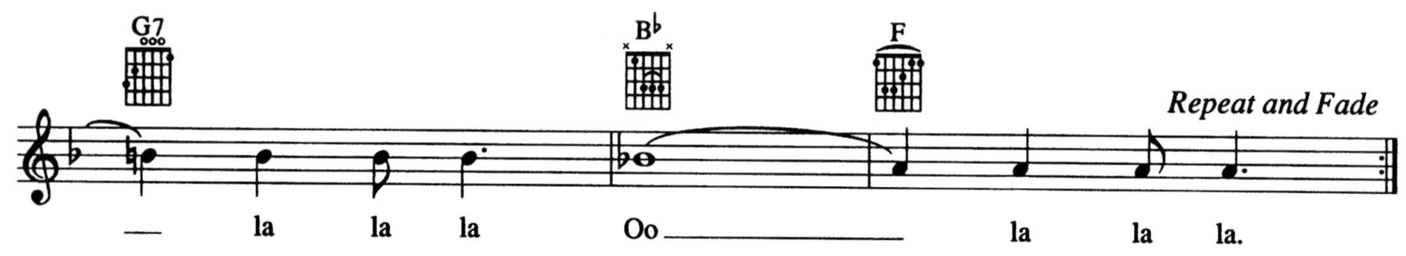
G7
B♭
F
Repeat and Fade
la la la
Oo
la la la.

Got To Get You Into My Life.

WORDS & MUSIC BY JOHN LENNON & PAUL McCARTNEY.

Moderately, with a strong beat

G

1. I was a - lone, I took a ride, I did - n't know what I would find
2. You did - n't run, you did - n't lie, you knew I want - ed just to hold
3. What can I do, what can I be when I'm with you I want to stay

F/G G

there. An - oth - er road, where may - be I
you. And had you gone you knew in time
there. If I'm true I'll nev - er leave

F/G

could see an - oth - er kind of mind there.
we'd meet a - gain for I'd have told you.
and if I do I know the way there.

Bm B♭+ Bm7/A Bm6/G♯ Bm B♭+

Ooh, then I sud - den - ly see you. Ooh, did I tell
Ooh, you were meant to be near me. Ooh, and I want
Ooh, then I sud - den - ly see you. Ooh, did I tell

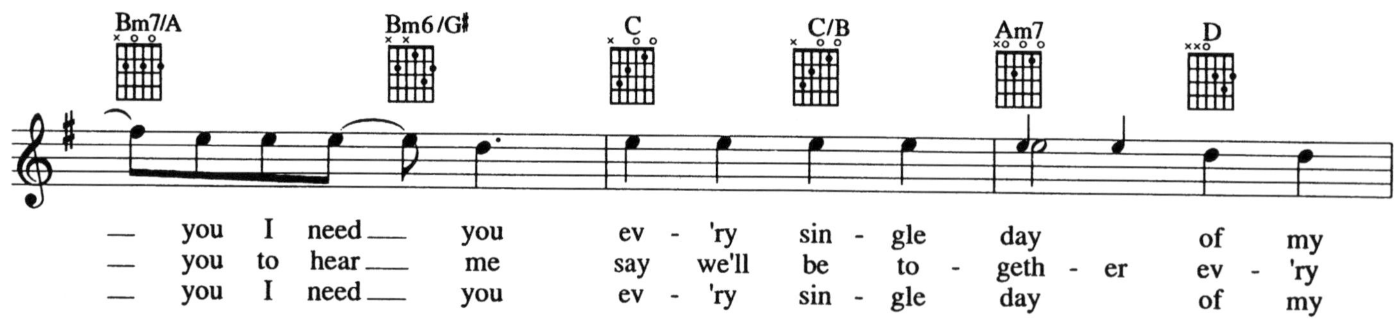
Bm7/A
Bm6/G♯
C
C/B
Am7
D
— you I need — you ev - 'ry sin - gle day of my
— you to hear — me say we'll be to - geth - er ev - 'ry
— you I need — you ev - 'ry sin - gle day of my

G
To Coda
1
2
G
life?
day.
life?
— Got to get you in - to my life! —

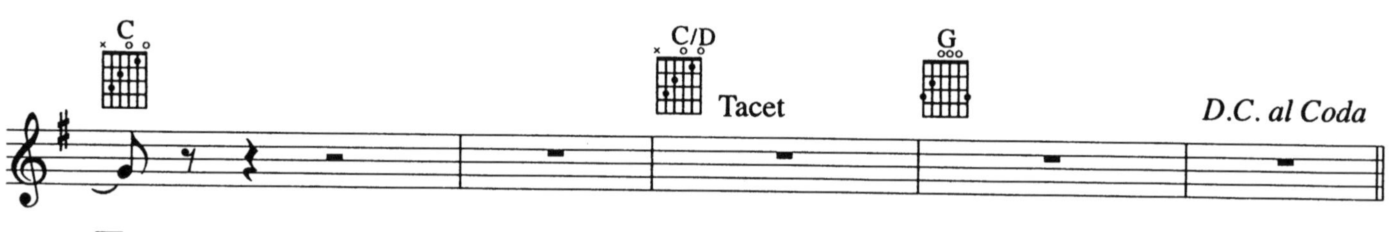
C
C/D
Tacet
G
D.C. al Coda
—

Coda
G
C
— Got to get you in - to my life! —

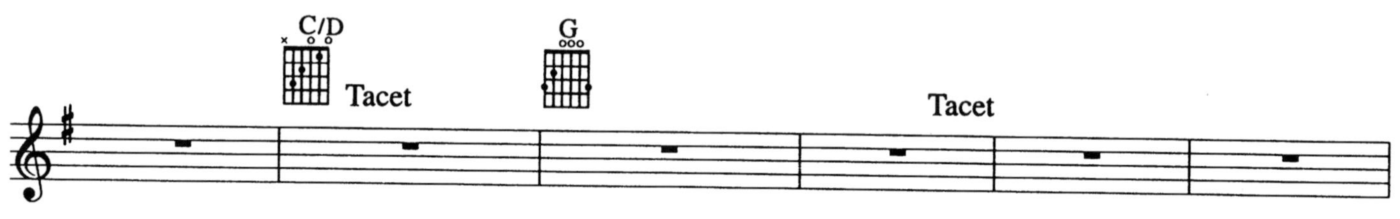
C/D
Tacet
G
Tacet

G
C
Got to get you in - to my life!

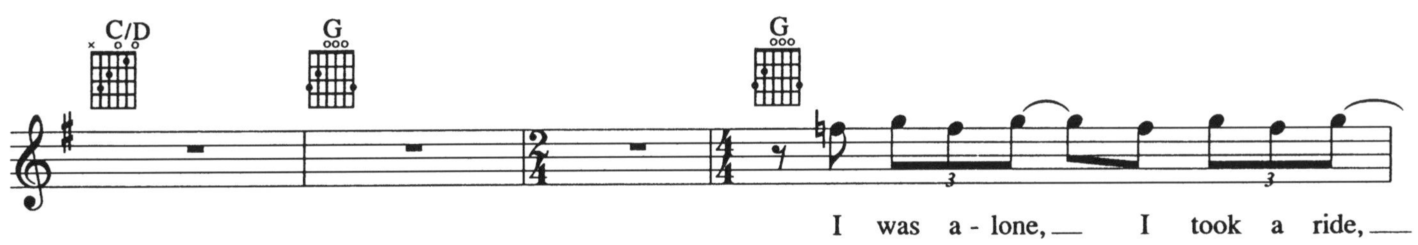
C/D
G
G
I was a - lone, I took a ride,

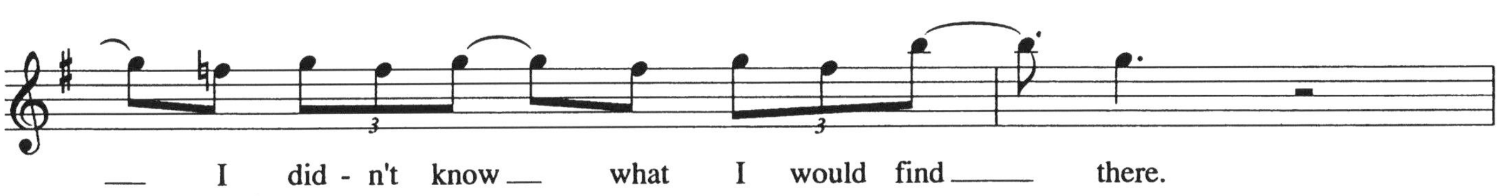
I did - n't know what I would find there.

An - oth - er road, where may - be I could see an - oth - er kind of mind

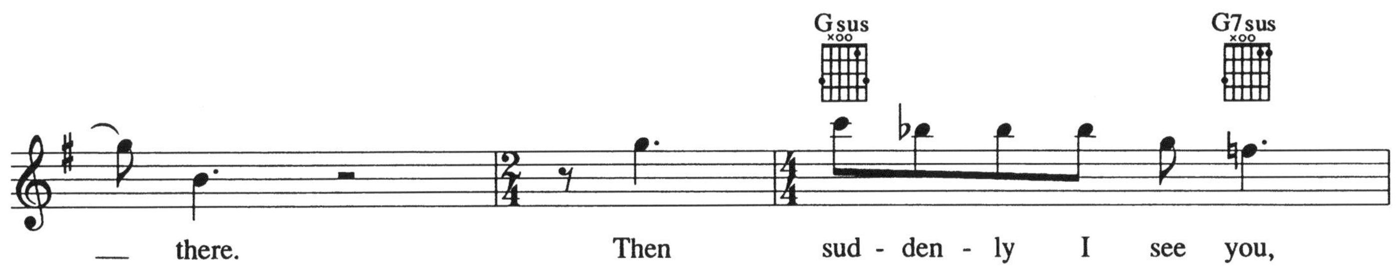
Gsus
G7sus
there. Then sud - den - ly I see you,

G
Gsus
G
did I tell you I need you?

You're Going To Lose That Girl.

Words & Music by John Lennon & Paul McCartney.

Moderately
C
Am7
Dm7
You're gon - na lose that girl.
You're gon - na lose that
G7
C
Em7
girl.
1.3. If you don't take her out to - night, she's gon - na
2. If you don't treat her right my friend, you're gon - na
Dm7
G7
C
Em7
change her mind.
find her gone.
And I will take her out to - night and I will
'Cause I will treat her right and then you'll be the
Dm7
G7
C
treat her kind.
lone - ly one.
You're gon - na lose that girl.
Am
Dm7
To Coda
1
G7
You're gon - na lose that girl.

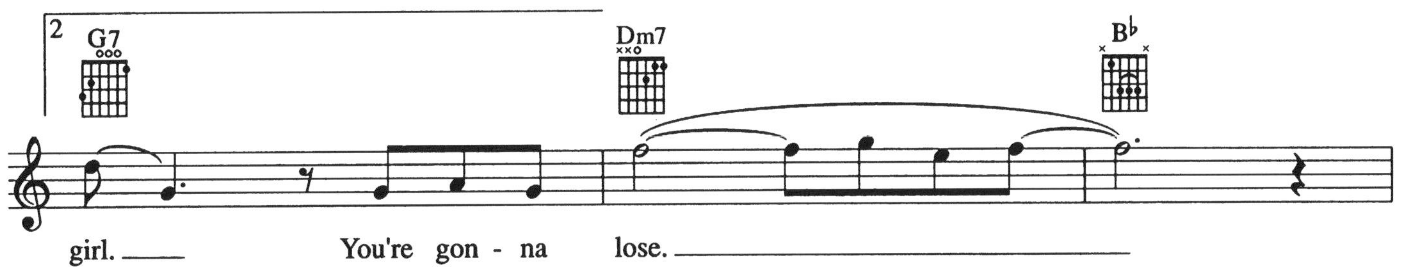
2
G7
Dm7
B♭
girl. You're gon - na lose.

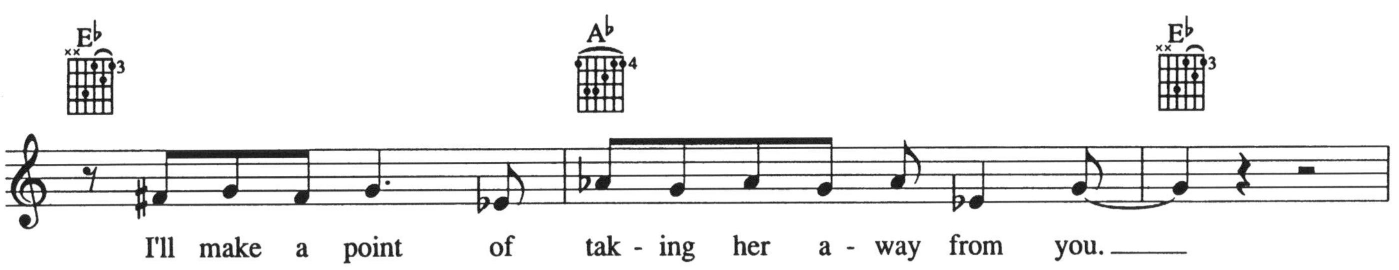
E♭
A♭
E♭
I'll make a point of tak - ing her a - way from you.

A♭
Yeah. The way you treat her, what else can I do?

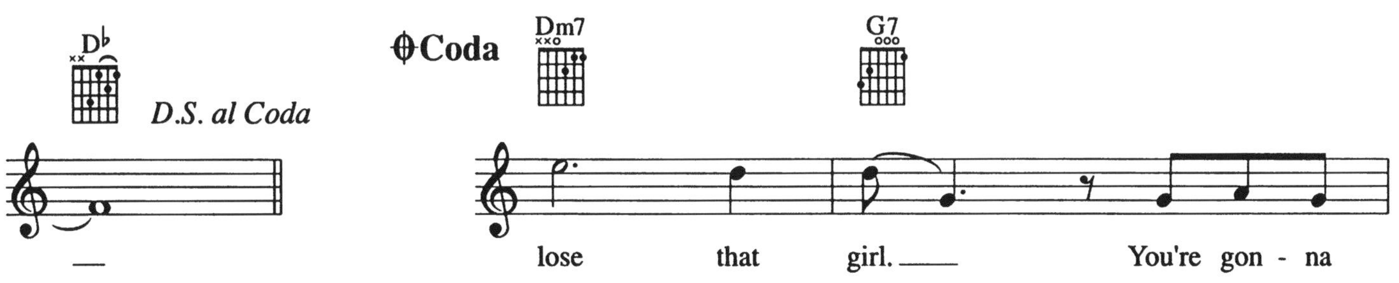
D♭
D.S. al Coda
Coda
Dm7
G7
lose that girl. You're gon - na

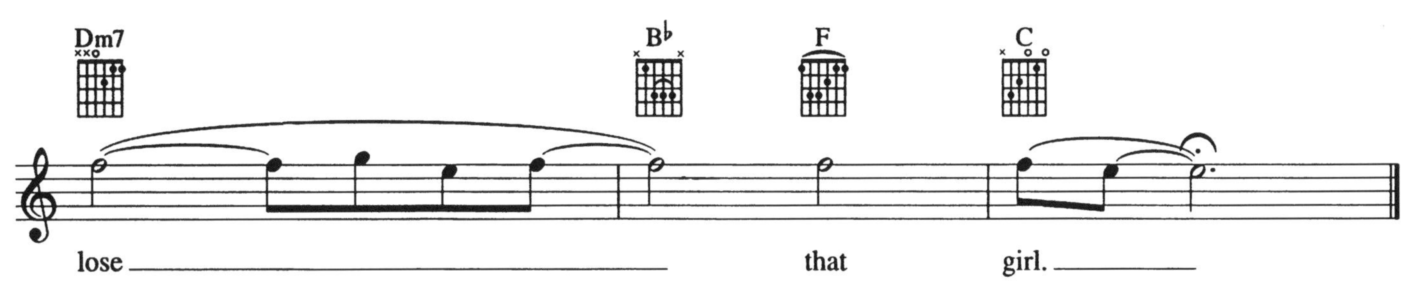
Dm7
B♭
F
C
lose that girl.

You've Got To Hide Your Love Away.

Words & Music by John Lennon & Paul McCartney.

Moderately
G D F G C
1. Here I stand with head in hand, turn my face to the
2. How can I ev - en try? I can nev - er
F C G D F G
wall. If she's gone I can't go on
win. Hear - ing them, see - ing them
C F C D G D
feel - ing two feet small. Ev - 'ry - where
in the state I'm in. How could she
F G C F C
peo - ple stare each and ev - 'ry day.
say to me, "Love will find a way?"
G D F G C
I can see them laugh at me And I hear them
Gath - er 'round all you clowns, Let me hear you

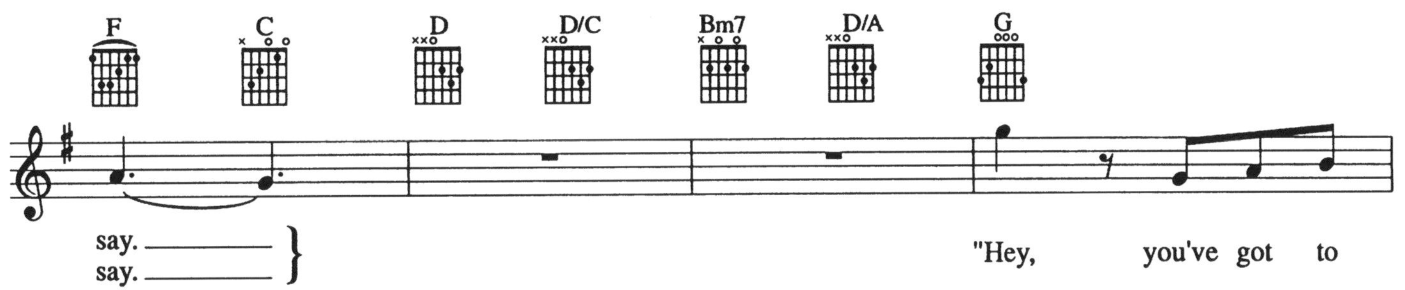
F
C
D
D/C
Bm7
D/A
G
say.
say.
"Hey, you've got to

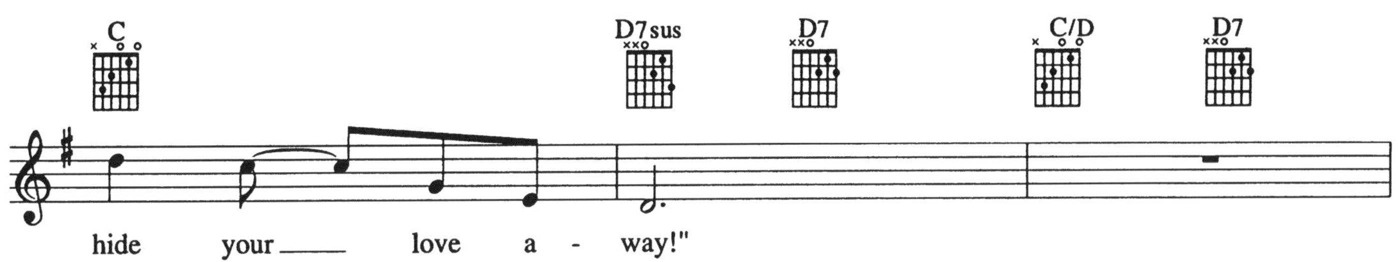
C
D7sus
D7
C/D
D7
hide your love a - way!"

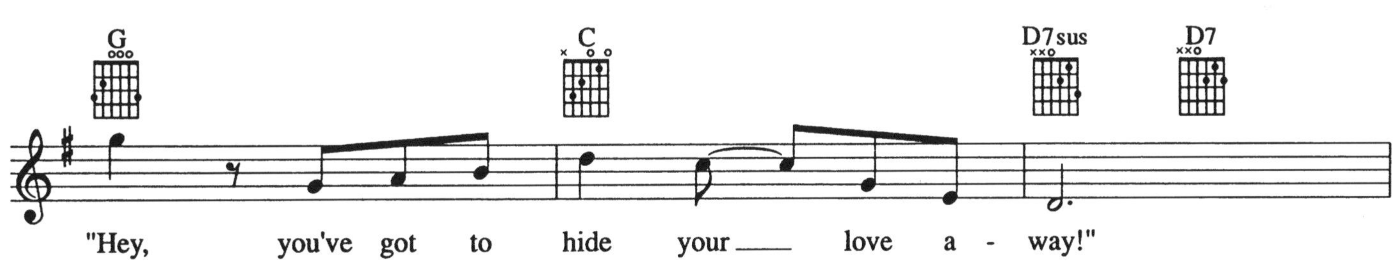
G
C
D7sus
D7
"Hey, you've got to hide your love a - way!"

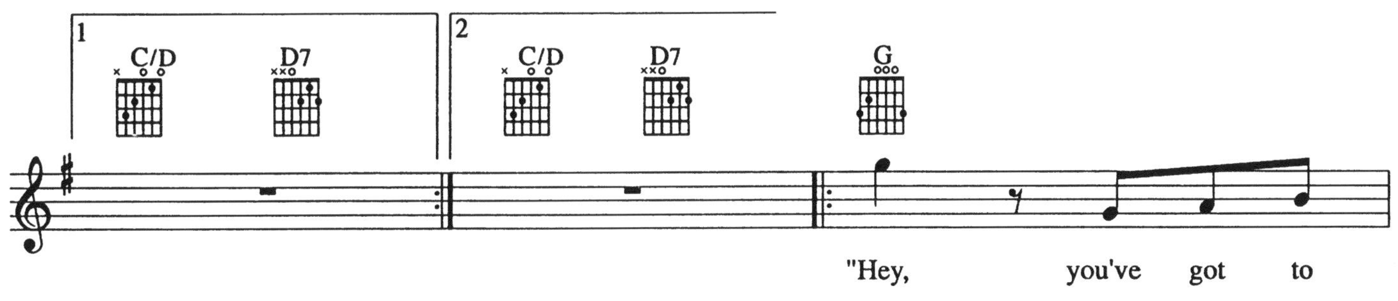
1
C/D
D7
2
C/D
D7
G
"Hey, you've got to

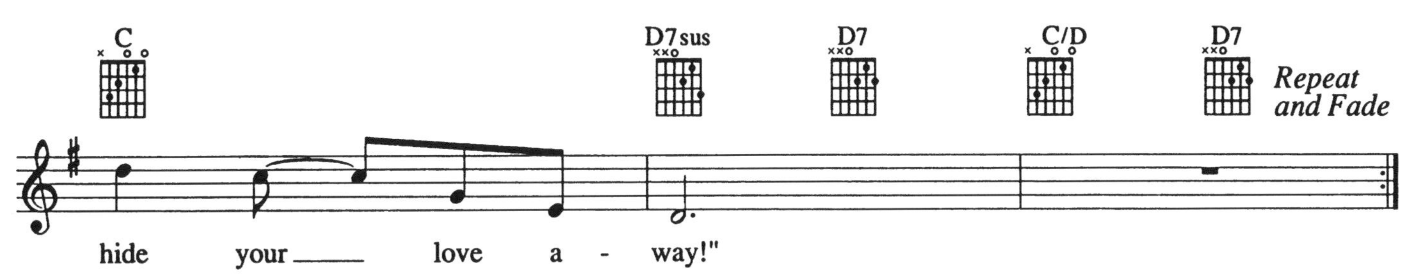
C
D7sus
D7
C/D
D7
Repeat and Fade
hide your love a - way!"

And Your Bird Can Sing.

Words & Music by John Lennon & Paul McCartney.

Moderately
E
1. Tell me that you've got ev - 'ry - thing you want,
2. You say you've seen sev - en won - ders,
F♯m
And your bird can sing, but you don't get me,
And your bird is green, but you can't see me,
A
F♯m7
E
1
2 E
You don't get me.
You can't see me.
G♯m
G+
B/F♯
When your prized pos - ses - sions start to weigh you down,
When your bird is bro - ken, will it bring you down?
C♯/F
E
F♯m7
Look in my di - rec - tion, I'll be 'round,
You may be a - wo - ken, I'll be 'round,

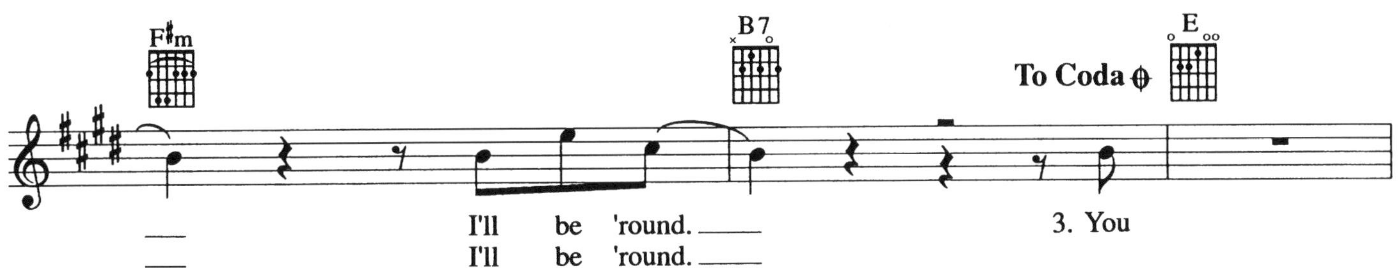
F♯m
B7
To Coda
E
I'll be 'round.
I'll be 'round.
3. You

F♯m7
B7/A
E
D.S. al Coda

Coda
E
B7/D
C♯m7
E/B
tell me that you've heard ev - 'ry sound there is, And your bird can

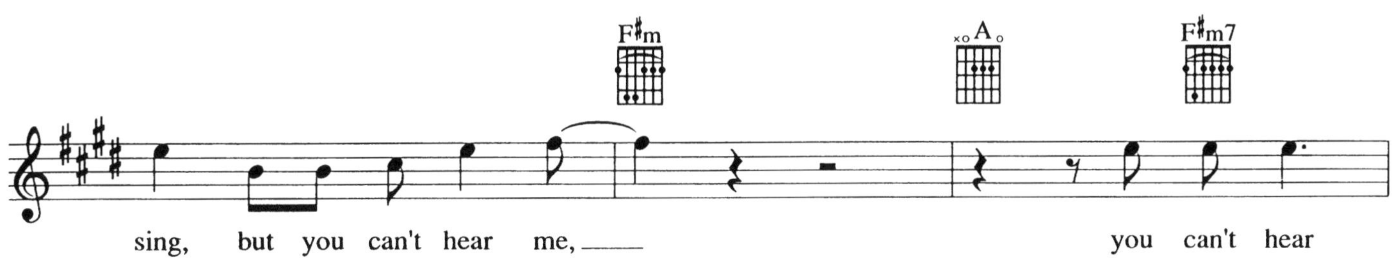
F♯m
A
F♯m7
sing, but you can't hear me,
you can't hear

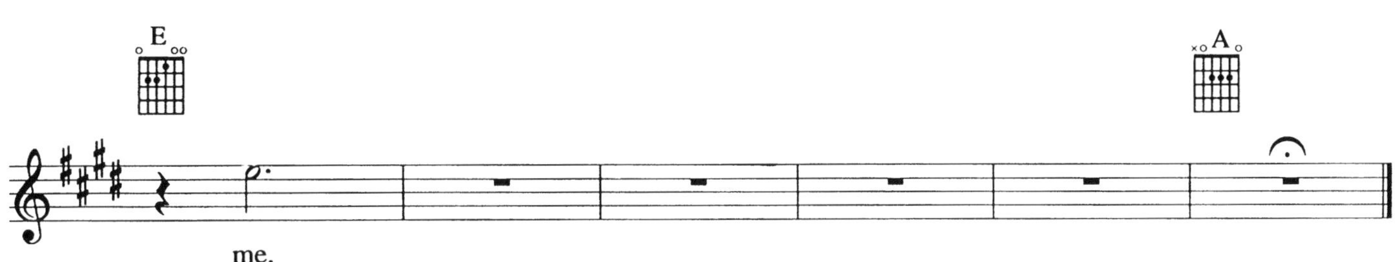
E
A
me.

Doctor Robert.

WORDS & MUSIC BY JOHN LENNON & PAUL McCARTNEY.

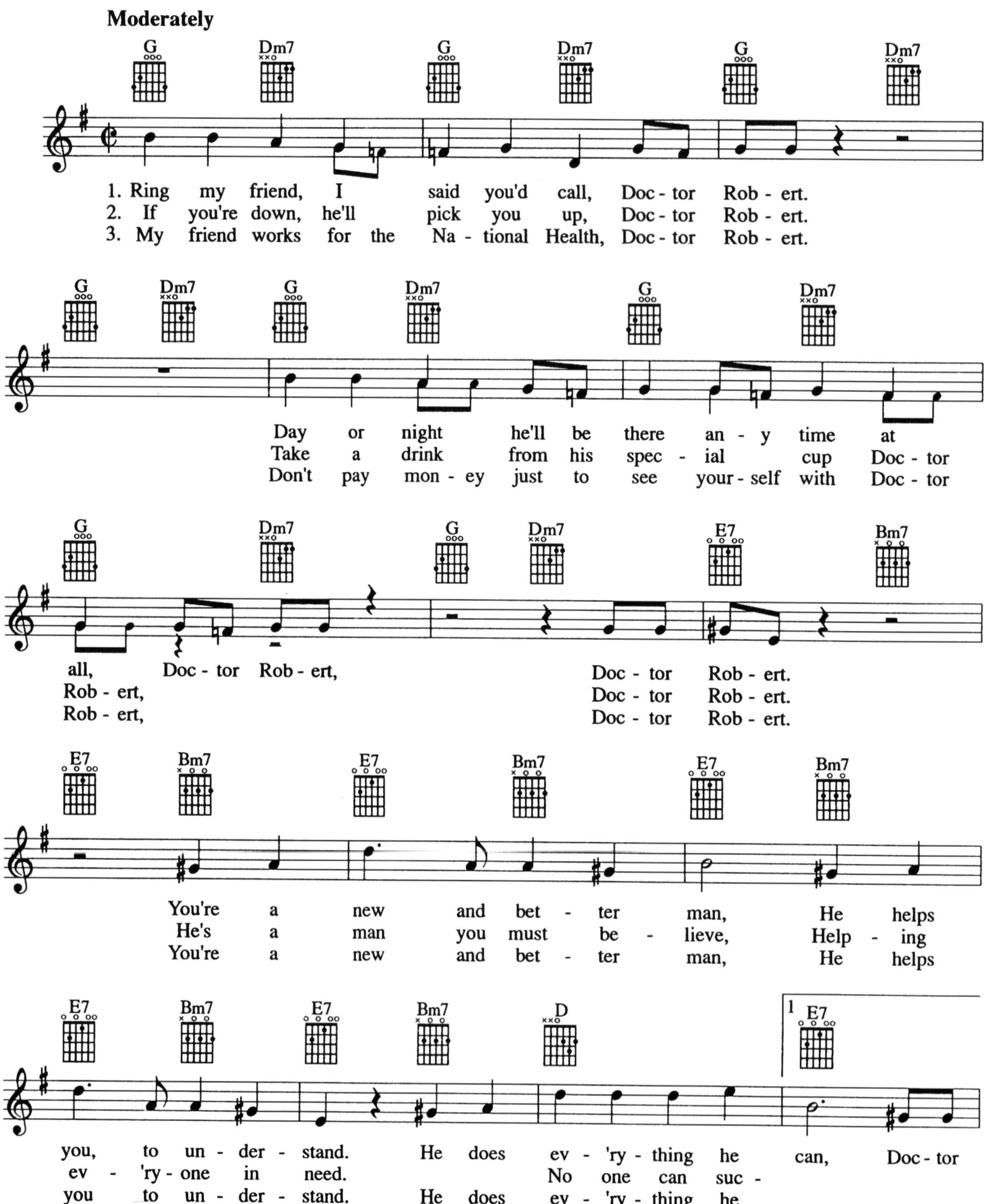
Moderately
G Dm7 G Dm7 G Dm7
1. Ring my friend, I said you'd call, Doc - tor Rob - ert.
2. If you're down, he'll pick you up, Doc - tor Rob - ert.
3. My friend works for the Na - tional Health, Doc - tor Rob - ert.
G Dm7 G Dm7 G Dm7
Day or night he'll be there an - y time at
Take a drink from his spec - ial cup Doc - tor
Don't pay mon - ey just to see your - self with Doc - tor
G Dm7 G Dm7 E7 Bm7
all, Doc - tor Rob - ert, Doc - tor Rob - ert.
Rob - ert, Doc - tor Rob - ert.
Rob - ert, Doc - tor Rob - ert.
E7 Bm7 E7 Bm7 E7 Bm7
You're a new and bet - ter man, He helps
He's a man you must be - lieve, Help - ing
You're a new and bet - ter man, He helps
E7 Bm7 E7 Bm7 D
1 E7
you, to un - der - stand. He does ev - 'ry - thing he can, Doc - tor
ev - 'ry - one in need. No one can suc -
you to un - der - stand. He does ev - 'ry - thing he

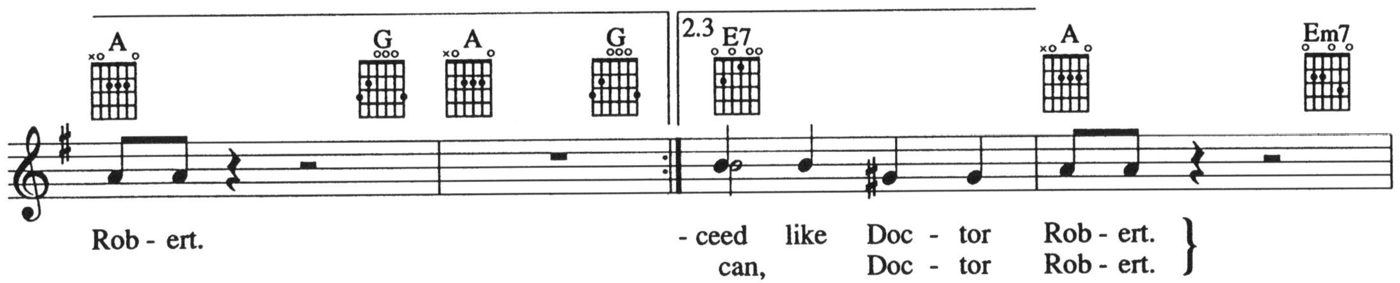
A
G
A
G
2.3
E7
A
Em7
Rob - ert.
- ceed like Doc - tor Rob - ert.
can, Doc - tor Rob - ert.

A
Em7
A
D/A
A
Well, well, well you're feel - ing fine.

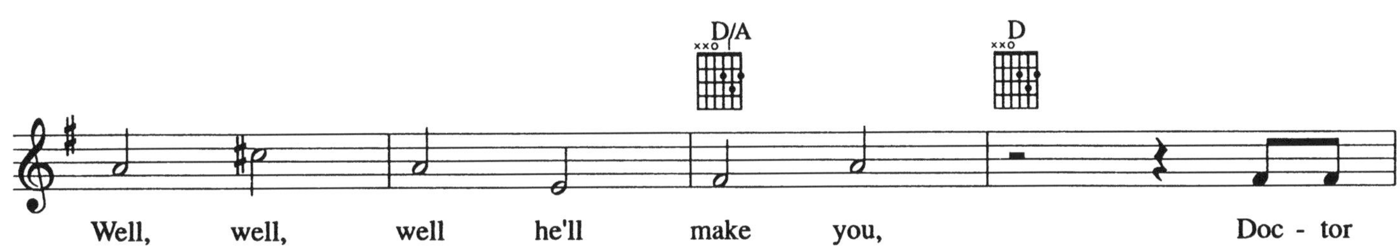
D/A
D
Well, well, well he'll make you, Doc - tor

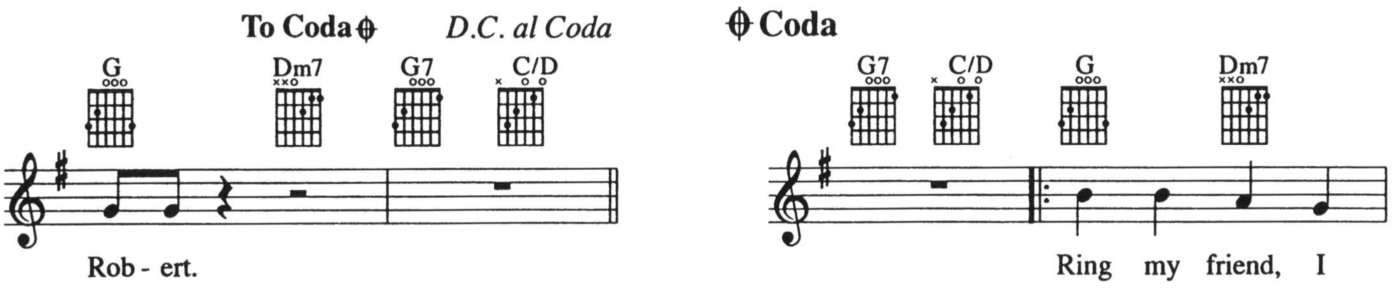
To Coda
D.C. al Coda
Coda
G
Dm7
G7
C/D
G7
C/D
G
Dm7
Rob - ert.
Ring my friend, I

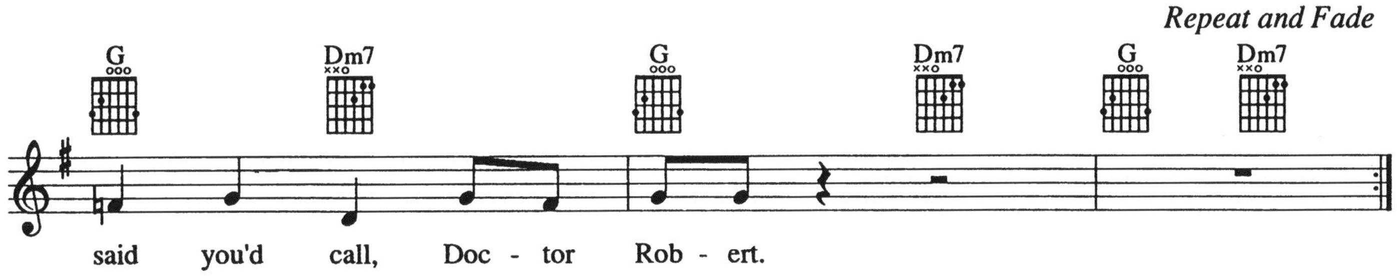
Repeat and Fade
G
Dm7
G
Dm7
G
Dm7
said you'd call, Doc - tor Rob - ert.

Eleanor Rigby.

WORDS & MUSIC BY JOHN LENNON & PAUL McCARTNEY.

Moderately
C
Em
Ah look at all the lone - ly peo - ple!

C
Em
Ah look at all the lone - ly peo - ple!

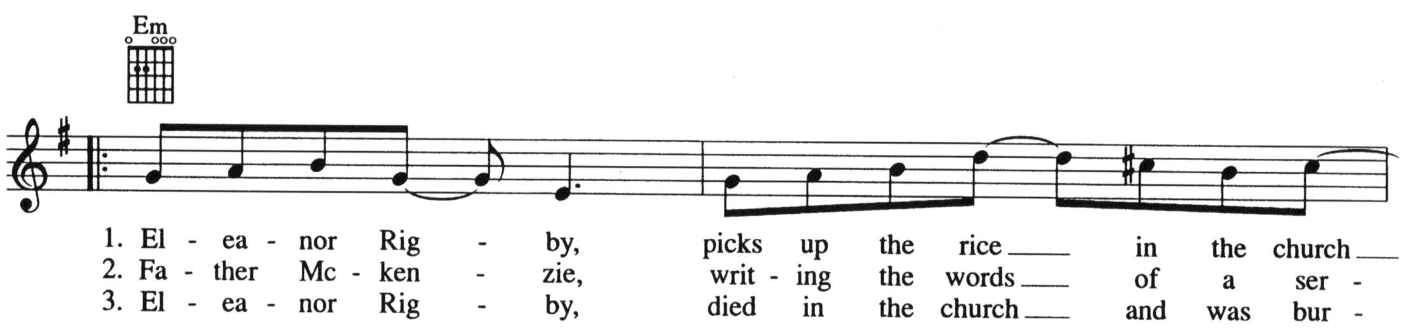
Em
1. El - ea - nor Rig - by, picks up the rice in the church
2. Fa - ther Mc - ken - zie, writ - ing the words of a ser -
3. El - ea - nor Rig - by, died in the church and was bur -

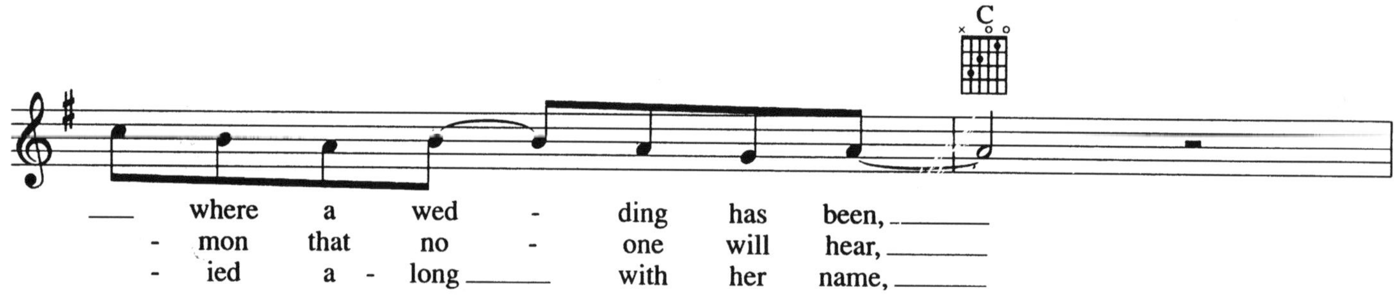
C
where a wed - ding has been,
- mon that no - one will hear,
- ied a - long with her name,

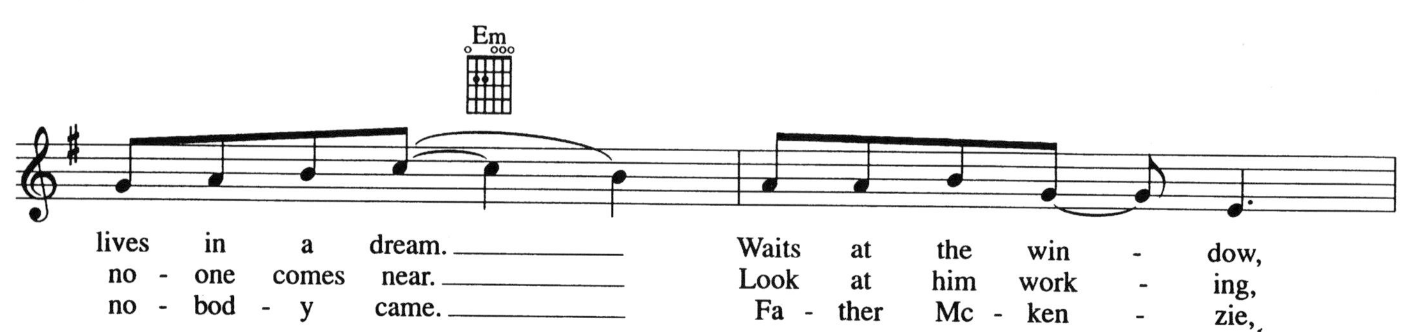
Em
lives in a dream. Waits at the win - dow,
no - one comes near. Look at him work - ing,
no - bod - y came. Fa - ther Mc - ken - zie,

wear - ing the face that she keeps in a jar by the door,
darn - ing his socks in the night when there's no - bod - y there,
wip - ing the dirt from his hands as he walks from the grave,

C
Em
Em7
who is it for?
what does he care?
no - one was saved.
All the lone - ly peo -

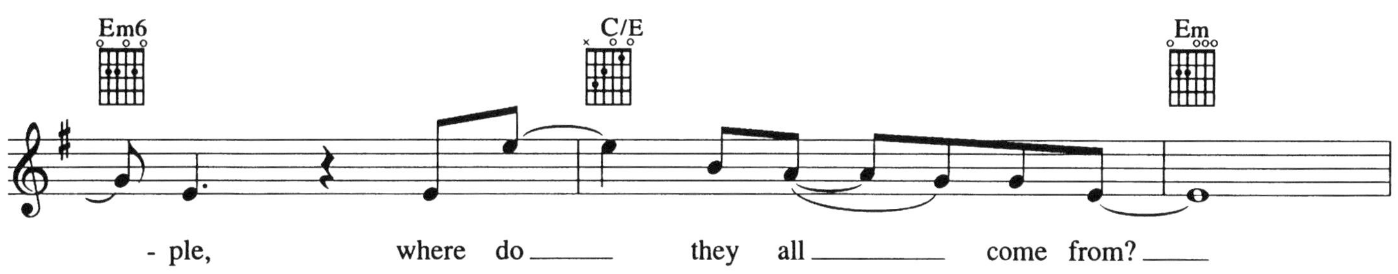
Em6
C/E
Em
- ple, where do they all come from?

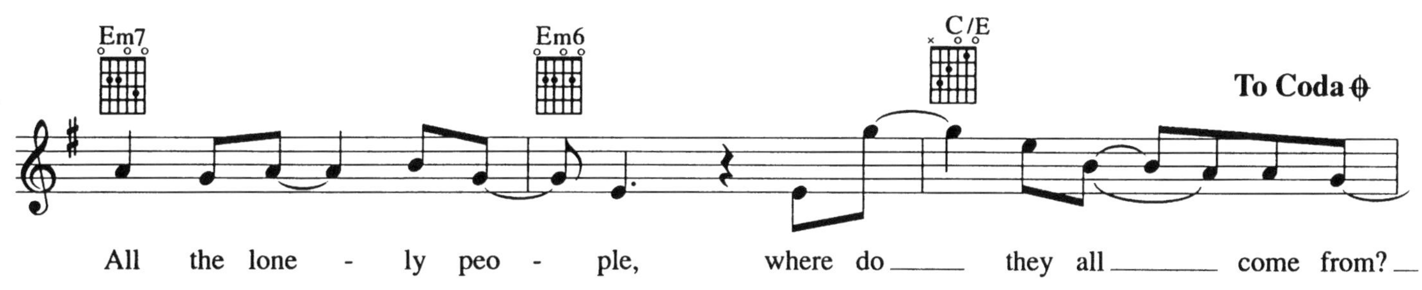
Em7
Em6
C/E
To Coda
All the lone - ly peo - ple, where do they all come from?

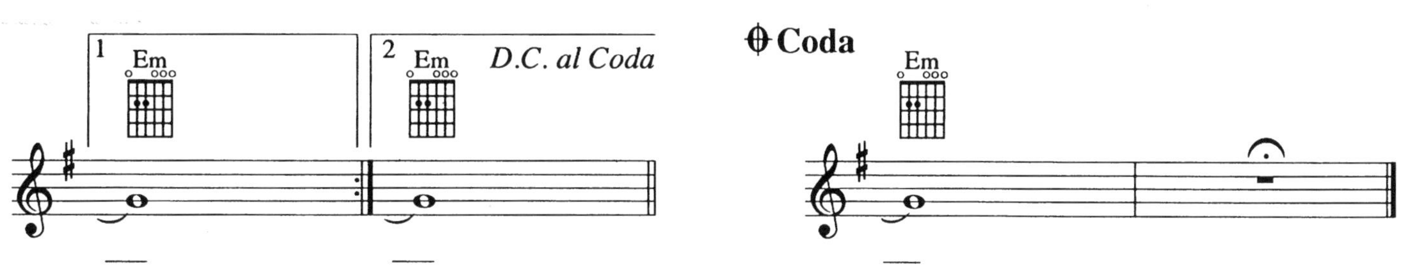
1
Em
2
Em
D.C. al Coda
Coda
Em

For No One.

Words & Music by John Lennon & Paul McCartney.

Moderately, (in 2)
C
Em/B
Am
1. Your day ___ breaks, your mind ___ aches, You find ___ that all ___
2. She wakes ___ up, she makes ___ up, She takes ___ her time ___
5. Your day ___ breaks, your mind ___ aches, There will ___ be times ___
C/G
F
B♭
___ her words of kind - ness lin - ger on ___ when she no
___ and does - n't feel she has to hur - ry, she no
___ when all the things she said will fill ___ your head, you
C
1
2, 3
long - er needs ___ you. ___
long - er needs ___ you. ___
won't for - get ___ her. ___
And in her
Dm
A7
Dm
C/E
eyes you see noth - ing, No sign of
Dm/F
C/G
Dm/A
A7/C♮
Dm
A7
love be - hind the tears ___ cried for no - one.

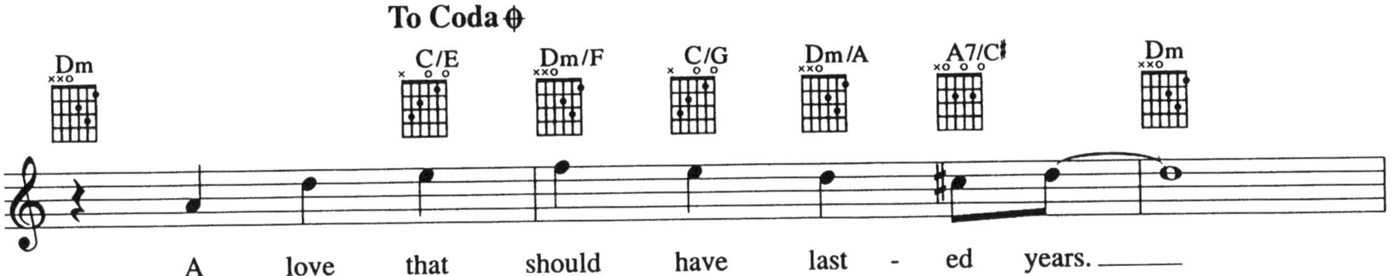
To Coda
Dm
C/E
Dm/F
C/G
Dm/A
A7/C♯
Dm
A love that should have last - ed years.

Dm7/G
G7
C
Em/B
3. You want her, you need her,
4. You stay home, she goes out,

Am
C/G
F
And yet you don't be - lieve her when she says her love
She says that long a - go she knew some - one but now

B♭
C
1
is dead: you think she needs you. And in her
he's gone; she does - n't need him.

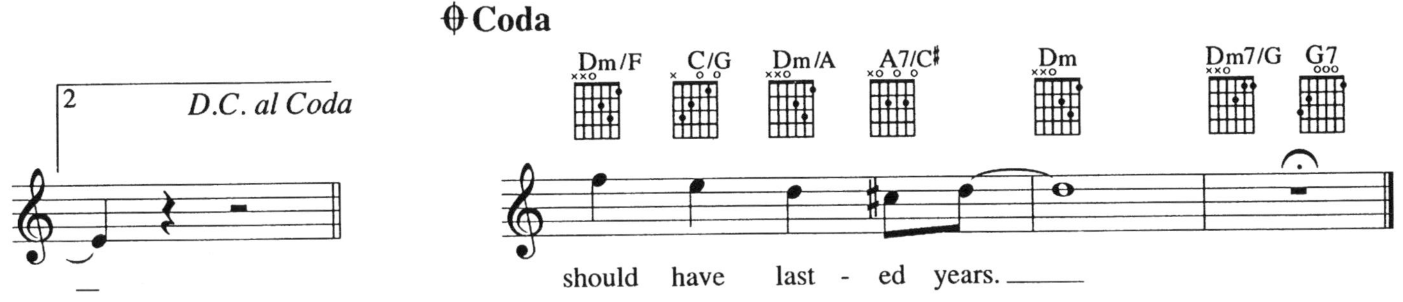
2
D.C. al Coda
Coda
Dm/F
C/G
Dm/A
A7/C♯
Dm
Dm7/G
G7
should have last - ed years.

Good Day Sunshine.

Words & Music by John Lennon & Paul McCartney.

Moderately
B
F♯
Good day sun - shine,
Good day sun - shine,
E
D/E
C♯m/E
Bm/E
Tacet
Good day sun - shine.
1. I need to
3. Then we'd
A
F♯7
B7
E7
laugh and when the sun is out
lie be - neath a shad - y tree,
I've got some - thing I can
I love her and she's
laugh a - bout. I feel good in a spec - ial way,
lov - ing me. She feels good she knows she's look - ing fine,
I'm in love and it's a sun - ny day.
I'm so proud to know that she is mine.
Good day sun - shine,
Good day sun - shine,
To Coda
Good day sun -

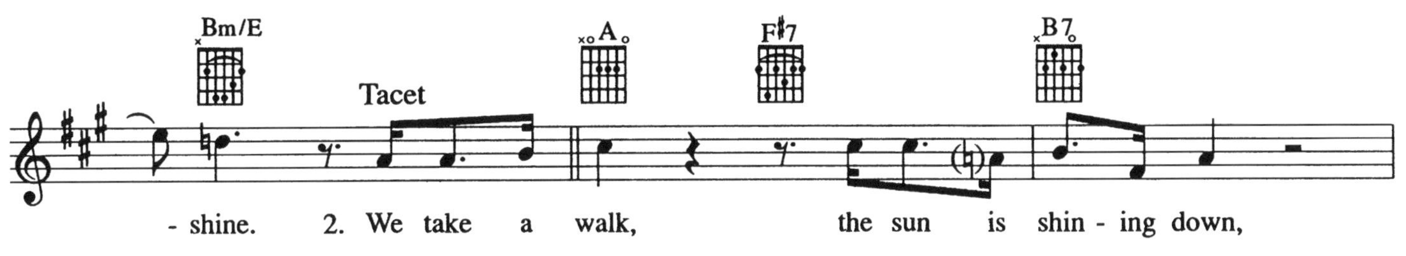
Bm/E
A
F♯7
B7
Tacet
- shine. 2. We take a walk, the sun is shin - ing down,
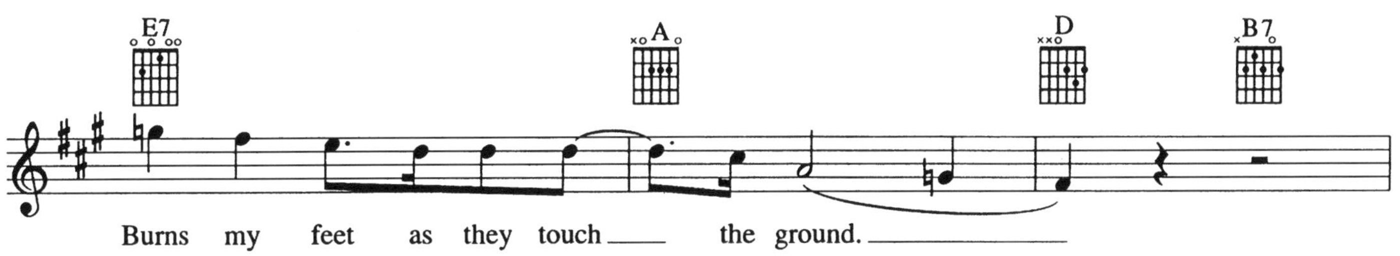
E7
A
D
B7
Burns my feet as they touch the ground.

E7
A7/E
D
D.C. al Coda
Coda
E
D/E
C♯m/E
Good day sun -
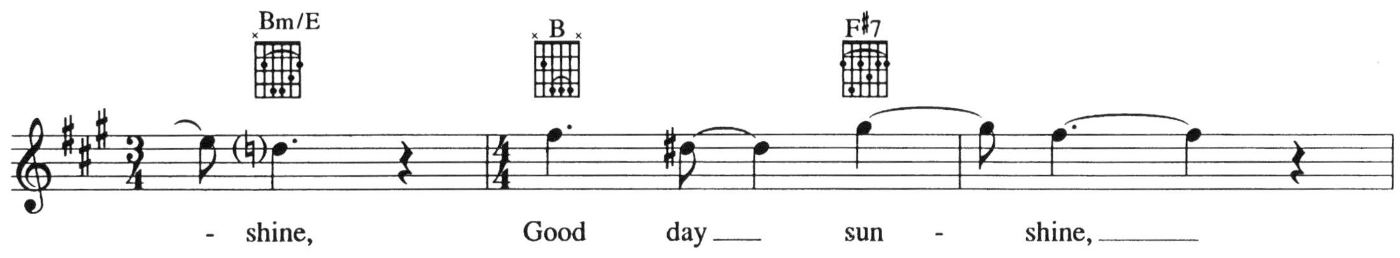
Bm/E
B
F♯7
- shine, Good day sun - shine,

B
F♯7
E
D/E
C♯m/E
Good day sun - shine, Good day sun -
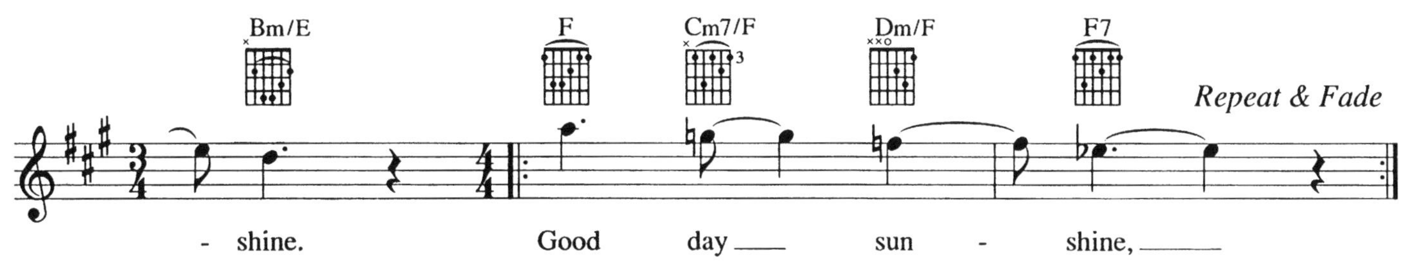
Bm/E
F
Cm7/F
Dm/F
F7
Repeat & Fade
- shine. Good day sun - shine,

Here, There And Everywhere.

Words & Music by John Lennon & Paul McCartney.

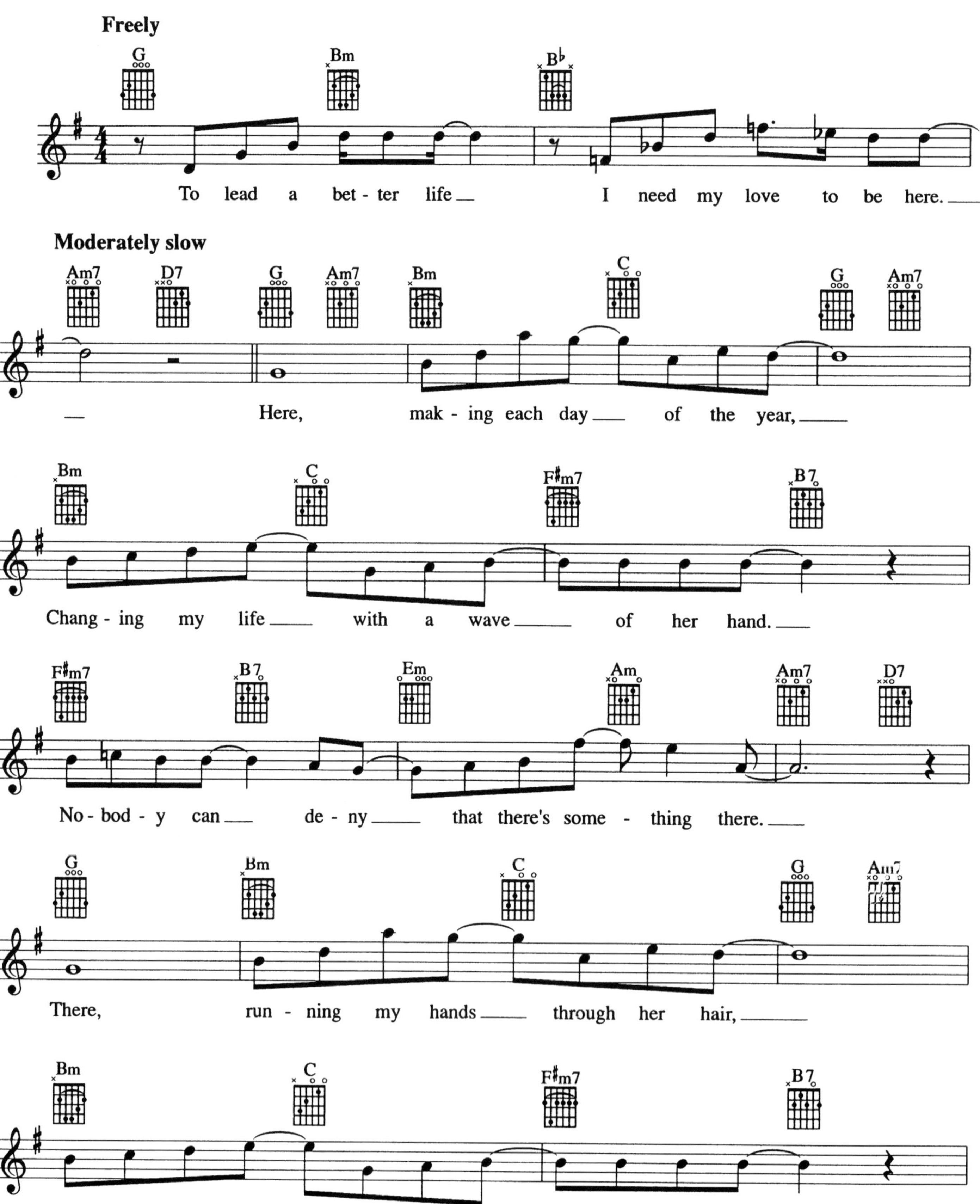
Freely
G Bm B♭
To lead a bet - ter life I need my love to be here.
Moderately slow
Am7 D7 G Am7 Bm C G Am7
Here, mak - ing each day of the year,
Bm C F♯m7 B7
Chang - ing my life with a wave of her hand.
F♯m7 B7 Em Am Am7 D7
No - bod - y can de - ny that there's some - thing there.
G Bm C G Am7
There, run - ning my hands through her hair,
Bm C F♯m7 B7
Both of us think - ing how good it can be.

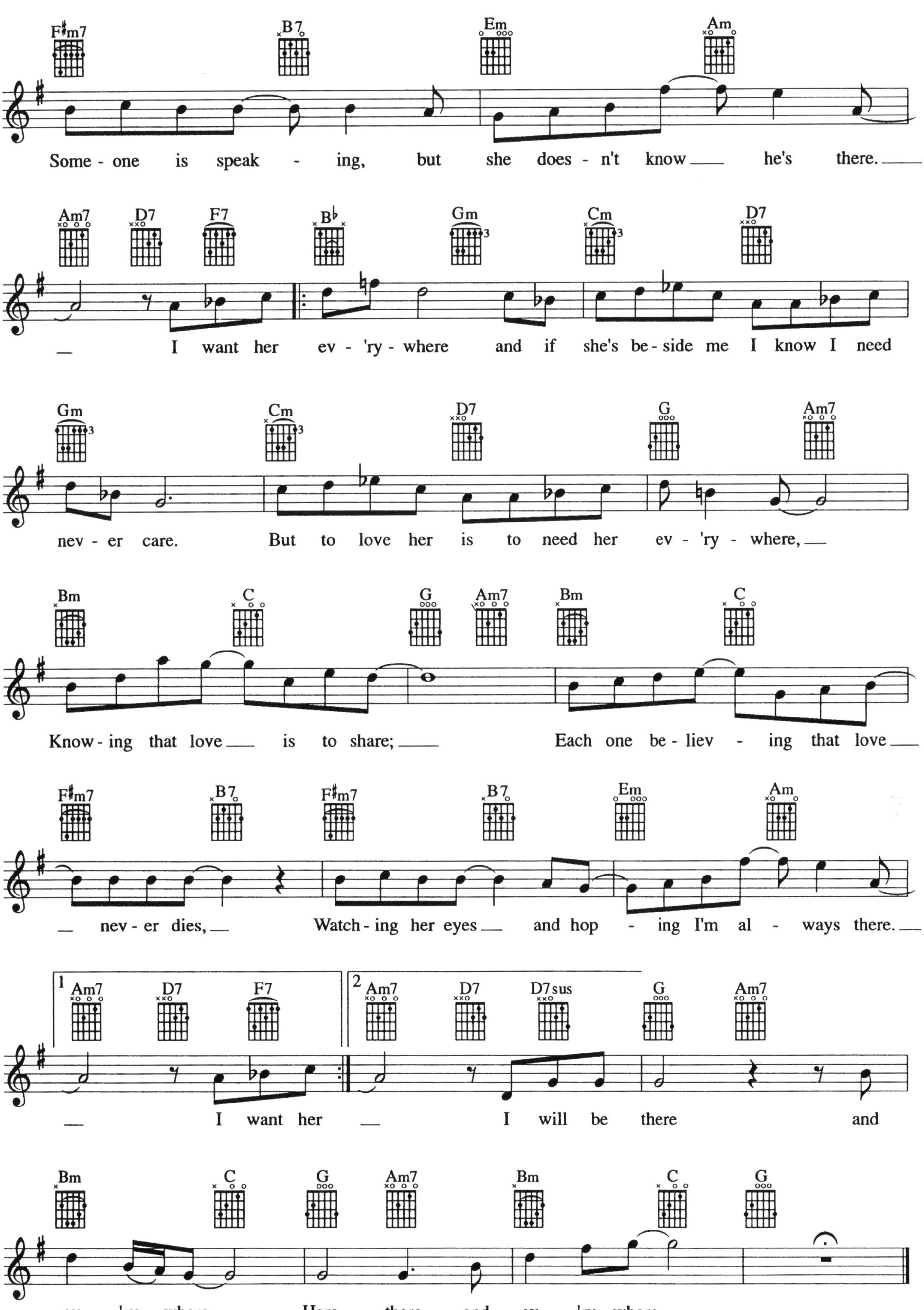
F♯m7
B7
Em
Am
Some - one is speak - ing, but she does - n't know he's there.
Am7
D7
F7
B♭
Gm
Cm
D7
I want her ev - 'ry - where and if she's be - side me I know I need
Gm
Cm
D7
G
Am7
nev - er care. But to love her is to need her ev - 'ry - where,
Bm
C
G
Am7
Bm
C
Know - ing that love is to share; Each one be - liev - ing that love
F♯m7
B7
F♯m7
B7
Em
Am
nev - er dies, Watch - ing her eyes and hop - ing I'm al - ways there.
1
Am7
D7
F7
2
Am7
D7
D7sus
G
Am7
I want her I will be there and
Bm
C
G
Am7
Bm
C
G
ev - 'ry - where, Here, there and ev - 'ry - where.

I Want To Tell You.

Words & Music by George Harrison.

Moderately
B♭
I want to tell you, My head is filled
with things to say.
C
F
When you're here,
All those words: they seem to slip a - way.
B♭
E♭sus
E♭
B♭
2. When I get near you, the games be - gin
3.4 I want to tell you, I feel hung up
to drag me down.
and I don't know why.
C
F
It's all right,
I don't mind,

To Coda
B♭
I'll make you maybe be next time a - round.
I could wait for - ev - er, I've got time.
E♭sus
E♭
Cm
E♭m6
But if I seem to act un - kind
Some - times I wish I knew you well
B♭
C
Cm
it's on - ly me, it's not my mind
then I could speak my mind and tell you;
E♭m6
B♭
B♭sus
1 B♭
That is con - fus - ing things.
May - be you'd un - der - stand.
2 B♭
D.S. al Coda
Coda
B♭
E♭sus
E♭
got time,
Repeat and Fade
B♭
E♭sus
E♭
B♭
E♭sus
E♭
I've got time.

I'm Only Sleeping.

Words & Music by John Lennon & Paul McCartney.

Moderately
Dm Gm F B♭
1.4. When I wake up ear - ly in the morn - ing. Lift my head,
3. Ev - 'ry - bod - y seems to think I'm la - zy. I don't mind, I
F A7 Dm Gm
I'm still yawn - ing. When I'm in the mid - dle of a dream,
think they're cra - zy. Run - nin' ev - 'ry - where at such a speed,
F B♭ F B♭ Gm
Stay in bed, float up - stream.
'til they find there's no need. (There's no need.)
F Gm7 Am
Please don't wake me, No, don't shake me. Leave me where I am,
Please don't spoil my day. I'm miles a - way. And af - ter all,
Gm7 B♭maj7 To Coda Dm
I'm on - ly sleep - ing.
I'm on - ly sleep - ing.
Cm7 D7 Gm
Keep - ing an eye on the world go - ing by my win - dow,

E♭maj7
Dm
Tak - ing my time.
3. Ly - ing there and star - ing at the
Gm
F
B♭
F
A7
Dm
ceil - ing, Wait - ing for a sleep - y feel - ing.
Gm
F
B♭
F
B♭
Gm
F
Please don't spoil my day.
Gm7
Am
Gm7
I'm miles a - way. And af - ter all, I'm on - ly
B♭maj7
Dm
sleep - ing.
Cm7
D7
Gm
Keep - ing an eye on the world go - ing by my win - dow,
E♭maj7
D.C. al Coda
Coda
Dm
Tak - ing my time.

Love You To.

WORDS & MUSIC BY GEORGE HARRISON.

Moderately
Cm
Each day just goes so fast, I turn around, it's past. You don't get time to hang a sign on me.
(2) - time is so short, A new one can't be bought. But what you've got means such a lot to me.
(3) - ple stand - ing 'round who'll screw you in the ground. They'll fill you in with all the things you'll see.
B♭
Cm
Love me while you can, or I'll get a plan.
Make love all day long, make love sing - ing songs.
I'll make love to you, If you want me to.
1.2
3
2. A life -
3. peo -

A Day In The Life.

Words & Music by John Lennon & Paul McCartney.

Slowly
G
Bm/F♯
Em
C
Em/B
1. I read the news to-day, oh boy, A-bout a luck-y man who
4. I read the news to-day, oh boy, Four thous-and holes in Black-burn,
Am
Cmaj7
G
Bm
Em
To Coda
made the grade; And though the news was rath-er sad,
Lan-ca-shire; And though the holes were rath-er small,
C
F
Em
Em/D
C
F
Well, I just had to laugh. I saw the pho-to-graph.
Em
Cmaj7
G
Bm/F♯
Em
2. He blew his mind out in a car,
3. I saw a film to-day oh boy,
C
Em/B
Am
Cmaj7
He did-n't no-tice that the lights had changed.
The Eng-lish ar-my had just won the war.
G
Bm
Em
C
F
A crowd of peo-ple stood and stared, They'd seen his face be-fore,
A crowd of peo-ple turned a-way, But I just had to look,

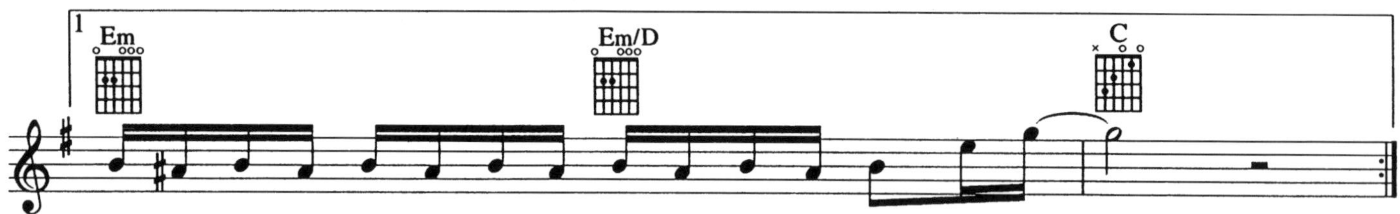
1
Em
Em/D
C
No - bod - y was real - ly sure if he was from the House of Lords.

2 Em
Em/D
C
Cmaj7
C
Bm/F♯
Hav - ing read the book I'd love to turn

G
Em/A
E
you on. Woke up,

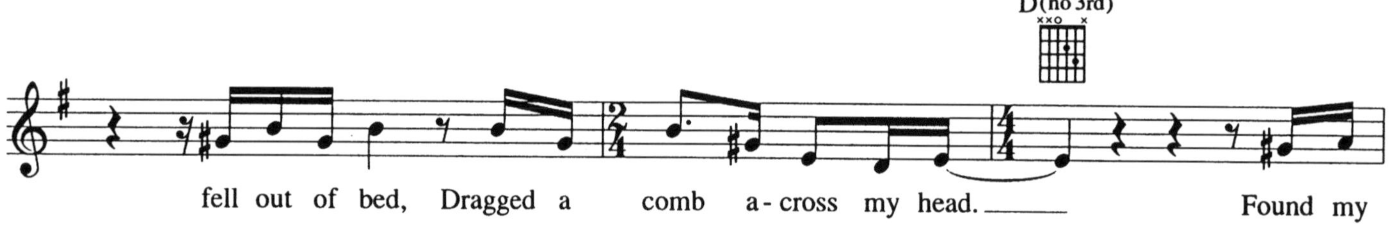
D(no 3rd)
fell out of bed, Dragged a comb a - cross my head. Found my

E
F♯m/B
E
F♯m/B
way down stairs and drank a cup, And look - ing up, I no - ticed I was late.

E
Found my coat and grabbed my hat, Made the bus in sec - onds

D(no 3rd)
E
F♯m/B
B7
flat. Found my way up - stairs and had a smoke And

E
F♯m/B
C
G
some - bod - y spoke and I went in - to a dream. Ah

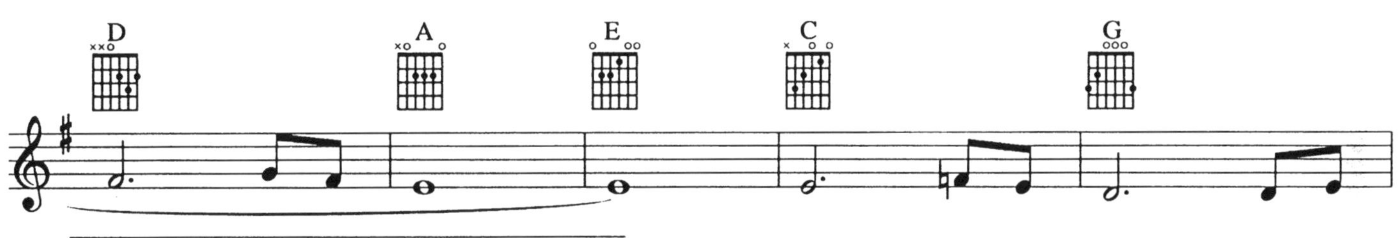
D
A
E
C
G

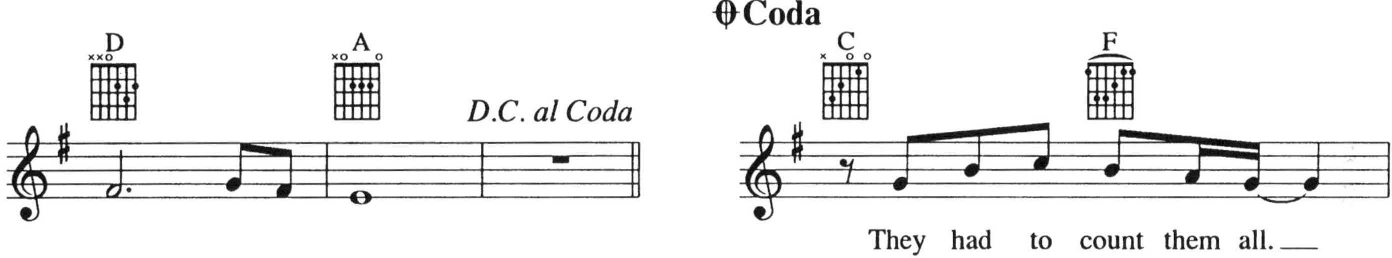
Coda
D
A
D.C. al Coda
C
F
They had to count them all.

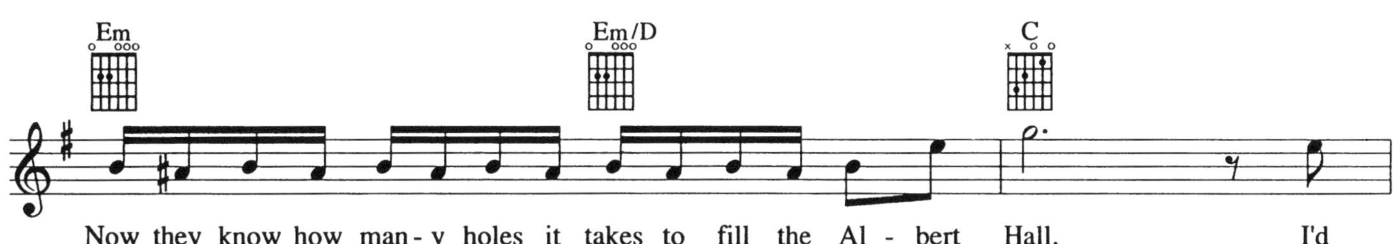
Em
Em/D
C
Now they know how man - y holes it takes to fill the Al - bert Hall. I'd

Bm/F♯
G
G/A
E
love to turn you on.

Paperback Writer.

Words & Music by John Lennon & Paul McCartney.

Bright Rock

Tacet
Pa - per-back wri - ter, Pa - per-back wri - ter.

G
1. Dear Sir or Mad - am will you
(3) thou - sand pag - es, give or

G7
G
read my book? It took me years to write; Will you take a look? It's
take a few; I'll be writ - ing more in a week or two. I can
G7
based on a nov - el by a man named Lear and I need a job so I
make it long - er if you like the style, I can change it round and I

C
want to be a Pa - per - back wri - ter, Pa - per - back
want to be a Pa - per - back wri - ter, Pa - per - back

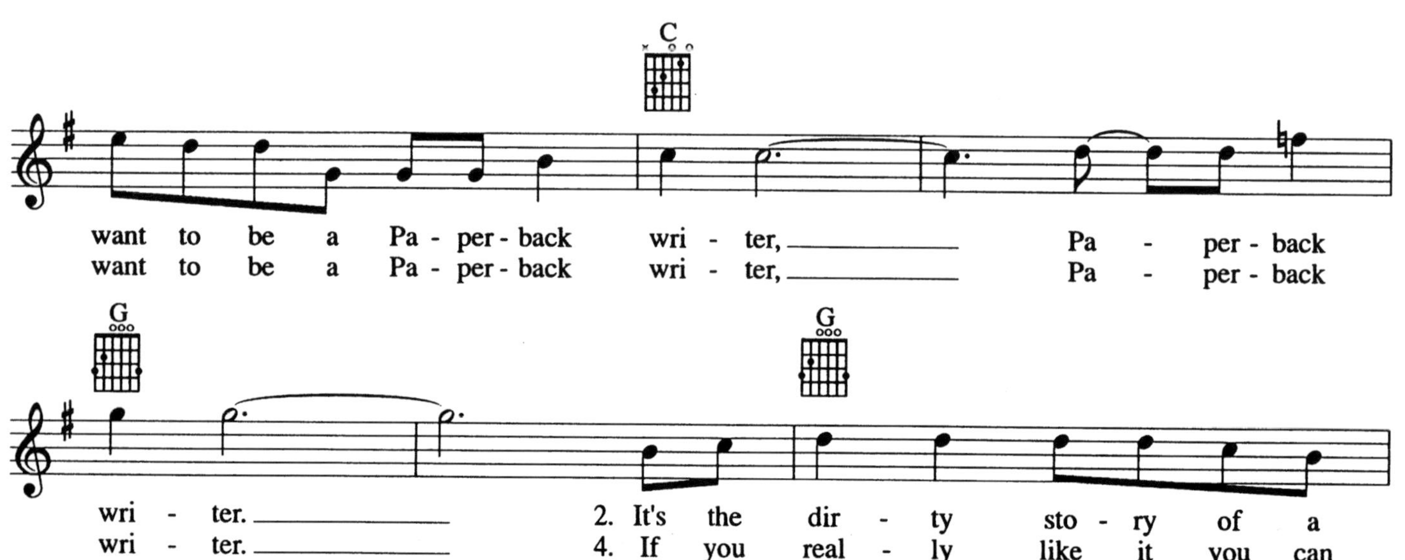
G
G
wri - ter. 2. It's the dir - ty sto - ry of a
wri - ter. 4. If you real - ly like it you can

dir - ty man, __ and his cling - ing wife __ does - n't un - der - stand. His
have the rights, __ It could make a mil - lion for you ov - er - night. If you

son is work - ing for the Dai - ly Mail; __ It's a stead - y job __ but he
must re - turn __ it, you can send it here, __ But I need a break __ and I

C
wants to be a Pa - per - back wri - ter, __ Pa - per - back
want to be a Pa - per - back wri - ter, __ Pa - per - back

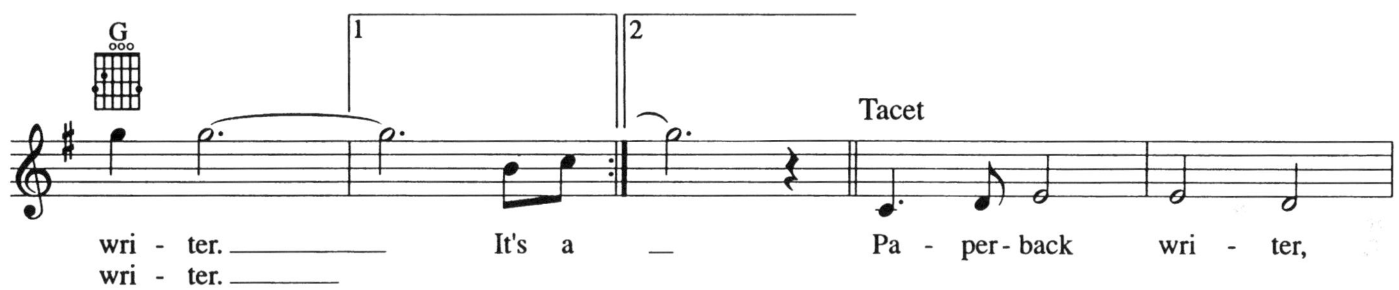
G
1
2
Tacet
wri - ter. __ It's a __ Pa - per - back wri - ter,
wri - ter. __

Pa - per - back wri - ter.

G
Repeat and Fade
Pa - per - back wri - ter. __

Words & Music by John Lennon & Paul McCartney.

Moderately

G C D G

If the rain comes, they run and hide their heads; They
sun shines, they slip in - to the shade And

C D G C

might as well be dead. If the rain comes, ___
sip their lem - on - ade. When the sun shines, ___

G 1 2

— If the rain comes. 2. When the shines.
— when the sun

G D7 C/G

Rain ___

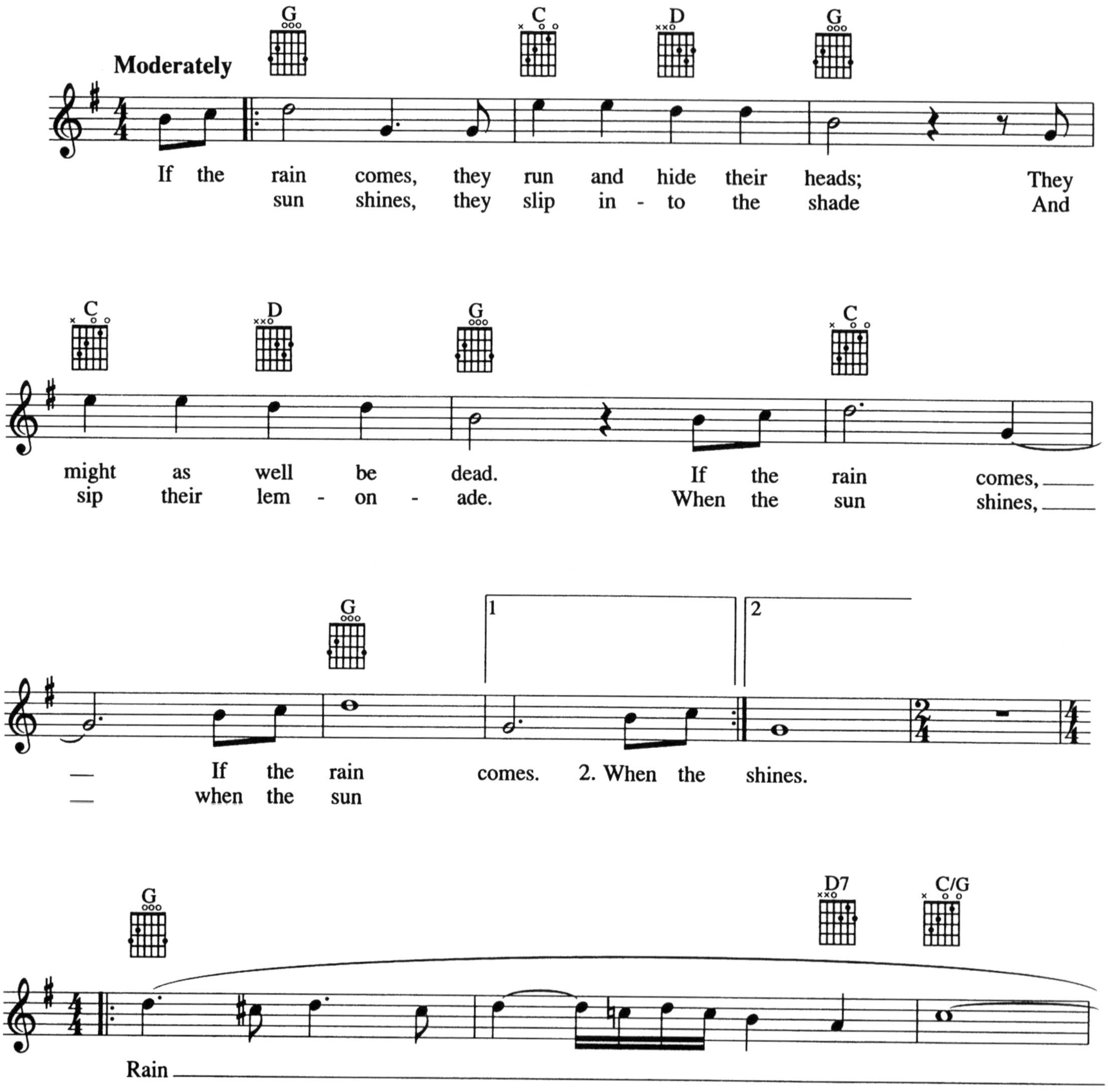

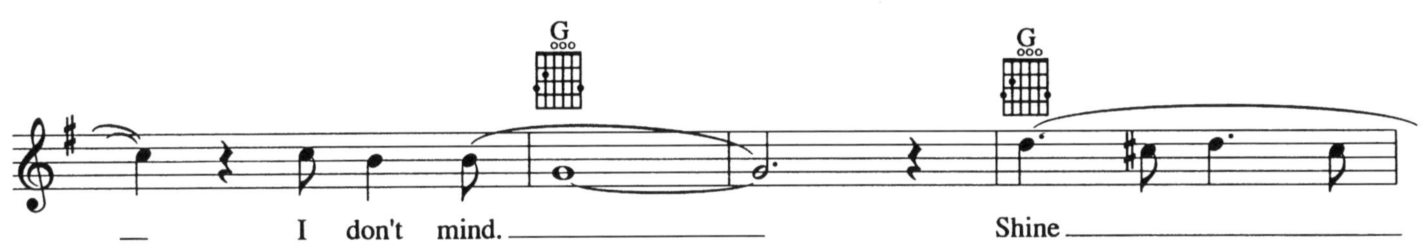
G
G
I don't mind.
Shine

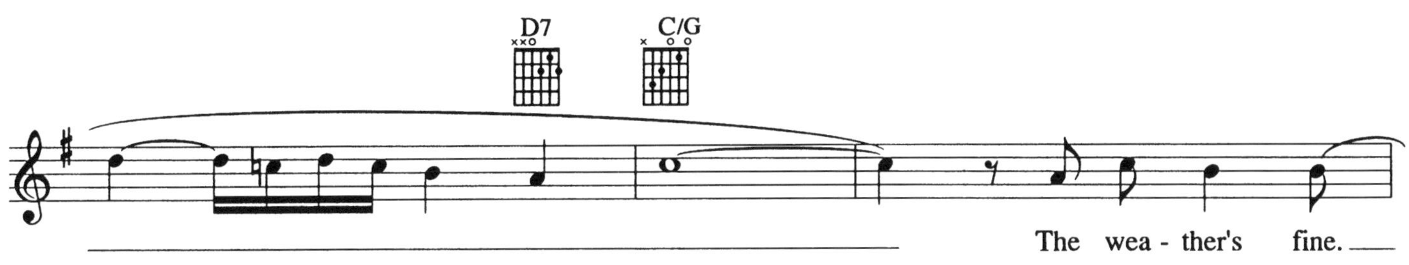
D7
C/G
The wea - ther's fine.

G
C
D
I can 1. show you that when it starts to
Can you 2. hear me that when it rains and

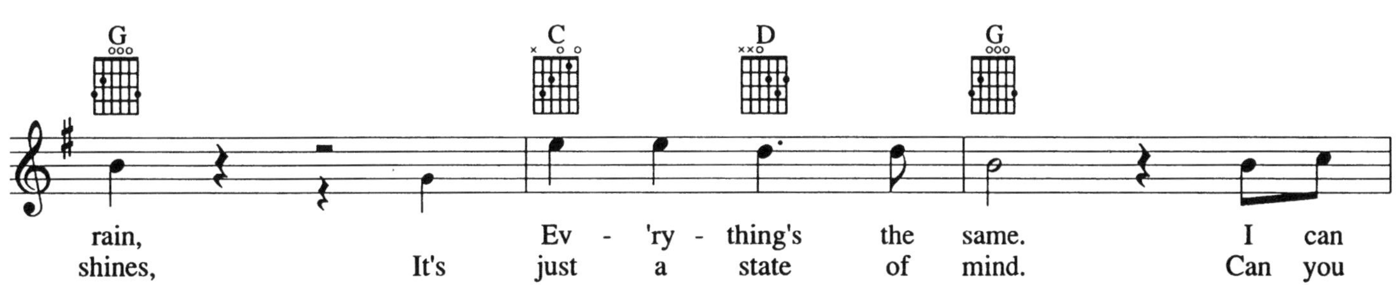
G
C
D
G
rain, Ev - 'ry - thing's the same. I can
shines, It's just a state of mind. Can you

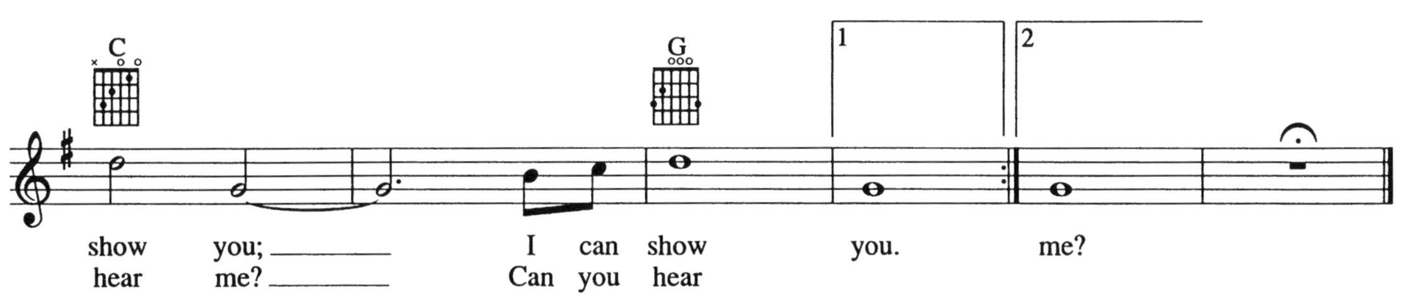
C
G
1
2
show you; I can show you. me?
hear me? Can you hear

She Said She Said.

Words & Music by John Lennon & Paul McCartney.

Slow rock
B♭ A♭ E♭ B♭ A♭ add 9
1. She said, "I know what it's like to be dead,
2. I said, "Who put all those things in your head,
E♭ B♭ A♭ add 9 E♭
I know what it is to be sad." And she's
things that make me feel that I'm mad." And you're
B♭ A♭ E♭ B♭ A♭
mak - ing me feel like I've nev - er been born.
mak - ing me feel like I've nev - er been born.
E♭ B♭ B♭ A♭ B♭
She said "You don't un - der - stand what I said." I said
A♭ B♭ Fm
"No, no no, you're wrong. When I was a boy
B♭ E♭ B♭7
ev - 'ry - thing was right, ev - 'ry - thing was

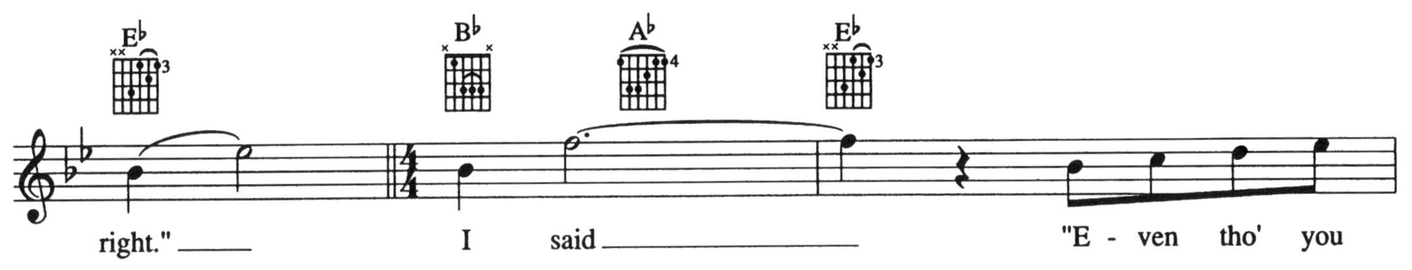
E♭
B♭
A♭
E♭
right." ___ I said ___ "E - ven tho' you

B♭
A♭ add 9
E♭
B♭
A♭ add 9
know what you know, I know that I'm read - y to leave,

E♭
B♭
A♭
E♭
B♭
'Cause you're mak - ing me feel ___ like I've nev - er been born." ___

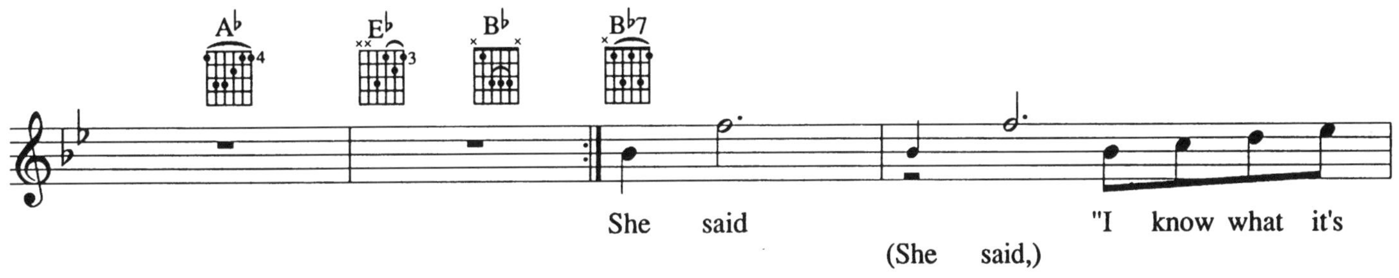
A♭
E♭
B♭
B♭7
She said "I know what it's
(She said,)

like to be dead, I know what it
("I know what it's like to be dead,)

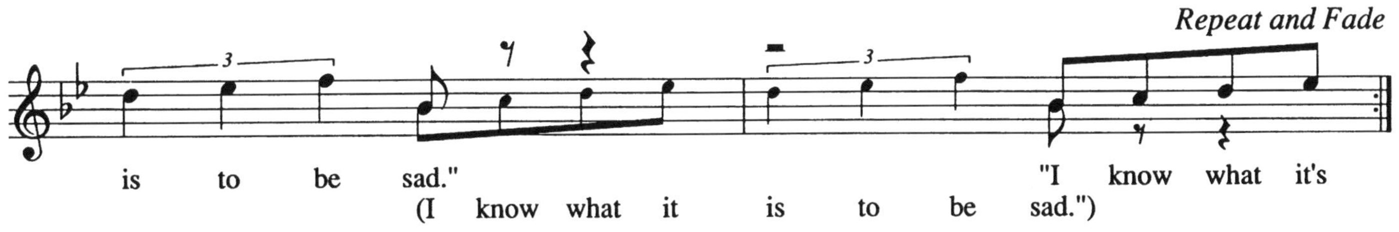
Repeat and Fade
is to be sad." "I know what it's
(I know what it is to be sad.")

Taxman.

Words & Music by George Harrison.

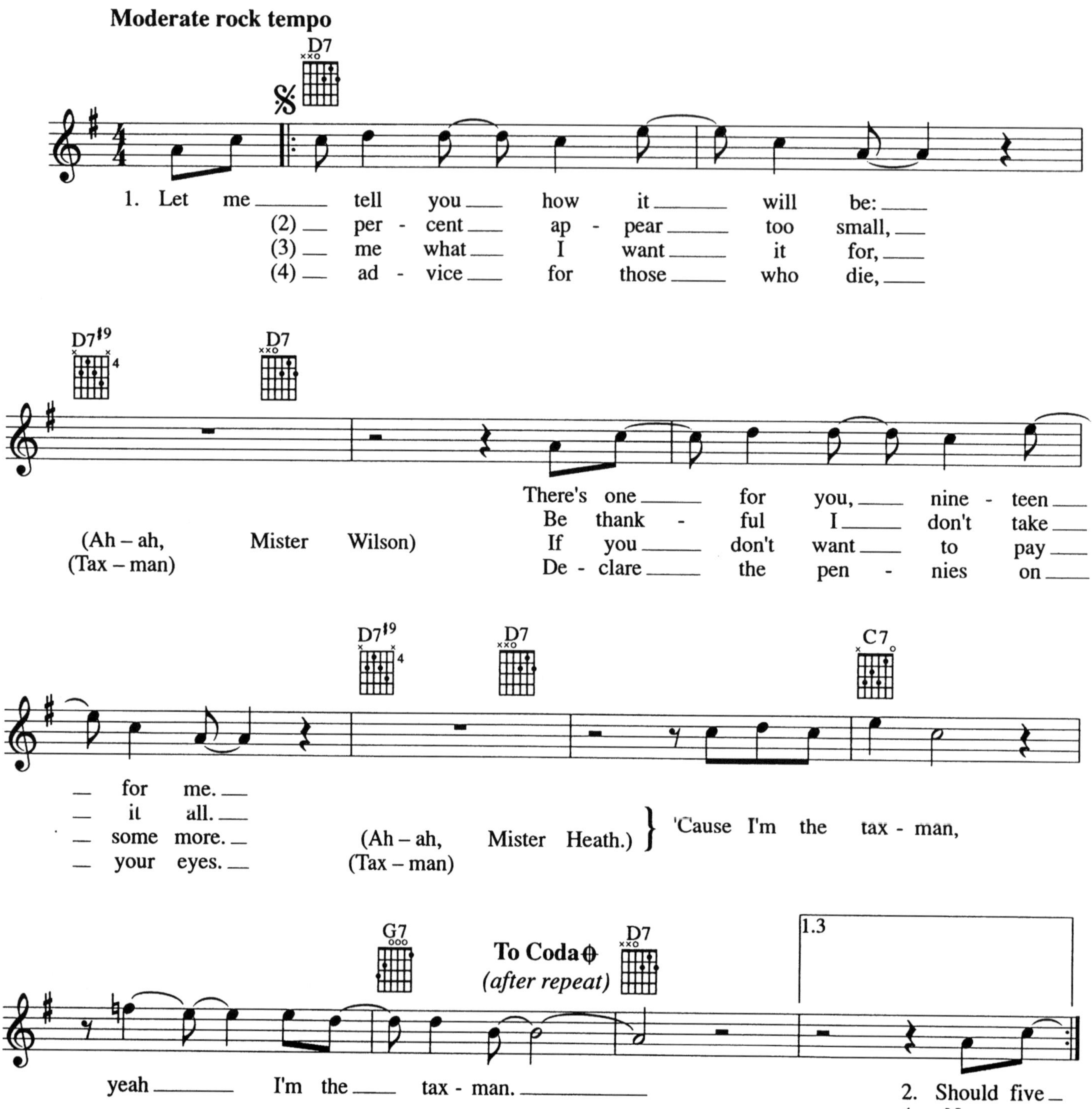
Moderate rock tempo
D7
1. Let me tell you how it will be:
(2) per - cent ap - pear too small,
(3) me what I want it for,
(4) ad - vice for those who die,
D7♯9
D7
(Ah – ah, Mister Wilson)
(Tax – man)
There's one for you, nine - teen for me.
Be thank - ful I don't take it all.
If you don't want to pay some more.
De - clare the pen - nies on your eyes.
D7♯9
D7
(Ah – ah, Mister Heath.)
(Tax – man)
C7
'Cause I'm the tax - man,
G7
To Coda
(after repeat)
D7
yeah I'm the tax - man.
1.3
2. Should five
4. Now my

2
D7
(If you drive a car;) I'll tax the street; (If you try

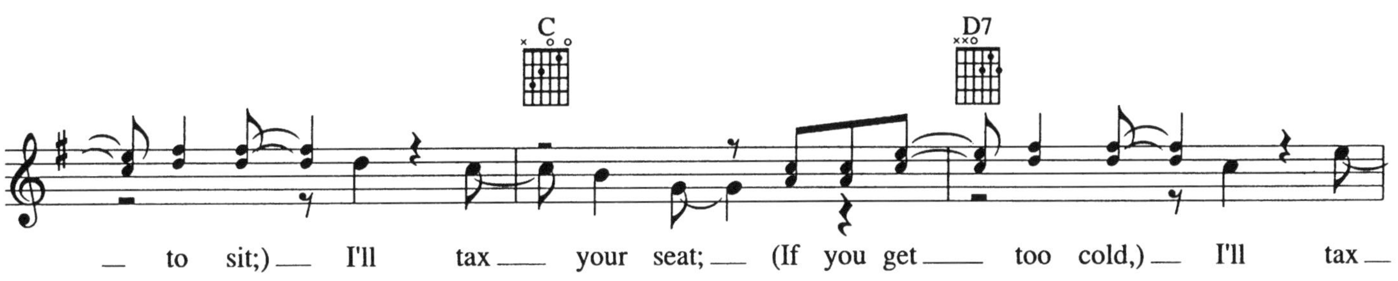
C
D7
to sit;) I'll tax your seat; (If you get too cold,) I'll tax

C
the heat; (If you take a walk,) I'll tax your feet.

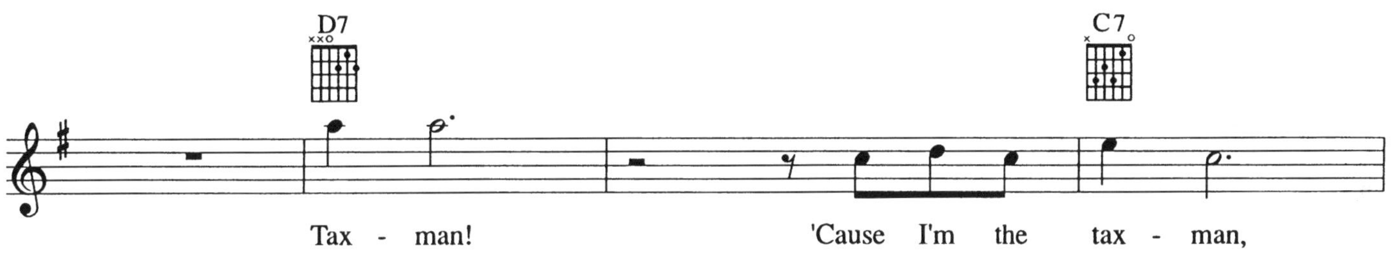
D7
C7
Tax - man! 'Cause I'm the tax - man,

G7
D7
D.S. al Coda
(with repeat)
yeah, I'm the tax - man. 3. Don't ask

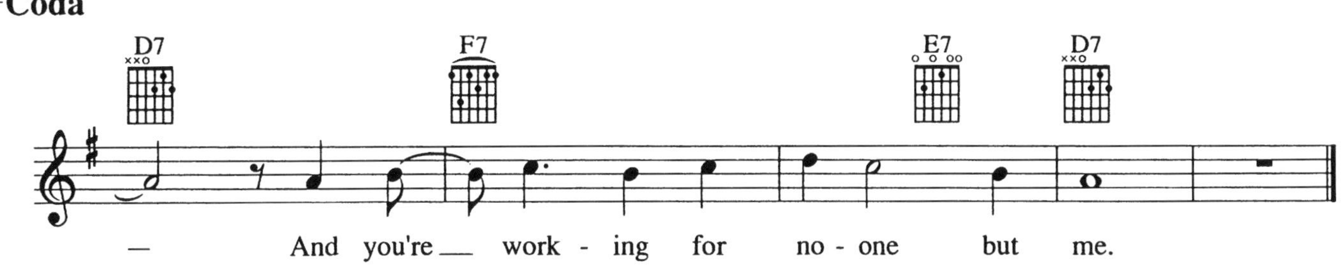
Coda
D7
F7
E7
D7
And you're work - ing for no - one but me.

Tomorrow Never Knows.

Words & Music by John Lennon & Paul McCartney.

Moderately
C
Turn off your mind, re - lax and float down - stream;
(2) is all and love is ev - 'ry - one;

B♭/C
3
It is not dy - ing, It is not
It is know - ing, It is

C
dy - ing. Lay down, all thought, sur - ren -
know - ing. When ig - nor - ance and haste

B♭/C
3
- der to the void; It is shin - ing,
may mourn the dead; It is be - liev - ing,

C
It is shin - ing.
It is be - liev - ing.
That you may see the mean -
But lis - ten to the col -

B♭/C
- ing of with - in,
- our of your dreams,
It is speak - ing,
It is not liv - ing,

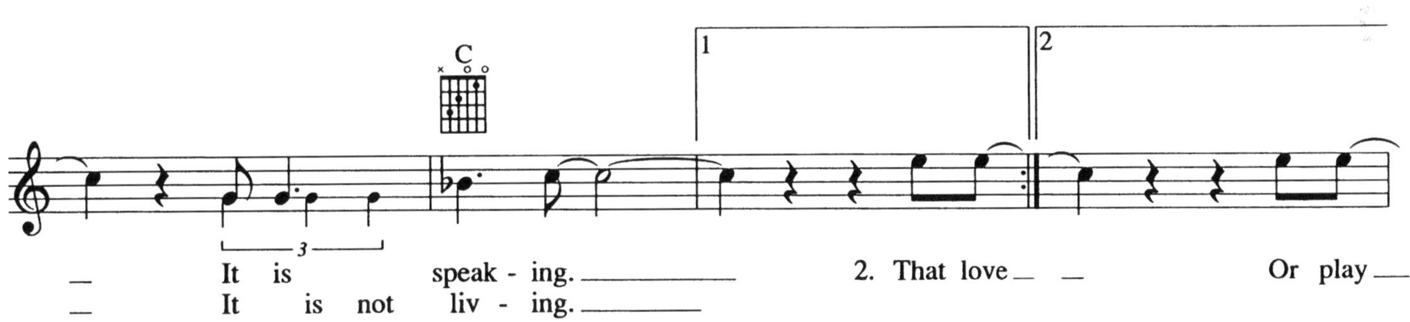
C
1
2
It is speak - ing.
It is not liv - ing.
2. That love
Or play

C
the game "Ex - is - tence" to the end
of the be -

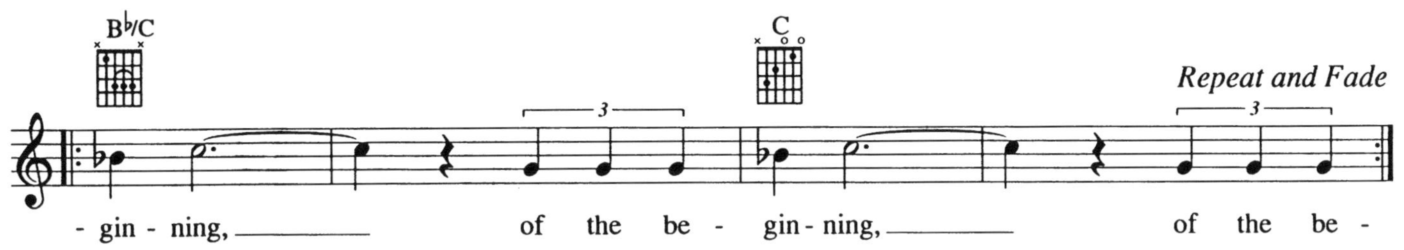
B♭/C
C
Repeat and Fade
- gin - ning,
of the be - gin - ning,
of the be -

Yellow Submarine.

Words & Music by John Lennon & Paul McCartney.

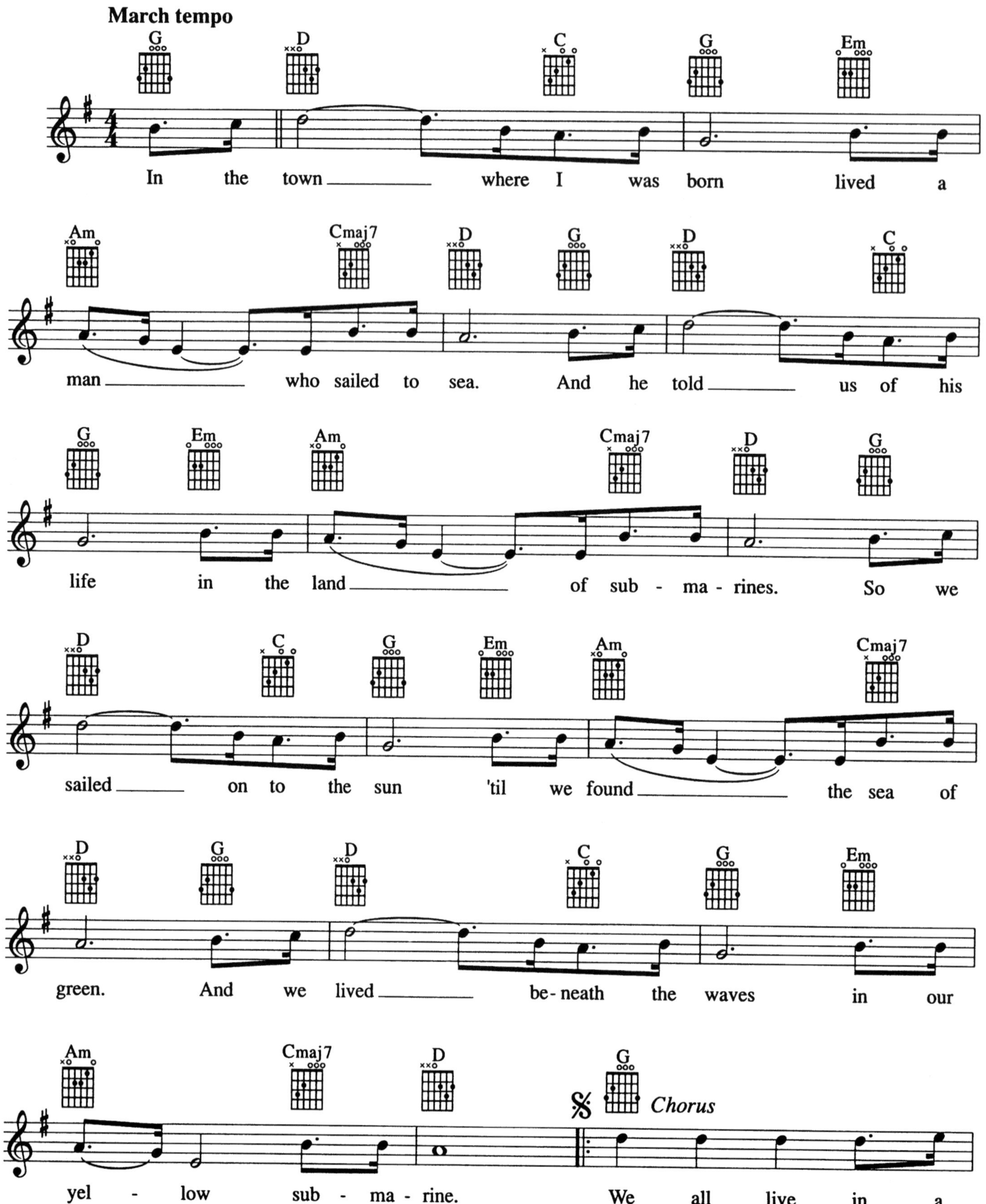
March tempo
G D C G Em
In the town ___ where I was born lived a
Am Cmaj7 D G D C
man ___ who sailed to sea. And he told ___ us of his
G Em Am Cmaj7 D G
life in the land ___ of sub - ma - rines. So we
D C G Em Am Cmaj7
sailed ___ on to the sun 'til we found ___ the sea of
D G D C G Em
green. And we lived ___ be-neath the waves in our
Am Cmaj7 D G
yel - low sub - ma - rine.
Chorus
We all live in a

D
G
yel - low sub - ma - rine, yel - low sub - ma - rine, yel - low sub - ma - rine.
G
D
We all live in a yel - low sub - ma - rine, yel - low sub - ma - rine,
G
D
C
yel - low sub - ma - rine.
And our friends are all a -
As we live a life of
G
Em
Am
Cmaj7
D
G
- board; ma - ny more of them live next door. And the
ease, ev - 'ry one of us has all we need. Sky of
D
C
1
G
band be - gins to play:
blue and sea of
2
G
Em
Am
Cmaj7
D
D.S. and Fade
green in our yel - low sub - ma - rine.

Oo You.

Words & Music by Paul McCartney.

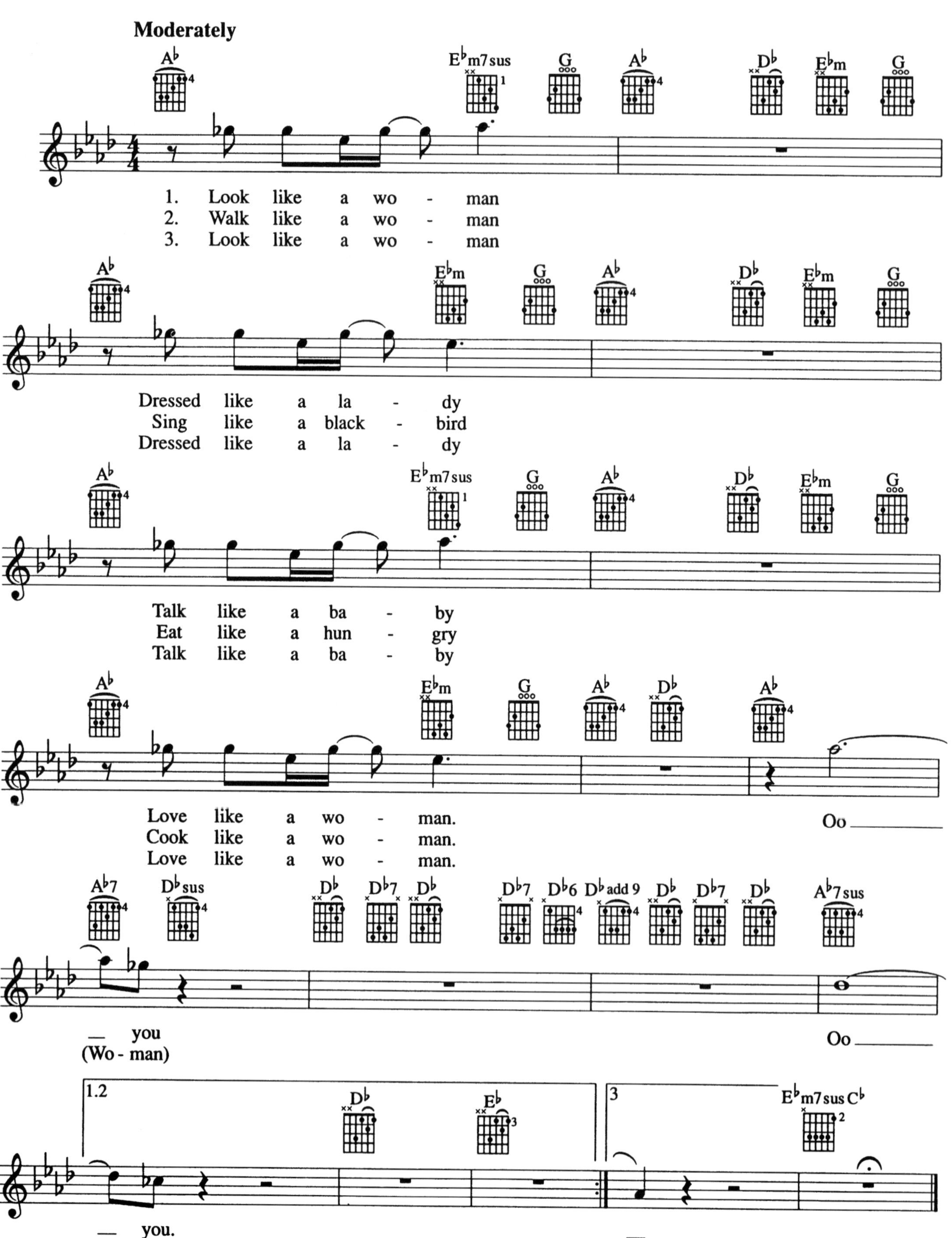
Moderately
A♭ E♭m7sus G A♭ D♭ E♭m G
1. Look like a wo - man
2. Walk like a wo - man
3. Look like a wo - man
A♭ E♭m G A♭ D♭ E♭m G
Dressed like a la - dy
Sing like a black - bird
Dressed like a la - dy
A♭ E♭m7sus G A♭ D♭ E♭m G
Talk like a ba - by
Eat like a hun - gry
Talk like a ba - by
A♭ E♭m G A♭ D♭ A♭
Love like a wo - man.
Cook like a wo - man.
Love like a wo - man.
Oo
A♭7 D♭sus D♭ D♭7 D♭ D♭7 D♭6 D♭add 9 D♭ D♭7 D♭ A♭7sus
you
(Wo - man)
Oo
1.2
D♭ E♭
you.
3
E♭m7sus C♭

Power To The People.

Words & Music by John Lennon & Paul McCartney.

Moderately
C
Tacet
Pow-er to the peo - ple, Pow-er to the peo - ple.
C Dm C Dm C Dm
Pow - er to the peo - ple, Pow - er to the peo -
C Dm C Dm C Dm
To Coda
4th time
- ple. Pow - er to the peo - ple,
C B♭ C Dm
Pow-er to the peo-ple, right on!
1. You say you want a rev - o - lu -
2. A mil-lion work - ers work-in' for noth-
3. We got-ta ask you com-rades and broth-
- tion, We bet-ter get on right a - way.
- ing, You bet-ter give them what they real - ly own.
- ers, How do you treat the old wo-man back home?
Well, you get
We got-ta
She got to
1.2
on your feet and in - to the street sing - ing:
put you down when we come in - to town sing - ing:
be her - self, so she can
3
D.C. al Coda
give her help sing-ing:
Coda
C B♭ C
Pow-er to the peo-ple, right on!

Baby You're A Rich Man.

Words & Music by John Lennon & Paul McCartney.

Moderately
G
C/G
G7
How does it feel to be one of the beau - ti - ful peo - ple,
G
F/G
F
G7
Now that you know who you are? What do you want to be,
C
G7
And have you trav - elled ve - ry far?
F
G7
C
G
Far as the eye can see. How does it feel to be
C
G7
G
one of the beau - ti - ful peo - ple,
How of - ten have you been there?
Tuned to a nat - ur - al E.
F/G
F
G7
C
Of - ten e - nough to know.
Hap - py to be that way,

G7
F/G
F
G7
What did you see when you were there?
Noth - ing that does - n't show.
Now that you've found an - oth - er key
What are you going to play?
C
G
C
Ba - by, you're a rich man, Ba - by, you're a rich man,
G
C
B♭
G7
Ba - by, you're a rich man too.
You keep all your mon - ey in a
C
G7
C
big brown bag in - side a zoo, what a thing to do;
G
C
G
To Coda
Ba - by, you're a rich man, Ba - by, you're a rich man, Ba - by, you're a rich man
C
D.S. al Coda
too.
Coda
C
G
too.
Ba - by, you're a rich man,
C
G
Repeat & Fade
Ba - by, you're a rich man, Ba - by, you're a rich man

Being For The Benefit Of Mr Kite.

WORDS & MUSIC BY JOHN LENNON & PAUL MCCARTNEY.

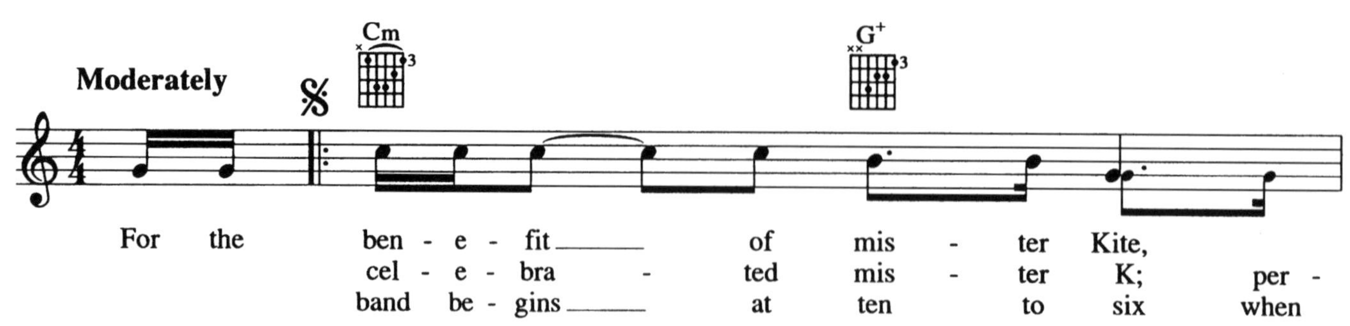
Moderately
Cm
G+
For the ben - e - fit of mis - ter Kite,
cel - e - bra - ted mis - ter K; per -
band be - gins at ten to six when

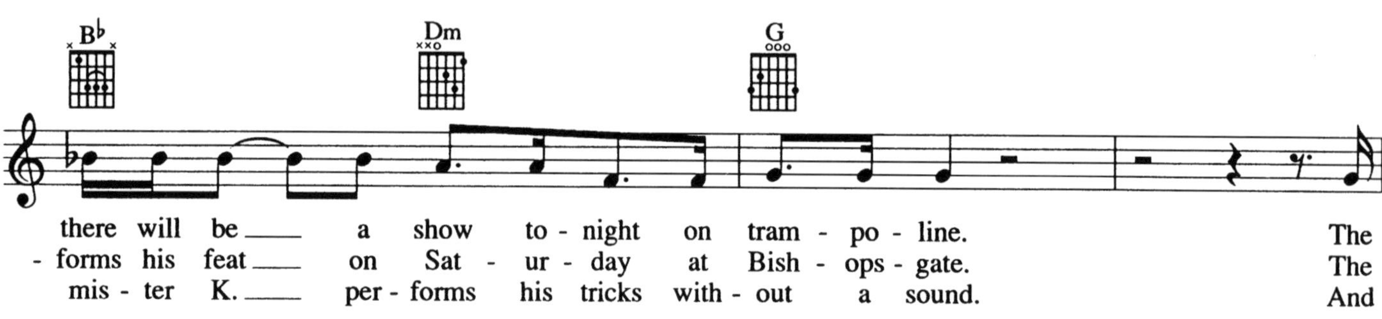
B♭
Dm
G
there will be a show to - night on tram - po - line. The
- forms his feat on Sat - ur - day at Bish - ops - gate. The
mis - ter K. per - forms his tricks with - out a sound. And

Cm
G+/E♭
B♭
Dm
Hen - der - sons will all be there, late of Pa - blo Fan - que's fair,
Hen - der - sons will dance and sing as mis - ter Kite flies through the ring;
mis - ter H. will dem - on - strate ten som - er - saults he'll un - der - take on

A
Dm
what a scene! O - ver men and hors - es, hoops and gar - ters,
don't be late. mes - s'rs K. and H. as - sure the pub - lic
sol - id ground. Hav - ing been some days in prep - ar - a - tion, a

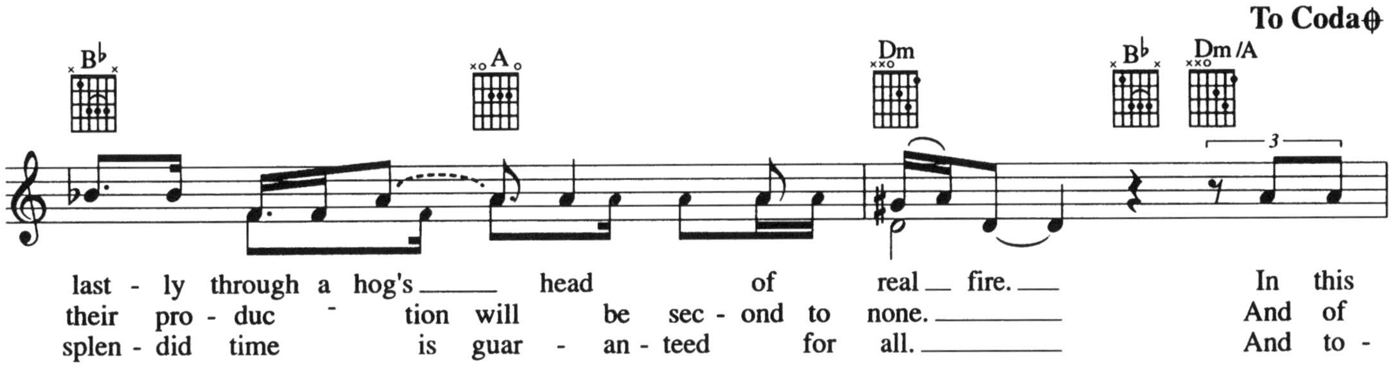
To Coda
B♭
A
Dm
B♭
Dm/A
last - ly through a hog's head of real fire. In this
their pro - duc - tion will be sec - ond to none. And of
splen - did time is guar - an - teed for all. And to -

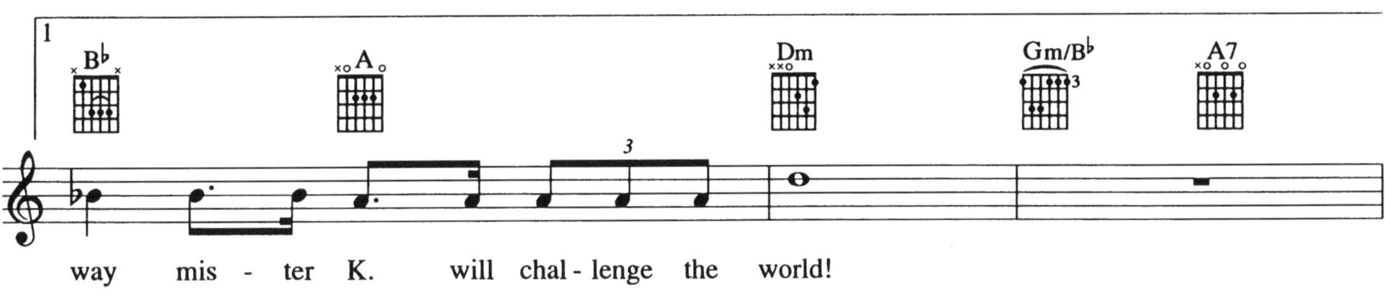
1
B♭
A
Dm
Gm/B♭
A7
way mis - ter K. will chal - lenge the world!

Dm
G
2
B♭
A
Dm
G7
D.S. al Coda
2. The course, Hen - ry, The horse danc - es the waltz. 3. The

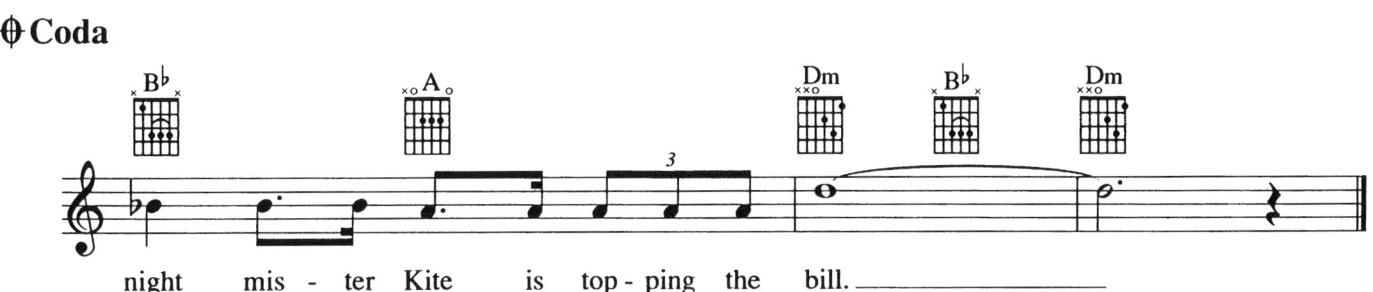
Coda
B♭
A
Dm
B♭
Dm
night mis - ter Kite is top - ping the bill.

Blue Jay Way.

WORDS & MUSIC BY GEORGE HARRISON.

Slowly
C
C°
1. There's a fog up on L. A. And my friends have lost their
show, And I told them where to
way. "We'll be ov - er soon" they said,
go. Ask a p'lice - man on the street,
Now they've lost them - selves in - stead.
There's so man - y there to meet.
Faster
Please don't
be long, please don't you be ver - y long,
Please don't be long,
or I may be a - sleep.
Slower
2. Well, it on - ly goes to
3. Now it's past my bed, I know, And I'd real - ly like to

C
C°
go. Soon will be the break of day, Sit - ting here in Blue Jay
C
Faster
Way. Please don't be long, please don't you
be ver - y long, Please don't be long, or I may be a -
sleep. Please don't be long, Please don't you
1,2
be ver - y long, Please don't be long.
3
Please don't be long. Don't be long, don't be long,
Don't be long, don't be long. Don't be long,
don't be long, Don't be long.

Fixing A Hole.

Words & Music by John Lennon & Paul McCartney.

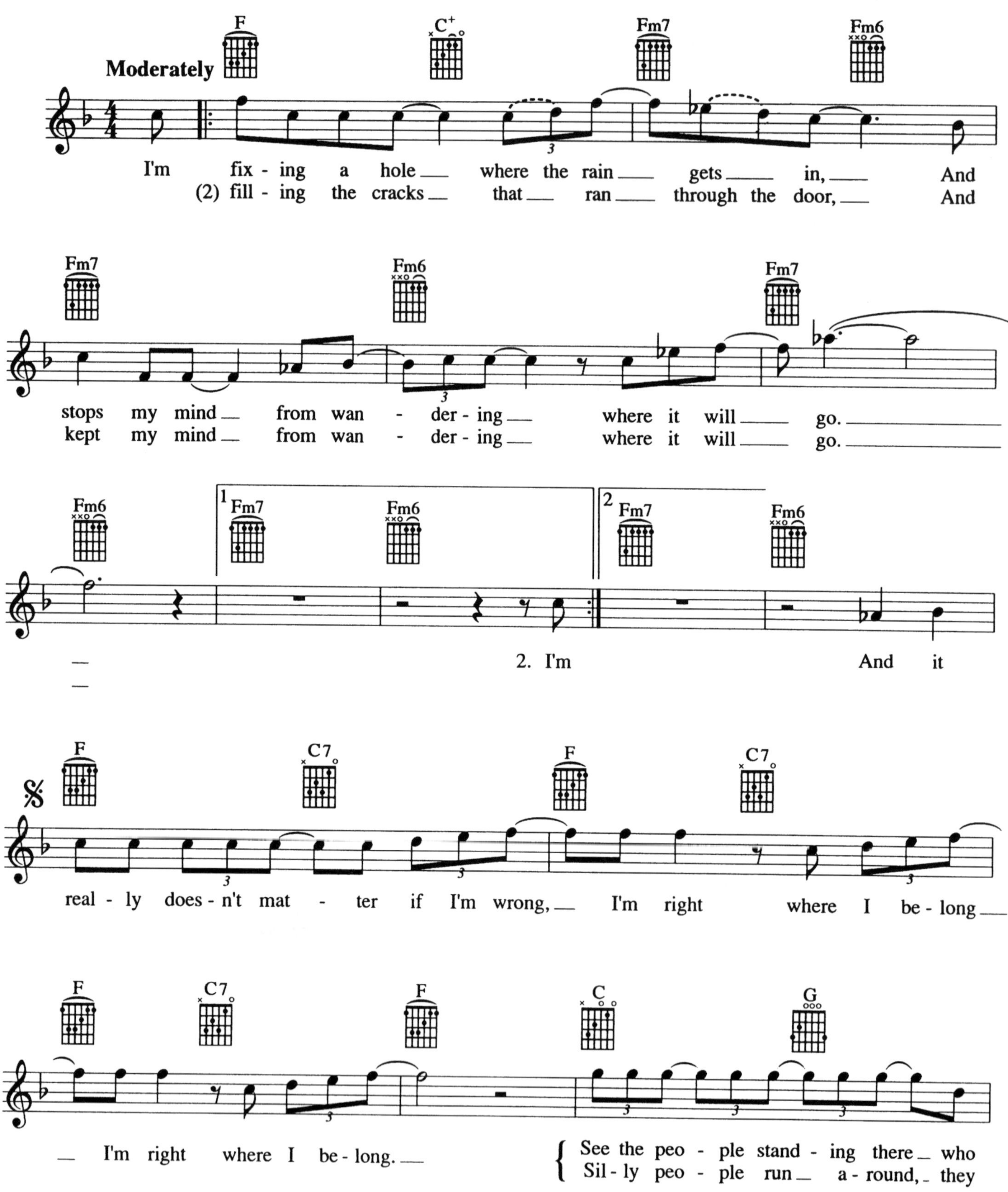
Moderately
F
C+
Fm7
Fm6
I'm fix - ing a hole where the rain gets in, And
(2) fill - ing the cracks that ran through the door, And
Fm7
Fm6
Fm7
stops my mind from wan - der - ing where it will go.
kept my mind from wan - der - ing where it will go.
Fm6
1 Fm7
Fm6
2 Fm7
Fm6
2. I'm
And it
F
C7
F
C7
real - ly does - n't mat - ter if I'm wrong, I'm right where I be - long
F
C7
F
C
G
I'm right where I be - long.
See the peo - ple stand - ing there who
Sil - ly peo - ple run a - round, they

C
G
C
G
dis - a - gree and nev - er win and won - der why they don't get in my
wor - ry me and nev - er ask me why they don't get past my door.

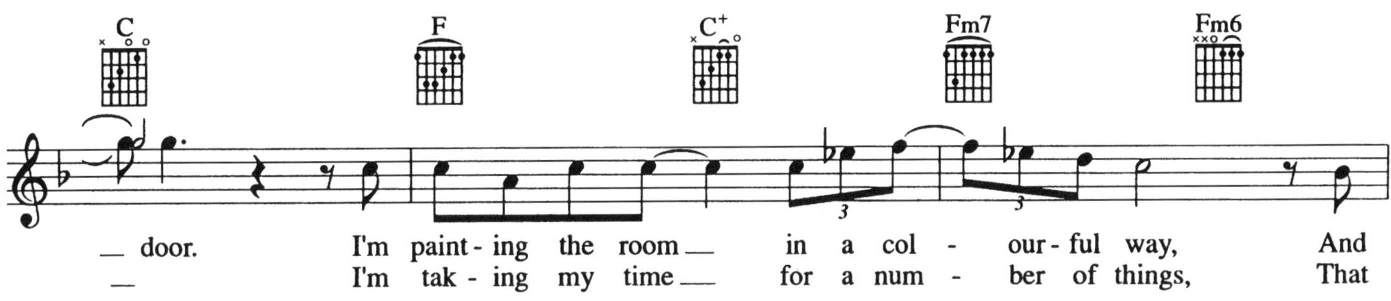
C
F
C+
Fm7
Fm6
door. I'm paint - ing the room in a col - our - ful way, And
I'm tak - ing my time for a num - ber of things, That

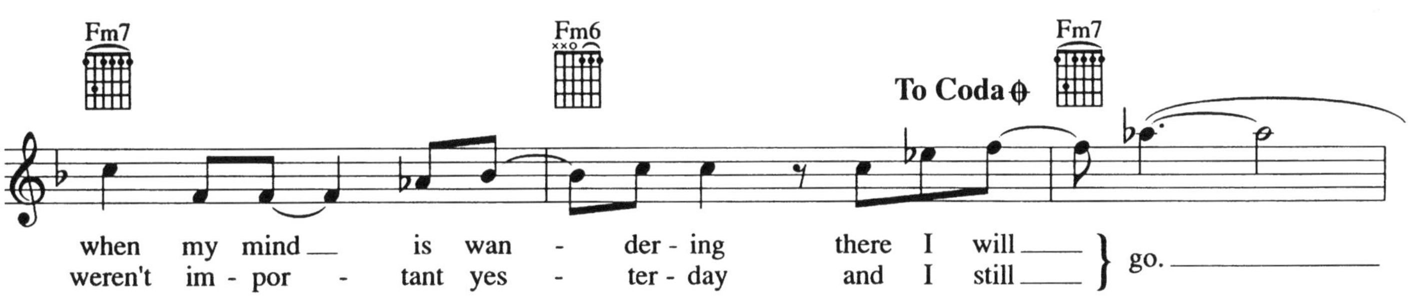
Fm7
Fm6
To Coda
Fm7
when my mind is wan - der - ing there I will
weren't im - por - tant yes - ter - day and I still
go.

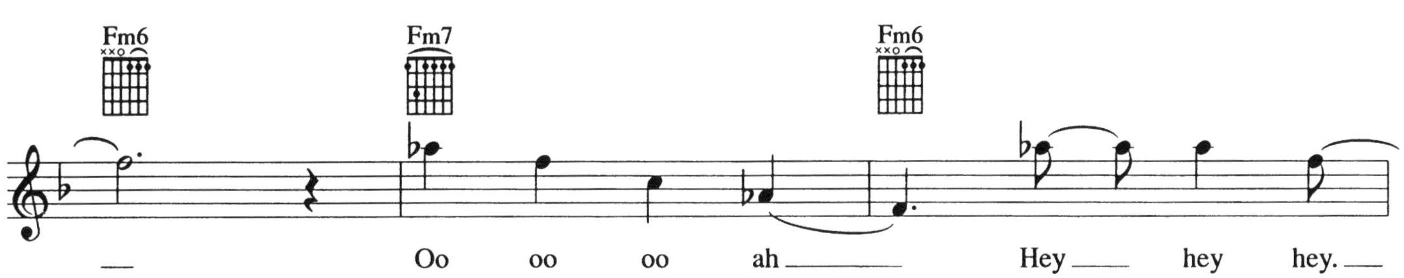
Fm6
Fm7
Fm6
Oo oo oo ah Hey hey hey.

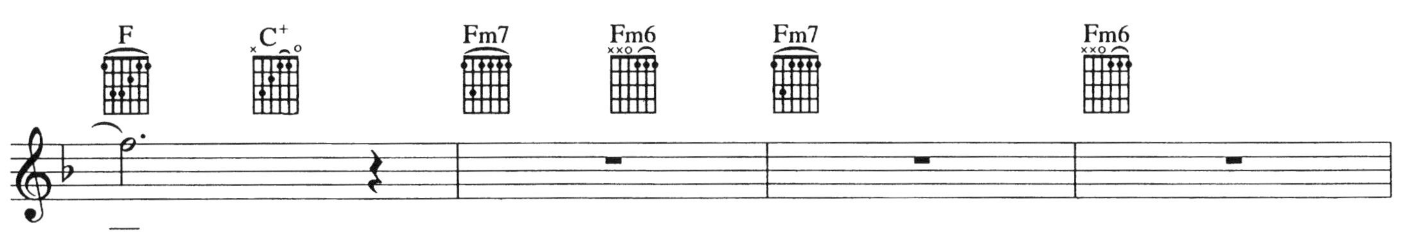
F
C+
Fm7
Fm6
Fm7
Fm6

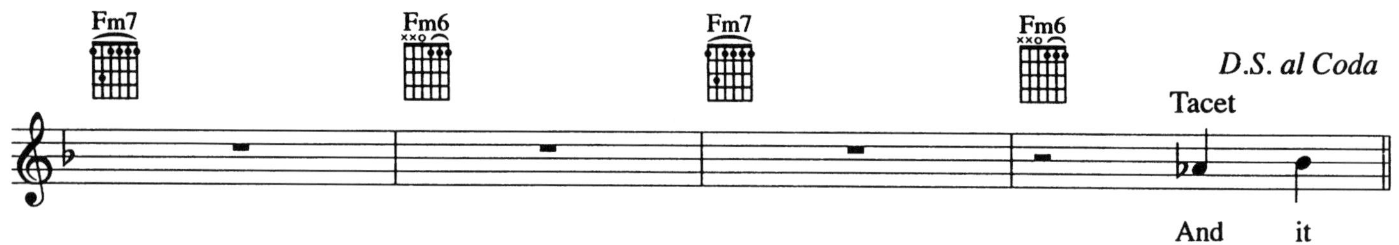
Fm7
Fm6
Fm7
Fm6
D.S. al Coda
Tacet
And it

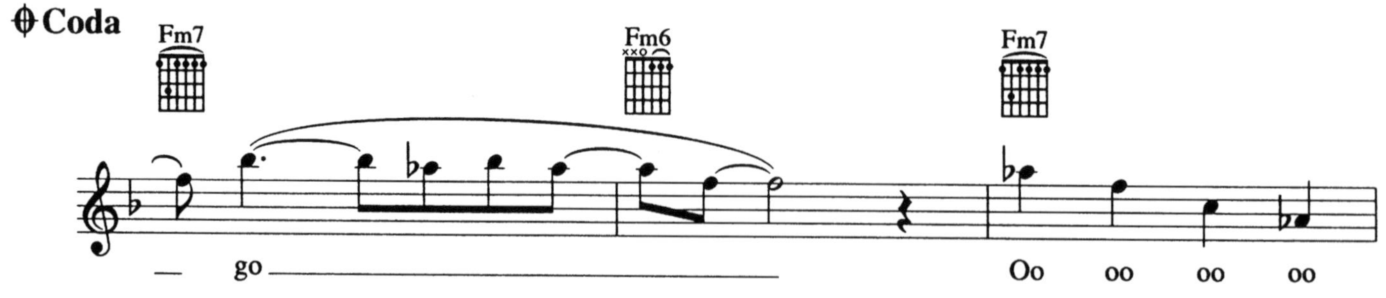
Coda
Fm7
Fm6
Fm7
go
Oo oo oo oo

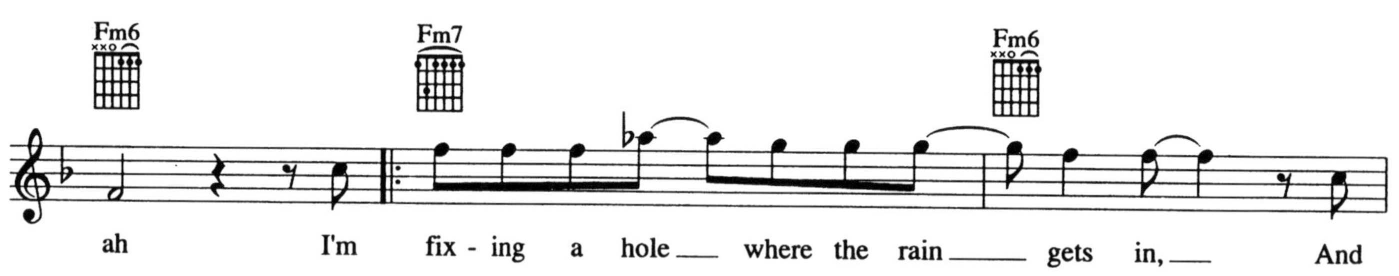
Fm6
Fm7
Fm6
ah I'm fix - ing a hole where the rain gets in, And

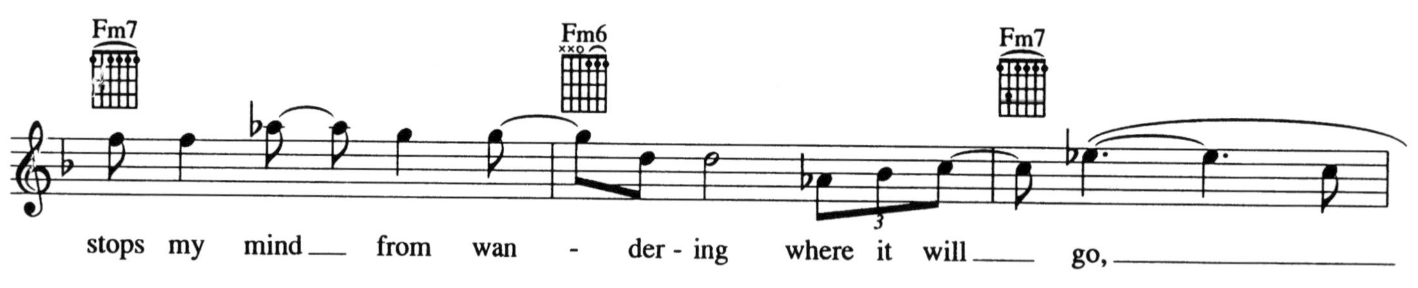
Fm7
Fm6
Fm7
stops my mind from wan - der - ing where it will go,

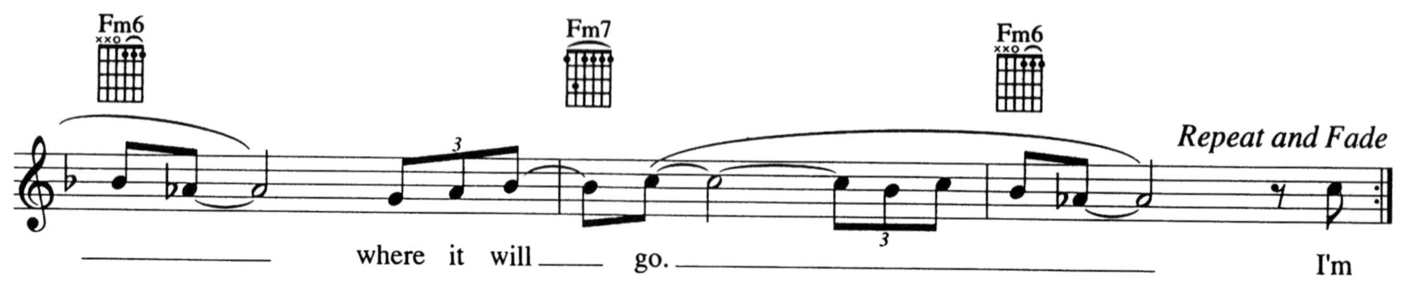
Fm6
Fm7
Fm6
Repeat and Fade
where it will go. I'm

Getting Better.

Words & Music by John Lennon & Paul McCartney.

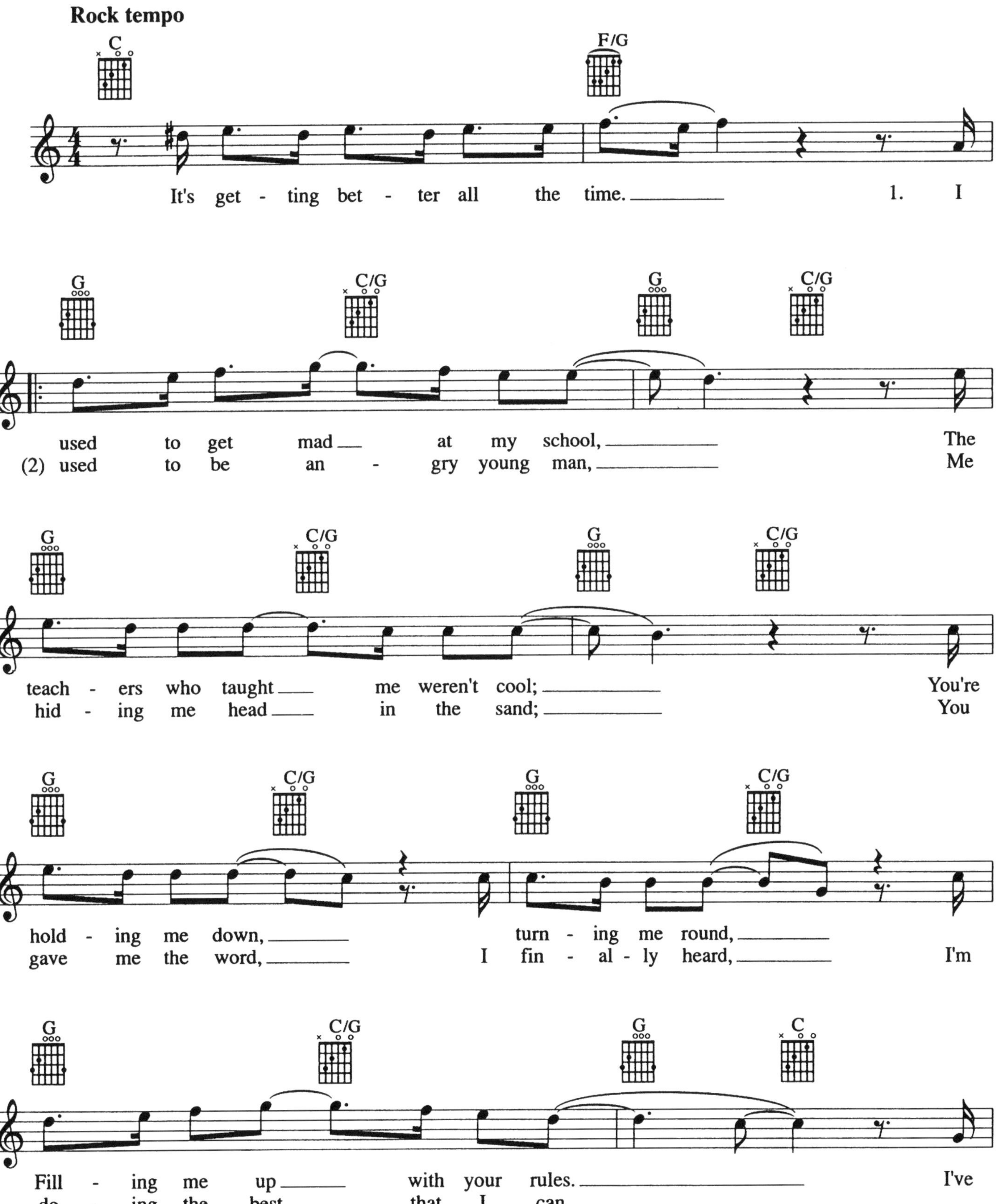
Rock tempo
C
F/G
It's get - ting bet - ter all the time.
1. I
G
C/G
used to get mad at my school, The
(2) used to be an - gry young man, Me
teach - ers who taught me weren't cool; You're
hid - ing me head in the sand; You
hold - ing me down, turn - ing me round,
gave me the word, I fin - al - ly heard, I'm
Fill - ing me up with your rules. I've
do - ing the best that I can.

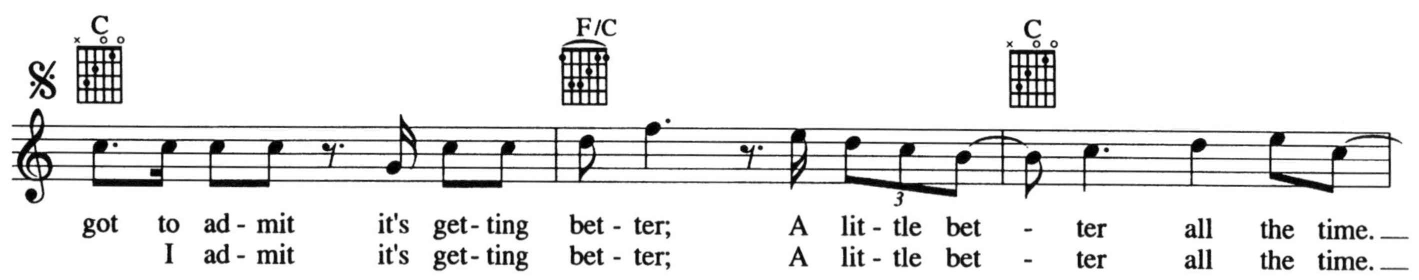
C
F/C
C
got to ad - mit it's get - ting bet - ter; A lit - tle bet - ter all the time.
I ad - mit it's get - ting bet - ter; A lit - tle bet - ter all the time.

Fmaj7
C
F/C
I have to ad - mit it's get - ting bet - ter, It's get - ting
Yes, I ad - mit it's get - ting bet - ter; it's get - ting

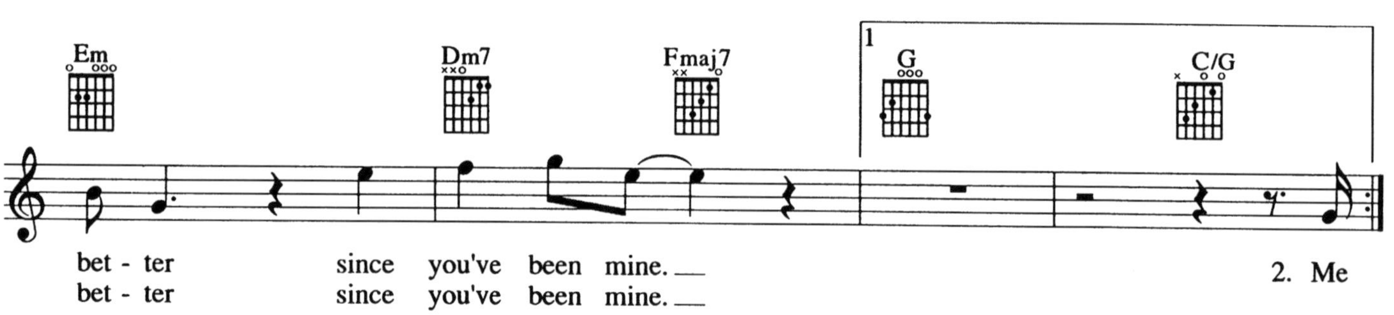
Em
Dm7
Fmaj7
1
G
C/G
bet - ter since you've been mine.
bet - ter since you've been mine.
2. Me

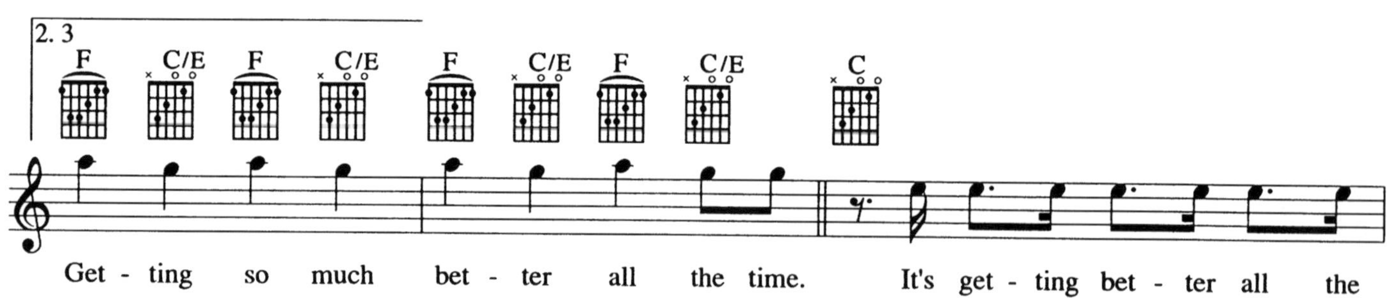
2. 3
F
C/E
F
C/E
F
C/E
F
C/E
C
Get - ting so much bet - ter all the time. It's get - ting bet - ter all the

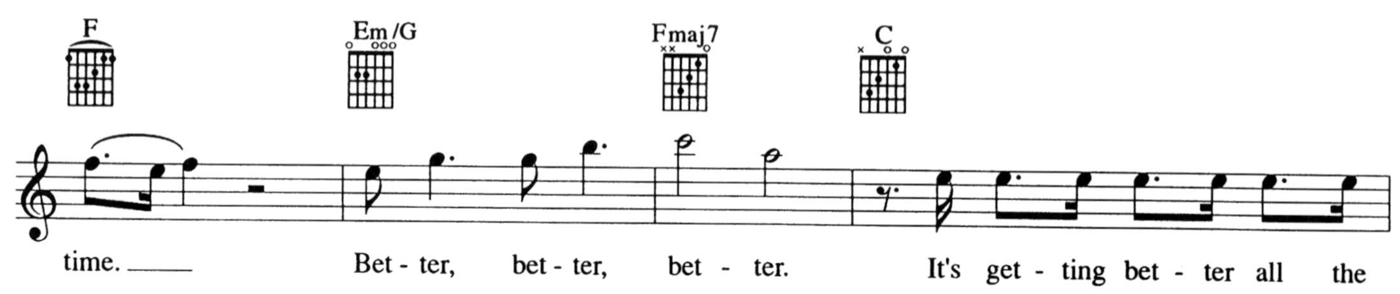
F
Em/G
Fmaj7
C
time. Bet - ter, bet - ter, bet - ter. It's get - ting bet - ter all the

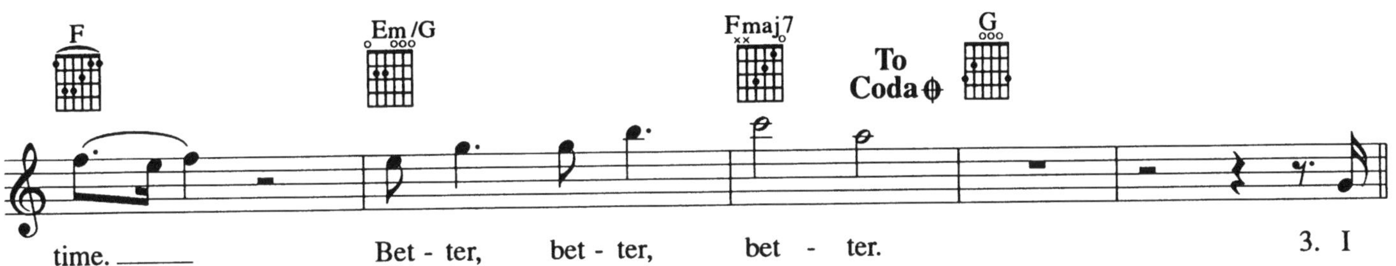
F
Em/G
Fmaj7
To Coda
G
time.
Bet - ter, bet - ter, bet - ter.
3. I

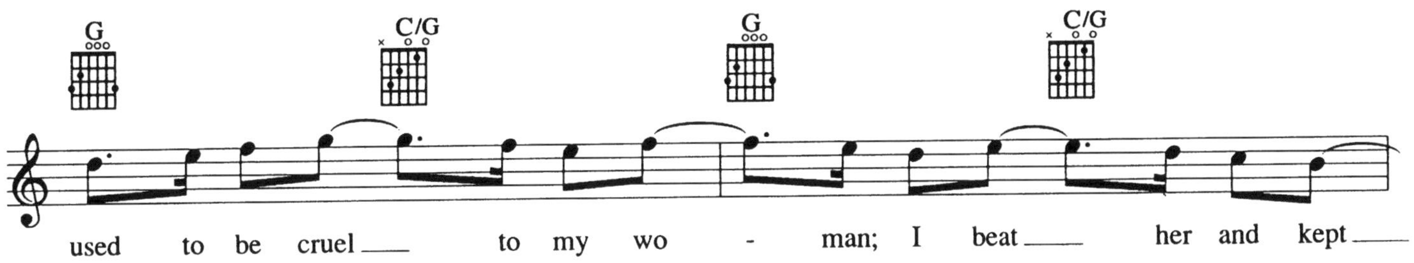
G
C/G
G
C/G
used to be cruel to my wo - man; I beat her and kept

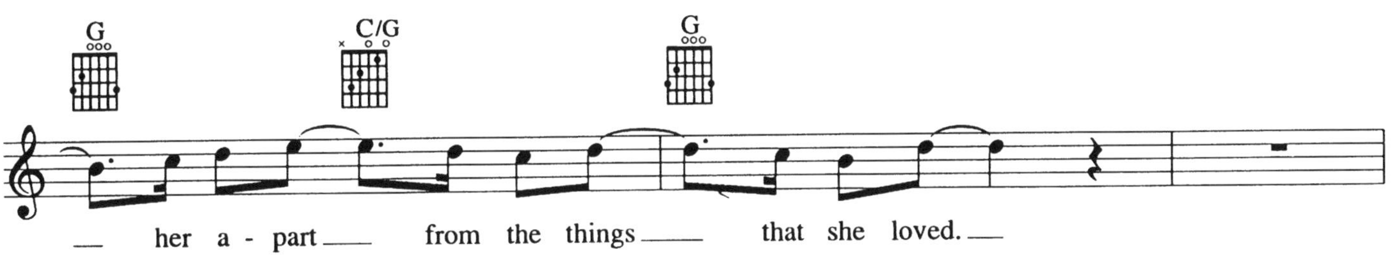
G
C/G
G
her a - part from the things that she loved.

Man, I was mean, but I'm chang - ing my scene, and I'm do -

D.S. al Coda
- ing the best that I can.

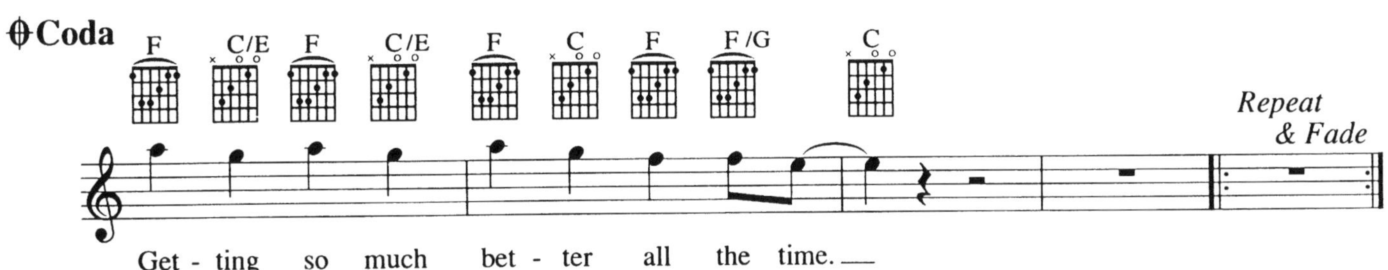
Coda
F
C/E
F
C/E
F
C
F
F/G
C
Repeat & Fade
Get - ting so much bet - ter all the time.

Good Morning, Good Morning.

WORDS & MUSIC BY JOHN LENNON & PAUL McCARTNEY.

Moderately
G C G C G C
Good morn - ing, good morn - ing, good morn - ing, good morn - ing, good
G D G F
morn - ing.
Noth - ing to do to save his life,
Af - ter a while you start to smile,
Some - bod - y needs to know the time,
G F
call his wife in. Noth - ing to say but, "What a day!
now you feel cool. Then you de - cide to take a walk
glad that I'm here. Watch - ing the skirts, you start to flirt,
G
How's your boy been?"
by the old school.
now you're in gear.
C D D7
Noth - ing to do, it's up to you,
Noth - ing has changed, it's still the same,
Go to a show, you hope she goes,
I've got

G
F
To Coda
G
C
noth - ing to say but "It's O. K.." Good morn - ing, good morn - ing, good

G
D
1
G
F
G
morn - ing. Go - ing to work, don't want to go, feel - ing low down.

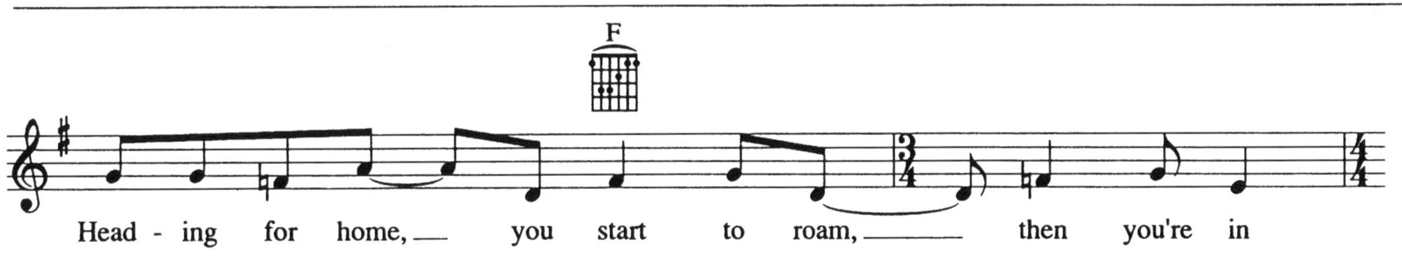
F
Head - ing for home, you start to roam, then you're in

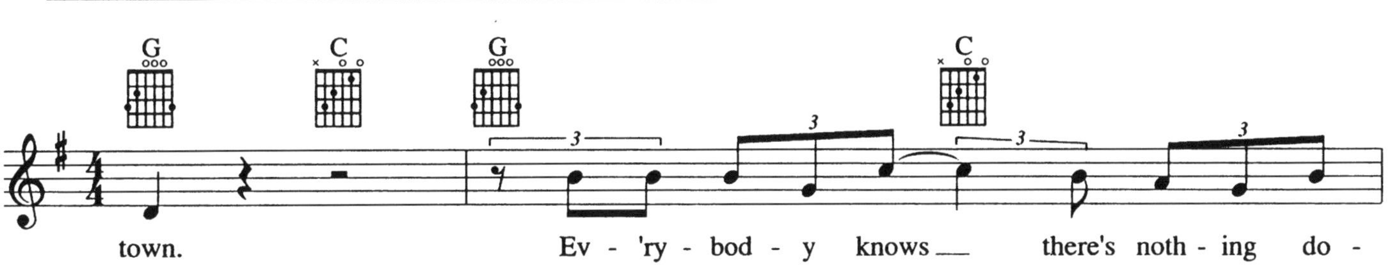
G
C
G
C
town. Ev - 'ry - bod - y knows there's noth - ing do -

G
C
G
C
- ing, Ev - ry - thing is closed, it's like a ru - in, Ev - 'ry one you see is half a - sleep

G C G D
— and you're on your own, — you're in the street. —
2
G F G F

G C G C
Peo - ple run - ning 'round — it's five o' - clock. —

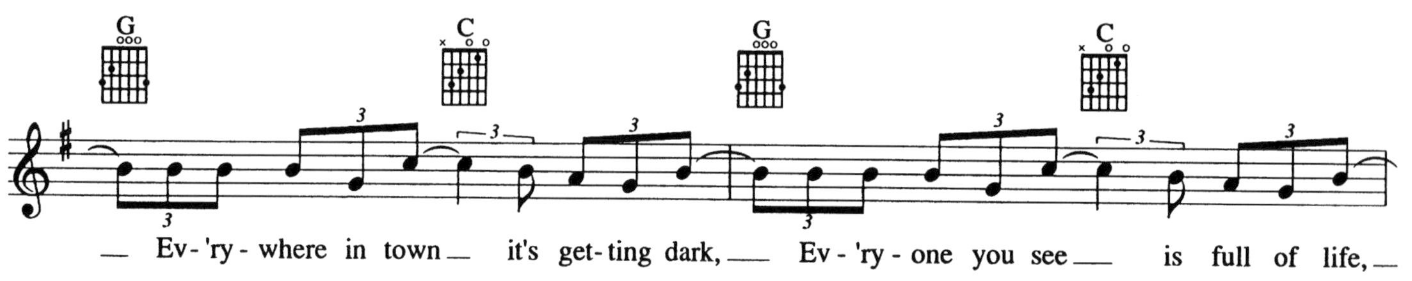
G C G C
— Ev - 'ry - where in town — it's get - ting dark, — Ev - 'ry - one you see — is full of life, —

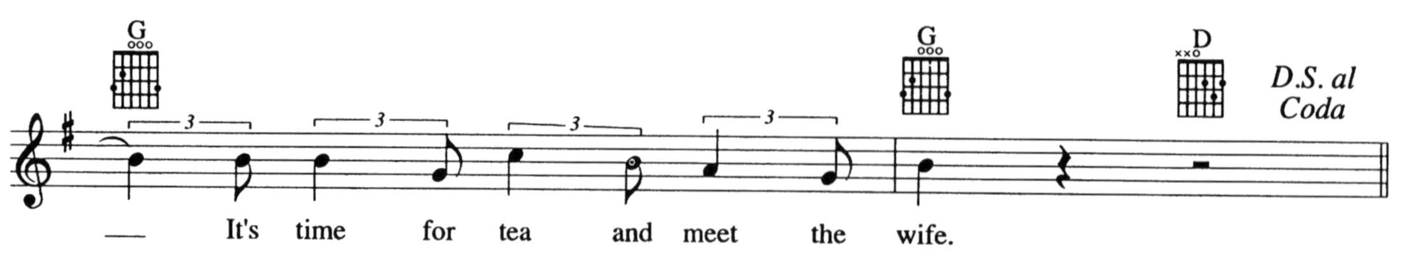
G G D
D.S. al Coda
— It's time for tea and meet the wife.

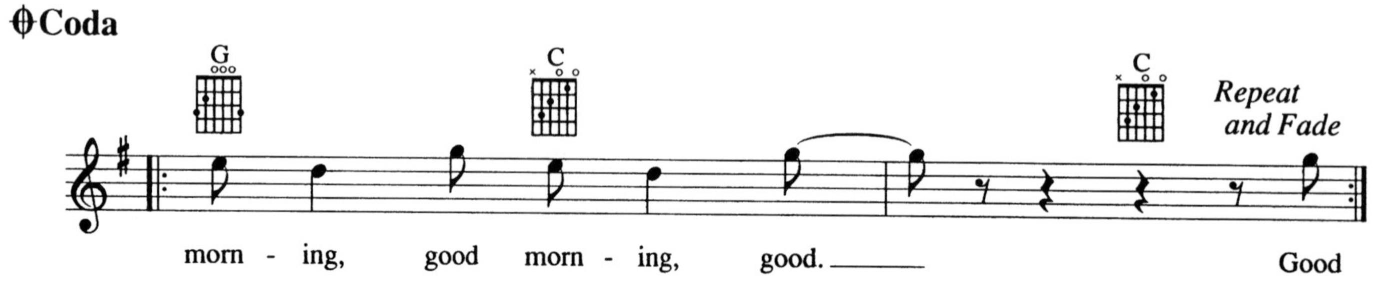
Coda
G C C
Repeat and Fade
morn - ing, good morn - ing, good. — Good

Hello Goodbye.

WORDS & MUSIC BY JOHN LENNON & PAUL McCARTNEY.

Moderately
F
C
G7
You say yes, I say no, You say stop and
Am
G7
Am
G7
I say go, go, go. Oh no.
G11
C
C/B
You say good-bye and I say hel-lo, hel-lo, hel-lo.
Am7
C/G
F
A♭
I don't know why you say good-bye, I say hel-lo,
C
C/B
Am7
C/G
hel-lo, hel-lo. I don't know

F
A♭
C
F
why you say good - bye, I say hel - lo.
I say high,
You say yes,

C
G7
Am
G7
You say low, You say why and I say I don't know.
I say no, You say stop and I say go, go, go.

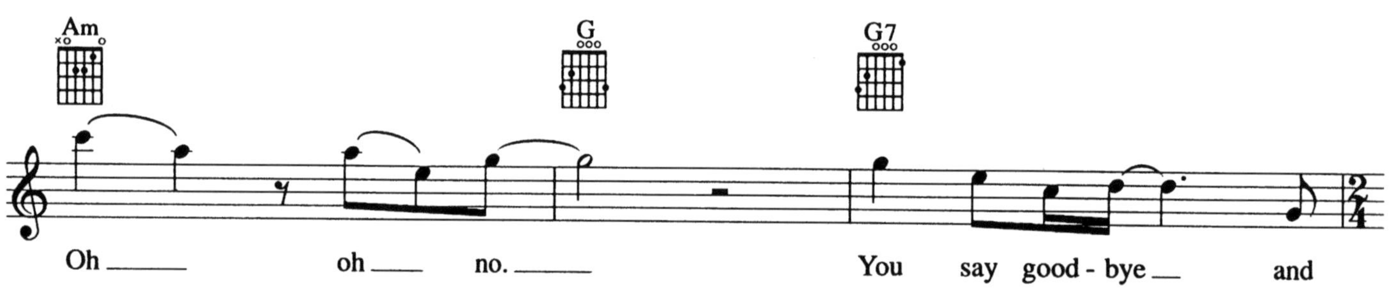
Am
G
G7
Oh oh no. You say good - bye and

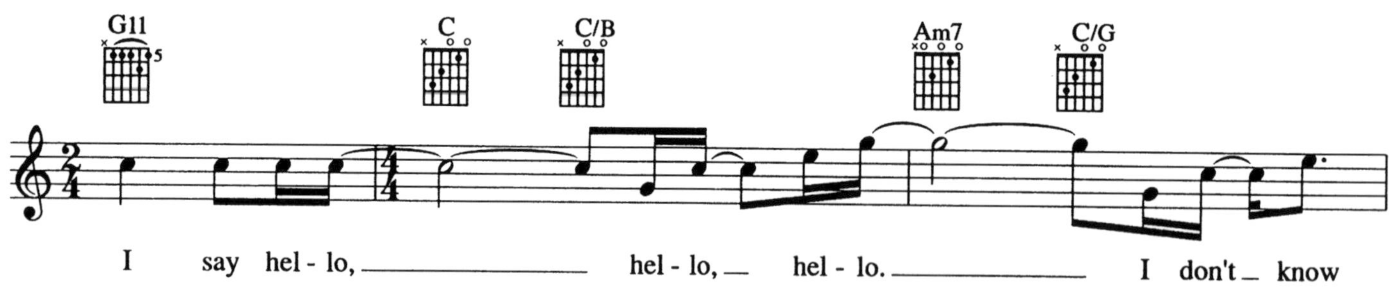
G11
C
C/B
Am7
C/G
I say hel - lo, hel - lo, hel - lo. I don't know

F
A♭
C
C/B
why you say good - bye, I say hel - lo, hel - lo, hel - lo.

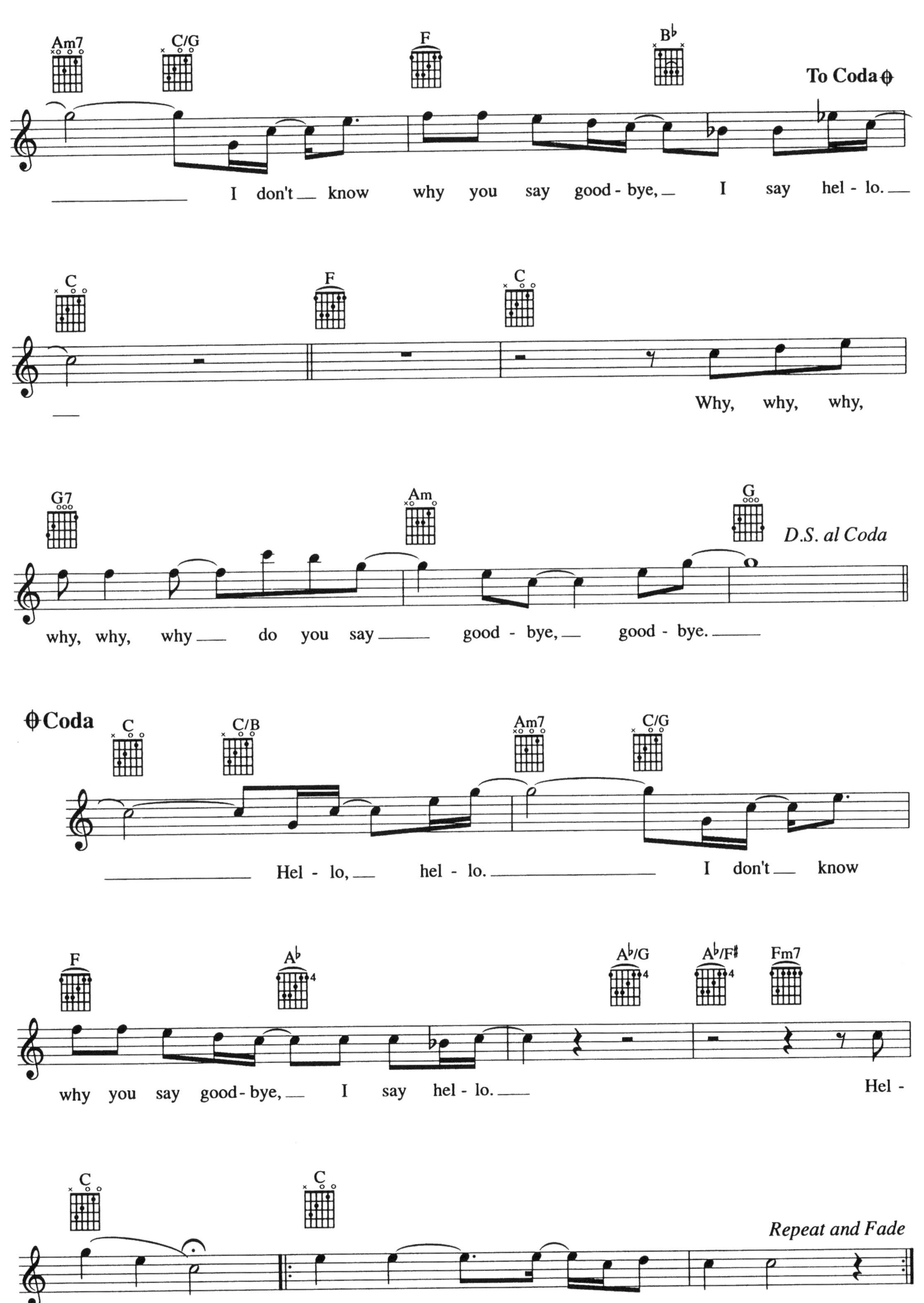
Am7
C/G
F
B♭
To Coda
I don't know why you say good-bye, I say hel-lo.
C
F
C
Why, why, why,
G7
Am
G
D.S. al Coda
why, why, why do you say good-bye, good-bye.
Coda
C
C/B
Am7
C/G
Hel-lo, hel-lo. I don't know
F
A♭
A♭/G
A♭/F♯
Fm7
why you say good-bye, I say hel-lo. Hel-
C
C
Repeat and Fade
-lo. Hel-la he-ba hel-lo-a.

I Am The Walrus.

Words & Music by John Lennon & Paul McCartney.

Slowly
G G/F B♭6 C D
I am he as you are he as you are me and we are all to-
Ex - pert tex - pert chok - ing smok - ers, don't you think the jok - er laughs at
G G/F B♭6
- geth - er.
you?
See how they run like pigs from a gun, see
See how they smile, like pigs in a sty, see
C G
how they fly. I'm cry - ing.
how they snied. I'm cry - ing.
G G/F C/E E♭maj7 F
Sit - ting on a corn - flake wait - ing for the van to come.
Yel - low mat - ter cus - tard drip - ping from a dead dog's eye.
Sem - o - li - na pil - chards climb - ing up the Eif - fel Tow -
G G/F E♭
- er.
Cor - po - ra - tion tee shirt, stu - pid blood - y Tues - day, man,
Crab - a - lock - er fish - wife, por - no - graph - ic priest - ess boy
El - e - men - t'ry pen - guin sing - ing Ha - re Krish - na man,
A
you been a naugh - ty boy, you let your face grow long.
you been a naugh - ty girl you let your knick - ers down.
you should have seen them kick - ing Ed - gar Al - lan Poe.
I am the

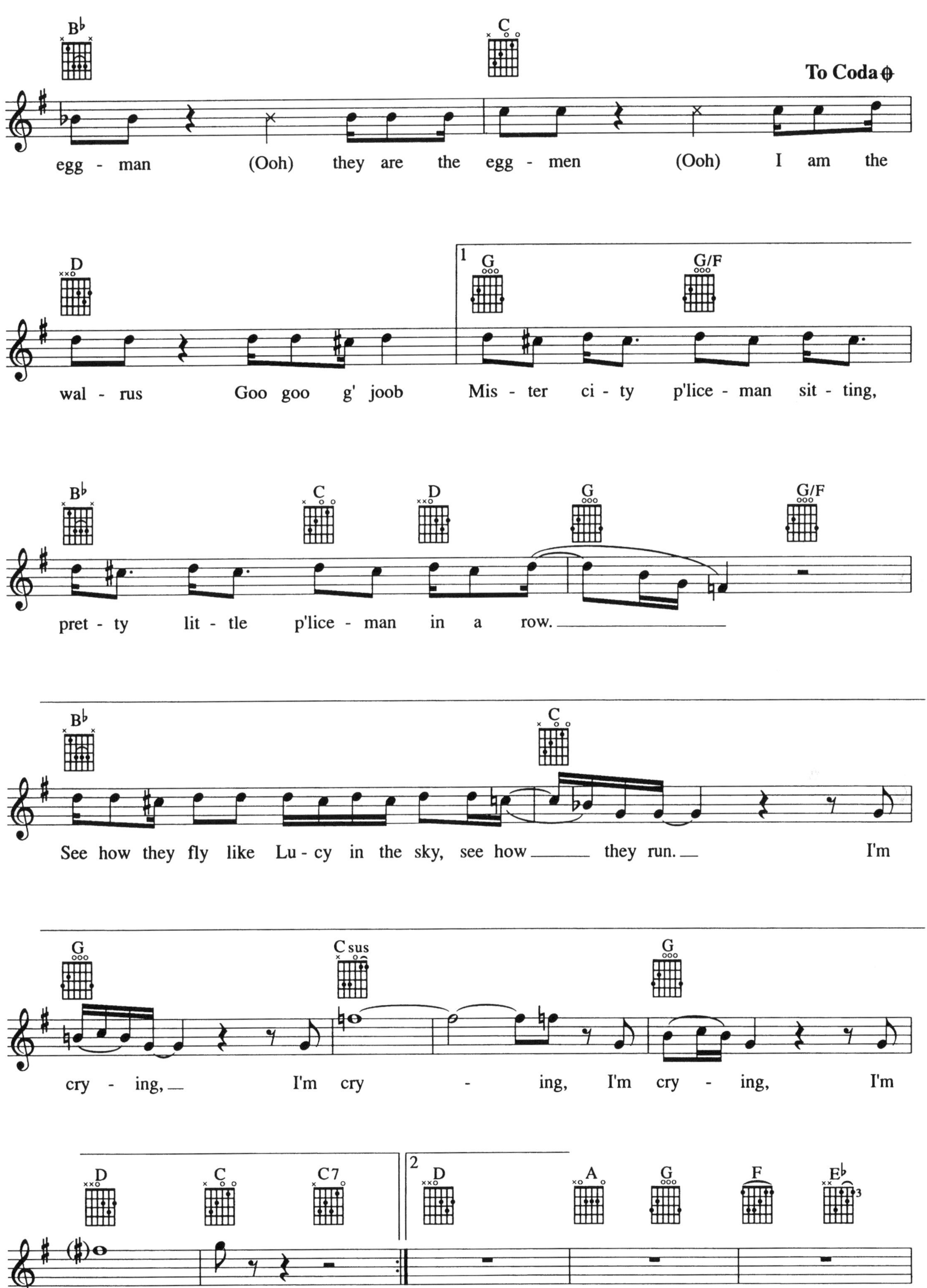
B♭
C
To Coda
egg - man (Ooh) they are the egg - men (Ooh) I am the
D
1 G
G/F
wal - rus Goo goo g' joob Mis - ter ci - ty p'lice - man sit - ting,
B♭
C
D
G
G/F
pret - ty lit - tle p'lice - man in a row.
B♭
C
See how they fly like Lu - cy in the sky, see how they run. I'm
G
C sus
G
cry - ing, I'm cry - ing, I'm cry - ing, I'm
D
C
C7
2 D
A
G
F
E♭
cry - ing.

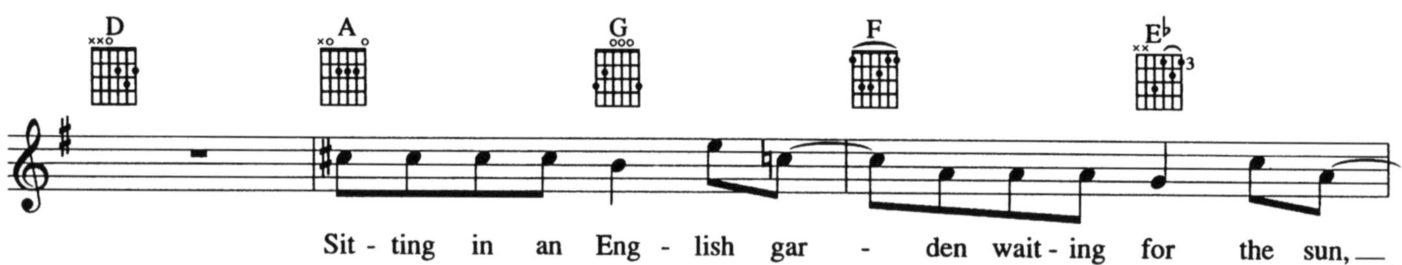
D A G F E♭
Sit - ting in an Eng - lish gar - den wait - ing for the sun,

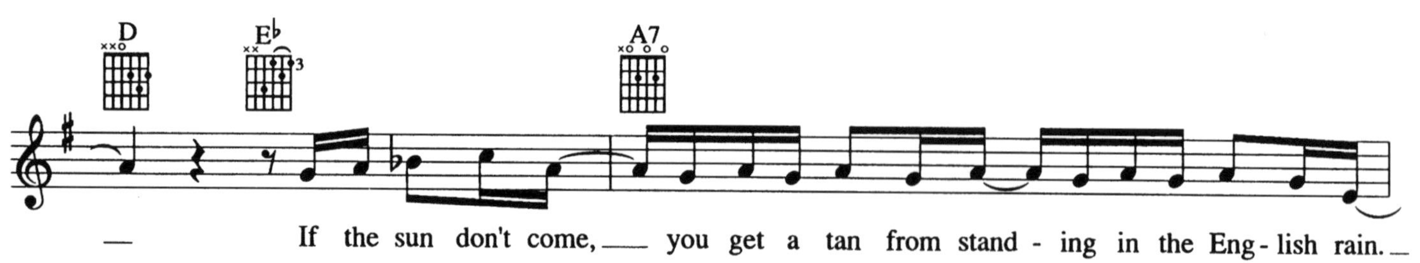
D E♭ A7
If the sun don't come, you get a tan from stand - ing in the Eng - lish rain.

A B♭ C C7
I am the egg - man, They are the egg - men I am the

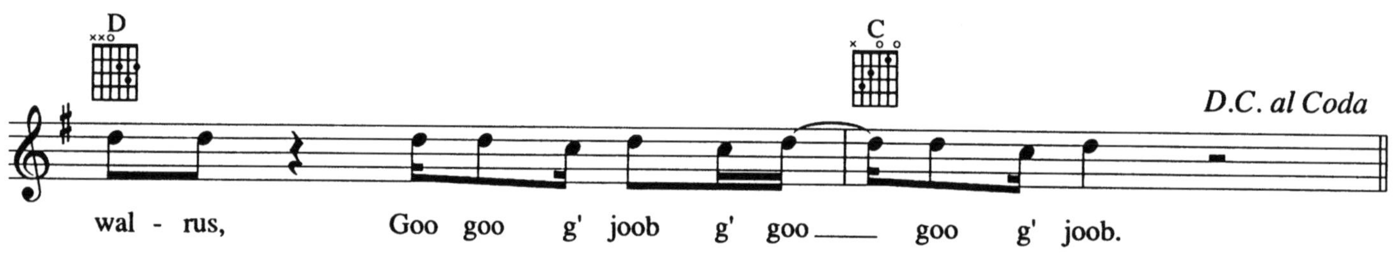
D C
D.C. al Coda
wal - rus, Goo goo g' joob g' goo goo g' joob.

Coda

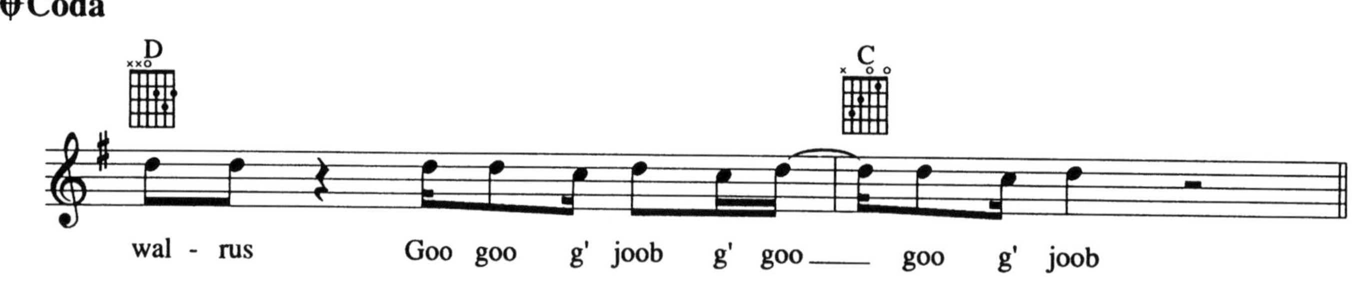
D C
wal - rus Goo goo g' joob g' goo goo g' joob

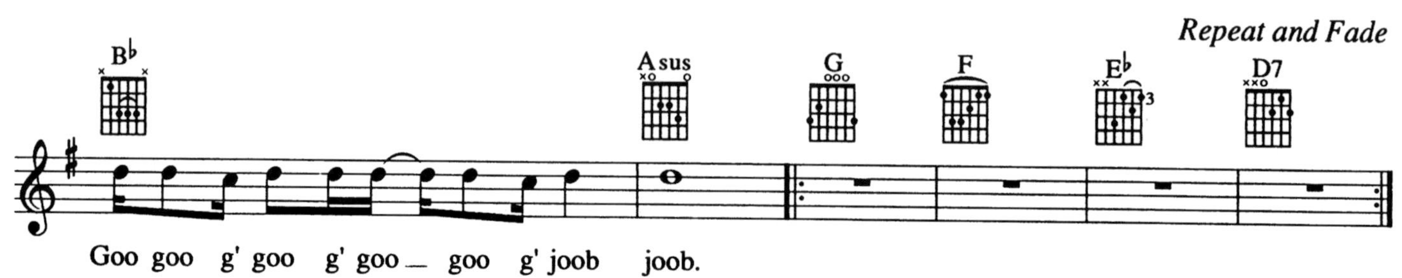
Repeat and Fade
B♭ Asus G F E♭ D7
Goo goo g' goo g' goo goo g' joob joob.

Penny Lane.

WORDS & MUSIC BY JOHN LENNON & PAUL McCARTNEY.

Moderately
C Am7 Dm7 G7sus
1. In Pen-ny Lane: there is a bar - ber show-ing pho - to-graphs of ev - 'ry head
shel - ter in the mid - dle of the round-a - bout, the pret - ty nurse
C Am Cm7 Am7♭5
he's had the pleas - ure to know, And all the peo - ple that come and go
is sell-ing pop - pies from a tray. And tho' she feels as if she's in a play
A♭maj7 G7sus G7 G7sus G7
stop and say "hel - lo" On the
she is an - y - way. In Pen - ny
C Am7 Dm7 G7sus
cor - ner is a bank - er with a mo - tor - car; The lit - tle chil -
Lane: the bar - ber shaves an - oth - er cus - tom - er, We see the bank -
C Am Cm7
- dren laugh at him be - hind his back. And the
- er sit - ting wait - ing for a trim. And then the
Am7♭5 A♭maj7 G7sus G7
bank - er nev - er wears a mac in the pour - ing rain.
fire - man rush - es in from the pour - ing rain

F
B♭
B♭/D
Ve - ry strange! Pen - ny Lane is in my ears and in my eyes.
Ve - ry strange! Pen - ny Lane is in my ears and in my eyes.
E♭
B♭
B♭/D
There be - neath the blue sub - ur - ban skies
There be - neath the blue sub - ur - ban skies
E♭
To Coda
G
C
Am7
I sit. And mean - while back in Pen - ny Lane there is a fire - man with an
I sit. And
Dm7
G7sus
C
Am
Cm7
hour - glass, And in his pock - et is a por - trait of the Queen. He likes to
Am7♭5
A♭maj7
G7sus
G7
keep his fire - en - gine clean; It's a clean ma - chine!
G7sus
G7
C
Am
Dm7
G
C
Am7
Cm7
Am7♭5

A♭maj7
G7sus
G7
F
B♭
Pen - ny Lane ___ is in my ears ___

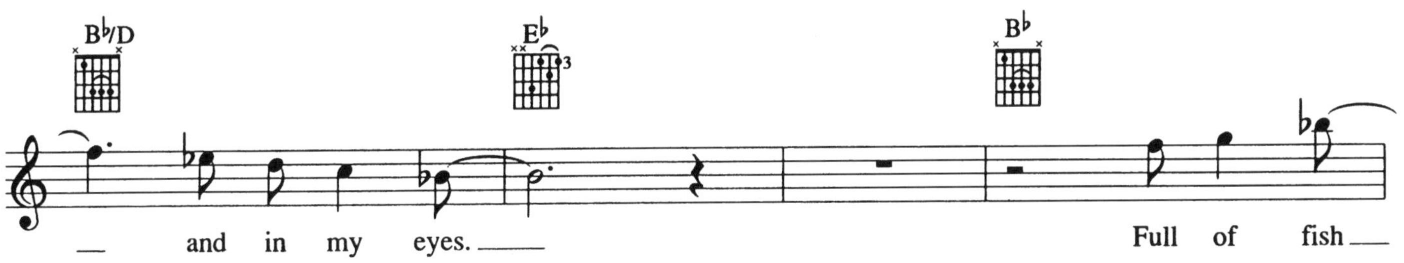
B♭/D
E♭
B♭
___ and in my eyes. ___ Full of fish ___

B♭/D
E♭
G
D.S. al Coda
___ and fin - ger pies ___ in sum - mer. Mean - while, Back be - hind the

Coda
G
C
mean - while back, Pen - ny Lane ___ is in my ears ___

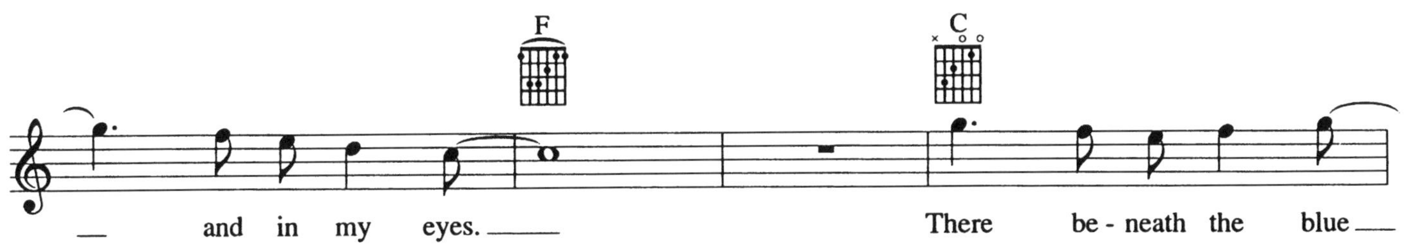
F
C
___ and in my eyes. ___ There be - neath the blue ___

C/E
F
C
___ sub - ur - ban skies ___ Pen - ny Lane ___

Lovely Rita.

WORDS & MUSIC BY JOHN LENNON & PAUL McCARTNEY.

Moderately
G F C G
Ah
Love - ly Ri - ta,
F C G
me - ter maid, Love - ly Ri - ta, me - ter maid.
C B♭ F C G
Love - ly Ri - ta, me - ter maid, noth - ing can come be - tween us;
Am D7 G
When it gets dark, I tow your heart a - way.
C F B♭ E♭
Stand - ing by a park - ing me - ter, when I caught a glimpse of Ri - ta,
Took her out and tried to win her, had a laugh, and o - ver din - ner;
C G C F
fill - ing in a tick - et in her lit - tle white book. In a cap she looked much old - er,
Told her I would real - ly like to see her a - gain. Got the bill and Ri - ta paid it,

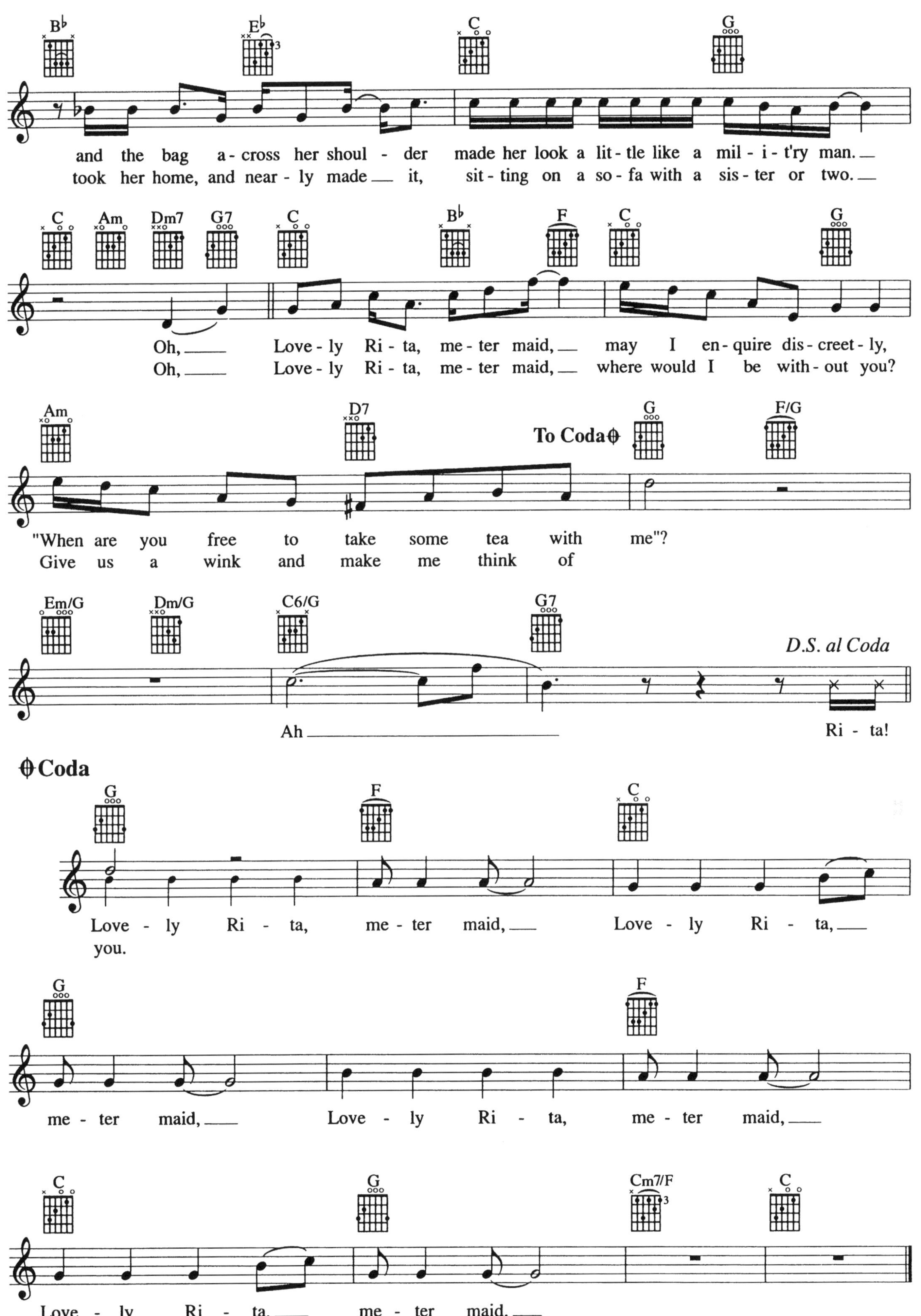
B♭ E♭ C G
and the bag a-cross her shoul-der made her look a lit-tle like a mil-i-t'ry man.
took her home, and near-ly made it, sit-ting on a so-fa with a sis-ter or two.
C Am Dm7 G7 C B♭ F C G
Oh, Love-ly Ri-ta, me-ter maid, may I en-quire dis-creet-ly,
Oh, Love-ly Ri-ta, me-ter maid, where would I be with-out you?
Am D7 To Coda G F/G
"When are you free to take some tea with me"?
Give us a wink and make me think of
Em/G Dm/G C6/G G7
D.S. al Coda
Ah Ri-ta!
Coda
G F C
Love-ly Ri-ta, me-ter maid, Love-ly Ri-ta,
you.
G F
me-ter maid, Love-ly Ri-ta, me-ter maid,
C G Cm7/F C
Love-ly Ri-ta, me-ter maid.

Lucy In The Sky With Diamonds.

Words & Music by John Lennon & Paul McCartney.

Moderately
A
A/G
F♯m7
Dm
1. Pic - ture your - self in a boat on a riv - er with
2. Fol - low her down to a bridge by a foun - tain where
3. Pic - ture your - self on a train in a sta - tion with
A/E
A/G
F♯m7
F
tan - ger - ine trees and mar - ma - lade skies.
rock - ing horse peo - ple eat marsh - mal - low pies.
plas - ti - cine por - ters with look - ing glass ties.
A/E
A/G
F♯m7
Dm
Some - bod - y calls you, you an - swer quite slow - ly, a
Ev - 'ry - one smile as you drift past the flow - ers that
Sud - den - ly some - one is there at the turn - stile, the
A/E
A/G
To Coda
F♯m
Dm
Dm/C
girl with ka - lei - do - scope eyes.
grow so in - cred - ib - ly high.
girl with ka - lei - do - scope
B♭
C9
F
Cel - lo - phane flow - ers of yel - low and green, tow - er - ing
News - pa - per tax - is ap - pear on the shore, wait - ing to

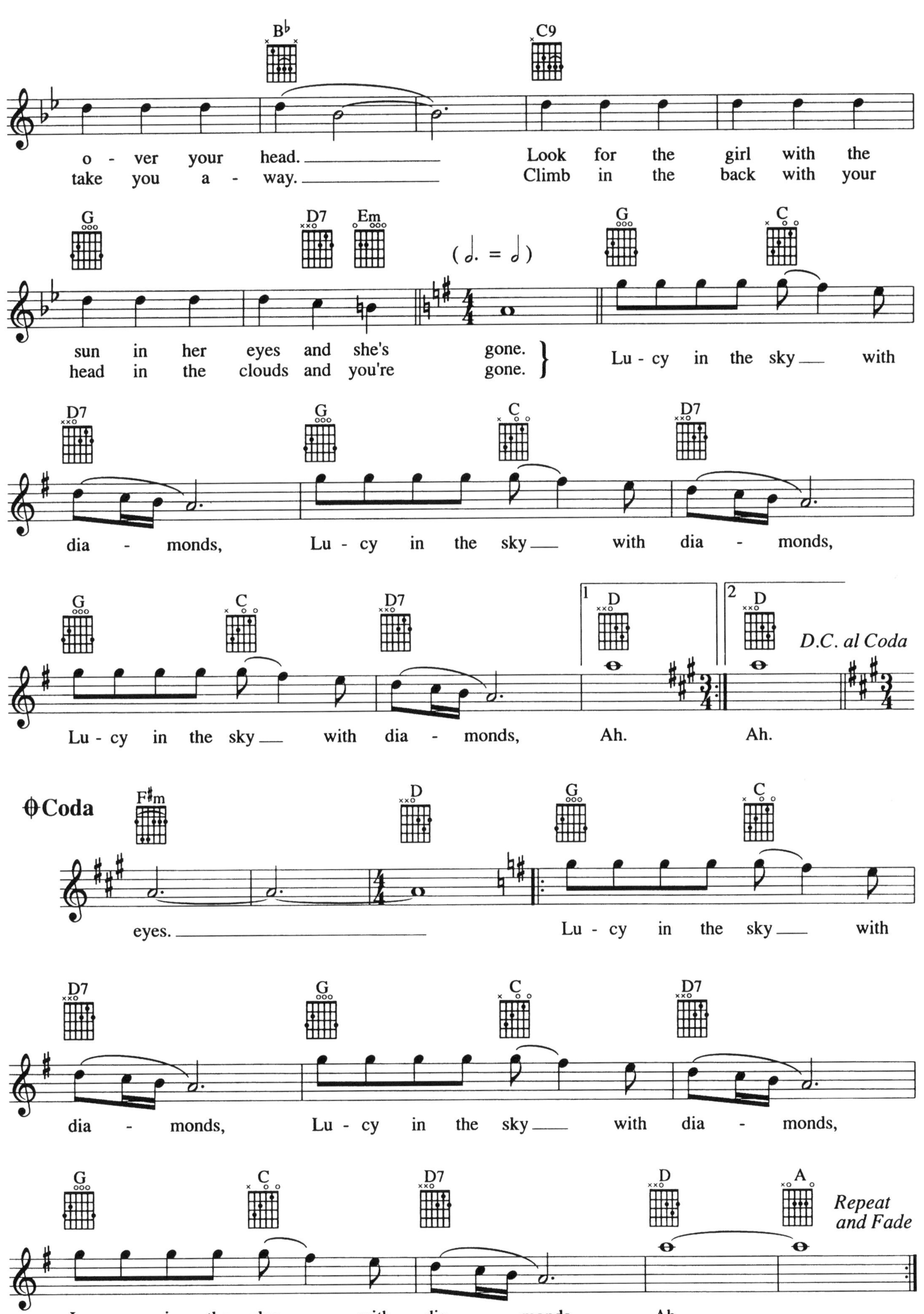
B♭
C9
o - ver your head. Look for the girl with the
take you a - way. Climb in the back with your
G
D7
Em
(♩. = 𝅗𝅥)
G
C
sun in her eyes and she's gone.
head in the clouds and you're gone.
Lu - cy in the sky with
D7
G
C
D7
dia - monds, Lu - cy in the sky with dia - monds,
G
C
D7
1
D
2
D
D.C. al Coda
Lu - cy in the sky with dia - monds, Ah. Ah.
Coda
F♯m
D
G
C
eyes. Lu - cy in the sky with
D7
G
C
D7
dia - monds, Lu - cy in the sky with dia - monds,
G
C
D7
D
A
Repeat and Fade
Lu - cy in the sky with dia - monds, Ah.

Magical Mystery Tour.

Words & Music by John Lennon & Paul McCartney.

Moderately, with a beat
F
C
G
G
(Spoken) Roll up, roll up for the Magical
Mystery Tour. Step right this way.
Roll up,
B♭
C
G
Roll up for the Mys - ter - y Tour.
Roll up,
B♭
C
Roll up for the Mys - ter - y Tour.
G
B♭
(1.3) Roll up, and that's an in - vi - ta - tion, Roll up for the Mys -
(2) Roll up, we've got ev - 'ry - thing you need, Roll up for the Mys -
C
G
- ter - y Tour. Roll up, to make a res - er - va - tion,
- ter - y Tour. Roll up, sat - is - fac - tion guar - an - teed.
B♭
To Coda
C
F
Fmaj7
Roll up for the Mys - ter - y Tour. The Mag - i - cal Mys -
Roll up for the Mys - ter - y Tour. The Mag - i - cal Mys -

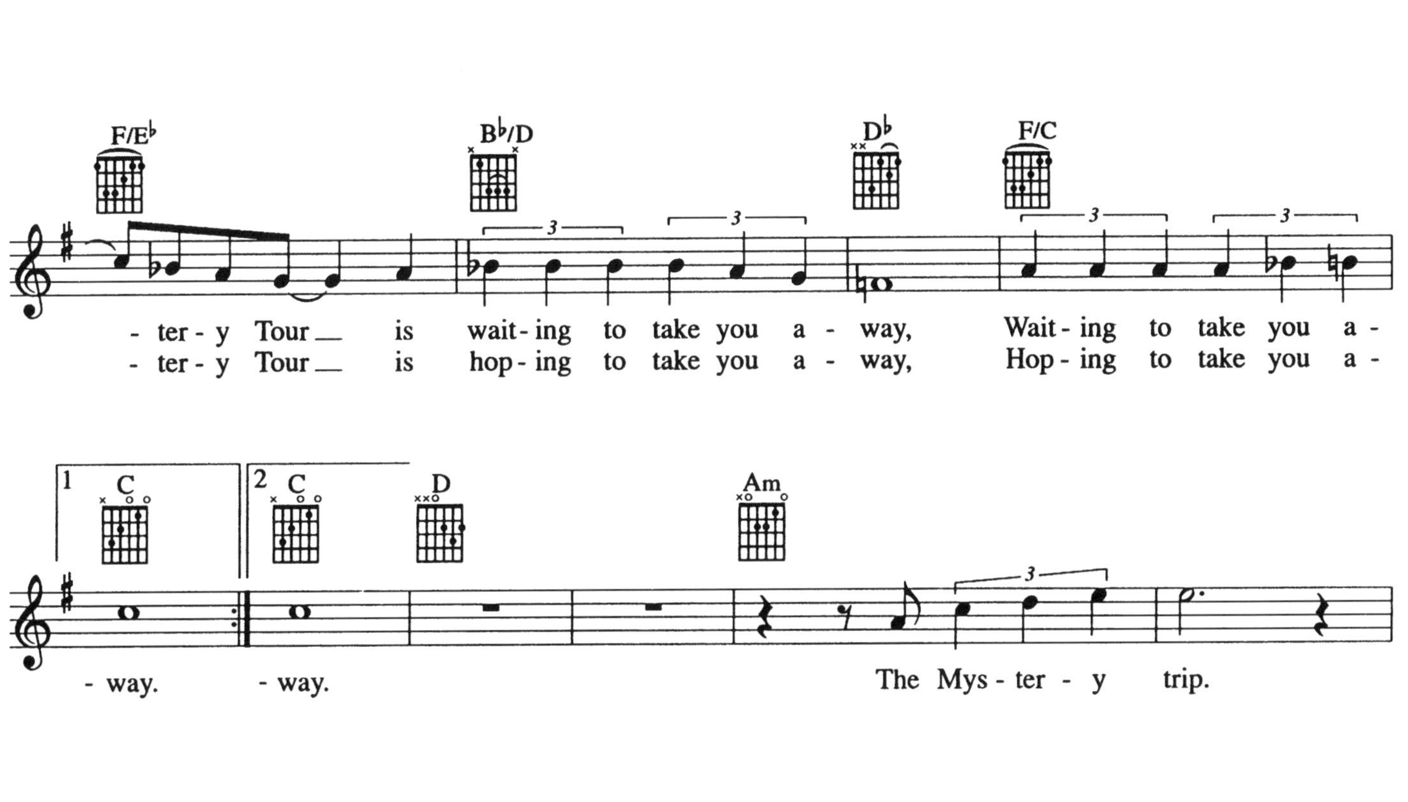
F/E♭
B♭/D
D♭
F/C
- ter - y Tour __ is wait - ing to take you a - way, Wait - ing to take you a -
- ter - y Tour __ is hop - ing to take you a - way, Hop - ing to take you a -

1 C
2 C
D
Am
- way. - way. The Mys - ter - y trip.

D
Am
C
D
D.S. al Coda
The Mys - ter - y trip.

Coda
C
F
F/E♭
- ter - y Tour. __ The Mag - i - cal Mys - ter - y Tour is
- ter - y Tour. __
B♭/D
D♭
F/C
com - ing / dy - ing to take you a - way. __ Com - ing / Dy - ing to

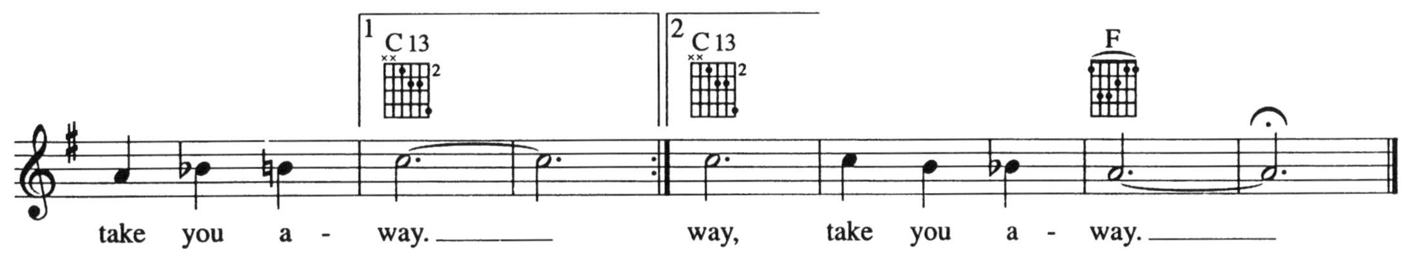
1 C13
2 C13
F
take you a - way. __ way, take you a - way. __

Sgt. Pepper's Lonely Hearts Club Band.

Words & Music by John Lennon & Paul McCartney.

Moderately slow, with a strong beat
G
A7
1. It was twen - ty years a - go to - day that Ser - geant
(2) real - ly want to stop the show but I
C
G
A7
Pep - per taught the band to play. They've been go - ing in and out of style, But they're
thought you might like to know That the sing - er's going to sing a song, And he
C
G
A7
guar - an - teed to raise a smile. So may I in - tro - duce you to the
wants you all to sing a - long. So let me in - tro - duce you to the
C
G
C
act you've known for all these years;
one and on - ly Bil - ly Shears.
Ser - geant Pep - per's Lone - ly Hearts Club
G
C7
F
C
D7
Band.
G
B♭
F
C
G
We're Ser - geant Pep - per's Lone - ly Hearts Club Band.
We
We

C G G B♭ F
hope you will en - joy the show.
hope you have en - joyed the show.
Ser - geant Pep - per's Lone - ly Hearts
Ser - geant Pep - per's Lone - ly Hearts
C G A7 D7
Club Band, Sit back and let the eve - ning go.
Club Band, We're sor - ry, but it's time to go.
C G A7
Ser - geant Pep - per's Lone - ly, Ser - geant Pep - per's Lone - ly, Ser -
C C/D G 1 C
- geant Pep - per's Lone - ly Hearts Club Band. It's won - der - ful to be here, It's
F7 C
cer - tain - ly a thrill, you're such a love - ly au - di - ence, we'd
D D7
like to take you home with us, we'd love to take you home. 2. I don't

2
G
B♭
F
C
G
Ser - geant Pep - per's Lone - ly Hearts Club Band. We'd

C
G
B♭
F
like to thank you once a - gain. Ser - geant Pep - per's one and on - ly

C
G
A7
D7
Lone - ly Hearts Club Band; It's get - ting ver - y near the end.

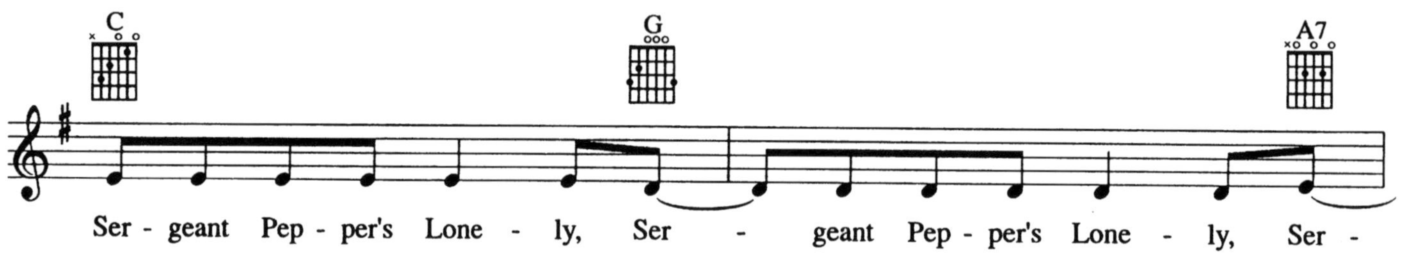
C
G
A7
Ser - geant Pep - per's Lone - ly, Ser - geant Pep - per's Lone - ly, Ser -

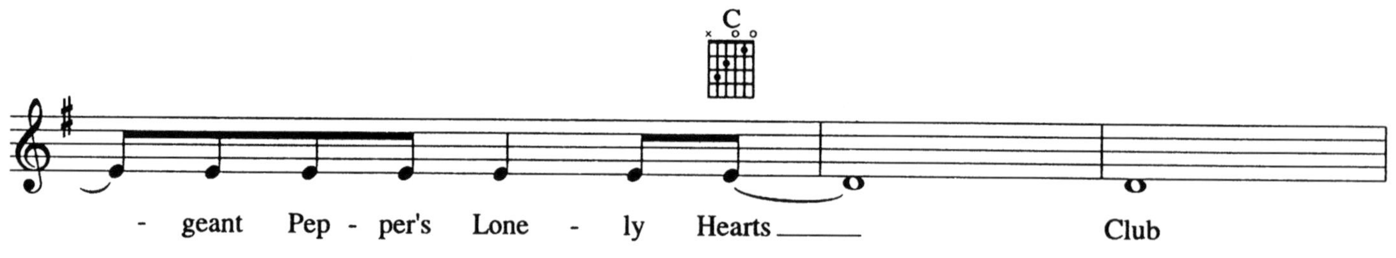
C
- geant Pep - per's Lone - ly Hearts Club

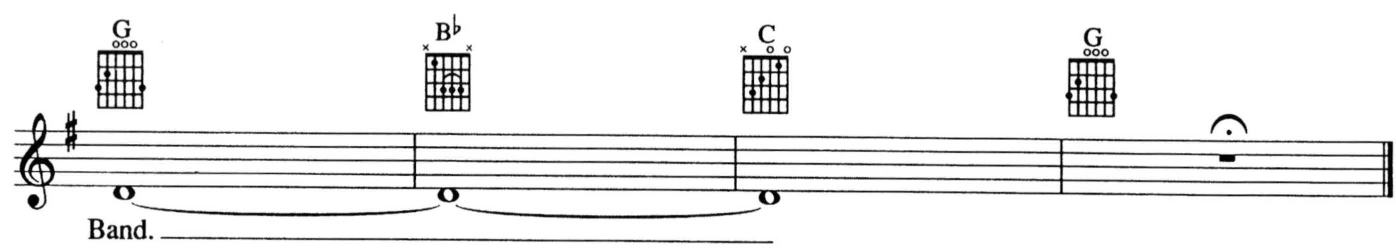
G
B♭
C
G
Band.

She's Leaving Home.

WORDS & MUSIC BY JOHN LENNON & PAUL McCARTNEY.

Moderately
E♭
B♭m
Fm7
A♭/C
Cm7
1. Wedn's - day morn - ing at five o' - clock as the day be - gins,
2. Fa - ther snores as his wife gets in - to her dres - sing gown,

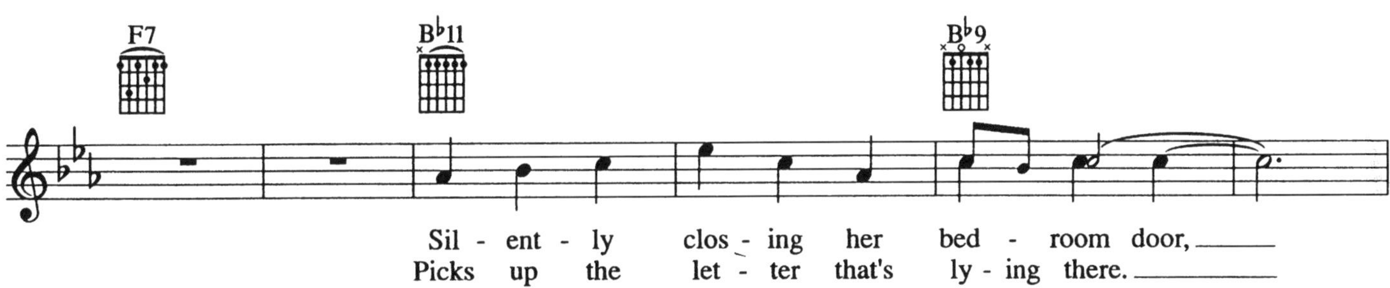
F7
B♭11
B♭9
Sil - ent - ly clos - ing her bed - room door,
Picks up the let - ter that's ly - ing there.

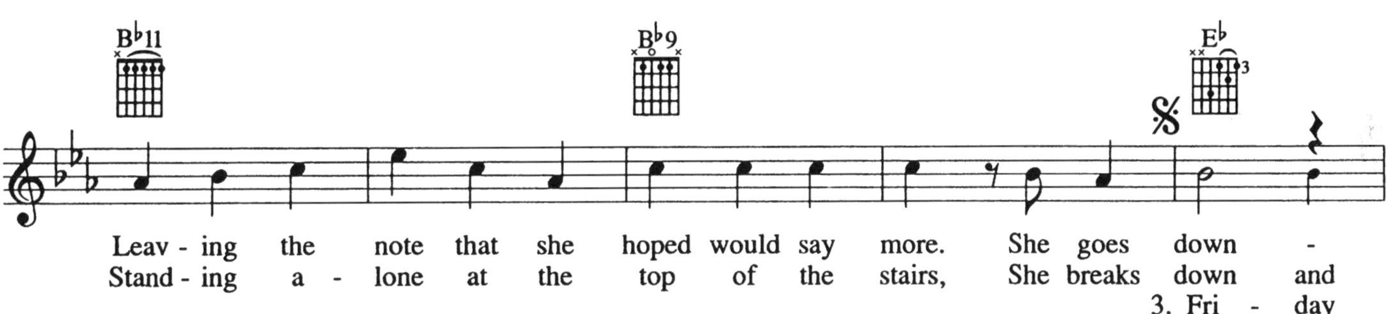
B♭11
B♭9
E♭
Leav - ing the note that she hoped would say more. She goes down -
Stand - ing a - lone at the top of the stairs, She breaks down and
3. Fri - day

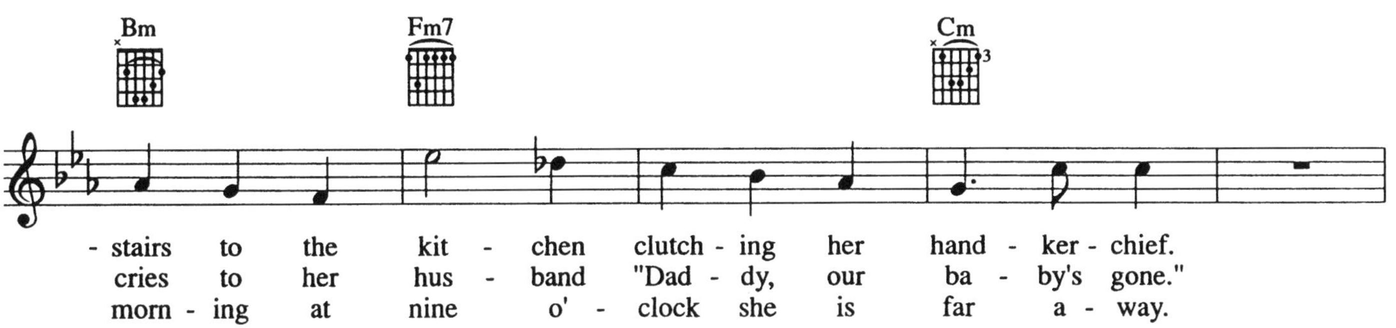
Bm
Fm7
Cm
- stairs to the kit - chen clutch - ing her hand - ker - chief.
cries to her hus - band "Dad - dy, our ba - by's gone."
morn - ing at nine o' - clock she is far a - way.

F7
B♭11
B♭9
Qui - et - ly turn - ing the back - door key,
Why would she treat us so thought - less - ly
Wait - ing to keep the ap - point - ment she made.

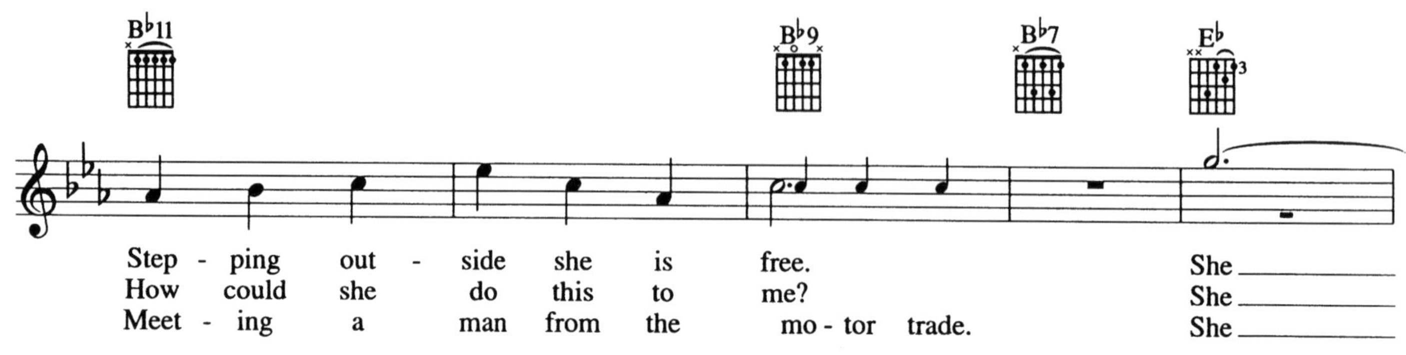
B♭11
B♭9
B♭7
E♭
Step - ping out - side she is free. She
How could she do this to me? She
Meet - ing a man from the mo - tor trade. She

(We gave her most of our lives) is leav - ing
(We nev - er thought of our - selves) is leav - ing
(What did we do that was wrong?) is hav - ing

(Sac - ri - ficed most of our lives) Home
(Nev - er a thought for our - selves) Home
(We did - n't know it was wrong.) Fun

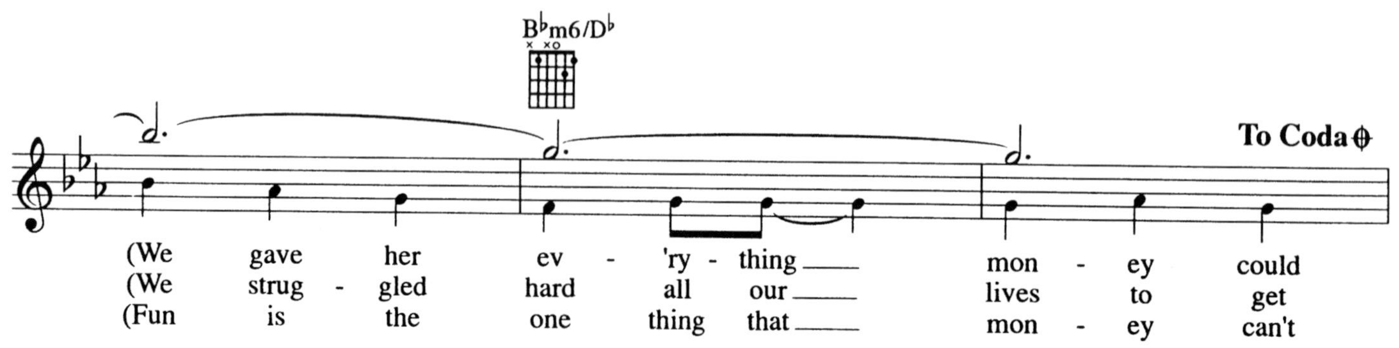
B♭m6/D♭
To Coda
(We gave her ev - 'ry - thing mon - ey could
(We strug - gled hard all our lives to get
(Fun is the one thing that mon - ey can't

Cm
F7
She's leav - ing home af - ter liv - ing a - lone for so
buy.
(Bye
by.
(Bye

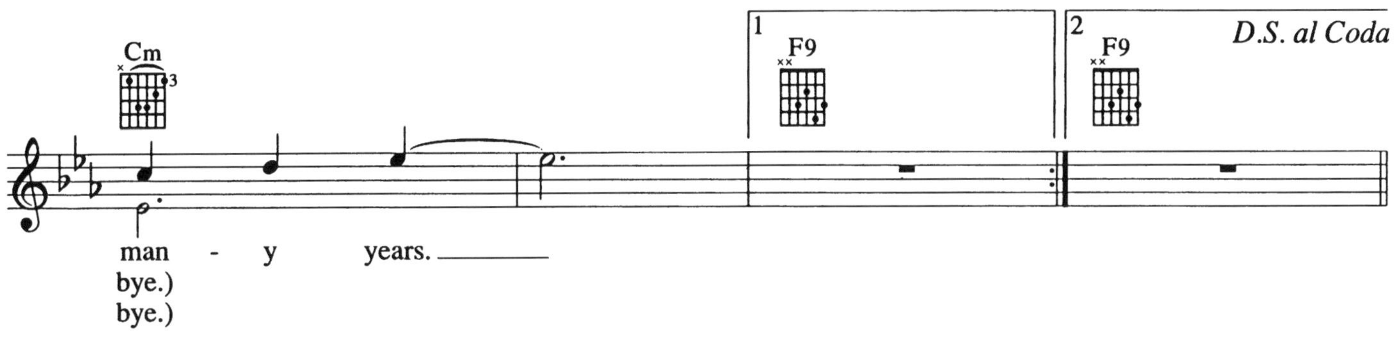
Cm
1
F9
2
F9
D.S. al Coda
man - y years.
bye.)
bye.)

Coda

Cm
F7
Some - thing in - side that was al - ways de - nied for so
buy.
Bye

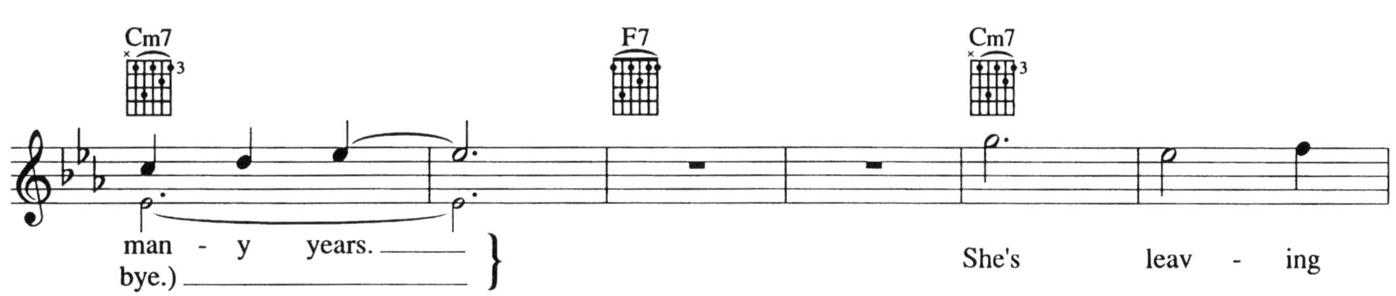
Cm7
F7
Cm7
man - y years.
bye.)
She's leav - ing

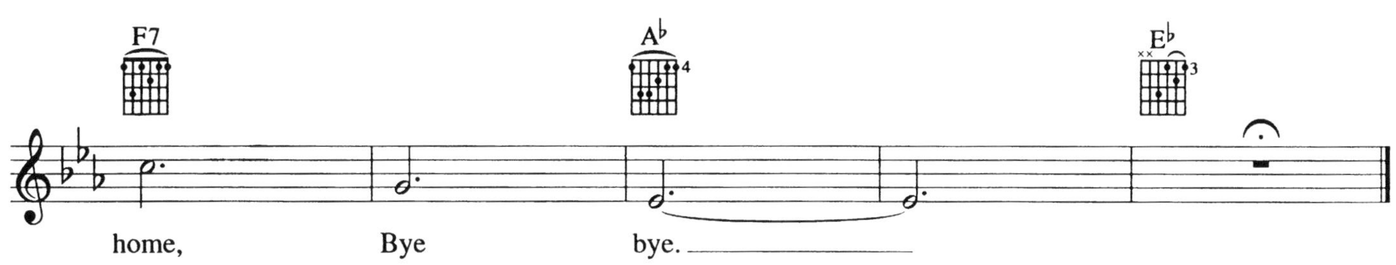
F7
A♭
E♭
home, Bye bye.

Strawberry Fields Forever.

Words & Music by John Lennon & Paul McCartney.

Slowly
G
Dm7
Let me take you down 'cause I'm go - in' to Straw - ber - ry
Dm
E7♭9
E7
Fields, Noth - ing is real, and
C
D
E7
Cmaj7
noth - ing to get hung a - bout; Straw - ber - ry Fields for -
G
D
Dmaj7
D7
Am7
C°
- ev - er.
1. Liv - ing is ea - sy with eyes closed,
2. No - one I think is in my tree,
3. Al - ways know some - times, think it's me;
Em
Em7/D
C
Mis - un - der - stand - ing all you see.
I mean it must be high or low.
But you know I know when it's a dream.
D7
G
Em
It's get - ting hard to be some - one, But it all works out,
That is, you know you can't tune in, But it's all right,
I think I know of thee, ah yes, But it's all wrong,

C
D
C
G
It does - n't mat - ter much to me.
That is, I think it's not too bad.
That is I think I dis - a - gree.
Let me take you down
Dm7
Dm
E7♭9
'cause I'm go - ing to Straw - ber - ry Fields,
Noth - ing is
E7
C
D
E7
real, and noth - ing to get hung a - bout;
1.2
Cmaj7
G
Straw - ber - ry Fields for - ev - er.
3
Cmaj7
G
Em7
Cmaj7
Straw - ber - ry Fields for - ev - er,
Straw - ber - ry Fields for -
G
Cmaj7
D
C
G
- ev - er,
Straw - ber - ry Fields for - ev - er.

The Fool On The Hill.

Words & Music by John Lennon & Paul McCartney.

Slowly
D6
Em/D
1. Day af - ter day A - lone on a hill, The
2. Well on the way Head in a cloud, The
D6
Em/D
man with the fool - ish grin is keep - ing per - fect - ly still; But
man of a thous - and voic - es talk - ing per - fect - ly loud; But
3
Em7
A
D6
Bm
no - bod - y wants to know him, They can see that he's just a fool, And
no - bod - y ev - er hears him, or the sound he ap - pears to make, And
Em7
A
Dm
B♭/D
Dm
he nev - er gives an ans - wer.
he nev - er seems to no - tice.
But the fool on the hill sees the sun
B♭/D
C
go - ing down, And the eyes in his head see the world

Dm
Dm7
D6
Em/D
spin - ning 'round.

D6
Em/D
Em7
A
No - bod - y seems to like him, They can
He nev - er lis - tens to them, He

D6
Bm
tell what he wants to do, And
knows that they're the fools,

Em7
A
Dm
B♭/D
Dm
he nev - er shows his feel - ings,
They don't like him,
But the fool on the hill sees the sun

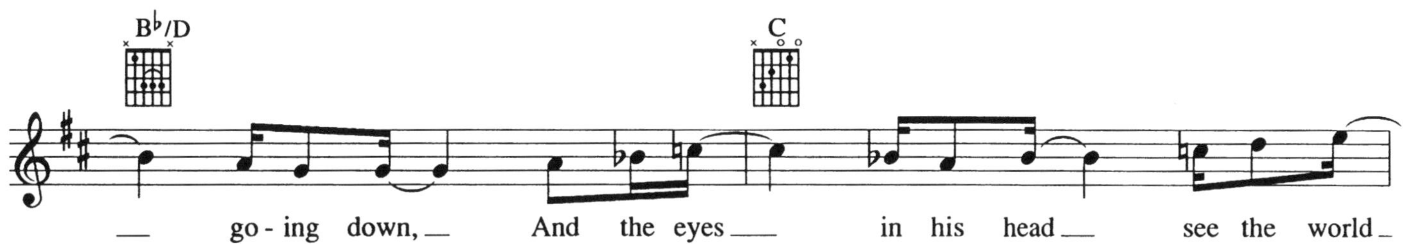
B♭/D
C
go - ing down, And the eyes in his head see the world

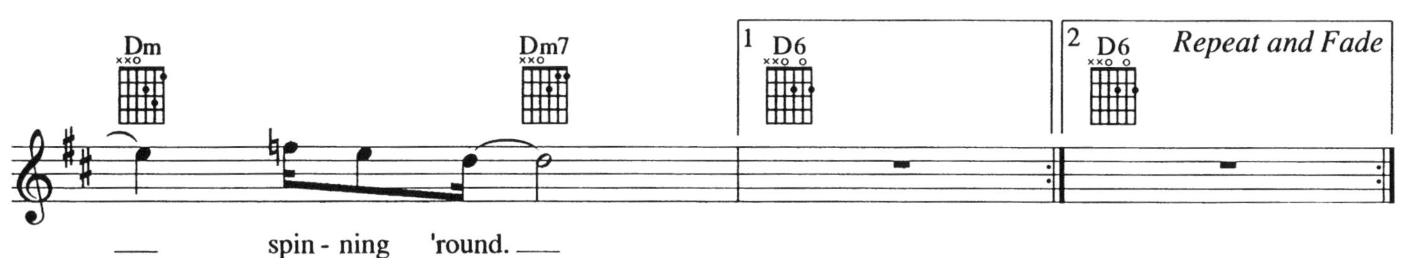
Dm
Dm7
1 D6
2 D6
Repeat and Fade
spin - ning 'round.

When I'm Sixty Four.

WORDS & MUSIC BY JOHN LENNON & PAUL McCARTNEY.

Steady 2 beat
C
When I get old - er, los - ing my hair many - y years from now;
G7
Will you still be send - ing me a val - en - tine,
Tacet
C
birth - day greet - ings, bot - tle of wine? If I'd been out till
C7
F
quar - ter to three would you lock the door?
A♭7♭5/G♭
C/G
A7
D9
G13
Will you still need me, will you still feed me when I'm six - ty
C
Am
G
Am
four? Oo You'll be

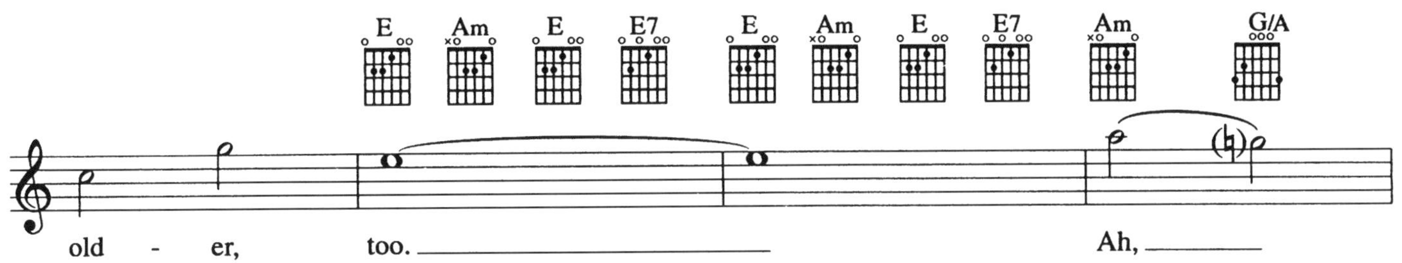
E
Am
E
E7
E
Am
E
E7
Am
G/A
old - er, too.
Ah,

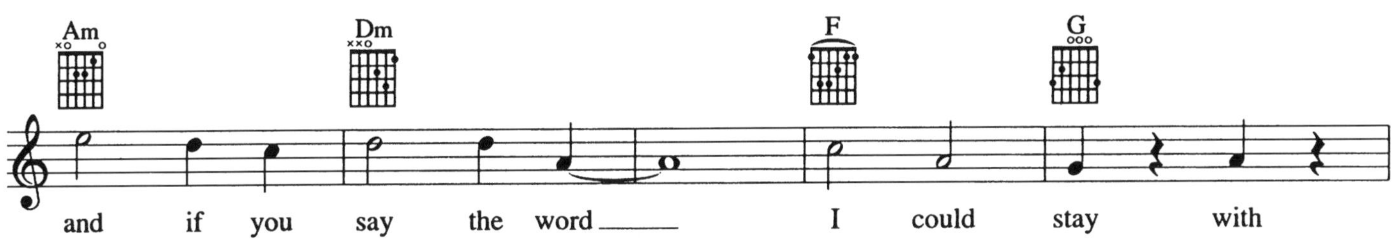
Am
Dm
F
G
and if you say the word
I could stay with

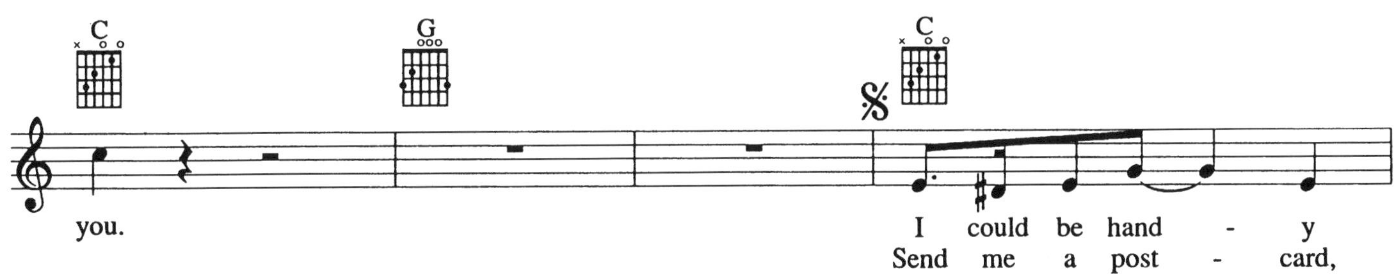
C
G
C
you.
I could be hand - y
Send me a post - card,

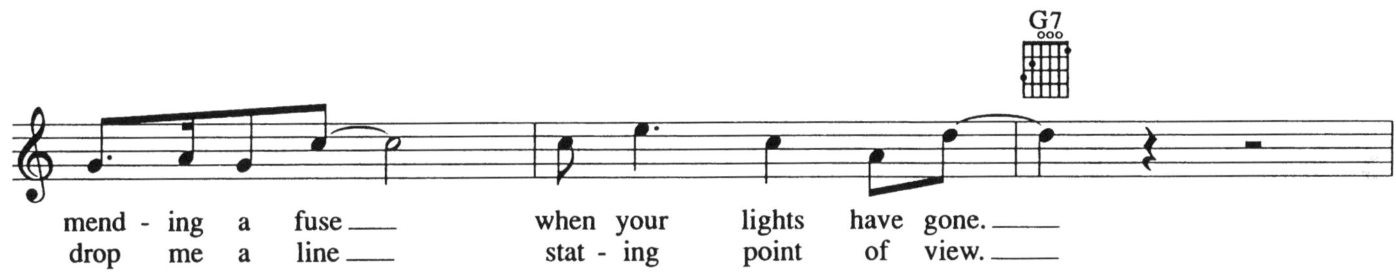
G7
mend - ing a fuse
when your lights have gone.
drop me a line
stat - ing point of view.

Tacet
You can knit a sweat - er by the fire side,
Sun - day morn - ings,
In - di - cate pre - cise - ly what you mean to say
yours sin - cere - ly

C
go for a ride.
Do - ing the gar - den,
wast - ing a - way.
Give me your an - swer,

C7 F
dig - ging the weeds; Who could ask for more?
fill in a form, mine for ev - er more.
A♭7♭5/G♭ C/G A7 D9 G13
To Coda
Will you still need me, will you still feed me, when I'm six - ty
Will you still need me, will you still feed me, when I'm six - ty
C Am
four? Ev - 'ry sum - mer we can rent a cot - tage in the Isle of Wight
G Am E Am E E7
if it's not too dear. We shall scrimp and save;
E Am E E7 Am G/A Am Dm
Grand - chil - dren on your knee;
F G C G
D.S. al Coda
Ve - ra, Chuck and Dave.
Coda
C F G11 G7 C
four?

With A Little Help From My Friends.

Words & Music by John Lennon & Paul McCartney.

Moderate swing feel (played as)
E♭
B♭/D
Fm
mf
1. What would you think if I sang out of tune? Would you stand up and walk out on me?
2. What do I do when my love is a - way, Does it wor - ry you to be a - lone?
3. Would you be - lieve in a love at first sight? Yes, I'm cer - tain that it hap - pens all the time.
B♭7
E♭
B♭
Lend me your ears and I'll sing you a song and I'll try not to sing out of key.
How do I feel by the end of the day, Are you sad be - cause you're on your own?
What do you see when you turn out the light? I can't tell you, but I know it's mine.
Fm
B♭7
E♭
D♭
A♭
Oh,
No,
Oh,
I get by with a lit - tle help from my friends.
E♭
D♭
A♭
Mm, I get high with a lit - tle help from my friends.

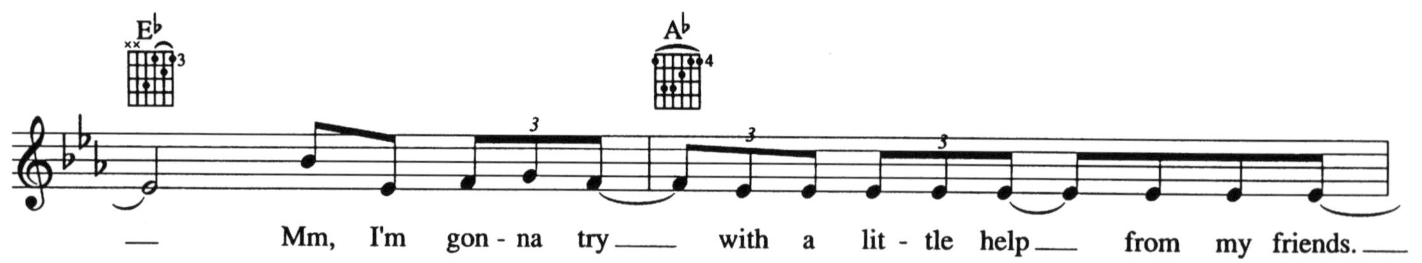
E♭
A♭
3
— Mm, I'm gon - na try___ with a lit - tle help___ from my friends.___

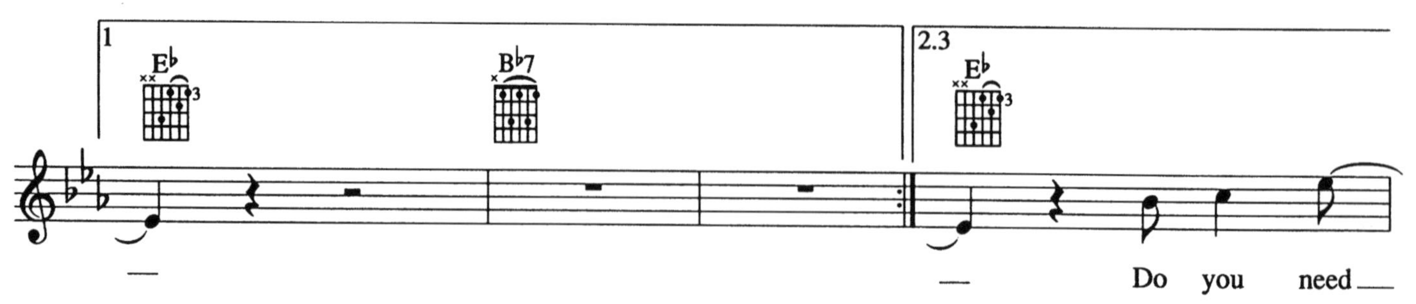
1
E♭
B♭7
2.3
E♭
— Do you need___

Cm
F7
E♭
D♭
— an - y - bod - y? I need some - bod - y to love.___

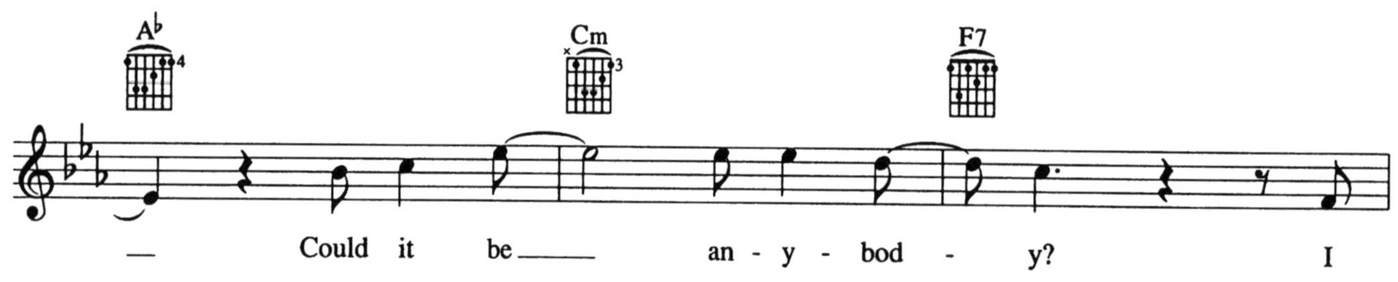
A♭
Cm
F7
— Could it be___ an - y - bod - y? I

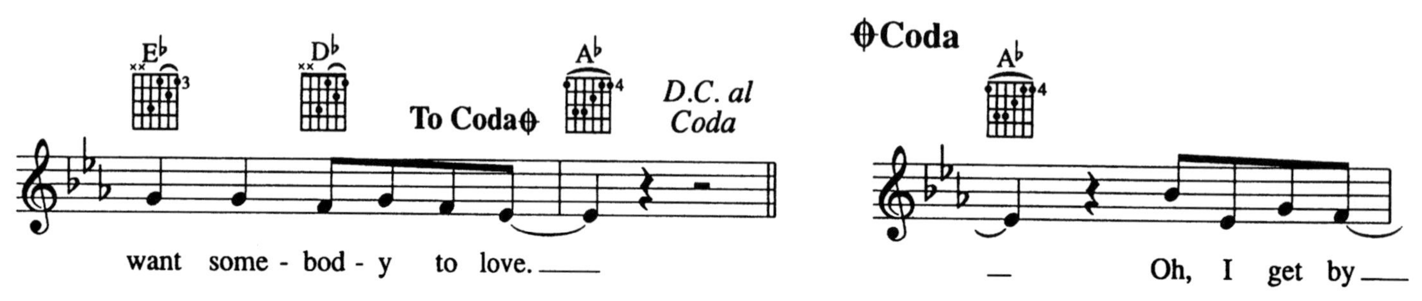
E♭
D♭
To Coda
A♭
D.C. al Coda
Coda
A♭
want some - bod - y to love.___
— Oh, I get by___

D♭
A♭
E♭
with a lit - tle help from my friends.
Mm, I'm gon - na try

D♭
A♭
E♭
with a lit - tle help from my friends.
Oh, I get high

A♭
E♭
with a lit - tle help from my friends.
Yes, I get by

D♭
A♭
with a lit - tle help from my friends,
with a lit - tle help from my friends.

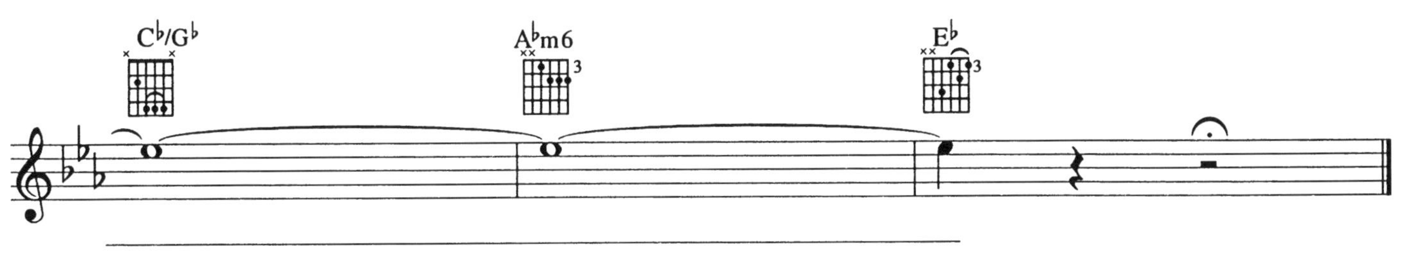
C♭/G♭
A♭m6
E♭

Within You Without You.

Words & Music by George Harrison.

Moderately
C
1. We were talk - ing a - bout the space be -
(2) talk - ing a - bout the love we
(3) talk - ing a - bout the love that's
- tween us all, And the peo - ple who hide them -
all could share, When we find it to try our
gone so cold, And the peo - ple who gain the
To Coda
1
- selves be - hind a wall of il - lu - sion; nev - er
best to hold it there with our
world and lose their
glimpse the truth, then it's far too late, and they pass a -
- way.
2. We were
2
love, with our
love we could save the world. If they on - ly
knew.

Slightly faster
Try to re - a - lize it's all with - in your - self, no -
And to see you're real - ly on - ly ver - y small, and
1
- one else can make you change.
2
life flows on

D.S. al Coda
with - in you and with - out you. 3. We were

Coda

soul. They don't know, They can't see. Are you

Slightly faster
one of them? When you've seen be - yond your - self, then
And the time will come when you see
you may find peace of mind is wait - ing there.
we're all one, and
1
2
life flows on with - in you and with - out you.

Your Mother Should Know.

Words & Music by John Lennon & Paul McCartney.

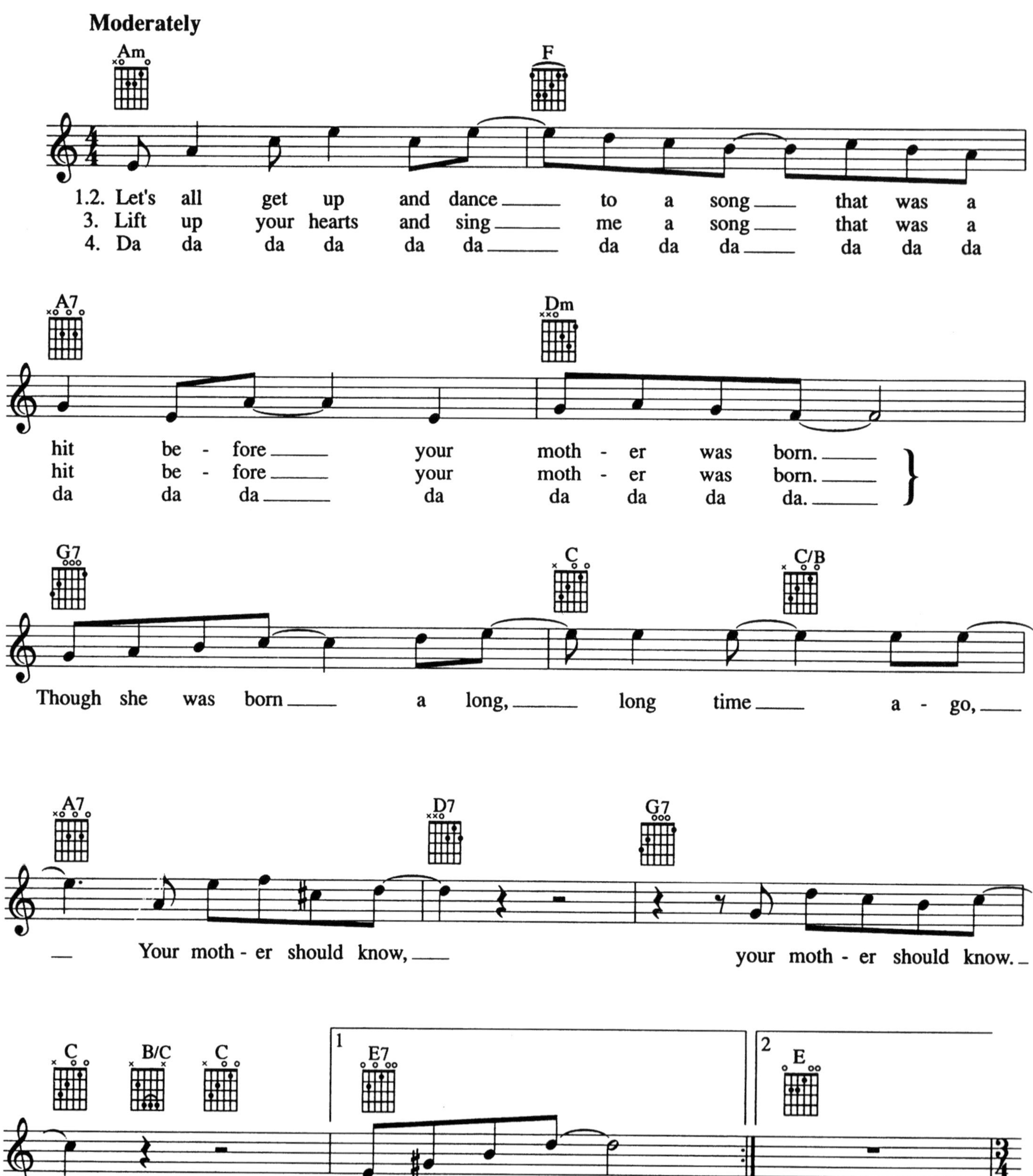
Moderately
Am
F
1.2. Let's all get up and dance to a song that was a
3. Lift up your hearts and sing me a song that was a
4. Da da da da da da da da da da da da
A7
Dm
hit be - fore your moth - er was born.
hit be - fore your moth - er was born.
da da da da da da da da.
G7
C
C/B
Though she was born a long, long time a - go,
A7
D7
G7
Your moth - er should know, your moth - er should know.
C
B/C
C
1
E7
2
E
Sing it a - gain;

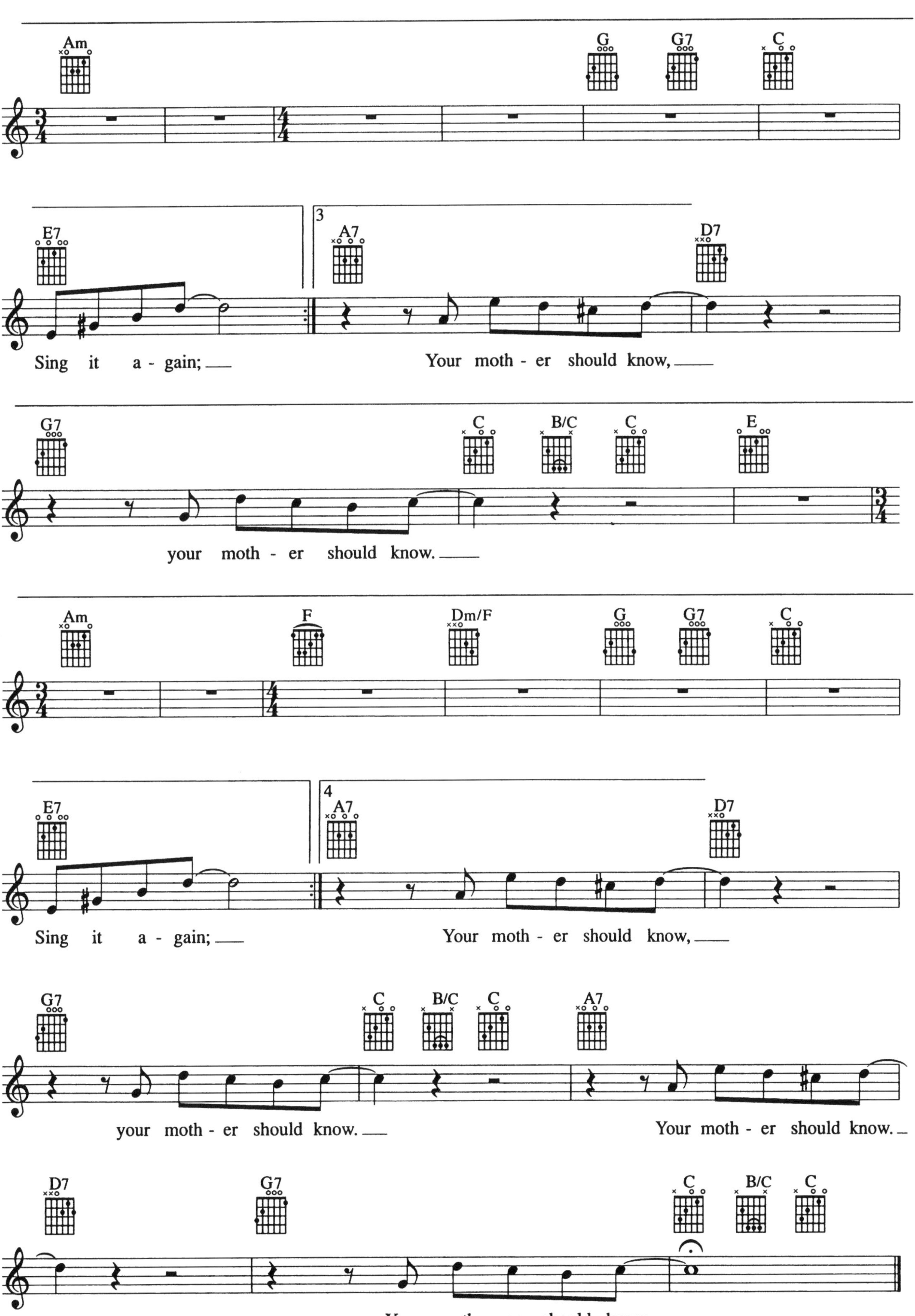
Am
G
G7
C
E7
3
A7
D7
Sing it a - gain;
Your moth - er should know,
G7
C
B/C
C
E
your moth - er should know.
Am
F
Dm/F
G
G7
C
E7
4
A7
D7
Sing it a - gain;
Your moth - er should know,
G7
C
B/C
C
A7
your moth - er should know.
Your moth - er should know.
D7
G7
C
B/C
C
Your moth - er should know

Across The Universe.

Words & Music by John Lennon & Paul McCartney.

Slowly
D♭ Fm
Words are fly - ing out __ like end - less rain __ in - to a pa - per cup, __ They
E♭m7 A♭ A♭7/E♭
slith - er while, __ they pass, they slip a - way ___ a - cross the u - ni - verse. __
D♭ Fm
Pools of sor - row, waves of joy are drift - ing through my o - pened mind, __ Pos -
E♭m7 G♭m D♭
- sess - ing and ca - ress - ing me. __ Jai __ Gu - ru ___ De __
E♭m7 A♭7
— va. __ Om. ___ Noth - ing's gon - na change my world, ___
G♭/D♭ D♭ A♭7
Noth - ing's gon - na change my world. __ Noth - ing's gon - na change my world, __

G♭/D♭
D♭
To Coda
Noth - ing's gon - na change my world.

Fm
Im - ag - es of bro - ken light which dance be - fore me like a mil - lion eyes

E♭m7
A♭
A♭7
They call me on and on a - cross the u - ni - verse,

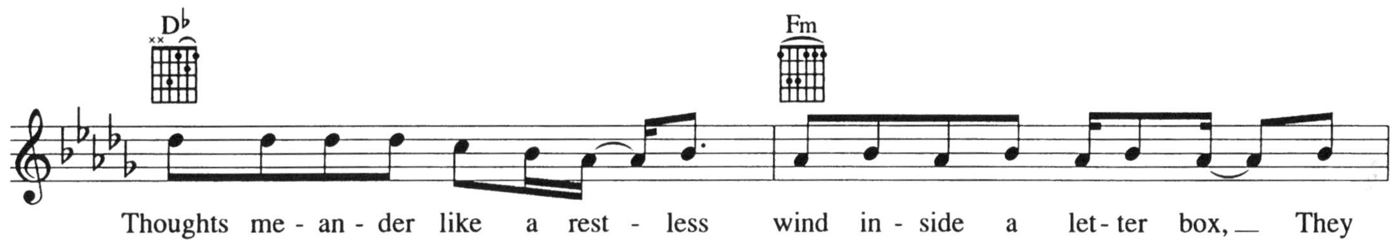
D♭
Fm
Thoughts me - an - der like a rest - less wind in - side a let - ter box, They

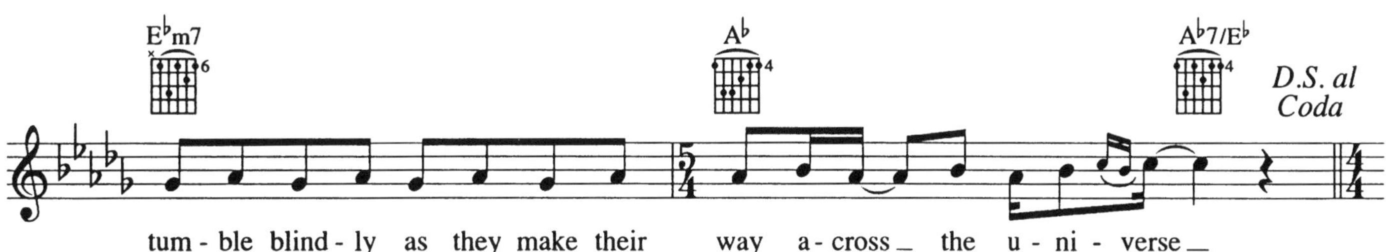
E♭m7
A♭
A♭7/E♭
D.S. al Coda
tum - ble blind - ly as they make their way a - cross the u - ni - verse

Coda
D♭
Fm
Sounds of laugh - ter, shades of earth are ring - ing through my o - pened ears, In -

E♭m7
G♭m
D♭
- cit - ing and in - vit - ing me.
Lim - it - less, un - dy - ing love, which
Fm
E♭m7
shines a - round me like a mil - lion suns, And calls me on and on a - cross
A♭
A♭7
D♭
the u - ni - verse.
Jai Gu - ru De
E♭m7
A♭7
va. Om
Noth - ing's gon - na change my world,
G♭/D♭
D♭
Noth - ing's gon - na change my world.
A♭7
G♭/D♭
Noth - ing's gon - na change my world,
Noth - ing's gon - na change my world.
D♭
Repeat & Fade
Jai Gu - ru De va.

All Together Now.

Words & Music by John Lennon & Paul McCartney.

Moderately
G
D7
1. One, two, three, four, can I have a lit - tle more?
2. A, B, C, D, can I bring my friend to tea?
G
D7
G
1
Five, six, sev - en, eight, nine, ten, I love you.
E, F, G, H, I, J, I love you.
2
C
G
(Bom, bom, bom, Bom - pa bom.) Sail the ship. (Bom - pa bom)
C
D
Chop the tree. (Bom - pa bom) Skip the rope. (Bom - pa bom)
D7
To Coda
G
Look at me! (all to - geth - er now) All to - geth - er

now, (All to - geth - er now) All to - geth - er now, (All to - geth - er now)

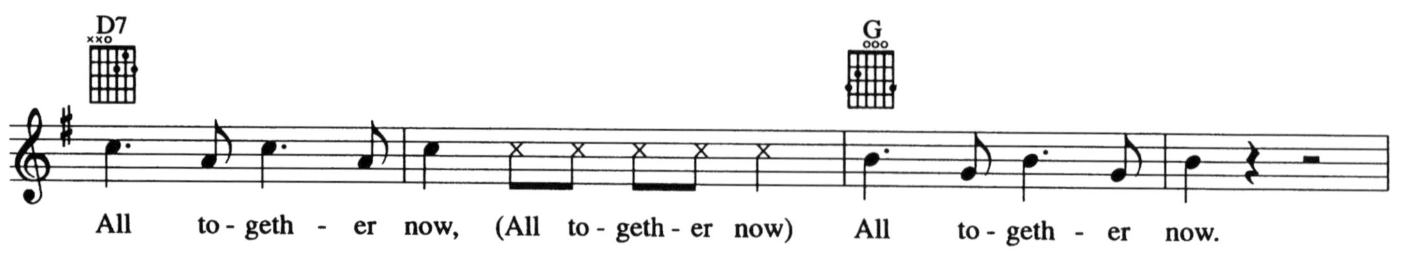
D7
G
All to - geth - er now, (All to - geth - er now) All to - geth - er now.

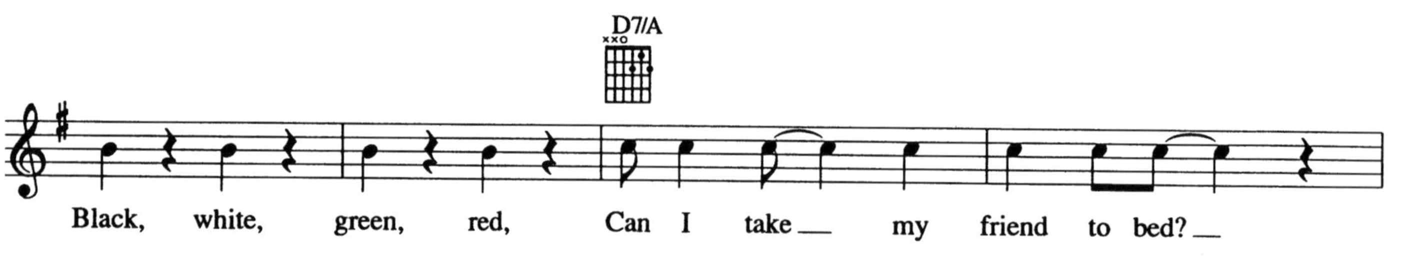
D7/A
Black, white, green, red, Can I take my friend to bed?

G
D7
G
Pink, brown, yel - low, or - ange and blue, I love you. (all to - geth - er now)

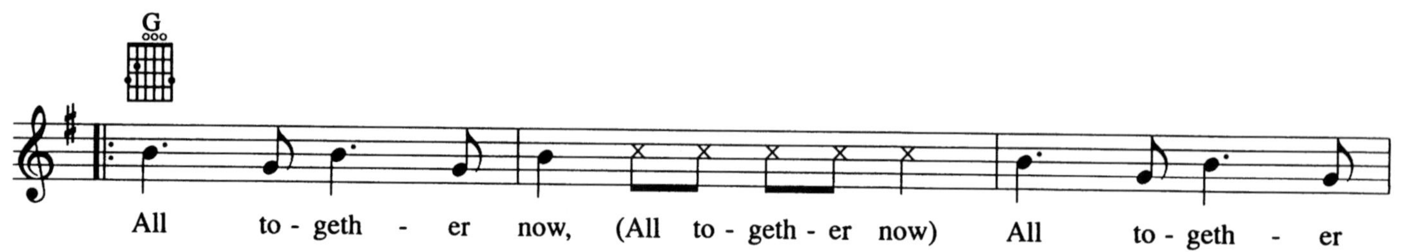
G
All to - geth - er now, (All to - geth - er now) All to - geth - er

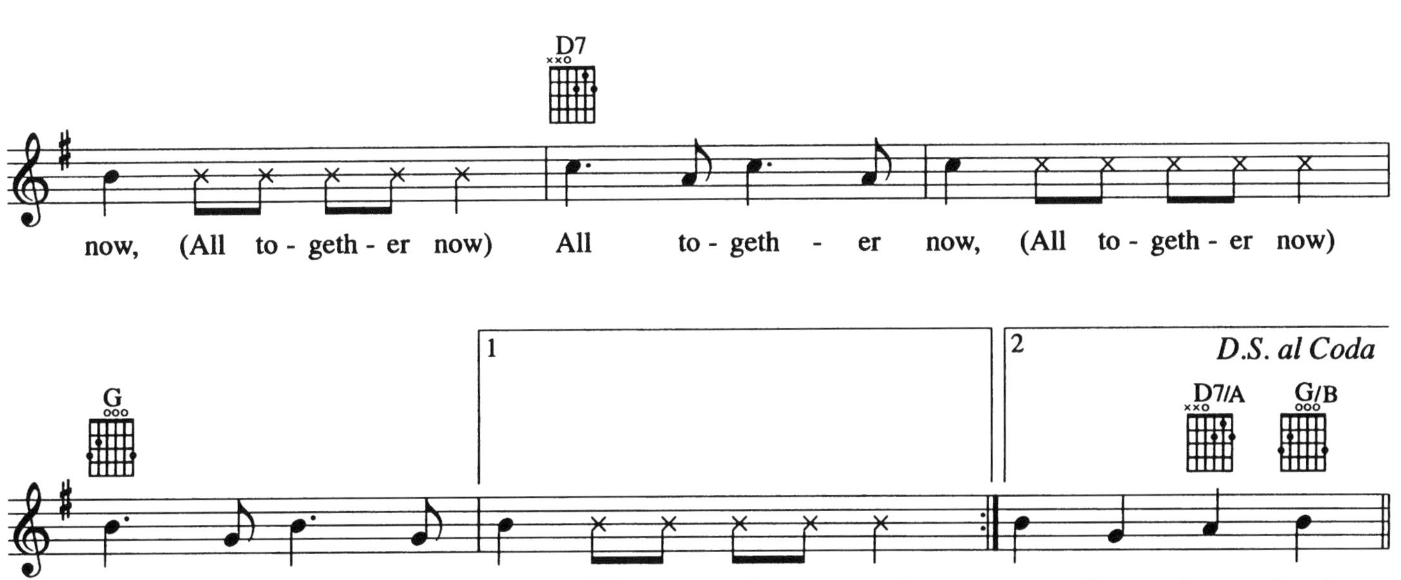
D7
now, (All to - geth - er now) All to - geth - er now, (All to - geth - er now)
1
2
D.S. al Coda
G
D7/A
G/B
All to - geth - er now, (All to - geth - er now) now. (bom, bom, bom)

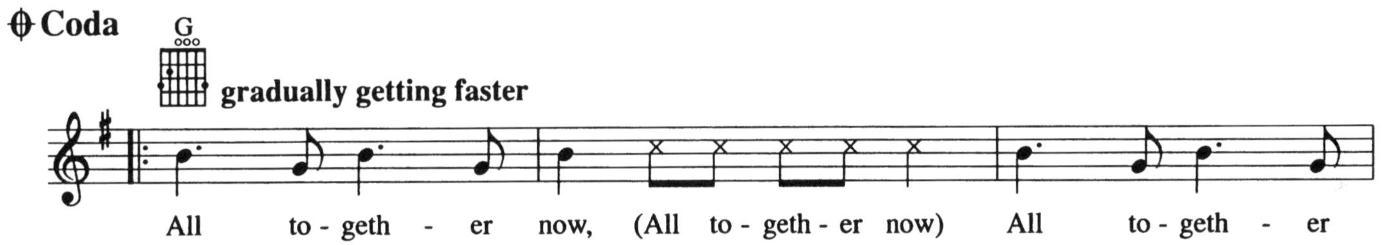
Coda
G
gradually getting faster
All to - geth - er now, (All to - geth - er now) All to - geth - er

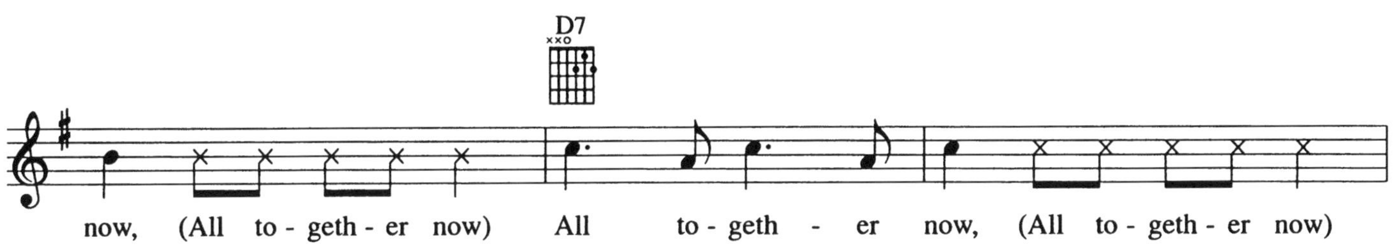
D7
now, (All to - geth - er now) All to - geth - er now, (All to - geth - er now)

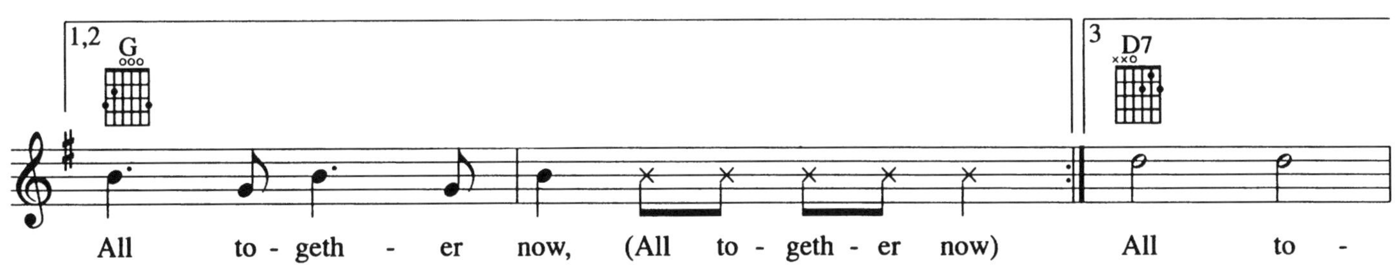
1,2
G
3
D7
All to - geth - er now, (All to - geth - er now) All to -

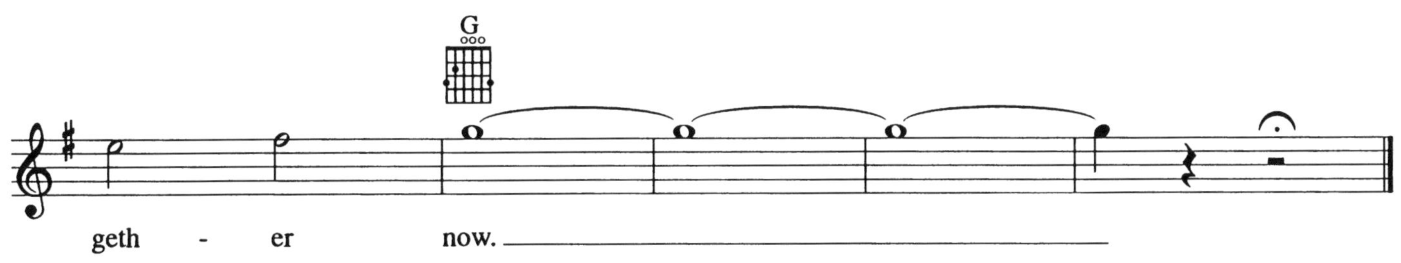
G
geth - er now.

Back In The USSR.

WORDS & MUSIC BY JOHN LENNON & PAUL McCARTNEY.

Rock Tempo
A D C D A D C D A C D
1. Flew in from Mi - a - mi Beach, B. O. A. C; Did - n't get to bed last night. On the way the pa - per bag was on my knee, Man, I had a dread - ful flight.
2. Been a - way so long I hard - ly knew the place, Gee it's good to get back home. Leave it 'till to - mor - row to un - pack my case, Hon - ey, dis - con - nect the phone.
3. Show me 'round your snow - peaked moun - tains way down south, Take me to your dad - dy's farm. Let me hear your bal - a - lai - kas ring - ing out, Come and keep your com - rade warm.
I'm back in the U. S. S. R. You don't know how luck - y you are, boy,
To Coda
1
D
Tacet
A
Back in the U. S. S. R.

D
E♭
E
2
D/E
Em7
Back in the U. S; back in the U. S;
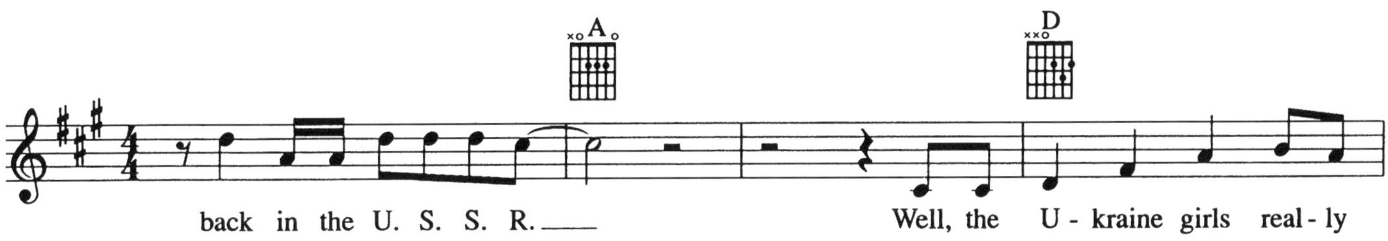
A
D
back in the U. S. S. R.
Well, the U - kraine girls real - ly
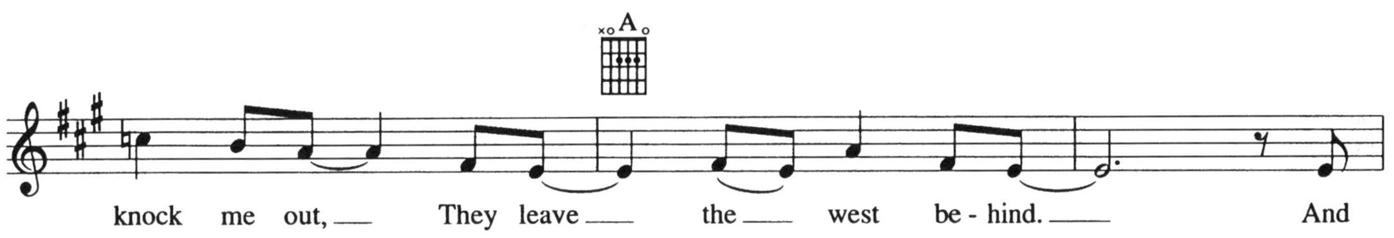
A
knock me out, They leave the west be - hind. And
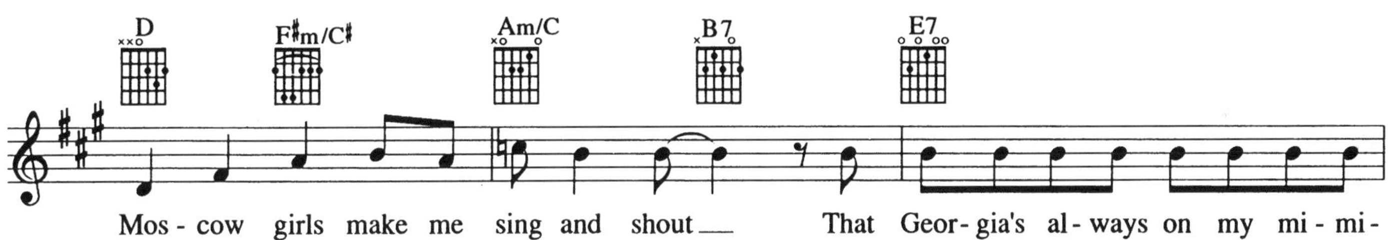
D
F♯m/C♯
Am/C
B7
E7
Mos - cow girls make me sing and shout That Geor - gia's al - ways on my mi - mi -

D.C. al Coda
D7
A
B7
E7
- mi - mi - mi - mi - mi - mi - mind.

Coda
D
Tacet
A
D
E♭
E
A
Back in the U. S. S. R.

Birthday.

Words & Music by John Lennon & Paul McCartney.

Moderately Bright

B♭7
You say it's your birth - day,
It's

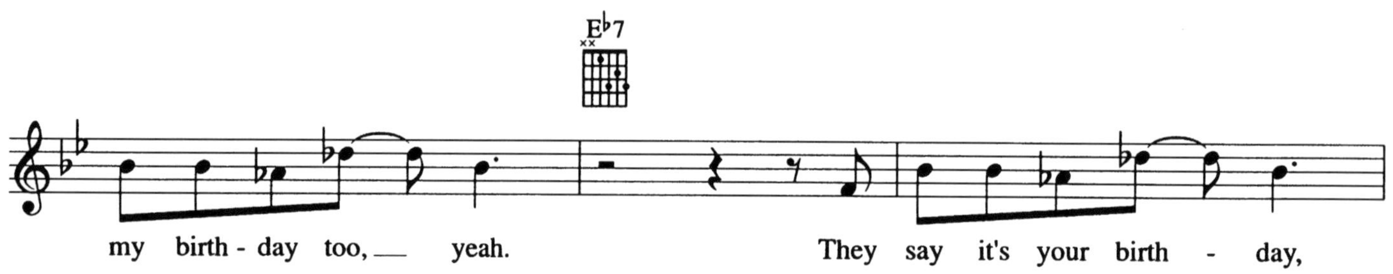
E♭7
my birth - day too, __ yeah.
They say it's your birth - day,

B♭7
F7
We're gon - na have a good time.
I'm

B♭7
To Coda
glad it's your birth - day,
Hap - py birth - day to __ you.

F
Yes, we're go - in' to a par - ty, par - ty,

Yes, we're go - in' to a par - ty, par - ty,
Yes, we're go - in' to a

D♭
A♭
par - ty, par - ty.
I would like you to dance,

D♭
A♭
D♭
(Birth - day) Take a cha - cha - cha - chance,
(Birth - day) I would

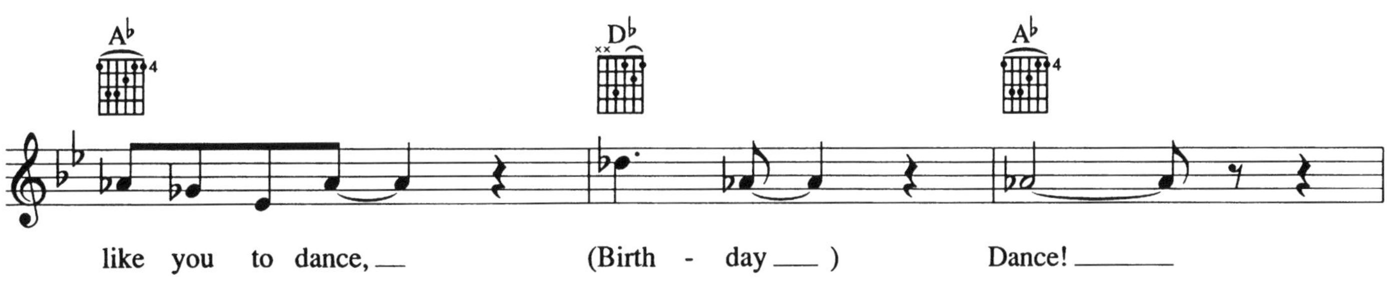
A♭
D♭
A♭
like you to dance,
(Birth - day)
Dance!

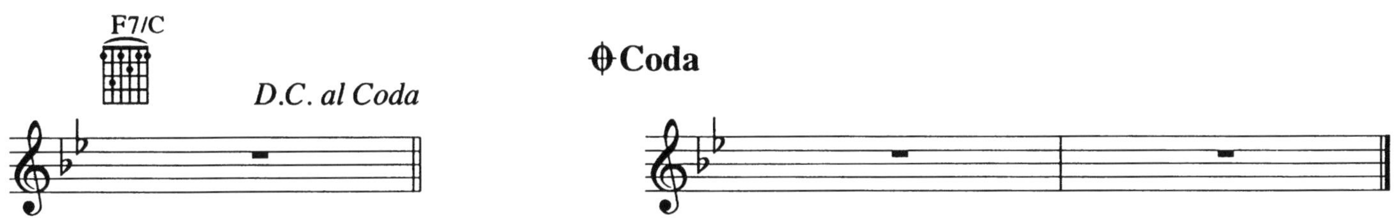
F7/C
D.C. al Coda
Coda

Blackbird.

WORDS & MUSIC BY JOHN LENNON & PAUL MCCARTNEY.

Slowly

G Am7 G/B G

1.3. Black - bird sing - ing in the dead of night
2. Black - bird sing - ing in the dead of night

C A7/C♯ D7 B7/D♯ Em Cm/E♭

Take these bro - ken wings and learn to fly;
Take these sunk - en eyes and learn to see;

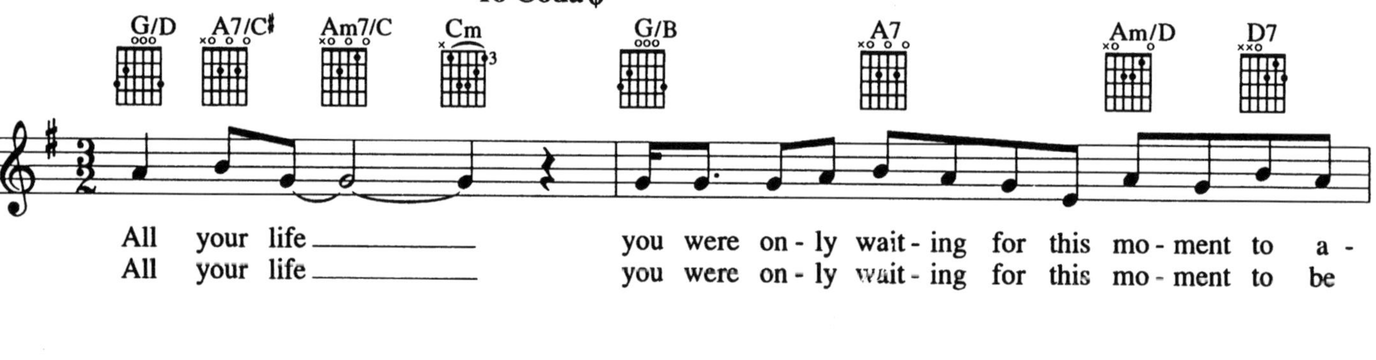
To Coda ⊕
G/D A7/C♯ Am7/C Cm G/B A7 Am/D D7
All your life
All your life
you were on - ly wait - ing for this mo - ment to a -
you were on - ly wait - ing for this mo - ment to be

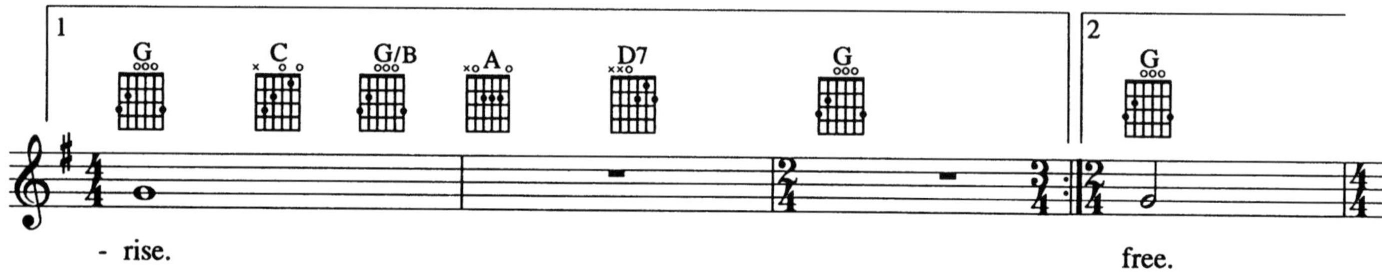
1
G C G/B A D7 G
- rise.
2
G
free.

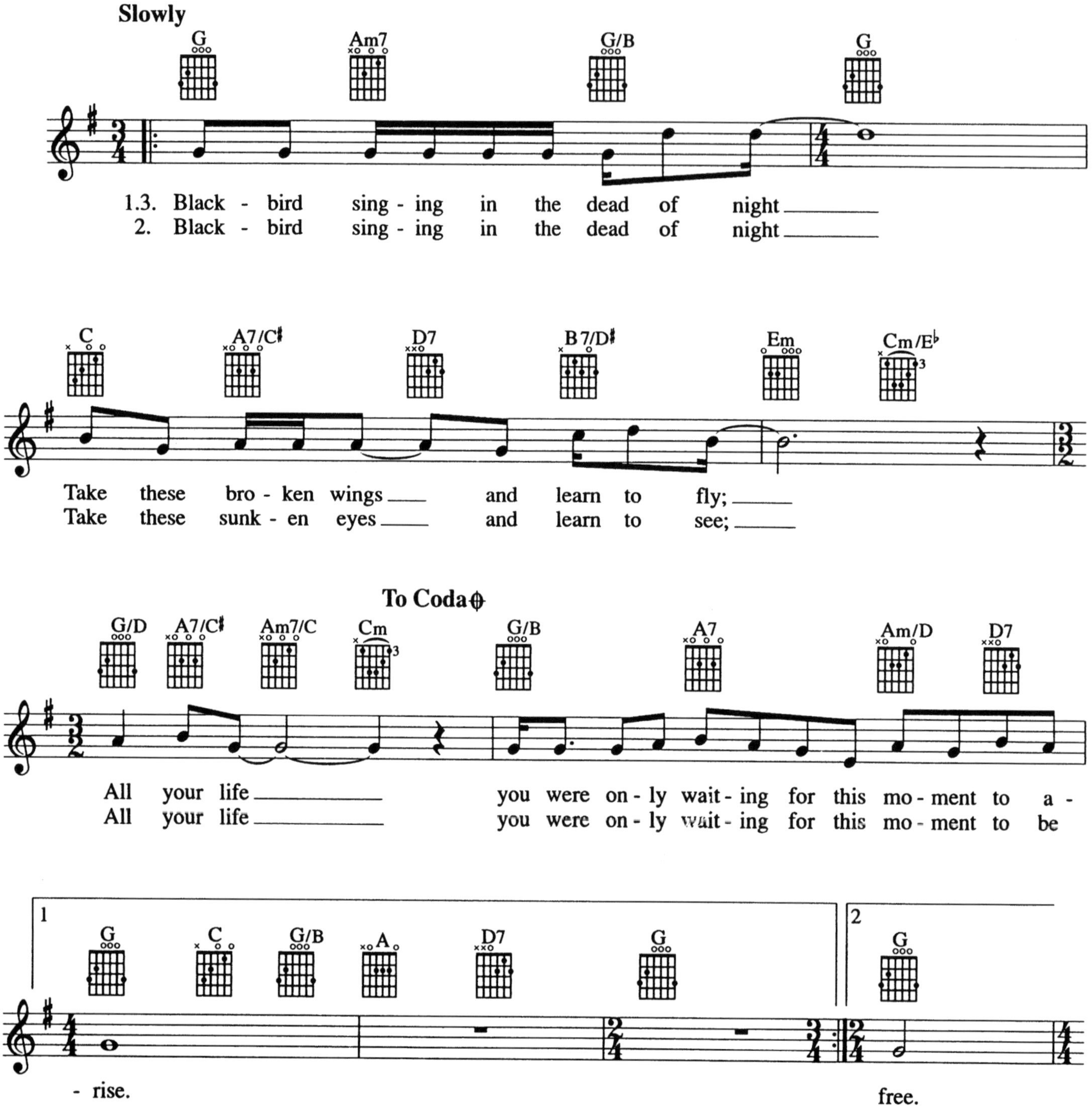

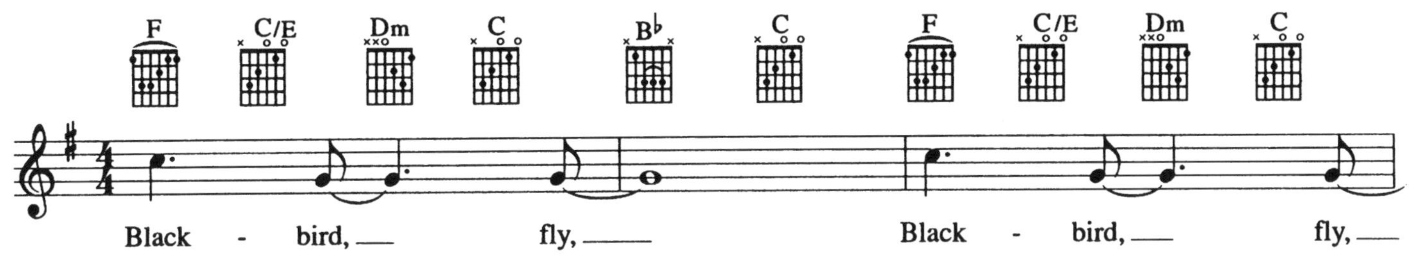
F C/E Dm C Bb C F C/E Dm C
Black - bird, fly, Black - bird, fly,

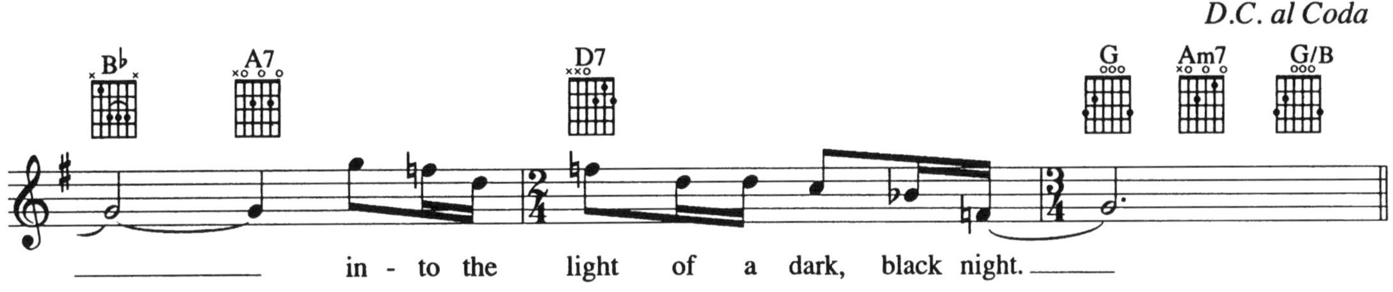
D.C. al Coda
Bb A7 D7 G Am7 G/B
in - to the light of a dark, black night.

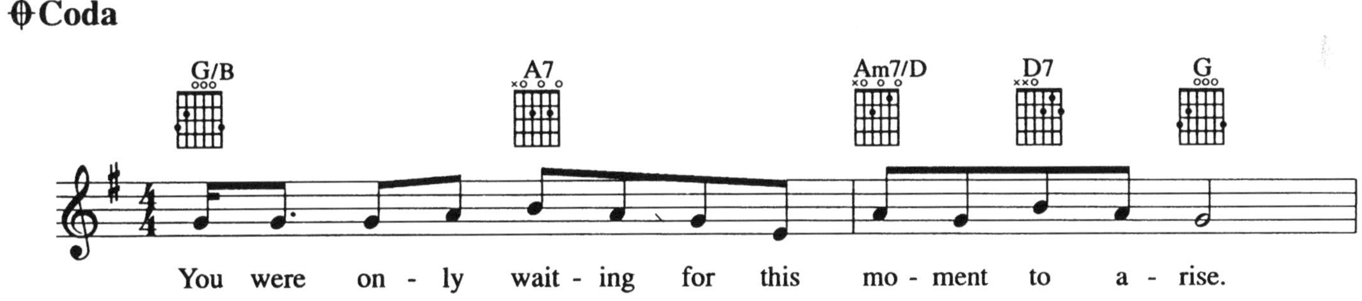
Coda
G/B A7 Am7/D D7 G
You were on - ly wait - ing for this mo - ment to a - rise.

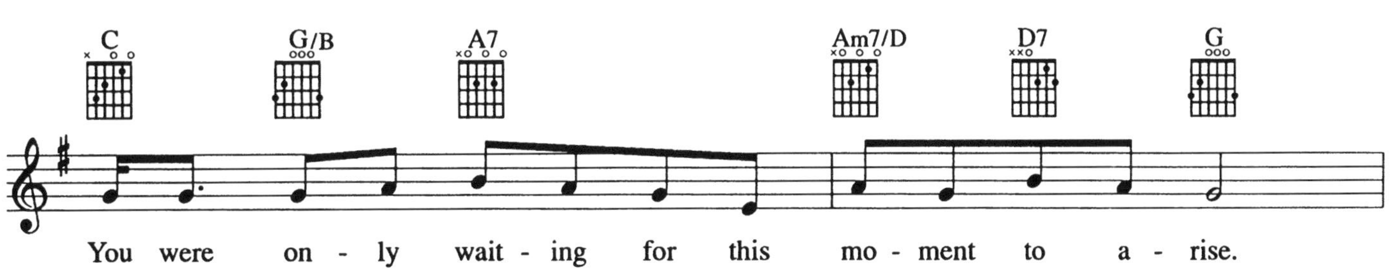
C G/B A7 Am7/D D7 G
You were on - ly wait - ing for this mo - ment to a - rise.

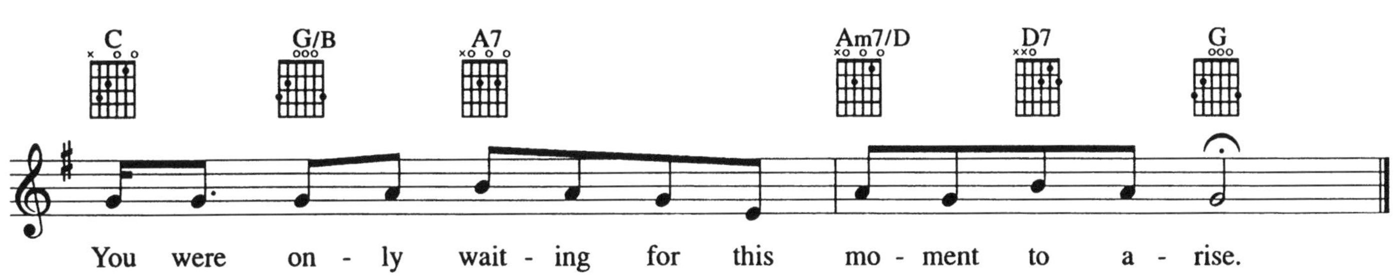
C G/B A7 Am7/D D7 G
You were on - ly wait - ing for this mo - ment to a - rise.

The Continuing Story Of Bungalow Bill.

Words & Music by John Lennon & Paul McCartney.

Fairly Fast
C G7 C Fm
Hey, Bun - ga - low Bill, What did you kill,
C Fm G A E7
Bun - ga - low Bill? Hey, Bun - ga - low Bill,
A Dm A Dm E
What did you kill, Bun - ga - low Bill? 1. He
Much Slower
Am Am/C F G
went out ti - ger hunt - ing with his el - e - phant and gun.
2. Deep in the jun - gle where the might - y ti - ger lies.
3. The child - ren asked him if to kill was not a sin.
Am Am/C F G
In case of ac - ci - dents, he al - ways took his Mom. He's the
Bill and his el - e - phants were tak - en by sur - prise.
"Not when he looked so fierce" his mom - my but - ted in.

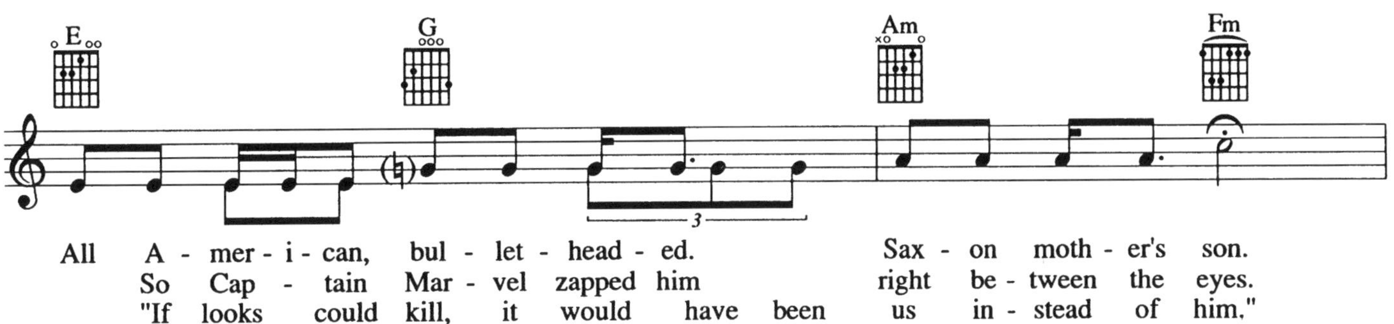
E
G
Am
Fm
All A - mer - i - can, bul - let - head - ed. Sax - on moth - er's son.
So Cap - tain Mar - vel zapped him right be - tween the eyes.
"If looks could kill, it would have been us in - stead of him."

1.2
Tempo 1
All the child - ren sing;
3
Tempo 1
All the child - ren sing;

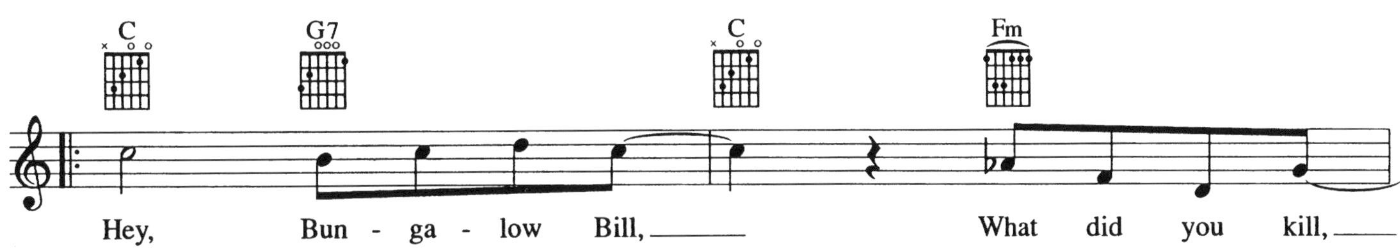
C
G7
C
Fm
Hey, Bun - ga - low Bill, What did you kill,

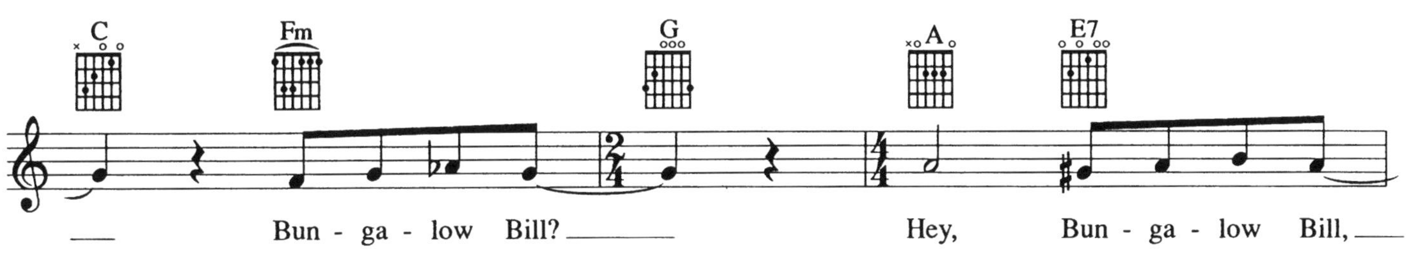
C
Fm
G
A
E7
Bun - ga - low Bill? Hey, Bun - ga - low Bill,

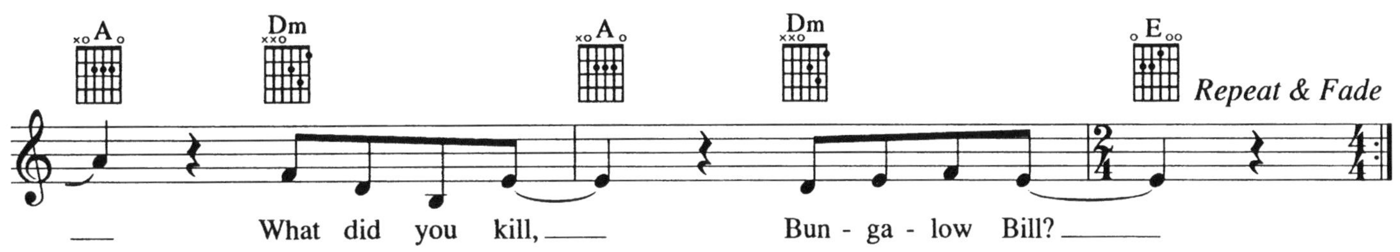
A
Dm
A
Dm
E
Repeat & Fade
What did you kill, Bun - ga - low Bill?

Cry Baby Cry.

WORDS & MUSIC BY JOHN LENNON & PAUL McCARTNEY.

Very slowly
G Am F G
Cry ba - by, cry, make your moth - er sigh, She's
Em7 A F
old en - ough to know bet - ter. 1. The
Em Em/D♯
King of Mar - i - gold was in the kitch -
King was in the gar - den pick - ing flow -
Duch - ess of Kir - cal - dy, al - ways smil -
twelve o - clock a meet - ing 'round the ta -
Em/D Em/C♯ C7 G
- en cook - ing break - fast for the Queen, The
- ers for a friend who came to play, The
- ing and ar - riv - ing late for tea, The
- ble for a se - ance in the dark, With
Em Em/D♯ Em/D Em/C♯
Queen was in the par - lour play - ing pian - o for the chil - dren of the King.
Queen was in the play - room paint - ing pic - tures for the chil - dren's hol - i - day.
Duke was hav - ing prob - lems with a mes - sage at the lo - cal Bird and Bee.
voic - es out of no - where put on spec - 'ly by the chil - dren for a lark.

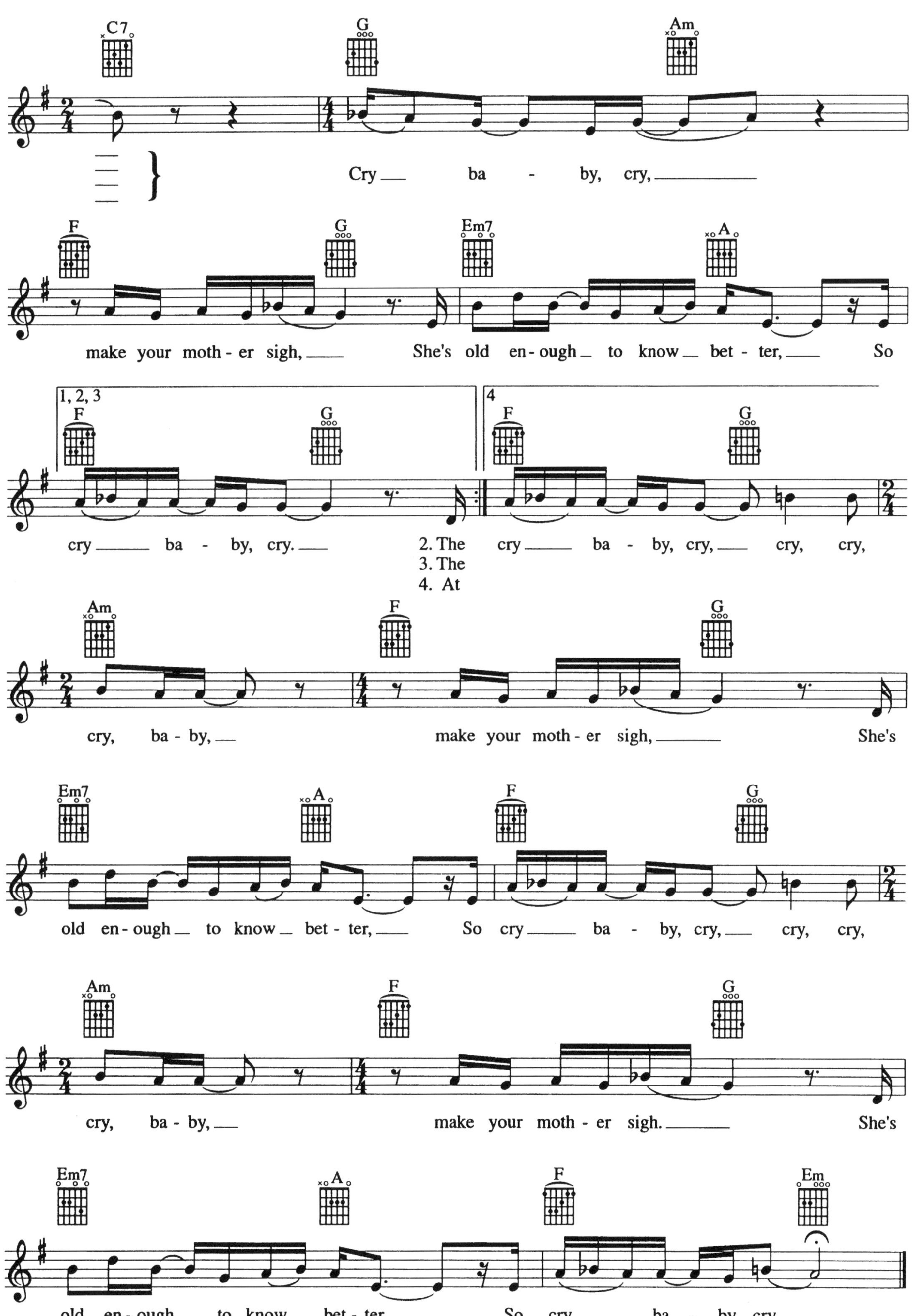
C7
G
Am
Cry ba - by, cry,
F
G
Em7
A
make your moth - er sigh,
She's old en - ough to know bet - ter,
So
1, 2, 3
4
cry ba - by, cry.
2. The
3. The
4. At
cry ba - by, cry, cry, cry,
cry, ba - by,
make your moth - er sigh,
She's
old en - ough to know bet - ter,
So cry ba - by, cry, cry, cry,
cry, ba - by,
make your moth - er sigh.
She's
Em
old en - ough to know bet - ter,
So cry ba - by, cry.

Dear Prudence.

Words & Music by John Lennon & Paul McCartney.

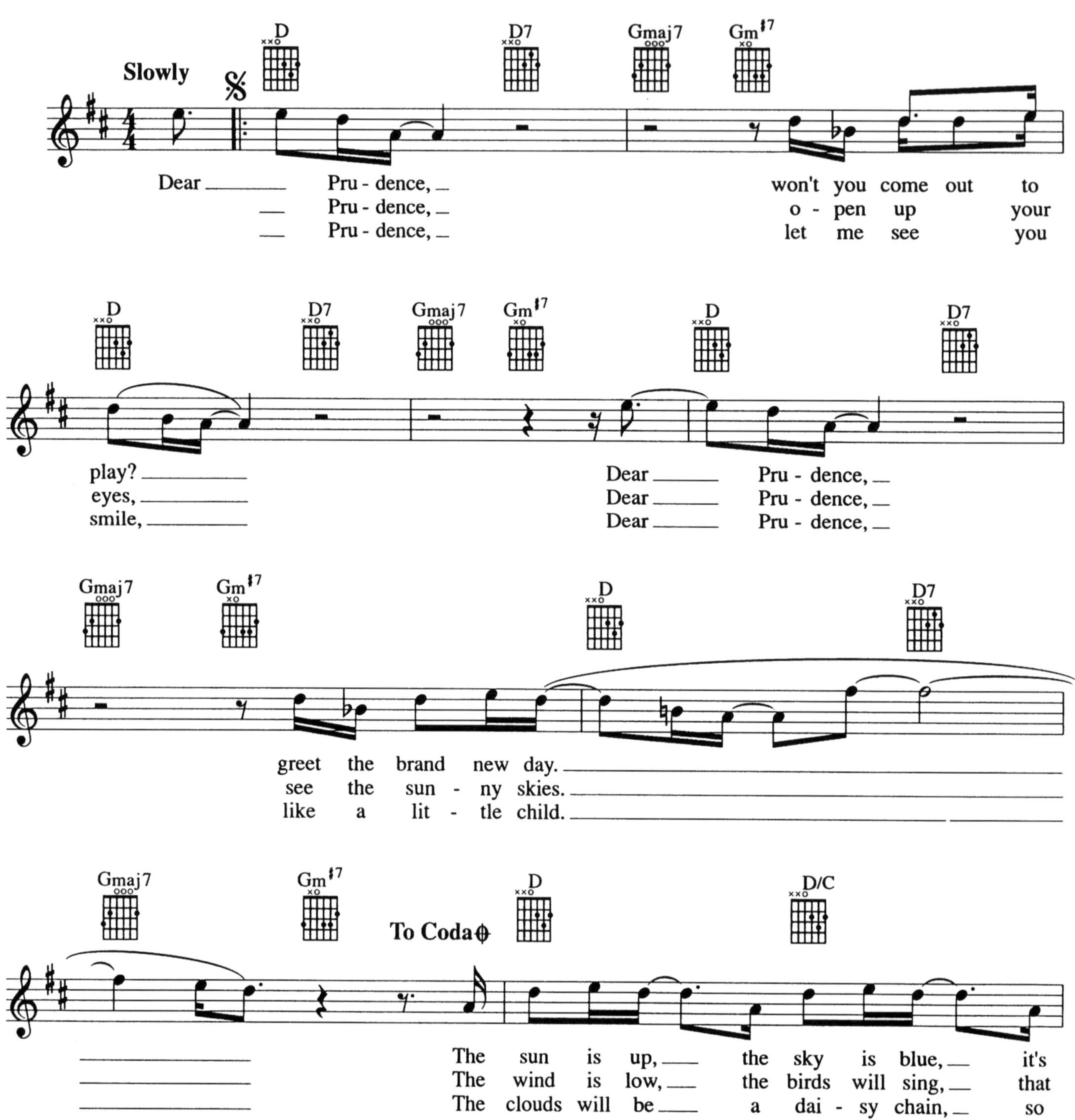
Slowly
D
D7
Gmaj7
Gm♮7
Dear ___ Pru - dence, _ won't you come out to
___ Pru - dence, _ o - pen up your
___ Pru - dence, _ let me see you
play? ___ Dear ___ Pru - dence, _
eyes, ___ Dear ___ Pru - dence, _
smile, ___ Dear ___ Pru - dence, _
greet the brand new day. ___
see the sun - ny skies. ___
like a lit - tle child. ___
To Coda
D/C
The sun is up, _ the sky is blue, _ it's
The wind is low, _ the birds will sing, _ that
The clouds will be _ a dai - sy chain, _ so

Gmaj7/B
Gm♮7/B♭
D/A
D7
beau - ti - ful and so are you. Dear Pru - dence,
you are part of ev - 'ry - thing. Dear Pru - dence,
let me see you smile a - gain. Dear Pru - dence,

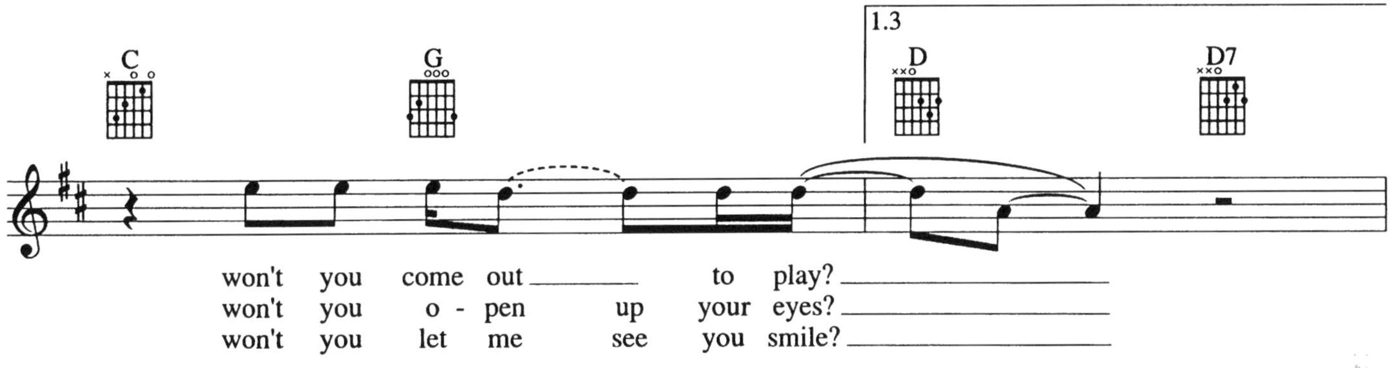
1.3
C
G
D
D7
won't you come out to play?
won't you o - pen up your eyes?
won't you let me see you smile?

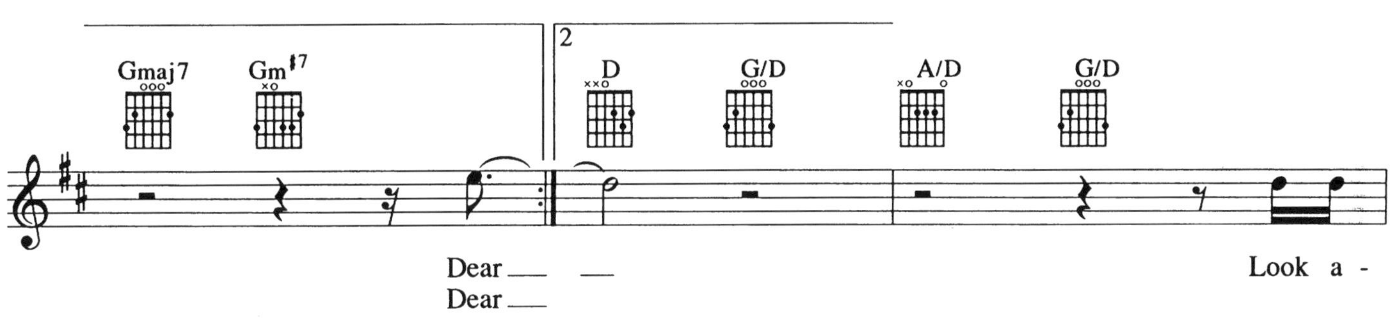
Gmaj7
Gm♮7
2
D
G/D
A/D
G/D
Dear
Dear
Look a -

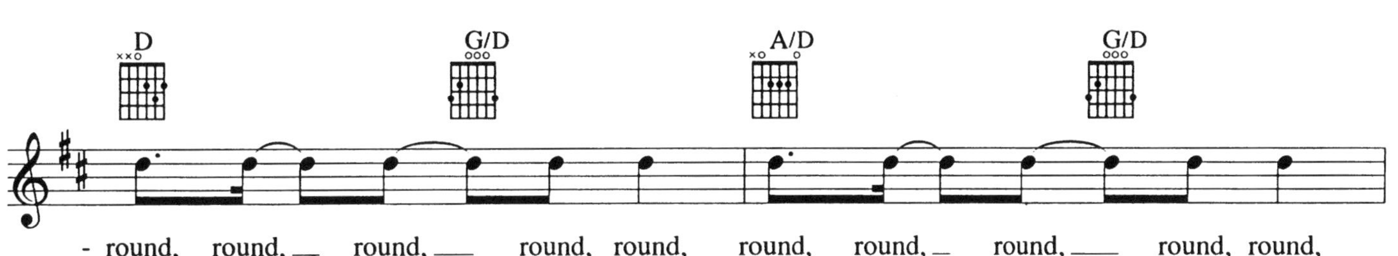
D
G/D
A/D
G/D
- round, round, round, round, round, round, round, round, round, round,

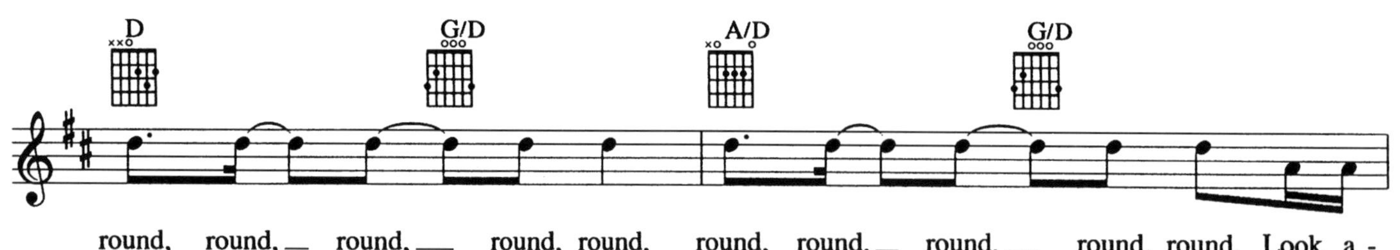
D G/D A/D G/D
round, round, round, round, round, round, round, round, round, round. Look a -

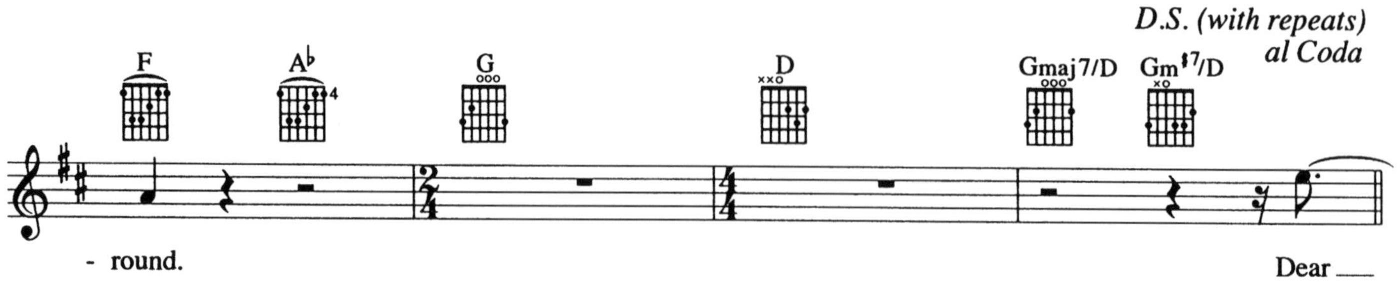
D.S. (with repeats) al Coda
F A♭ G D Gmaj7/D Gm♯7/D
- round. Dear

Coda
D D/C G/B
sun is up, the sky is blue, it's beau - ti - ful, and

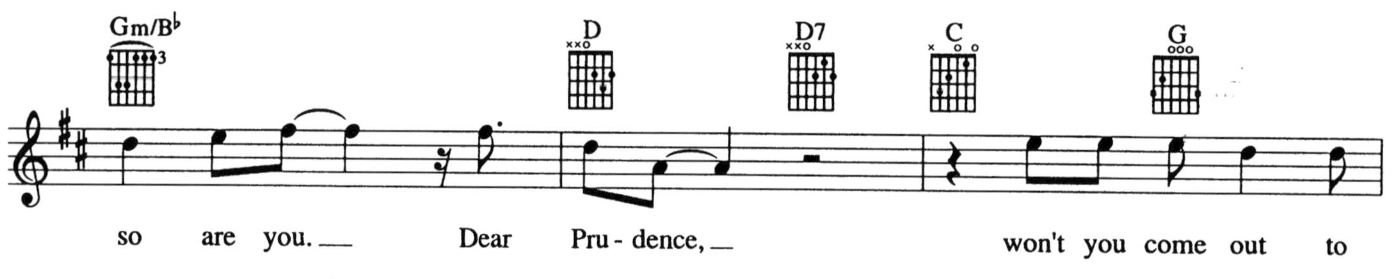
Gm/B♭ D D7 C G
so are you. Dear Pru - dence, won't you come out to

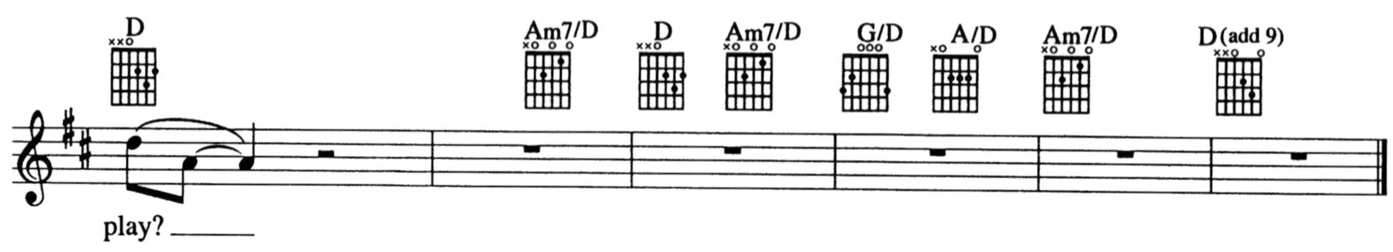
D Am7/D D Am7/D G/D A/D Am7/D D(add 9)
play?

Don't Pass Me By.

Words & Music by Ringo Starr.

Moderately
C
I lis - ten for your foot - steps com - ing up the drive,
F
Lis - ten for your foot - steps, but they don't ar - rive,
G
Wait - ing for your knock, dear, on my old front door, I don't
F
hear it. Does it mean you don't love me an - y - more?
C
C
2. I hear the clock a - tick - ing
(3) sor - ry that I doub - ted you,
on the man - tle shelf,
I was so un - fair,
F
See the hands a - mov - ing,
You were in a car crash

G
But I'm by my - self. I won - der where you are
and you lost your hair. You said that you would

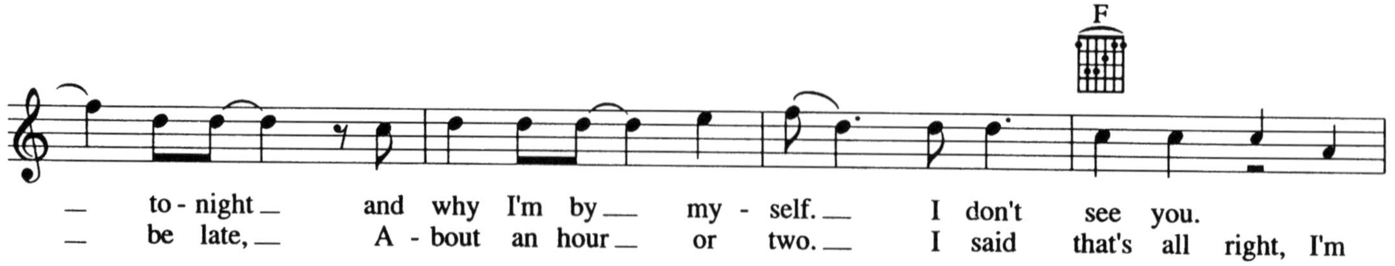
F
to - night and why I'm by my - self. I don't see you.
be late, A - bout an hour or two. I said that's all right, I'm

C
Does it mean you don't love me an - y - more?
wait - ing here, just wait - ing to hear from you.

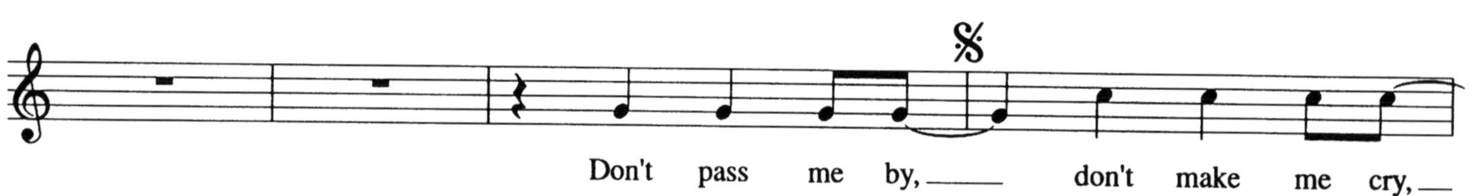
Don't pass me by, don't make me cry,

F
don't make me blue, 'cause you know, dar - ling, I

C
love on - ly you. You'll nev - er know it hurt me so,

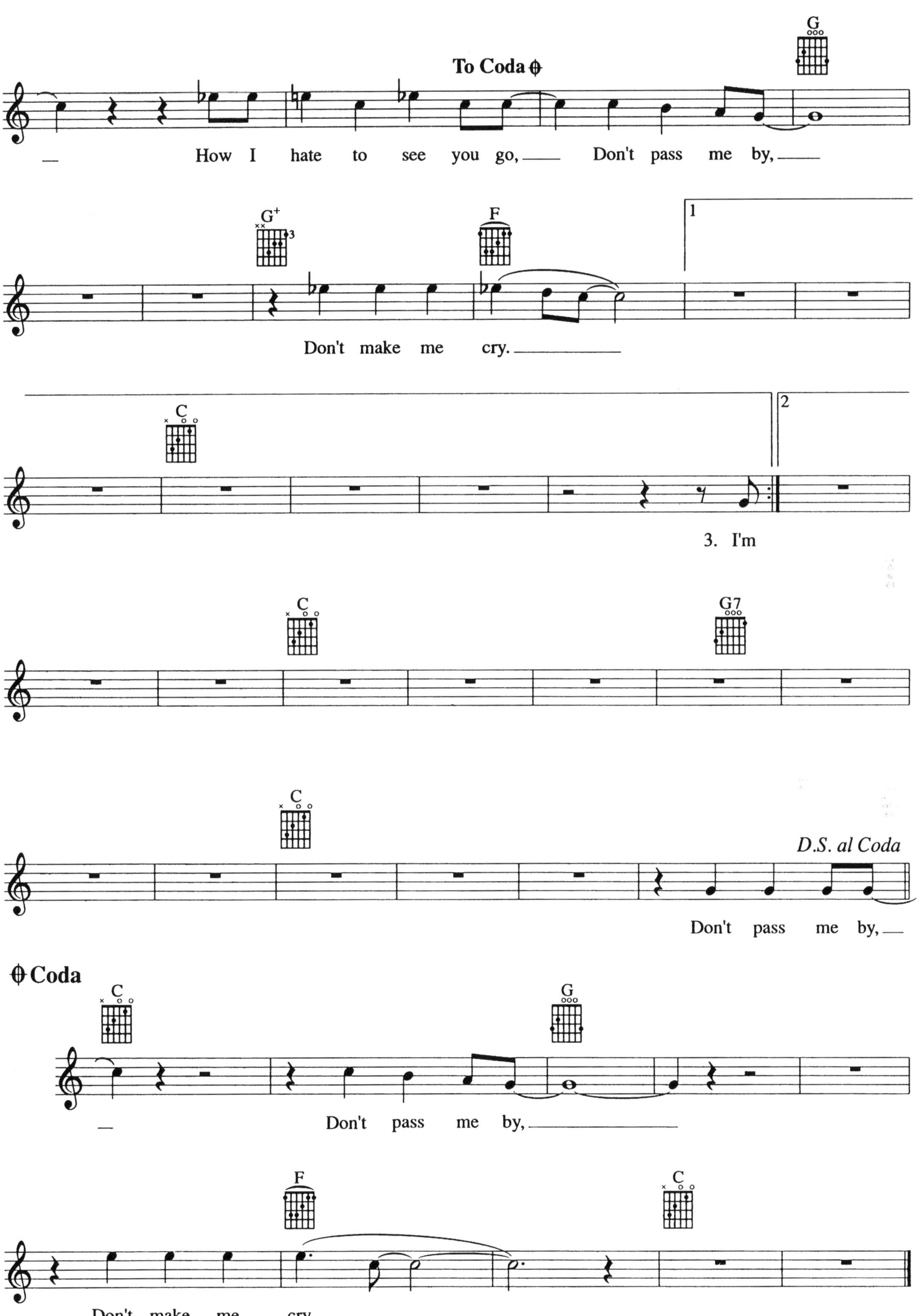
To Coda
G
How I hate to see you go, Don't pass me by,
G+
F
1
Don't make me cry.
C
2
3. I'm
C
G7
C
D.S. al Coda
Don't pass me by,
Coda
C
G
Don't pass me by,
F
C
Don't make me cry.

Everybody's Got Something To Hide Except Me And My Monkey.

Words & Music by John Lennon & Paul McCartney.

Slowly, with a beat
E♭
Come on, come on,
Come on, come on.
E♭
Come on is such a joy,
Come on is such a joy.
1.3. Come on is take it eas - y.
2. Come on is make it eas - y.
Come on is take it eas - y.
Come on is make it eas - y.
Take it
A♭
eas - y.
D♭
Take it eas - y.
B♭7
Ev - 'ry - bod - y's got some - thing to hide

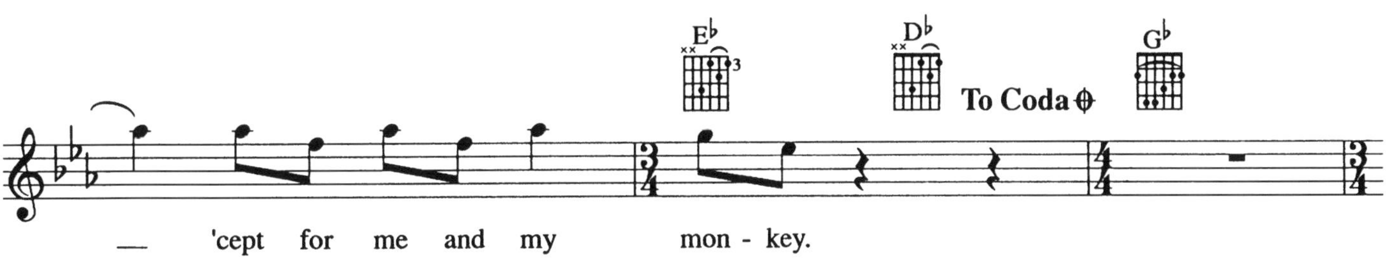
E♭
D♭
To Coda
G♭
'cept for me and my mon - key.

E♭
G♭
D♭
E♭
The deep - er you go, the
Your in - side is out when your

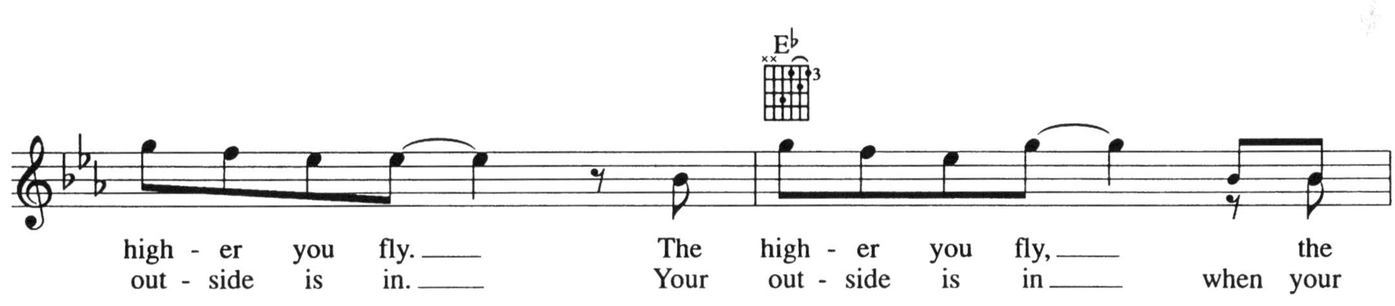
E♭
high - er you fly. The high - er you fly, the
out - side is in. Your out - side is in when your

A♭
deep - er you go so come on. Come on.
in - side is out so come on. Come on.

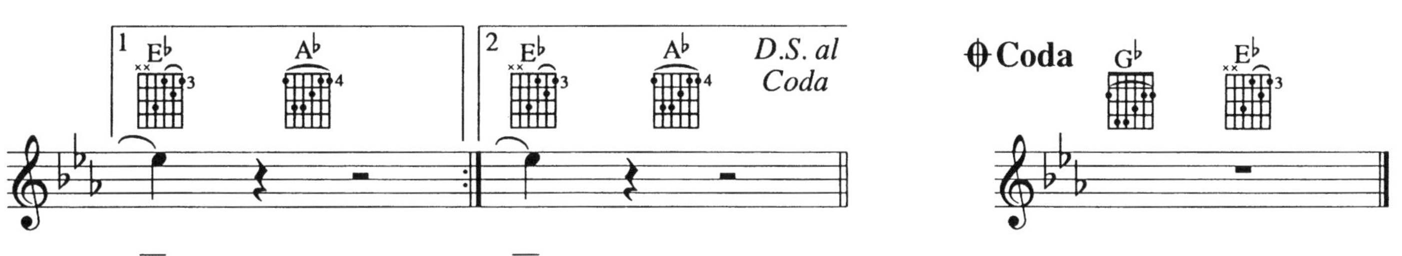
1
E♭
A♭
2
E♭
A♭
D.S. al Coda
Coda
G♭
E♭

Flying.

By John Lennon, Paul McCartney, George Harrison and Richard Starkey.

Moderately

Csus C Csus C Csus C Csus C F7

C7 C Csus C G F G7

C

(2nd time only) La, la la___ la la.___ La, la la___ la la.___

C7 F

___ La, la la___ la la.___

C G F

La, la la___ la la.___ Ah, ah,

1 C G7

2 C

ah.

Goodnight.

Words & Music by John Lennon & Paul McCartney.

Slowly
G
Bm7
Am7
Cmaj7
Now it's time to say good - night;
Close your eyes and I'll close mine.
Good night,
C/G
D7/F♯
sleep tight.
1.3. Now the sun turns out his light;
2. Now the moon be - gins to shine;
Good night, sleep tight.
To Coda
Gmaj7
Am/G
Dream sweet dreams for me.
Dream sweet dreams for you.
1
2
you.
Am
A
Dm
G7
C
Mm.
mm
mm
D.C. al Coda
C/E
D7
Coda
Dream sweet dreams for you.

Glass Onion.

Words & Music by John Lennon & Paul McCartney.

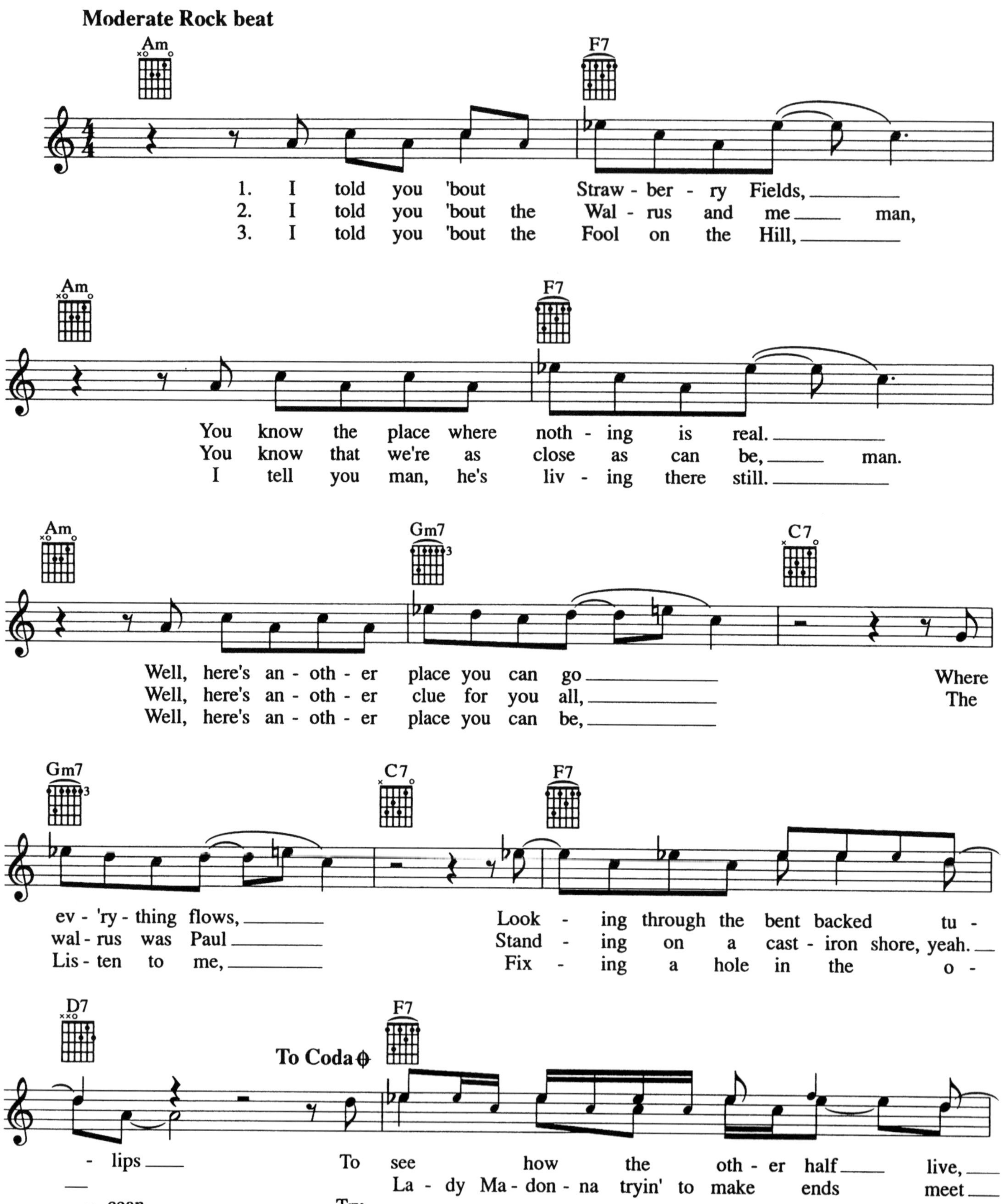
Moderate Rock beat
Am
F7
1. I told you 'bout Straw - ber - ry Fields,
2. I told you 'bout the Wal - rus and me man,
3. I told you 'bout the Fool on the Hill,
Am
F7
You know the place where noth - ing is real.
You know that we're as close as can be, man.
I tell you man, he's liv - ing there still.
Am
Gm7
C7
Well, here's an - oth - er place you can go Where
Well, here's an - oth - er clue for you all, The
Well, here's an - oth - er place you can be,
Gm7
C7
F7
ev - 'ry - thing flows, Look - ing through the bent backed tu -
wal - rus was Paul Stand - ing on a cast - iron shore, yeah.
Lis - ten to me, Fix - ing a hole in the o -
D7
To Coda
F7
- lips To see how the oth - er half live,
La - dy Ma - don - na tryin' to make ends meet
- cean Try -

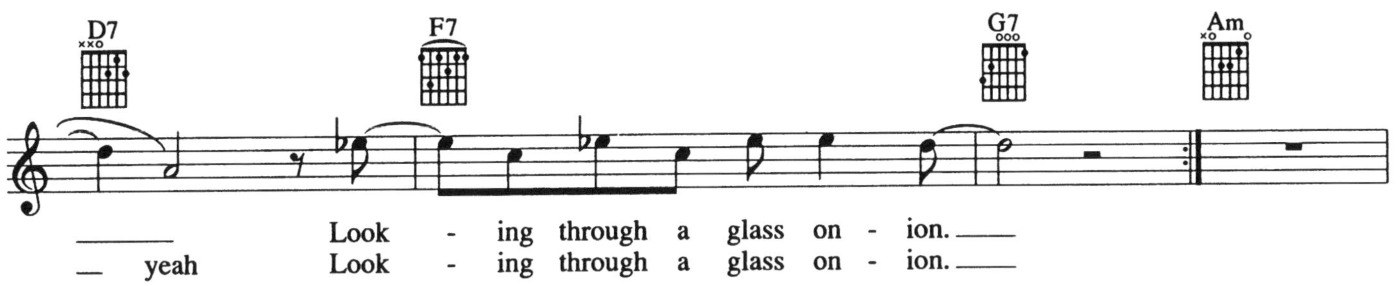
D7
F7
G7
Am
Look - ing through a glass on - ion.
yeah Look - ing through a glass on - ion.

F
Am6
Oh yeah
Oh yeah,
Oh

Am7
F7
G7
D.C. al Coda
yeah,
Look - ing through a glass on - ion.

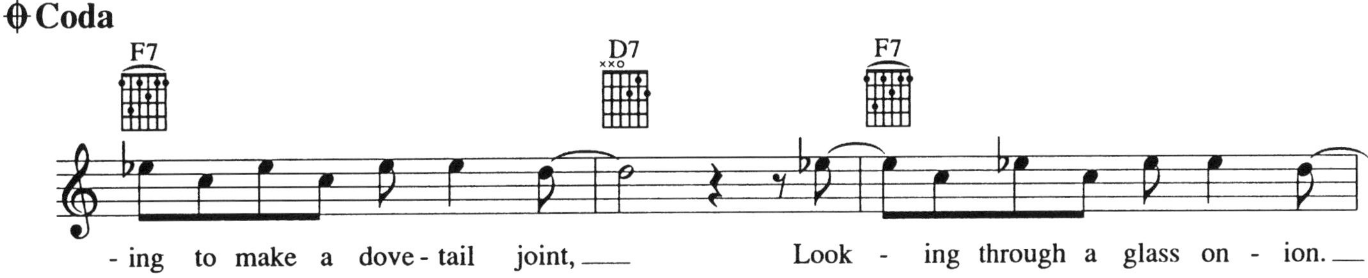
Coda
F7
D7
F7
- ing to make a dove - tail joint,
Look - ing through a glass on - ion.

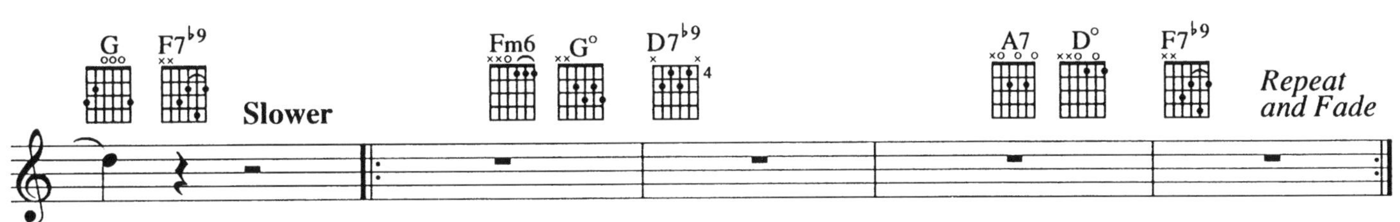
G
F7♭9
Slower
Fm6
G°
D7♭9
A7
D°
F7♭9
Repeat and Fade

Happiness Is A Warm Gun.

Words & Music by John Lennon & Paul McCartney.

Very slowly
Am7
Am6
Em
She's not a girl who miss - es much,
Du du du du du du
oh, yeah.
Dm
She's well ac - quaint - ed with the touch of the vel - vet hand. Like a liz - ard on a
Am
win - dow pane, The man in the crowd with the mul - ti - col - oured mir - rors on his
hob - nail boots. Ly - ing with his eyes while his hands are bus - y work - ing
o - ver - time. A soap im - pres - sion of his
wife which he ate and do - nat - ed to the Na - tion'l Trust.

Double tempo
A7
C
Am
A7
I need a fix 'cause I'm
go - in' down, Down to the bits that I left up
C
A7
town; I need a fix 'cause I'm go - in' down.
A7
C
A7
Moth - er Su - per - i - or jump the gun. Moth - er Su - per - i - or
G7
Half Tempo
C
Am
F
Play 3 times
jump the gun. Hap - pi - ness is a warm gun,
Double tempo
C
Am
F
G7
C
Hap - pi - ness is a warm gun, ma - ma. When I

Am Fmaj7 G7 C Am
hold you in my arms, And I feel my
F G7 C Am7
fin - ger on your trig - ger I know no -
Half Tempo
F G7 C Am
- bod - y can do me no harm be - cause Hap - pi - ness is a
F G7 C Am Fmaj7 G7
warm gun, ma - ma; Hap - pi - ness is a warm gun, yes it is,
Fm7 C Am F G7
Hap - pi - ness is a warm, yes, it is, gun. Well, don't you know that
C Am F G7 C
hap - pi - ness is a warm gun, ma - ma yeah.

Helter Skelter.

WORDS & MUSIC BY JOHN LENNON & PAUL McCARTNEY.

Rock Tempo (bright 4)

E7

When I get to the bot - tom I go back to the top of the slide, __

A C

__ Where I stop and I turn, and I go for a ride __ till I get to the

G E7

bot - tom and I see you a - gain. __ Yeah, yeah, yeah, __ yeah.

E7

But do you, don't you want __ me to love __ you?

E7

I'm com - ing down fast, but I'm miles a - bove __ you.

E G

Tell me, tell me, tell __ me, come on tell __ me the an - swer. __

A

__ Well, you may be a lov - er, but you ain't no __ danc -

E
A7
E
- er. __ Now hel - ter, skel - ter. Hel - ter, skel - ter,
A7
E
Hel - ter, skel - ter, ye - ah. __
E7
Well, will you, won't you want __
do you, don't you want __
__ me to make __ you?
__ me to make __ you?
I'm com - ing down fast, but
G
don't let me break you. Tell me, tell me, tell __
A
__ me __ the an - swer. You may be a lov - er, but you ain't no danc - er.
E
A7
Look out! __ Hel - ter, skel - ter,
E
A7
To Coda
E
Hel - ter, skel - ter, Hel - ter, skel - ter, Ooh. __

Look out! 'Cause here she comes!
A
E7
A
E
E7
When I get to the bot - tom, I go
A/E
back to the top of the slide, And I stop and I turn, and I go for a ride
C/E
G
and I get to the bot - tom and I see you a - gain.
E
D.S. al Coda
Yeah, yeah, yeah, yeah. Well,
Coda
E
(shout) Look out! Hel - ter, skel - ter she's
E
Repeat ad lib. and Fade
com - ing down fast. Yes, she is.

Hey Bulldog.

Words & Music by John Lennon & Paul McCartney.

Slow Rock
F7
Cm
1. Sheep dog, stand - ing in the rain,
2. Child - like, no one un - der - stands,
3. Big man, wait - ing in the dark,
F7
Cm
Bull frog do - ing it a - gain.
Jack knife in your sweat - y hands.
Wig - wam, fright - ened of the dark.
E♭
Cm
B♭
B♭7
Some kind of hap - pi - ness is meas - ured out in miles.
Some kind of in - no - cence is meas - ured out in years.
Some kind of sol - i - tude is meas - ured out in you.
E♭
Cm
1
F7
What makes you think you're some - thing spec - ial when you smile?
You don't know what it's like to
You think you know me, but you

2.3
F7
Fm
D♭/F
lis - ten to your fears. __
have - n't got a clue
You can talk __ to me, __

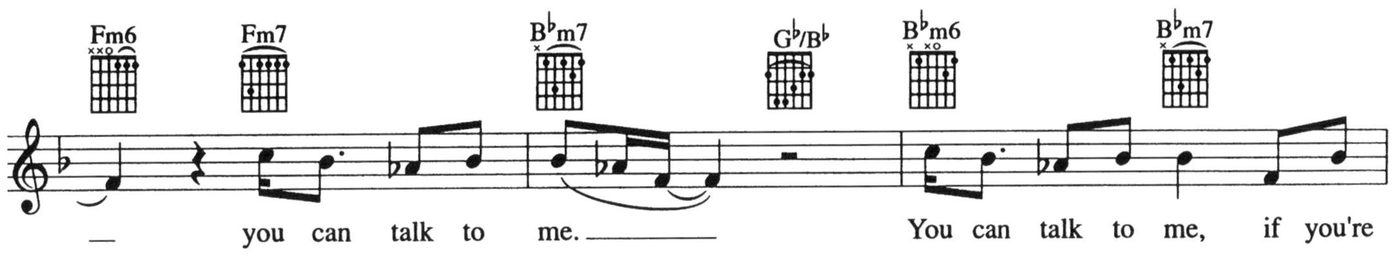
Fm6
Fm7
B♭m7
G♭/B♭
B♭m6
B♭m7
__ you can talk to me. __
You can talk to me, if you're

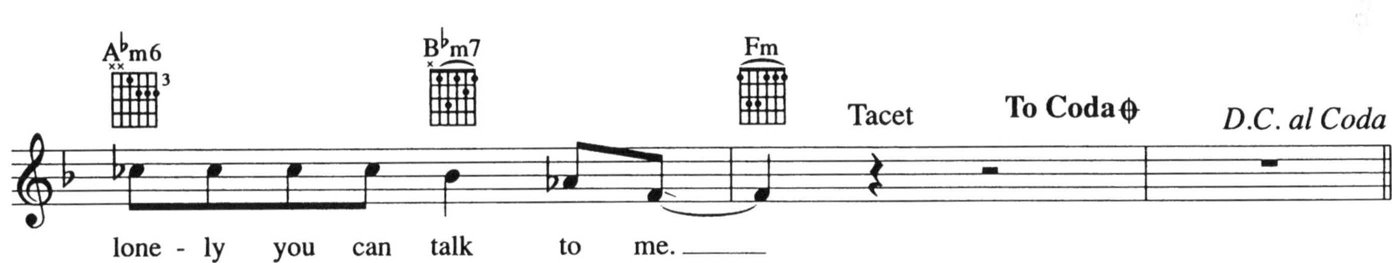
A♭m6
B♭m7
Fm
Tacet
To Coda
D.C. al Coda
lone - ly you can talk to me. __

Coda

Hey, __ Bull -

F
Cm7
F7
Repeat and Fade
ad lib.
- dog. __
Hey, __ Bull - dog. __

Honey Pie.

Words & Music by John Lennon & Paul McCartney.

Slowly, ad lib.
Em A7 D9 Cm G
She was a work - ing girl North of Eng - land way.
Em A7 D11 Cm G
(Half spoken) Now she's hit the big time in the U. S. A.
A7 D7 Am7 D7 Am7
And if she could on - ly hear me, this is what I'd
D7 a tempo (moderately) G
say: Hon - ey Pie, you are mak - ing me
E♭ E A7 A7♭5
cra - zy, I'm in love, but I'm la - zy,
D7 G E♭ D11 D7
So won't you please come home. Oh

G
E♭
Hon - ey Pie, my po - si - tion is trag - ic,
E
A7
A7♭5
D7
Come and show me the mag - ic of your Hol - ly - wood song.
G
F♯
F
G6/B
You be - came a leg -
Will the wind that blew
A/C♯
G/D
G7
- end of the sil - ver screen, And now the
her boat a - cross the sea,
C
E7
Am
thought of meet - ing you makes me weak in the knees.
kind - ly send her sail - ing back to me.
D7
C/E
D7/F♯
G
T - t - tee. Oh Hon - ey Pie, you are driv - ing me
Now Hon - ey Pie, you are mak - ing me

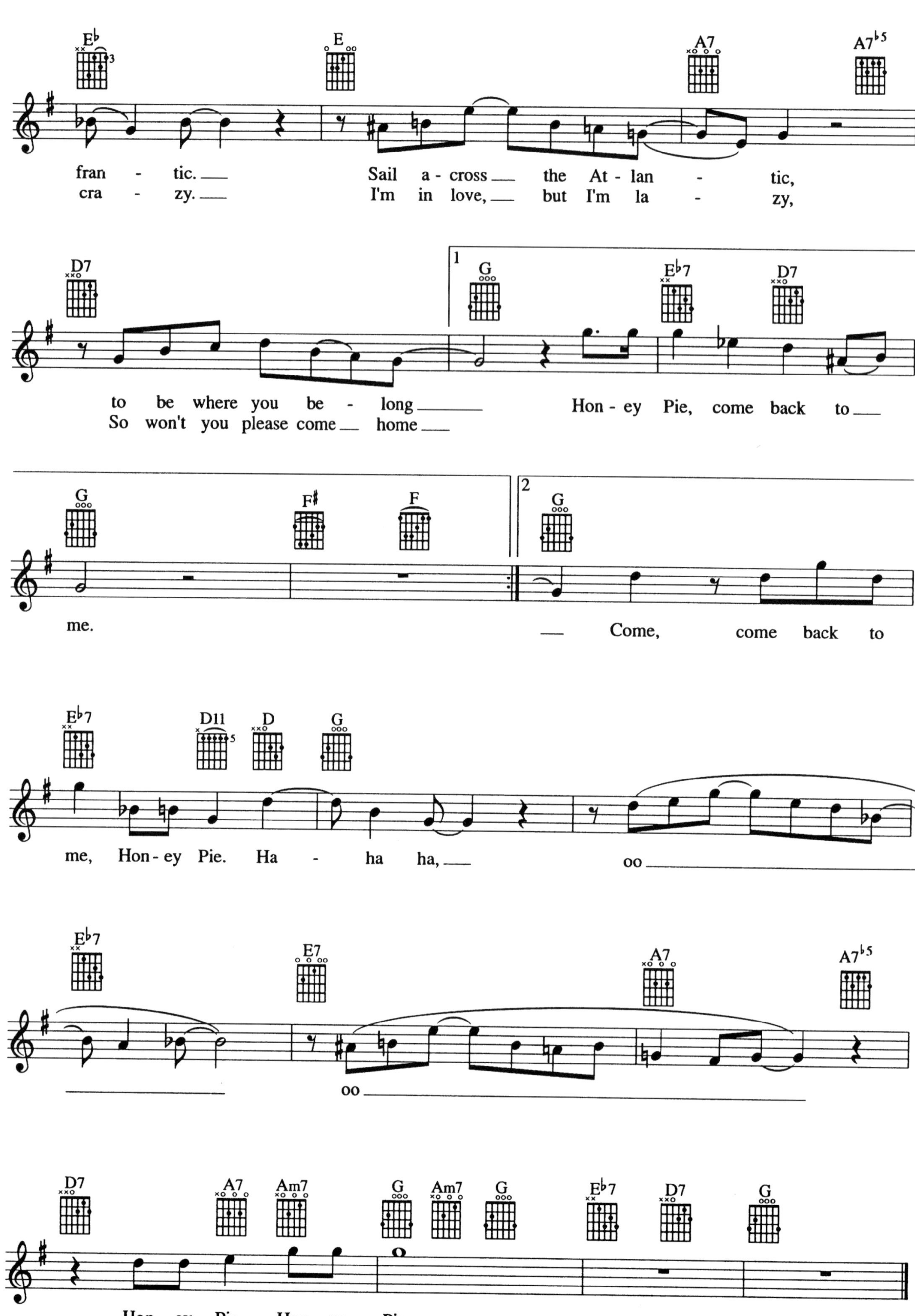
E♭ E A7 A7♭5
fran - tic. Sail a - cross the At - lan - tic,
cra - zy. I'm in love, but I'm la - zy,
D7 G E♭7 D7
to be where you be - long Hon - ey Pie, come back to
So won't you please come home
G F♯ F G
me. Come, come back to
E♭7 D11 D G
me, Hon - ey Pie. Ha - ha ha, oo
E♭7 E7 A7 A7♭5
oo
D7 A7 Am7 G Am7 G E♭7 D7 G
Hon - ey Pie, Hon - ey Pie.

It's All Too Much.

Words & Music by George Harrison.

Heavy rock beat
C/G
G
C/G
G
C/G
G
C/G
1
G
It's all too much.

2
G
G
When I look in - to your eyes, your
Float - ing down the stream of time, from
Sail me on a sil - ver sun, where

love is there for me.
life to life with me.
I know that I'm free.
And the more I go
Makes no dif - f'rence where
Show me that I'm ev -

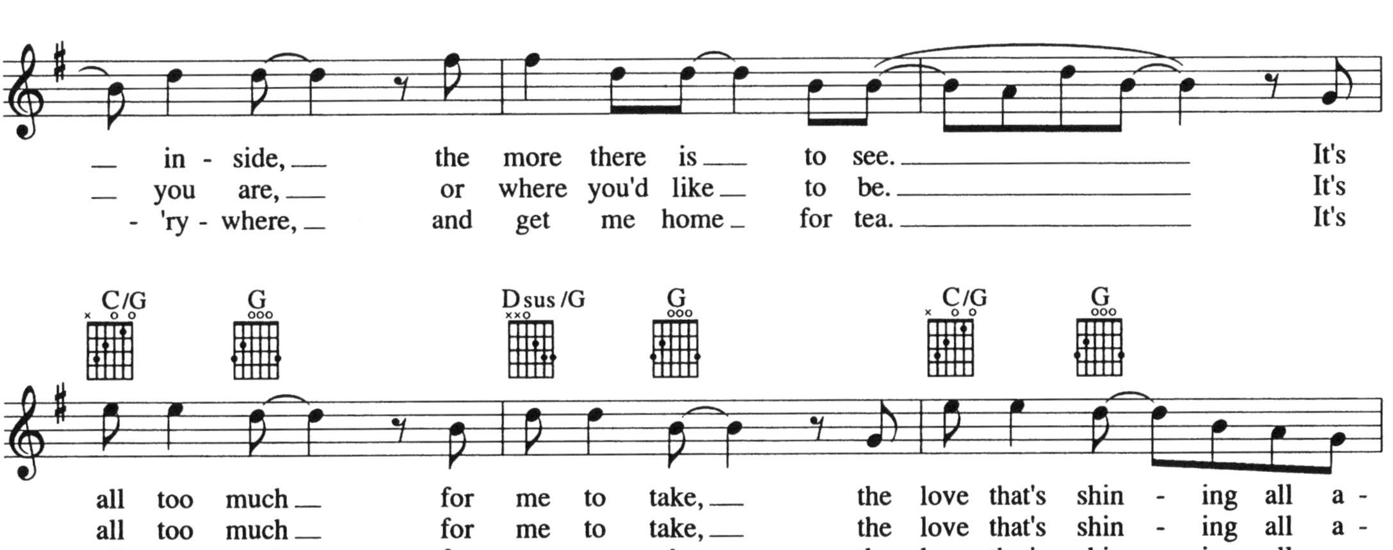
in - side, the more there is to see.
you are, or where you'd like to be.
- 'ry - where, and get me home for tea.
It's
It's
It's
C/G
G
Dsus/G
G
C/G
G
all too much for me to take, the love that's shin - ing all a -
all too much for me to take, the love that's shin - ing all a -
all too much for me to take, the love that's shin - ing all a -

C/G
G
Dsus/G
G
round you. Ev - 'ry - where, it's what you make, for
round here. All the world is birth - day cake, so
round here. The more I have, the less I know, and

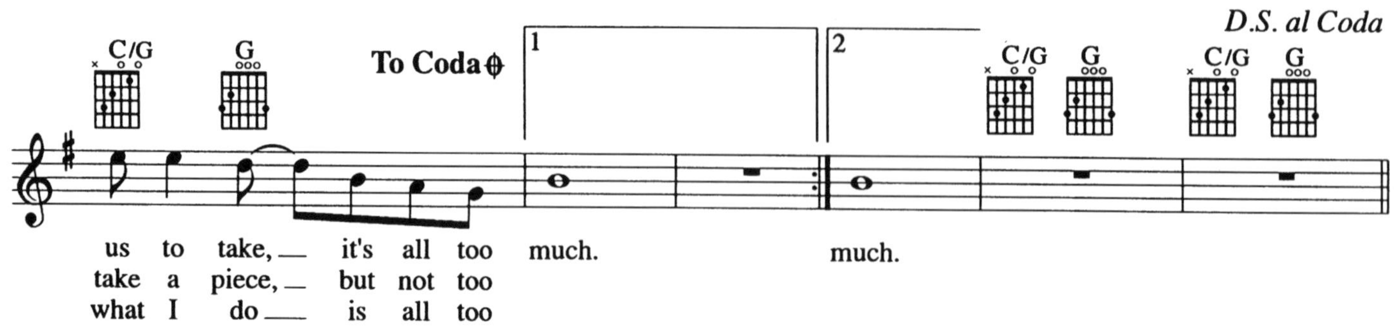
D.S. al Coda
C/G
G
To Coda
1
2
C/G
G
C/G
G
us to take, it's all too much. much.
take a piece, but not too
what I do is all too

Coda

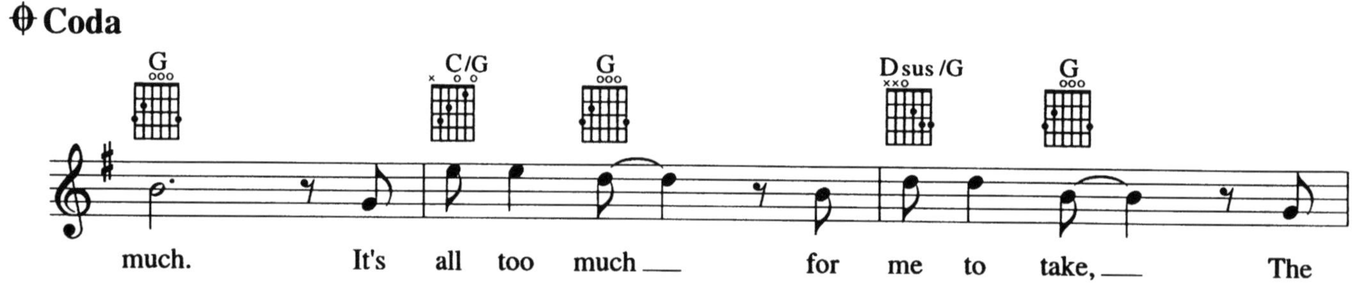
G
C/G
G
Dsus/G
G
much. It's all too much for me to take, The

C/G
G
C/G
G
love that's shin - ing all a - round you. Ev - 'ry - where it's

Dsus/G
G
C/G
G
C/G
G
what you make, for us to take, it's all too much. It's

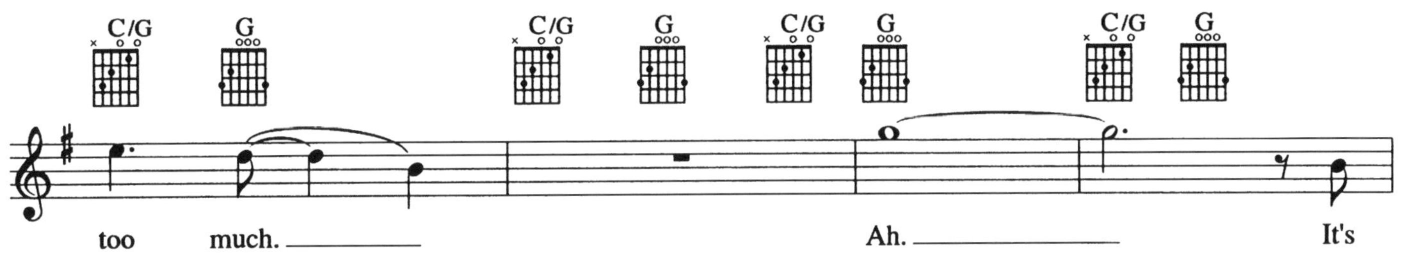

C/G
G
C/G
G
C/G
G
C/G
G
too much.
Ah.
It's

C/G
G
C/G
G
too much.
With your long blonde hair and your eyes

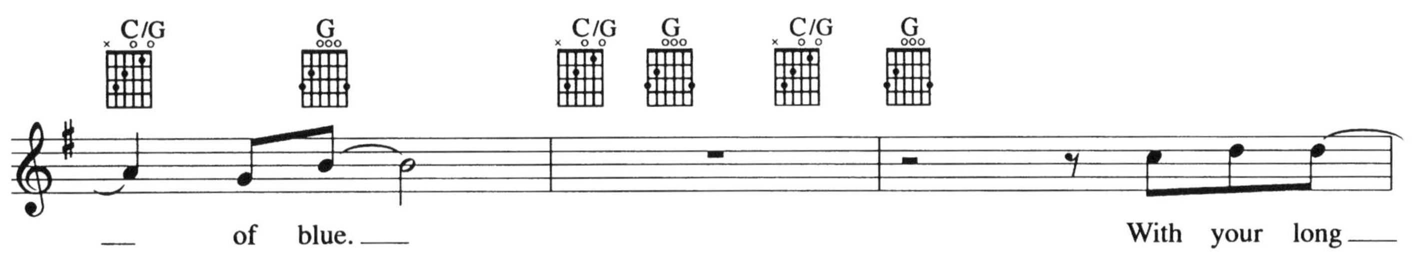

C/G
G
C/G
G
C/G
G
of blue.
With your long

C/G
G
C/G
blonde hair and your eyes of blue.

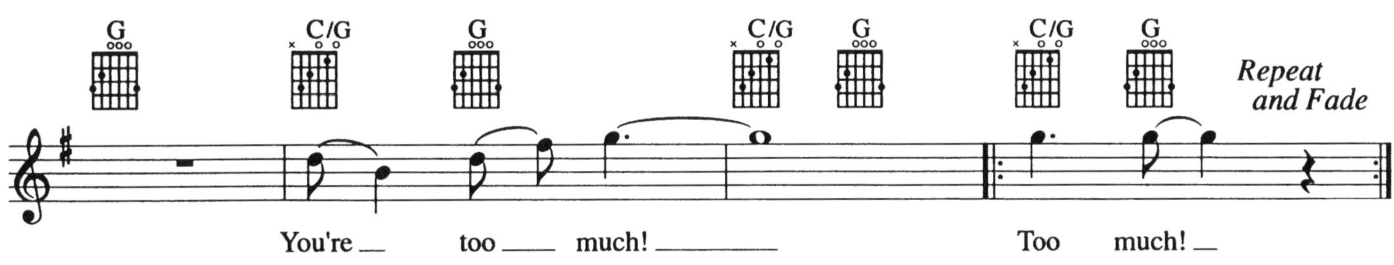

G
C/G
G
C/G
G
C/G
G
Repeat and Fade
You're too much!
Too much!

I Will.

WORDS & MUSIC BY JOHN LENNON & PAUL McCARTNEY.

Moderately

F Dm7 Gm7 C7

Who knows how long I've loved you? You know
I ev - er saw you, I did -

F Dm Am F7 B♭ C7

I love you still. Will I wait a lone - ly life -
- n't catch your name, But it nev - er real - ly mat -

Dm F/A B♭ C7 1. F Dm7

- time? If you want me to, I will.
- tered, I will al - ways feel the same.

Gm7 C7 2. F F7 B♭ Am Dm7

For if Love you for - ev - er and for - ev - er,

Gm C7 F F7 B♭ Am

Love you with all my heart. Love you when - ev - er we're

Dm7 G7 C7

to - geth - er, Love you when we're a - part. And when

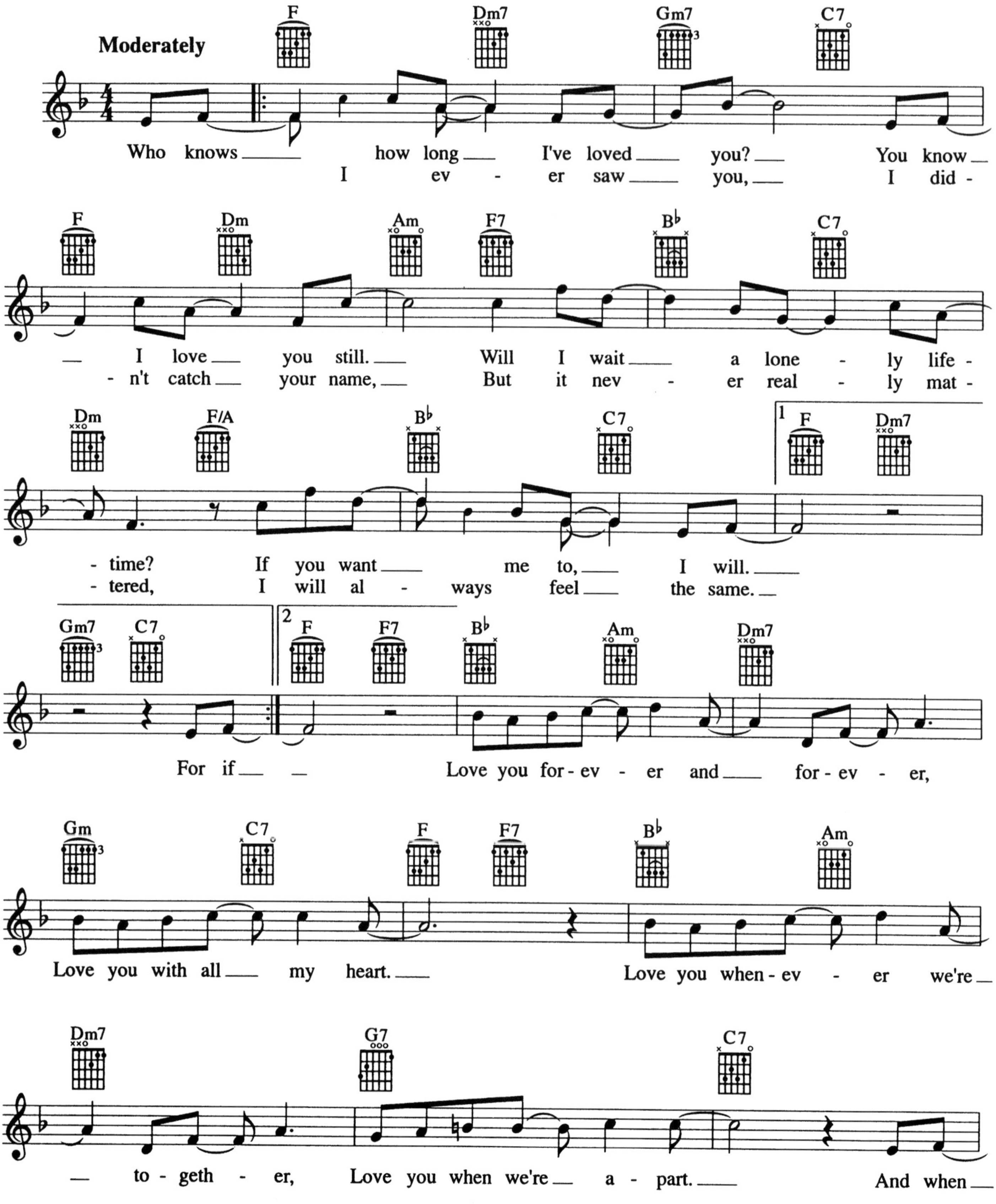

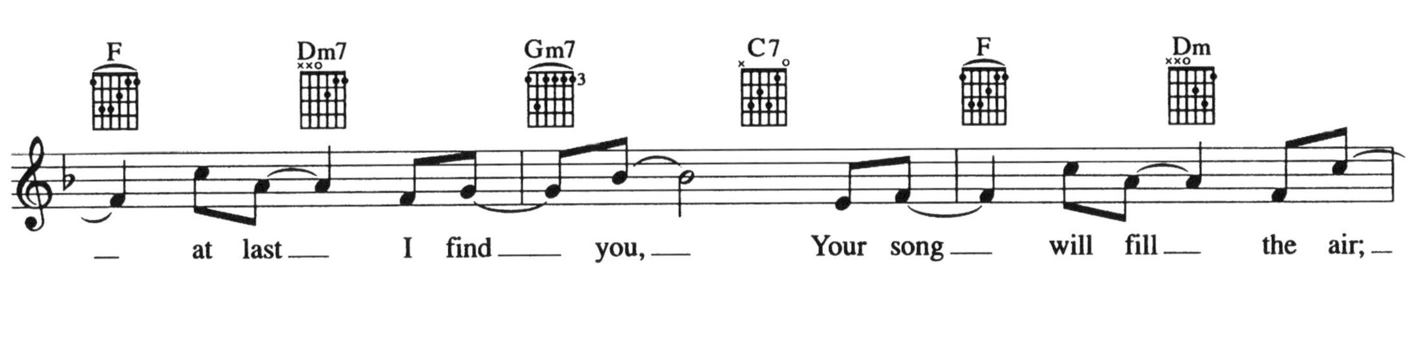
F Dm7 Gm7 C7 F Dm
at last I find you, Your song will fill the air;

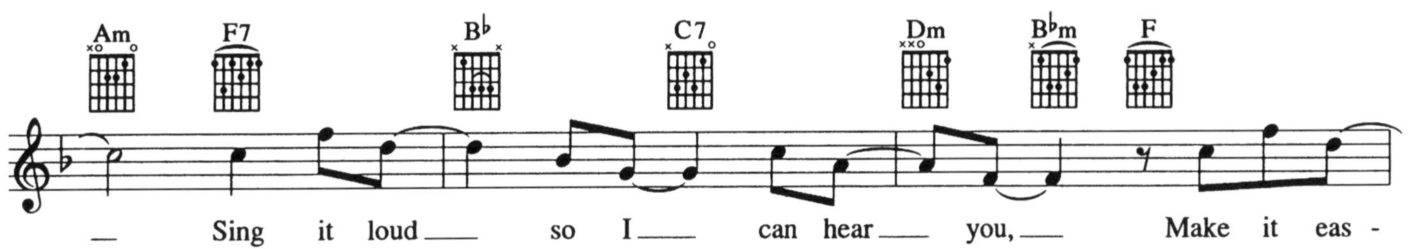
Am F7 B♭ C7 Dm B♭m F
Sing it loud so I can hear you, Make it eas -

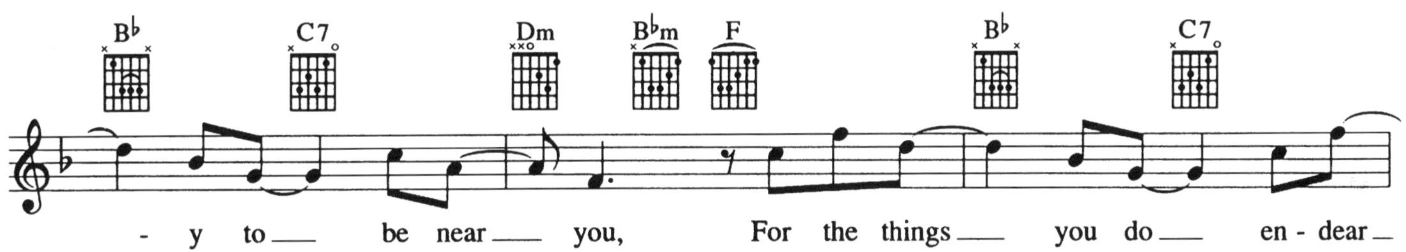
B♭ C7 Dm B♭m F B♭ C7
- y to be near you, For the things you do en - dear

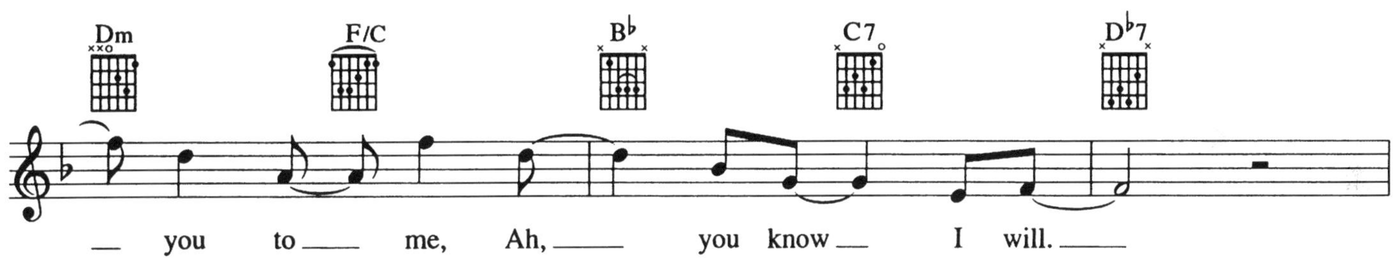
Dm F/C B♭ C7 D♭7
you to me, Ah, you know I will.

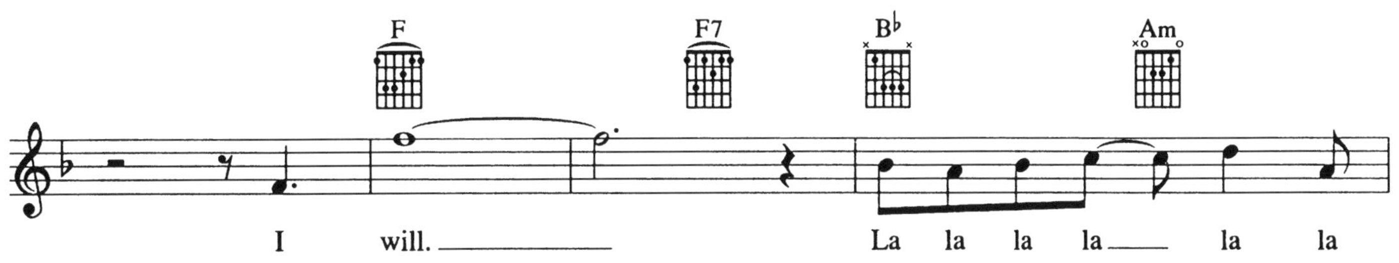
F F7 B♭ Am
I will. La la la la la la

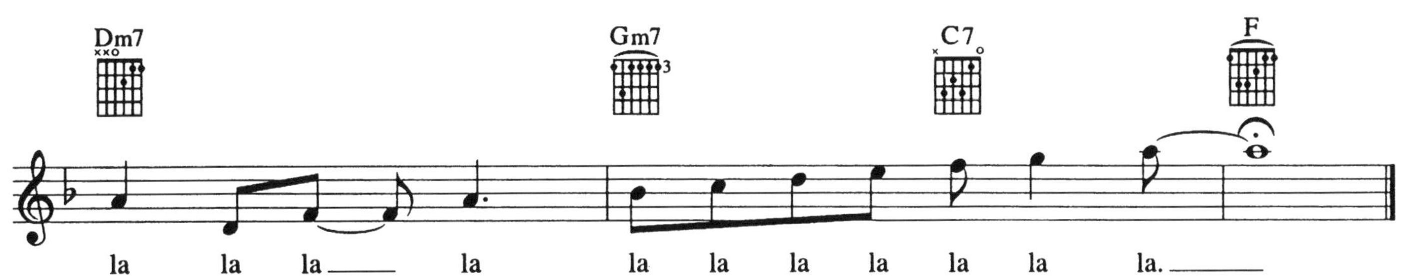
Dm7 Gm7 C7 F
la la la la la la la la la la la.

I'm So Tired.

Words & Music by John Lennon & Paul McCartney.

Slowly

B♭maj9 A E♭ F7

I'm so tired, I have-n't slept a wink; I'm
(2) so tired, I don't know what to do, I'm

B♭ Gm7 E♭ F7

so tired, my mind is on the blink. I
so tired, my mind is set on you. I

1 B♭ F+ Gm E♭m7

won-der should I get up and fix my-self a drink, no, no, no. 2. I'm

2 B♭ F+ Gm7 E♭m7 E♭m6 E♭m

won-der should I call you, but I know what you would do.

B♭
You'd say I'm put-ting you on, but it's no joke; It's do-ing me harm you know I

F7
can't sleep, I can't stop my brain, you know it's three weeks, I'm go-ing in-sane you know I'd

E♭
To Coda
B♭
Tacet
give you ev-'ry-thing I got for a lit-tle peace of mind. I'm

B♭maj9
A
E♭
F7
B♭
Gm7
so tired, I'm feel-ing so up-set. Al-though I'm so tired,

E♭
F7
B♭
F+
I'll have an-oth-er cig-ar-ette, And curse Sir Wal-ter Ra-leigh, he was

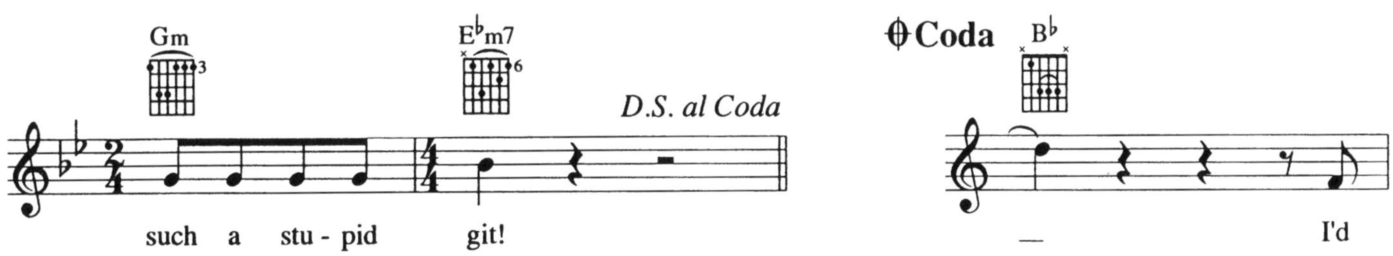
Gm
E♭m7
D.S. al Coda
Coda
B♭
such a stu-pid git!
I'd

E♭
B♭
give you ev-'ry-thing I got for a lit-tle peace of mind.

Julia.

WORDS & MUSIC BY JOHN LENNON & PAUL MCCARTNEY.

Moderately slow with feeling
F
Dm7
Am
Half of what I say is mean - ing - less.
When I can - not sing my heart,
F
Dm7
Am
C
But I say it just to reach you, Ju - li - a.
I can on - ly speak my mind. Ju - li -
F
Dm7
Cm
Cm7
Ju - li - a.
- a.
Ju - li - a,
Sea - shell eyes,
Sleep - ing sand,
D
B♭9
B♭m7
To Coda
F
o - cean child, calls me.
wind - y smile, calls me.
si - lent cloud, touch me.
So I sing a song
Dm7
Am
C
F
of love, Ju - li - a.
Em
F
Her hair of float - ing sky is shim - mer - ing,

Dm7
Dm6
Am7
Am6
Am♯5
glim - mer - ing in the sun.
Am
F
Dm7
Cm
Cm7
Ju - li - a.
Ju - li - a,
D
B♭9
B♭m7
F
morn - ing moon touch me. So I sing a song
Dm7
Am
C
F
D.C. al Coda
of love, Ju - li - a.
Coda
F
Dm7
Am
C
F
So I sing a song of love, Ju - li - a.
Dm7
Cm
Cm7
D
B♭9
Mmm
calls
B♭m7
F
Dm7
C
C7
me. So I sing a song of love for Ju - li -
F
C
C7
F
Am
C
Fmaj7
- a. Ju - li - a, Ju - li - a.

Lady Madonna.

Words & Music by John Lennon & Paul McCartney.

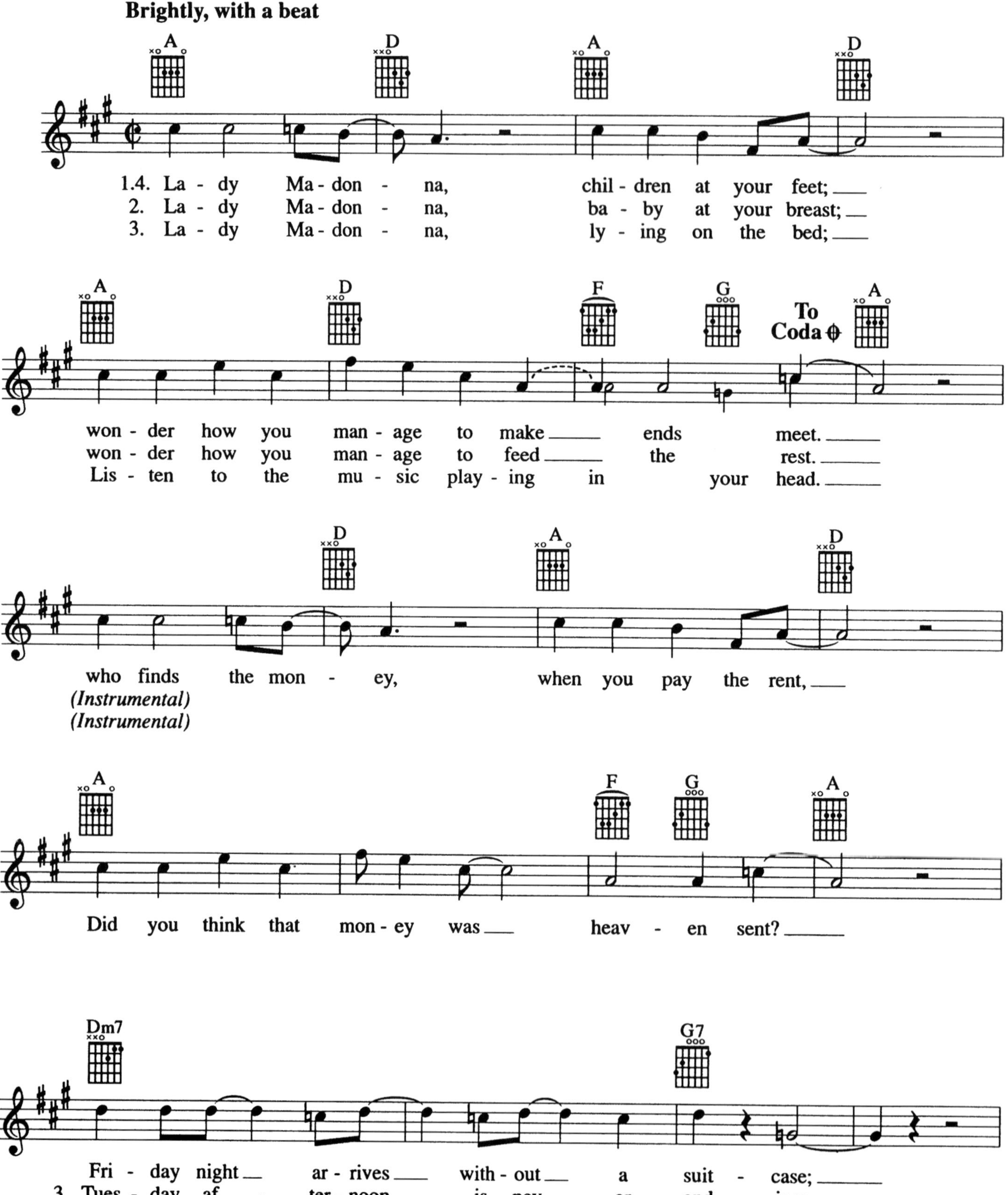
Brightly, with a beat
A D A D
1.4. La - dy Ma - don - na, chil - dren at your feet;
2. La - dy Ma - don - na, ba - by at your breast;
3. La - dy Ma - don - na, ly - ing on the bed;
A D F G To Coda A
won - der how you man - age to make ends meet.
won - der how you man - age to feed the rest.
Lis - ten to the mu - sic play - ing in your head.
D A D
who finds the mon - ey, when you pay the rent,
(Instrumental)
(Instrumental)
A F G A
Did you think that mon - ey was heav - en sent?
Dm7 G7
Fri - day night ar - rives with - out a suit - case;
3. Tues - day af - ter - noon is nev - er end - ing;

C
Am
Sun - day morn - ing creep in like a nun.
Wednes - day morn - ing pa - pers did - n't come.

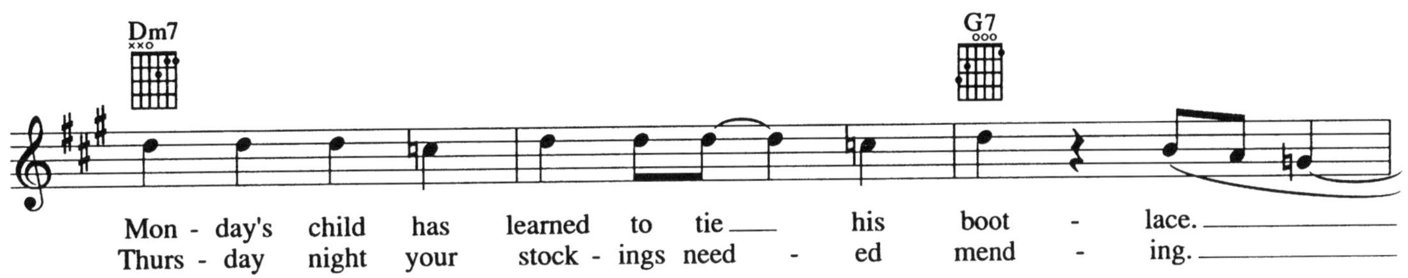
Dm7
G7
Mon - day's child has learned to tie his boot - lace.
Thurs - day night your stock - ings need - ed mend - ing.

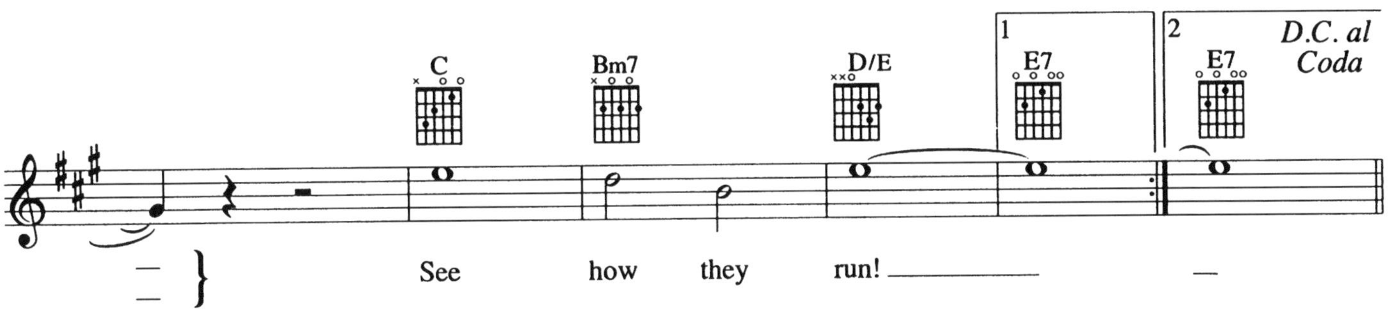
C
Bm7
D/E
1
E7
2
E7
D.C. al Coda
See how they run!

Coda
A
Bm
C°
E7sus
A

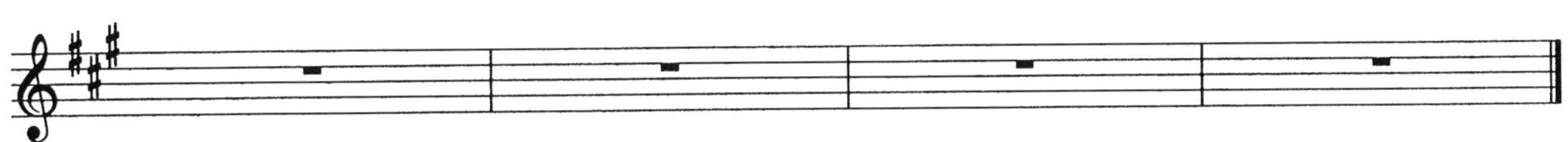

Long Long Long.

Words & Music by George Harrison.

Moderately
B♭
Am
Gm
C9
F
Gm
F
It's been a long, long, long time;
long, long, long time;
see you, be you;
C
Gm
F
C
How could I ev - er have lost you?
Now I'm so hap - py I found you.
How can I ev - er mis - place you?
Gm
To Coda
F
C
C7
1 C
When I loved you.
How I love you.
How I
It took a
2
B♭
F
C
Gm
So man - y years; I was search - ing.

B♭
F
C
So man - y tears I was wast -

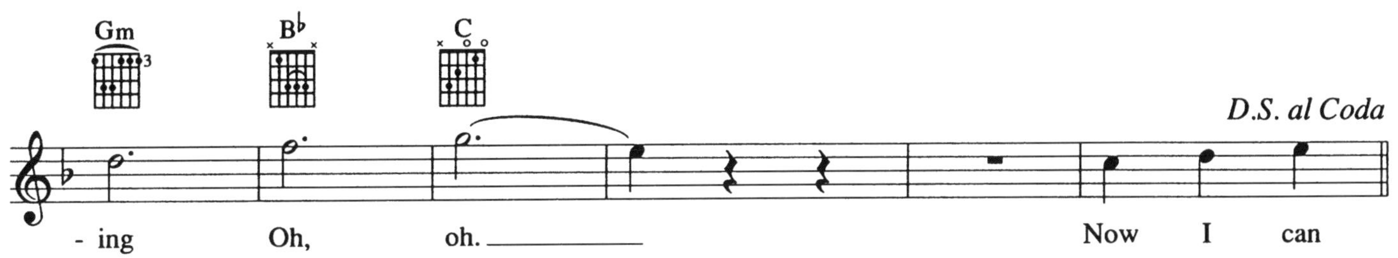

Gm
B♭
C
D.S. al Coda
- ing Oh, oh.
Now I can

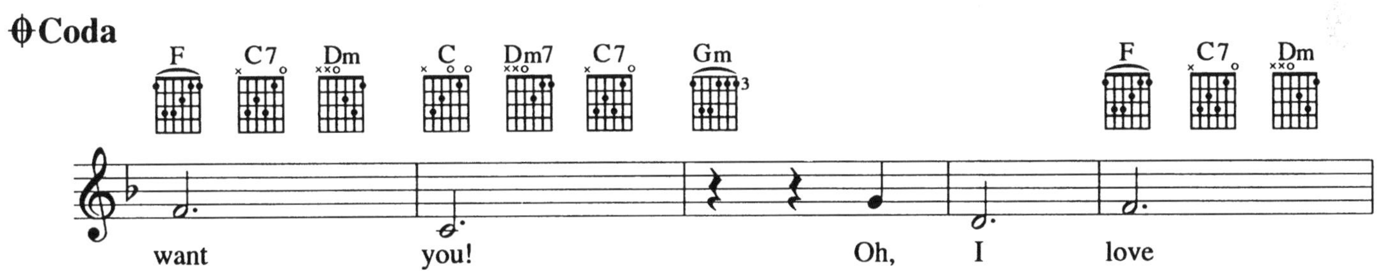

Coda
F
C7
Dm
C
Dm7
C7
Gm
F
C7
Dm
want you! Oh, I love

C
Dm7
C7
Gm
F
C
Dm
C
you! you know that I need you!

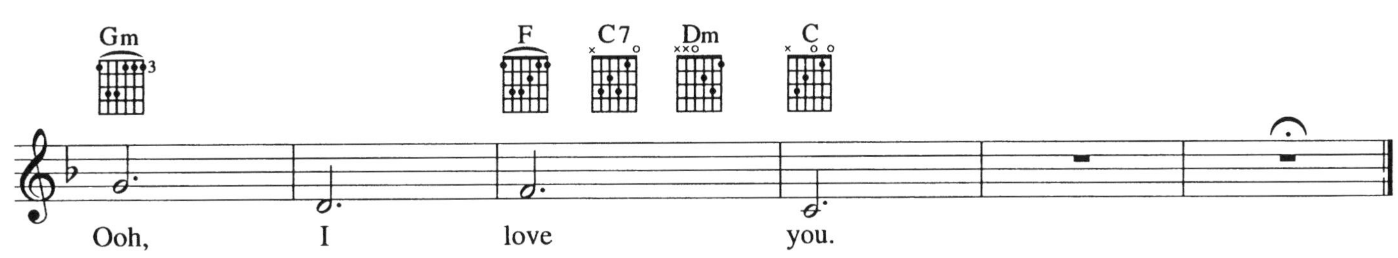

Gm
F
C7
Dm
C
Ooh, I love you.

Martha My Dear.

Words & Music by John Lennon & Paul McCartney.

Moderately
E♭
Dm
Mar - tha, my dear, though I spend my
Gm
C7
F
days in con - ver - sa - tion, please, re - mem - ber
B♭
A♭
B♭7
A♭
me; Mar - tha, my love. Don't for - get me,
B♭7
A♭
B♭7
Dm7
Mar - tha, my dear. Hold your head
Hold your hand
Gm7
F
up, you sil - ly girl; Look what you've done.
out, you sil - ly girl; See what you've done.

Gm/C
When you find your - self in the
C7
Gm/C
A
thick of it, Help your - self to a bit of what is all a - round
Dm7
Gm7
To Coda
Tacet
you, sil - ly girl. Take a
Dm7
G9
Dm7
good look a - round you, Take a good look, you're
G7
C11
bound to see that you and me were
B♭maj7
Dm7
meant to be for each oth - er,

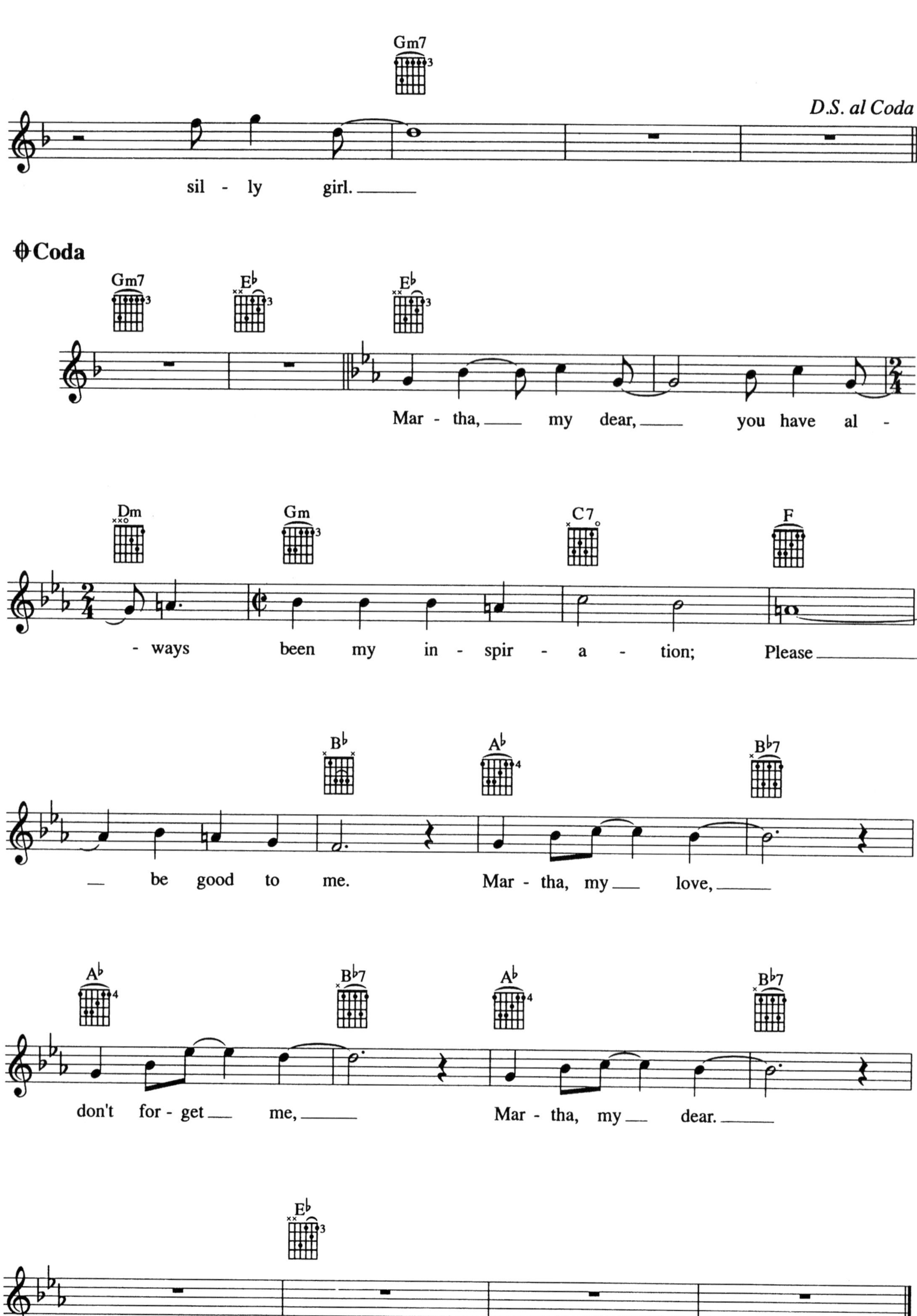
Gm7
D.S. al Coda
sil - ly girl.
Coda
Gm7
E♭
E♭
Mar - tha, my dear, you have al -
Dm
Gm
C7
F
- ways been my in - spir - a - tion; Please
B♭
A♭
B♭7
be good to me. Mar - tha, my love,
A♭
B♭7
A♭
B♭7
don't for - get me, Mar - tha, my dear.
E♭

Mother Nature's Son.

Words & Music by John Lennon & Paul McCartney.

Slowly
D G/D D Bm Bm/A E9
Born a poor young coun - try boy. Moth - er Na - ture's son.
A D/A A D/A A D/A A D/A D Dm
All day long I'm sit - ting, sing - ing songs for ev - 'ry - one.
G/D D Dm G/D D D G/D D
Sit be - side a moun - tain stream.
Find me in my field of grass.
Bm Bm/A E9 A D/A A D/A A D/A A D/A
See her wa - ters rise. Lis - ten to the pret - ty sound of mu - sic as she flies.
Moth - er Na - ture's son. Sway - ing dais - ies sing a la - zy song be - neath the sun.
D Dm G/D D G/D D
Du du du du du du du du du du du
G/D D Dmaj7 D7 Am7/D D7
du du du du du du du du du, du du
G/D Gm/D 1 D 2 D Dm G/D D7
du. Hm, hm, Moth - er Na - ture's son.

Ob-La-Di, Ob-La-Da.

WORDS & MUSIC BY JOHN LENNON & PAUL McCARTNEY.

Bright Tempo
B♭ F7
1. Des - mond had a bar - row in the mar - ket place, Mol -
2. Des - mond takes a trol - ly to the jewel - ler's store, Buys
B♭
- ly is the sing - er in a band. Des - mond says to
a twen - ty car - at gold - en ring. Takes it back to
E♭ B♭
Mol - ly "Girl I like your face", and Mol - ly says this as she
Mol - ly wait - ing at the door and as he gives it to her
F7 B♭
takes him by the hand.
she be - gins to sing:
Ob - la - di, Ob - la - da, life goes on
Dm Gm B♭ F7 B♭
bra. la la how the life goes on.
Dm Gm
Ob - la - di, Ob - la - da, life goes on bra. la

B♭
F7
B♭
1
2
— la how the life goes on. ___

E♭
In a cou - ple of years they have built a home ___ sweet home. ___

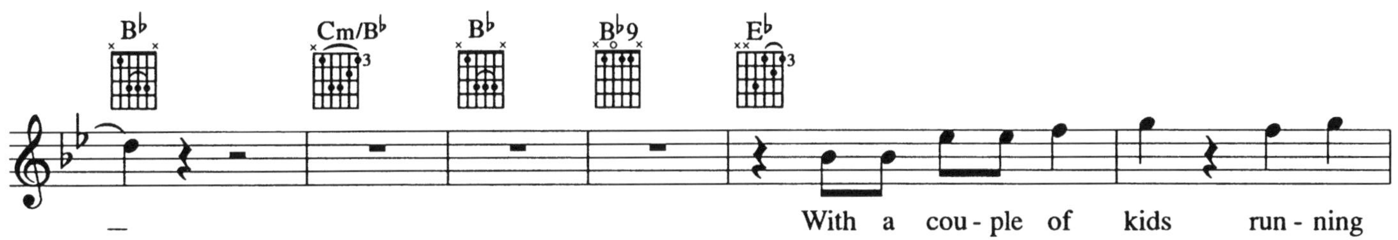
B♭
Cm/B♭
B♭
B♭9
E♭
— With a cou - ple of kids run - ning

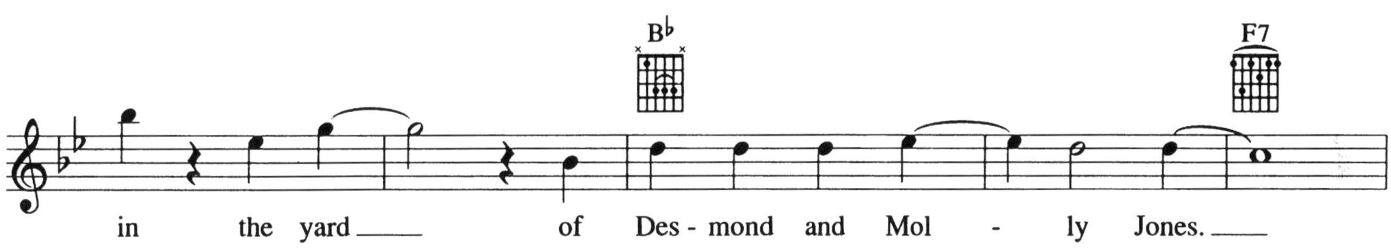
B♭
F7
in the yard ___ of Des - mond and Mol - ly Jones. ___

B♭
F7
Hap - py ev - er af - ter in the mar - ket place; ___ Des -
Hap - py ev - er af - ter in the mar - ket place; ___ Mol -

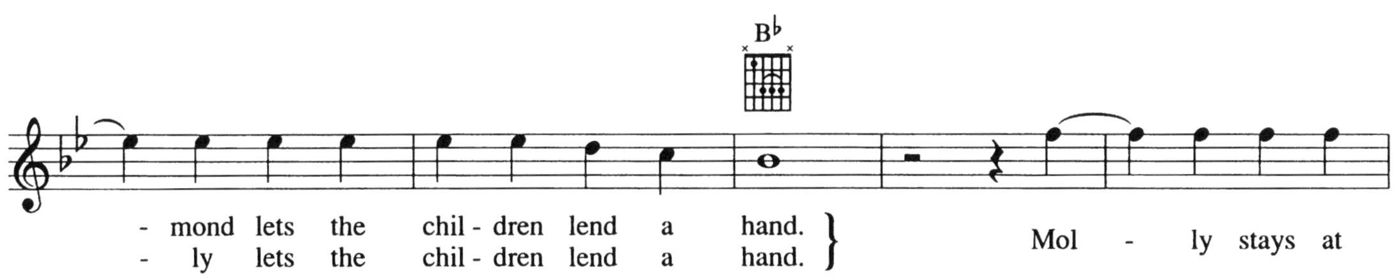
B♭
- mond lets the chil - dren lend a hand.
- ly lets the chil - dren lend a hand.
Mol - ly stays at

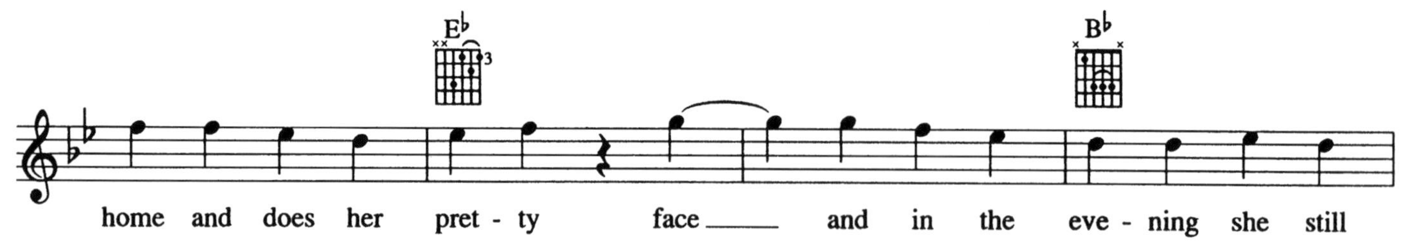
E♭
B♭
home and does her pret - ty face and in the eve - ning she still

F7
B♭
sings it with the band;
Ob - la - di, Ob - la - da, life goes on

Dm
Gm
B♭
F7
B♭
bra. la la how the life goes on. Ob - la - di,

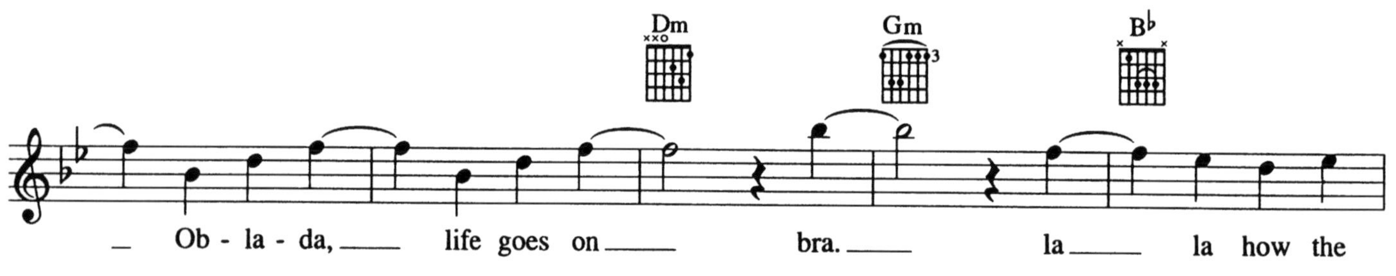
Dm
Gm
B♭
Ob - la - da, life goes on bra. la la how the

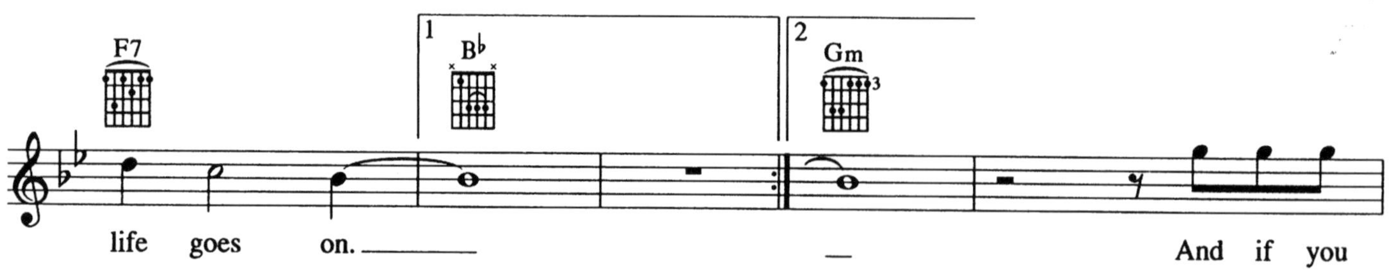
F7
1
B♭
2
Gm
life goes on. And if you

F7
B♭
want some fun take ob - la - di - bla - da.

Savoy Truffle.

Words & Music by George Harrison.

Moderately, with a beat
E7
Cream ___ tan - ger - (3) ine and Mon - tel - i - mar, ___
(2) - cream, and a nice ap - ple tart, ___
F♯
A Gin - ger Sling ___
I feel your taste ___
A
with a pine - ap - ple heart. ___
all the time ___ we're a - part. ___
G
Cof - fee des - sert, ___ yes, you know ___ it's good news, ___
Co - co - nut fudge ___ real - ly blows ___ down those blues, ___
B7
Em
C/E
But you'll have to have them all pulled out ___

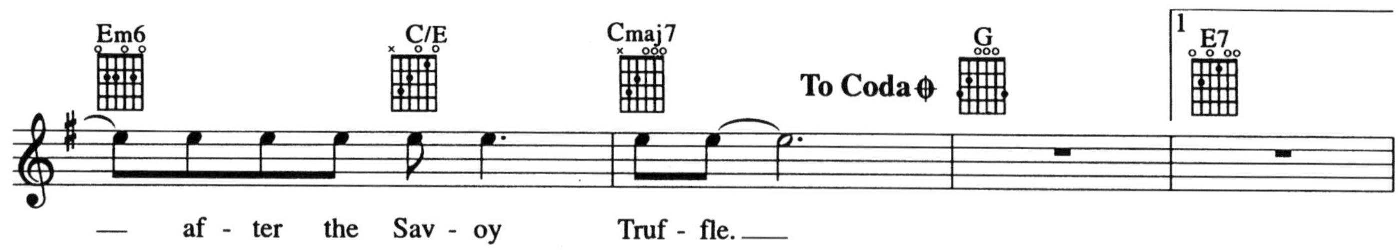
Em6
C/E
Cmaj7
To Coda
G
1
E7
— af - ter the Sav - oy Truf - fle. —

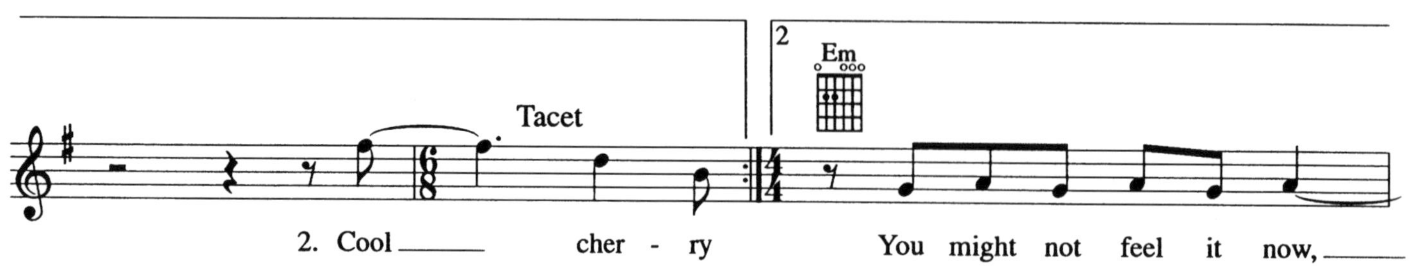
Tacet
2
Em
2. Cool — cher - ry You might not feel it now, —

A
Asus
A
G
B
— But when the pain cuts through, — you're gon - na know, and how. — The

Em
A
Asus
A
sweet is gon - na fill your head; — When it be - comes too much — you'll

G
B
Em
C/E
shout a - loud. — But you'll have to have them all pulled out —

Em6
C/E
Cmaj7
G
— af - ter the Sav - oy Truf - fle. — You

Em
A
Asus
A
know that what you eat, you are; — But what is sweet now — turns

G
B
Em
A
so sour, — We all know "ob - la - di - bla - da," — but can you

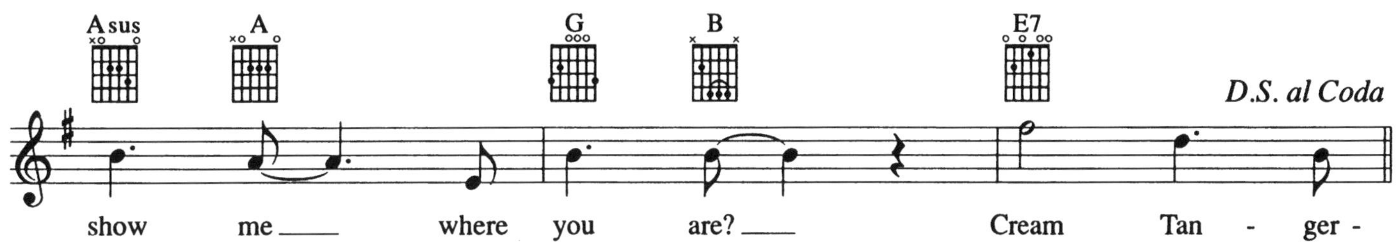
Asus
A
G
B
E7
D.S. al Coda
show me — where you are? — Cream Tan - ger -

Coda
G
Em6
C/E
yes, you'll have to have them all pulled out —

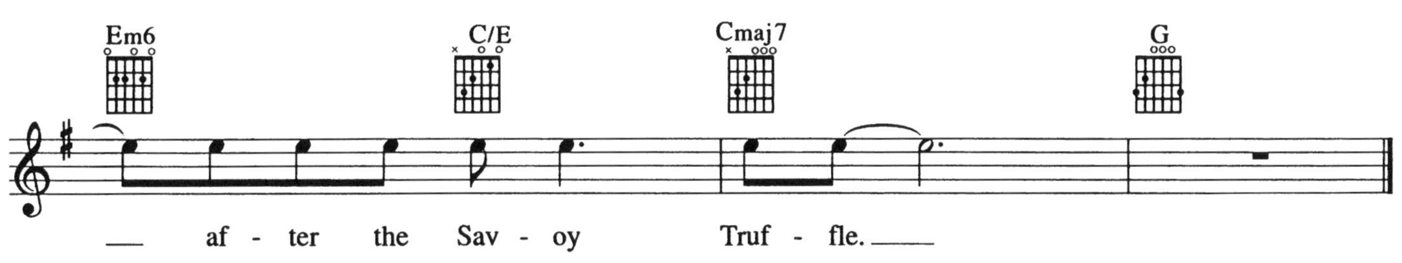
Em6
C/E
Cmaj7
G
— af - ter the Sav - oy Truf - fle. —

Only A Northern Song.

Words & Music by George Harrison.

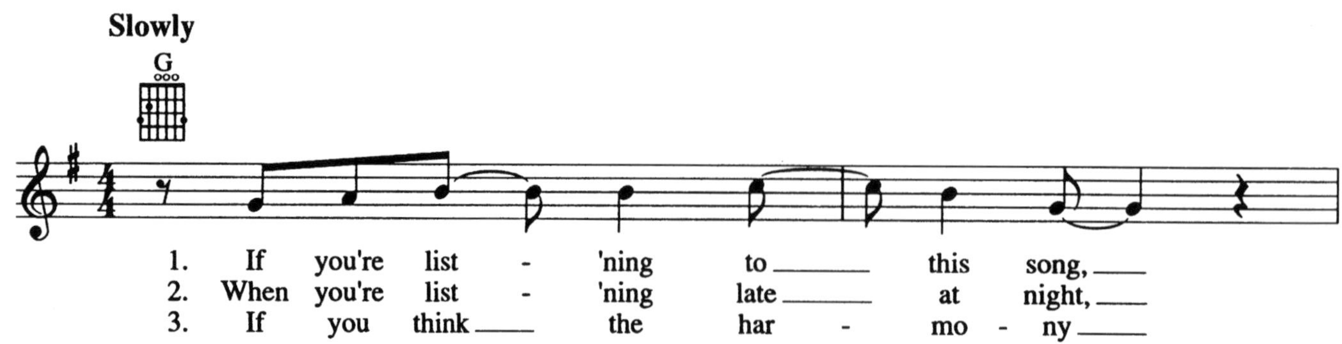
Slowly
G
1. If you're list - 'ning to this song,
2. When you're list - 'ning late at night,
3. If you think the har - mo - ny

You may think the chords are go - in' wrong;
You may think the bands are not quite right;
Is a lit - tle dark and out of key;

C/D D C/D D7

But they're not, He just wrote
But they are, they just play
You're cor - rect: there's no -

To Coda ⊕ 1 C 2 C

it like that. that. It
it like
bod - y

D Am F B7 E7

does - n't real - ly mat - ter what chords I play, what words I say or
does - n't real - ly mat - ter what clothes I wear, or how I fare, or

Am
E7
C
G
time of day it is As it's on - ly a North - ern
if my hair is brown When it's on - ly a North - ern

1
Dsus
G
song.

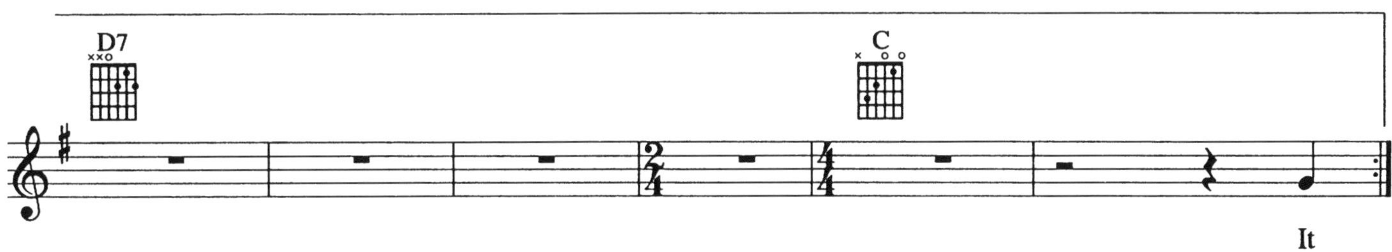
D7
C
It

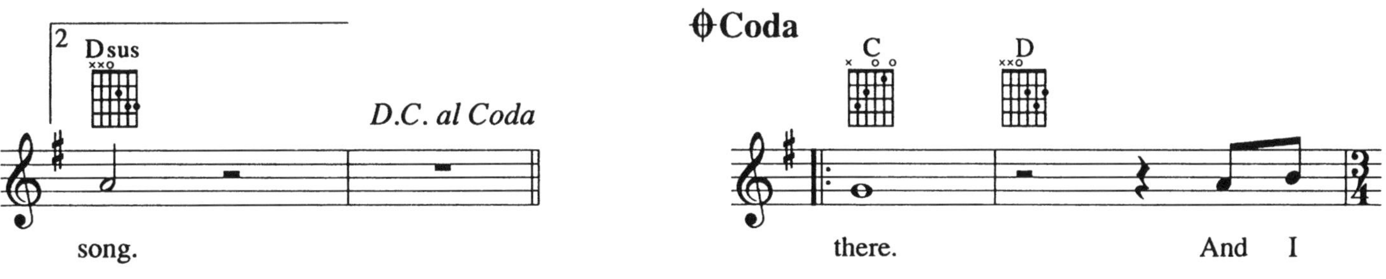
2
Dsus
D.C. al Coda
song.
Coda
C
D
there. And I

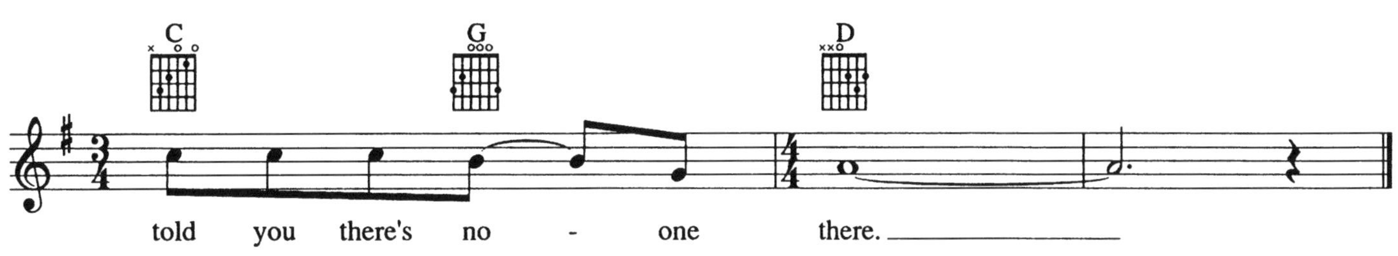
C
G
D
told you there's no - one there.

Piggies.

WORDS & MUSIC BY GEORGE HARRISON.

Slow 4
A♭ E♭7 A♭ E♭
1. Have you seen the lit - tle pig - gies crawl - ing in the dirt?
2. Have you seen the big - ger pig - gies in their starched white shirts?
A♭ E♭ Fm B♭
And for all the lit - tle pig - gies life is get - ting worse.
You will find the big - ger pig - gies stir - ring up the dirt.
Fm B♭ E♭ Fm7 F♯° E♭/G A♭ E♭
Al - ways hav - ing dirt to play a - round in.
Al - ways have clean shirts to play a - round in.
1 A♭ E♭
2 A♭ C7 B♭m C7
In their styles with all their back - ing,
D♭ A♭ E♭
They don't care what goes on a - round;

B♭m C7 D♭ E♭
In their eyes there's some-thing lack-ing, What they need's a damn good whack-ing!
E♭7 A♭ E♭7 A♭ E♭ A♭ E♭7
3. Ev-'ry-where there's lots of pig-gies
A♭ E♭ A♭ E♭7
liv-ing pig-gy lives, You can see them out for din-ner
Fm B♭ Fm B♭
with their pig-gy wives; Clutch-ing forks and knives to
E♭ Fm7 F♯° E♭/G A♭ E♭ A♭m E♭
eat their ba-con.
A♭m E♭7 B♭7 E♭ A E

Revolution.

Words & Music by John Lennon & Paul McCartney.

Moderate Shuffle
C
You say you want a rev - o - lu - tion, Well
(2) say you got a real so - lu - tion, Well
(3) say you'll change the con - sti - tu - tion, Well
F
you know, We all want to change the
you know, We'd all love to see the
you know, We all want to change your
C
C
3
world. You tell me that it's e - vo - lu -
plan. You ask me for a con - tri - bu -
head. You tell me it's the in - sti - tu -
F
- tion, Well you know,
- tion, Well you know,
- tion, Well you know,
G7
We all want to change the world.
We're all do - ing what we can.
You bet - ter free your mind in - stead.
3

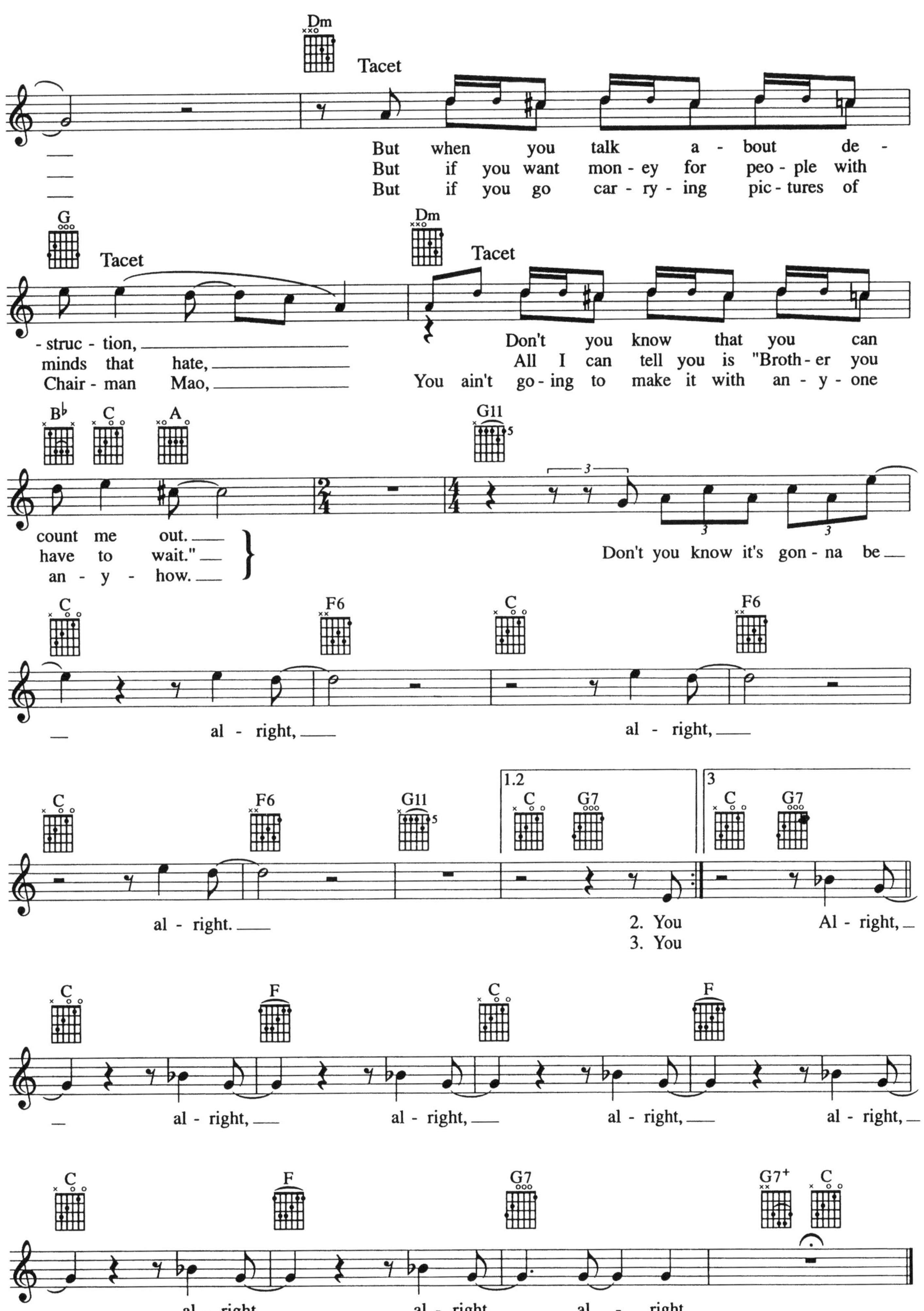
Dm
Tacet
But when you talk a - bout de -
But if you want mon - ey for peo - ple with
But if you go car - ry - ing pic - tures of
G
Tacet
Dm
Tacet
- struc - tion,
minds that hate,
Chair - man Mao,
Don't you know that you can
All I can tell you is "Broth - er you
You ain't go - ing to make it with an - y - one
B♭ C A
G11
count me out.
have to wait."
an - y - how.
Don't you know it's gon - na be
C F6 C F6
al - right,
al - right,
C F6 G11
1.2 C G7
3 C G7
al - right.
2. You
3. You
Al - right,
C F C F
al - right,
al - right,
al - right,
al - right,
C F G7 G7+ C
al - right,
al - right,
al - right.

Rocky Raccoon.

Words & Music by John Lennon & Paul McCartney.

Bright 4
Am7
(Spoken) Now some - where in the Black Moun - tain hills of Da - ko - ta there lived a

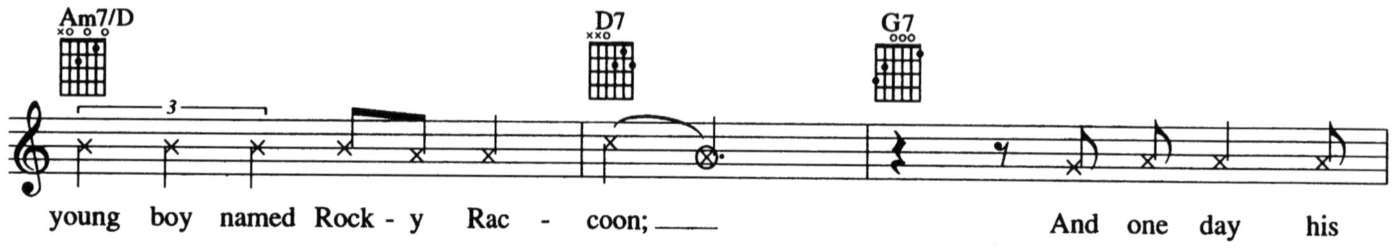
Am7/D
D7
G7
3
young boy named Rock - y Rac - coon;
And one day his

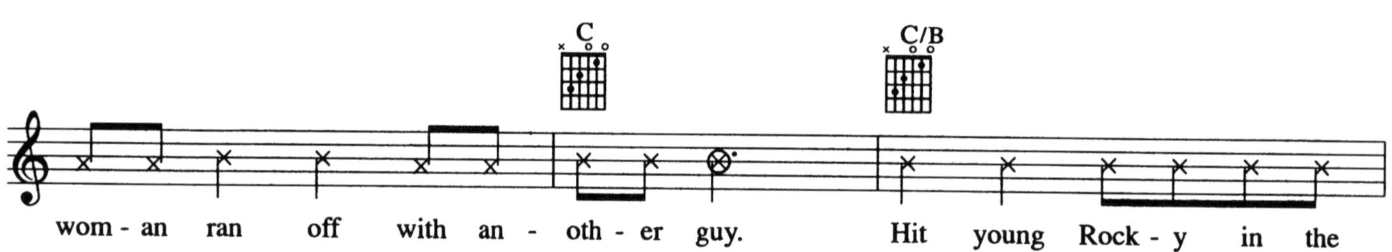
C
C/B
wom - an ran off with an - oth - er guy.
Hit young Rock - y in the

Am7
Am7/D
eye. Rock - y did - n't like that, he said I'm gon - na get that boy.

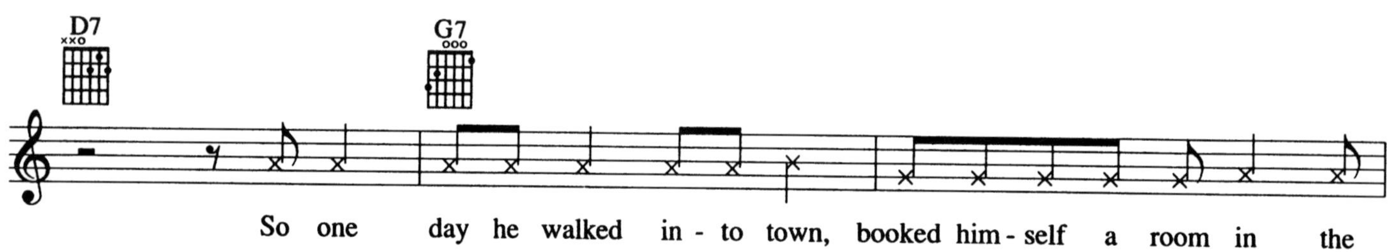
D7
G7
So one day he walked in - to town, booked him - self a room in the

C
C/B
Am7
lo - cal sal - oon. Rock - y Rac - coon checked
she and her man who

Am7/D
D7
G7
in - to his room on - ly to find Gid - eon's Bi -
called him - self Dan were in the next room at the hoe -

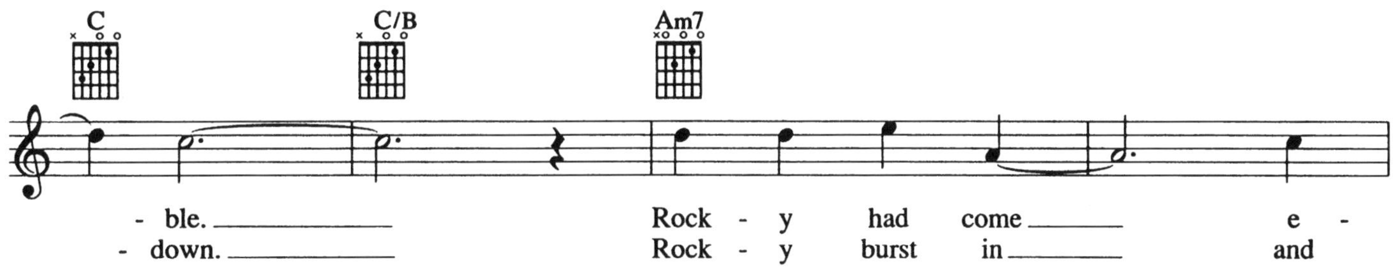
C
C/B
Am7
- ble. Rock - y had come e -
- down. Rock - y burst in and

Am7/D
D7
G7
- quipped with a gun to shoot off the legs
grin - ning a grin, He said "Dan - ny boy, this

C
C/B
Am7
of his ri - val. His ri - val it seems
is a show - down." But Dan - iel was hot,

Am7/D
D7
G7
— had brok - en his dreams by steal - ing the girl
— he drew first and shot and Rock - y col - lapsed
C
1 C/B
Am7
— of his fan - cy. Her name was Ma - gill, And she
— in the cor - ner.
D7
G7
called her - self Lil, but ev - 'ry - one knew her as Nan -
C
C/B
2 C/B
Am7
- cy. Now Now the doc - tor came in
Am7/D
D7
G7
— stink - ing of gin and pro - ceed - ed to lie
C
C/B
Am7
— on the ta - ble. He said, "Rock - y, you met your match,"

Am7/D
D7
And Rock - y said, "Doc, it's on - ly a scratch,
And I'll be

G7
C
C/B
bet - ter, I'll be bet - ter Doc, as soon as I am a - ble."
Now

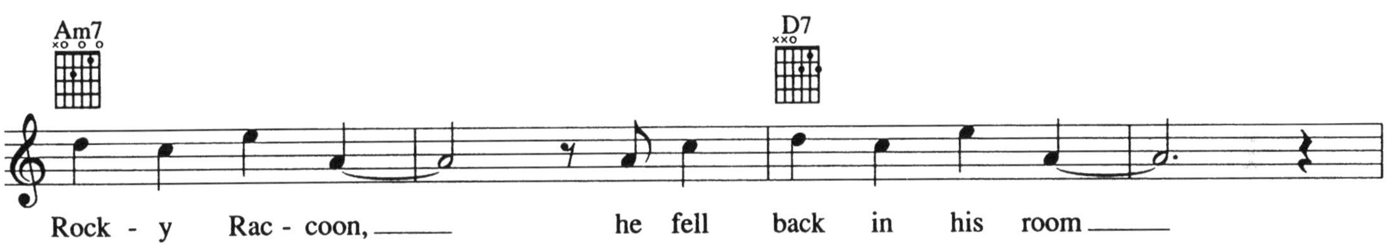
Am7
D7
Rock - y Rac - coon, he fell back in his room

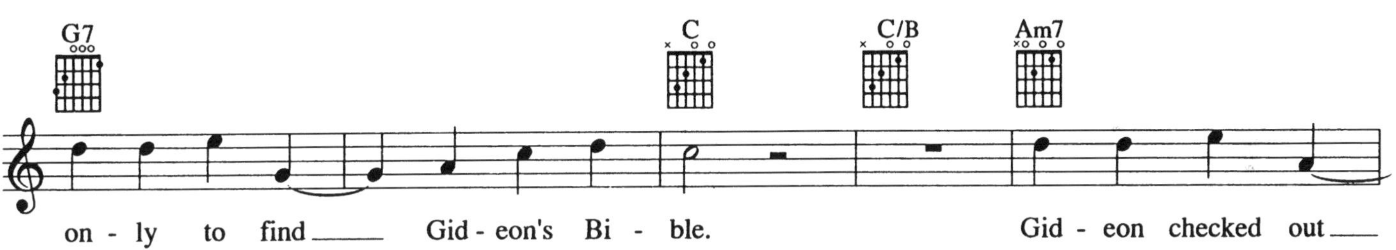
G7
C
C/B
Am7
on - ly to find Gid - eon's Bi - ble.
Gid - eon checked out

Am7/D
D7
G7
and he left in no doubt to help with good Rock -

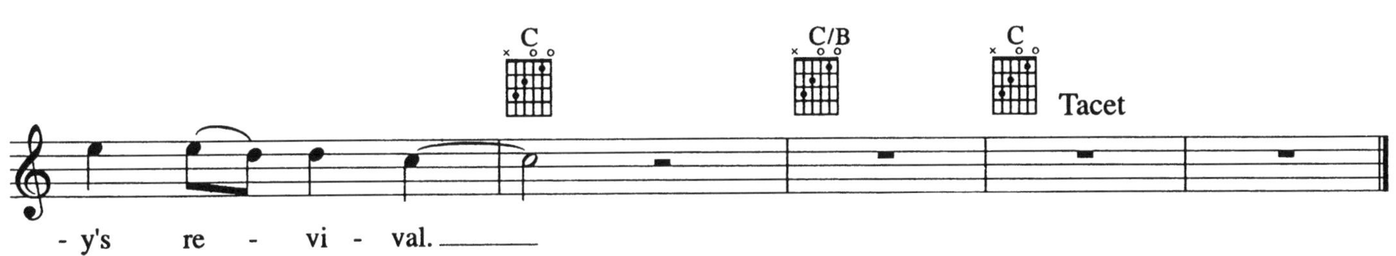
C
C/B
C
Tacet
- y's re - vi - val.

Sexy Sadie.

Words & Music by John Lennon & Paul McCartney.

Very slowly
G F♯7 Bm Bm7
Sex - y Sa - die, what have you done?
Sex - y Sa - die, you broke the rules.
C D G F♯
You made a fool of ev - 'ry - one,
You laid it down for all to see,
C D G F♯
You made a fool of ev - 'ry - one.
You laid it down for all to see.
Sex - y
Sex - y
1 F D
Sa - die, oh what have you done?
2 F D
Sa - die, oh you broke the rules.
G Am Bm C
One sun - ny day, the world was wait - ing for a lov - er;
We gave you ev - 'ry - thing you owned just to sit at her ta - ble;
G Am Bm C
She came a - long to turn on ev - 'ry - one.
Just a smile would light - en ev - 'ry - thing.
Sex - y Sa -
Sex - y Sa -

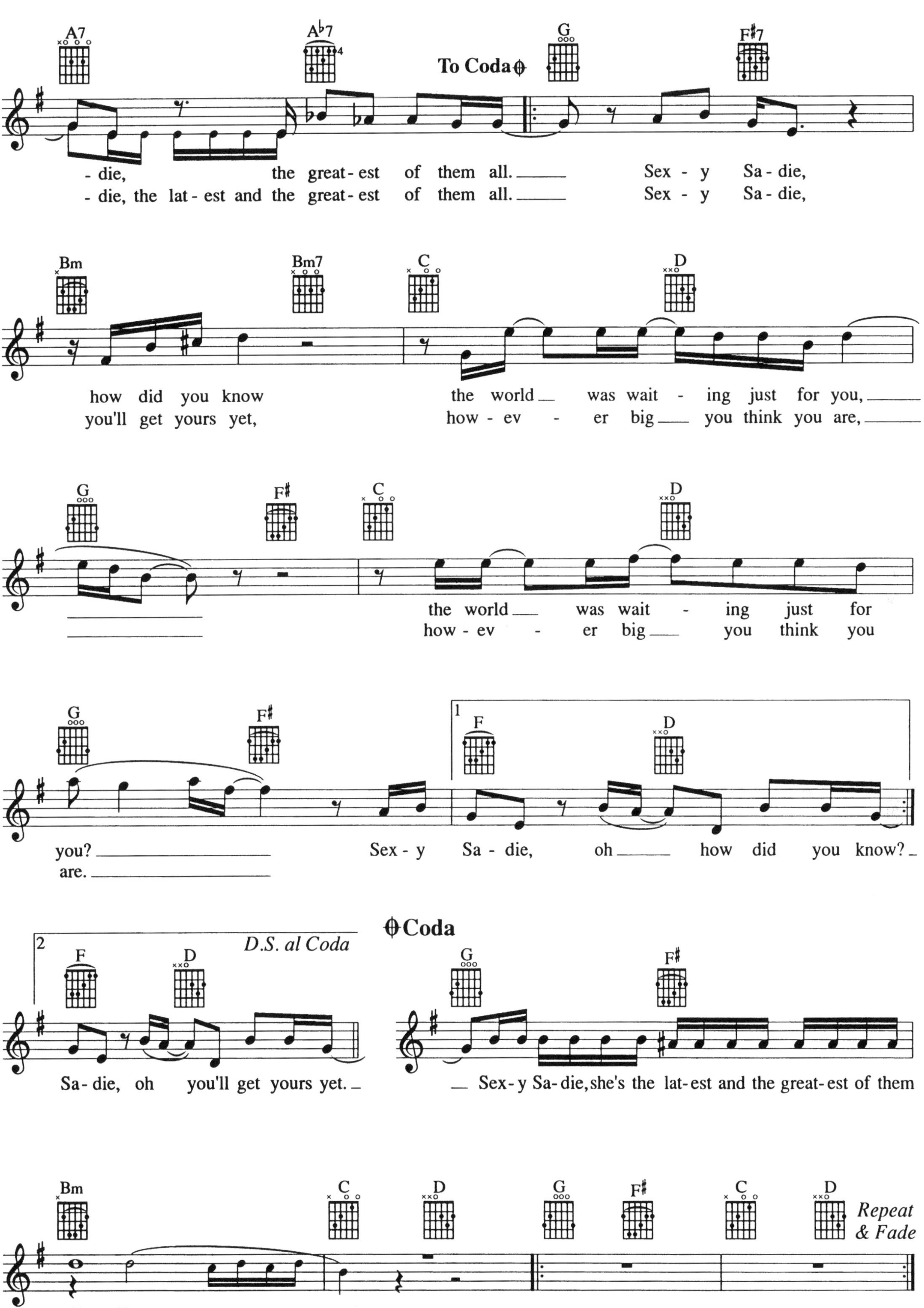

A7
A♭7
To Coda
G
F♯7
- die, the great-est of them all. Sex - y Sa - die,
- die, the lat - est and the great - est of them all. Sex - y Sa - die,
Bm
Bm7
C
D
how did you know the world was wait - ing just for you,
you'll get yours yet, how - ev - er big you think you are,
G
F♯
C
D
the world was wait - ing just for
how - ev - er big you think you
G
F♯
1
F
D
you? Sex - y Sa - die, oh how did you know?
are.
2
F
D
D.S. al Coda
Coda
G
F♯
Sa - die, oh you'll get yours yet. Sex - y Sa - die, she's the lat - est and the great - est of them
Bm
C
D
G
F♯
C
D
Repeat & Fade
all. (Oo)

Step Inside Love.

Words & Music by John Lennon & Paul McCartney.

Moderately
C
Gm7
Step in - side love, Let me find you a place
(2) tired, love, Let me turn down the light,
(3) leave me, Say you'll see me a - gain,
G♭9♭5
G♭7
F
Where the cares of the day will be car - ried a - way by the
Come in out of the cold, rest your head on my shoul - der and
For I'll know in my heart we will not be a - part and I'll
Fm7
E7♭9
E♭
smile on your face. We are to - geth - er now and for -
love me to - night. I'll al - ways be here if you should
miss you till then. We'll be to - geth - er now and for -
F
G7
Tacet
Dm7
- ev - er, come my way.
need me, night and day.
- ev - er, come my way.
Step in - side, love
G7
C
E♭
B♭
F
C
E♭
and stay; Step in - side, love. Step in - side,
B♭
F
C
E♭
B♭
F
C
love, Step in - side, love, I want you to stay.
B♭/C
1.2
C
G7
Tacet
3
C
B♭/C
Repeat and Fade
2. You look
3. When you

Wild Honey Pie.

Words & Music by John Lennon & Paul McCartney.

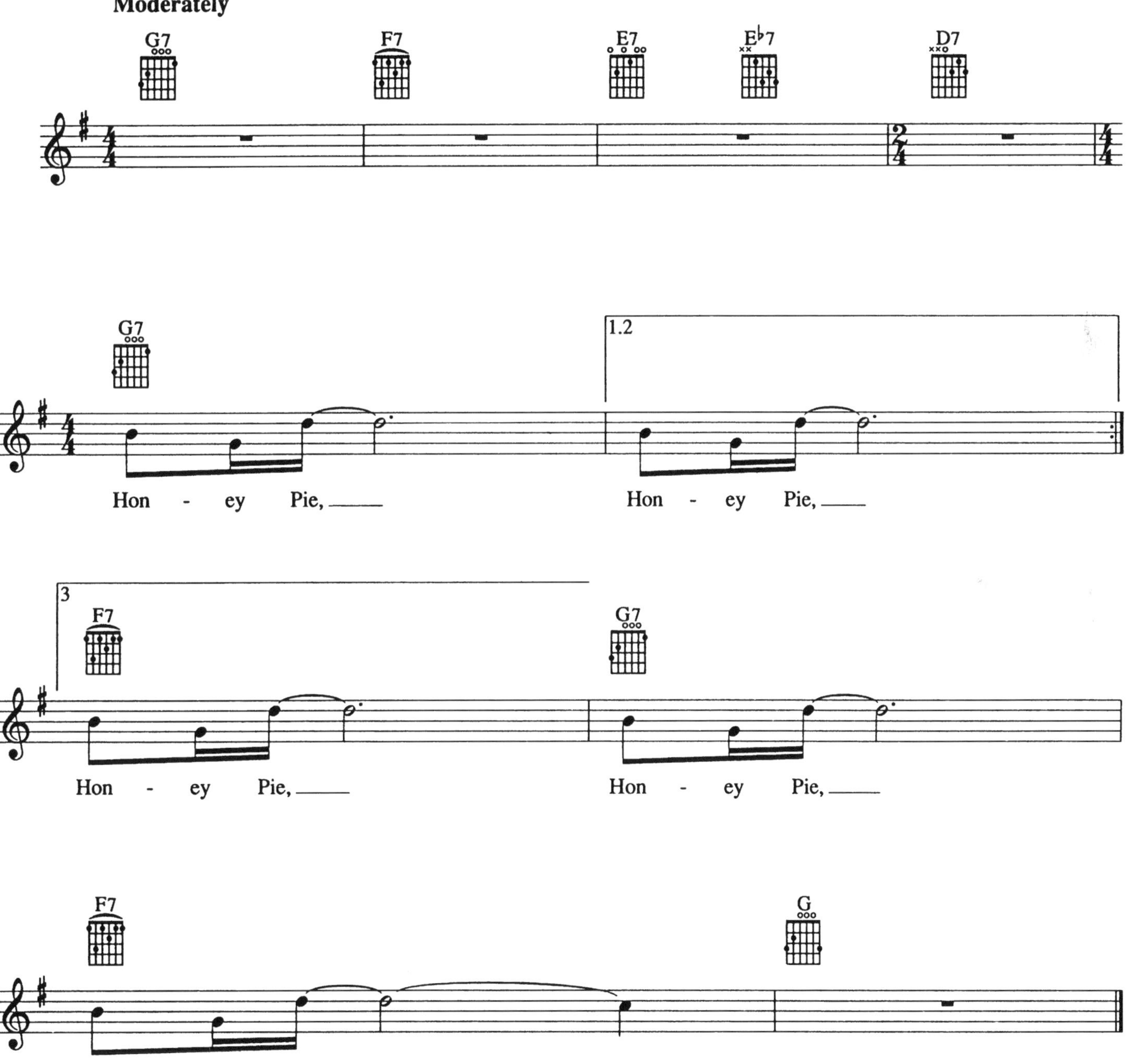
Moderately
G7
F7
E7
E♭7
D7
G7
1.2
Hon - ey Pie,
Hon - ey Pie,
3
F7
G7
Hon - ey Pie,
Hon - ey Pie,
F7
G
Hon - ey Pie,
(Spoken:) I love you honey pie!

The Inner Light.

Words & Music by George Harrison.

Moderately
E♭
E♭7
Fm/E♭
With - out go - ing out of my door I can
- out go - ing out of your door you can
A♭/E♭
know all things on earth.
With - out look - ing out of my
know all things on earth.
With - out look - ing out of your
win - dow I could know the ways of heav - en.
win - dow you can know the ways of heav - en.
The
far - ther one trav - els, the less one knows,
The less one real - ly knows.
To Coda

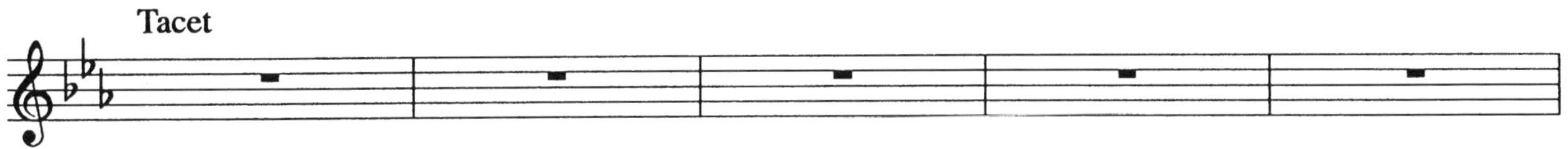
Tacet

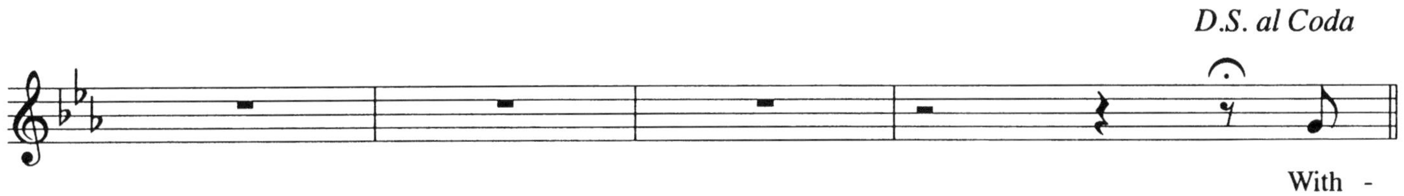
D.S. al Coda
With -

Coda

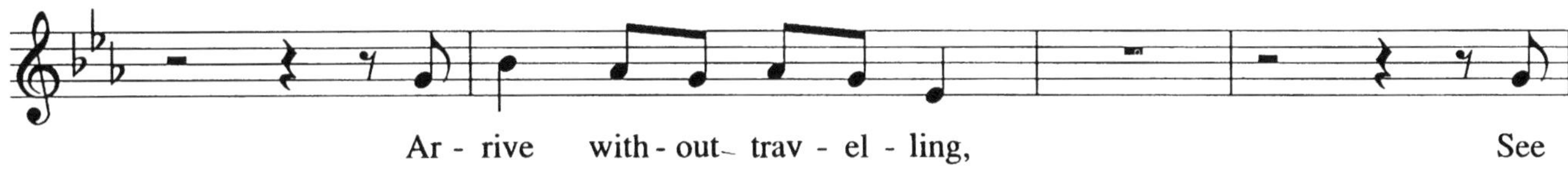
Ar - rive with - out trav - el - ling,
See

all with - out look - ing, do all with - out do - ing.

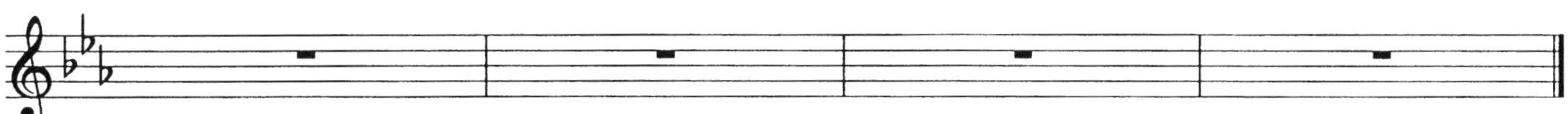

While My Guitar Gently Weeps.

Words & Music by George Harrison.

Moderately
Am
Am/G
F♯m7♭5
I look at you all, see the love there that's sleep -
(2) at the world, and I no - tice it's turn -
Fmaj7
Am
G
D
- ing,
- ing,
While my gui - tar gen - tly weeps.
E7
Am
Am/G
I look at the floor, and I see
With ev - 'ry mis - take we must sure -
F♯m7♭5
Fmaj7
Am
G
it needs sweep - ing,
- ly be learn - ing,
Still my gui - tar gen - tly weeps.
C
E7
A
C♯m7
I don't know why
I don't know how
F♯m
C♯m
Bm
no - bo - dy told you, how to un -
you were di - vert - ed, you were per -

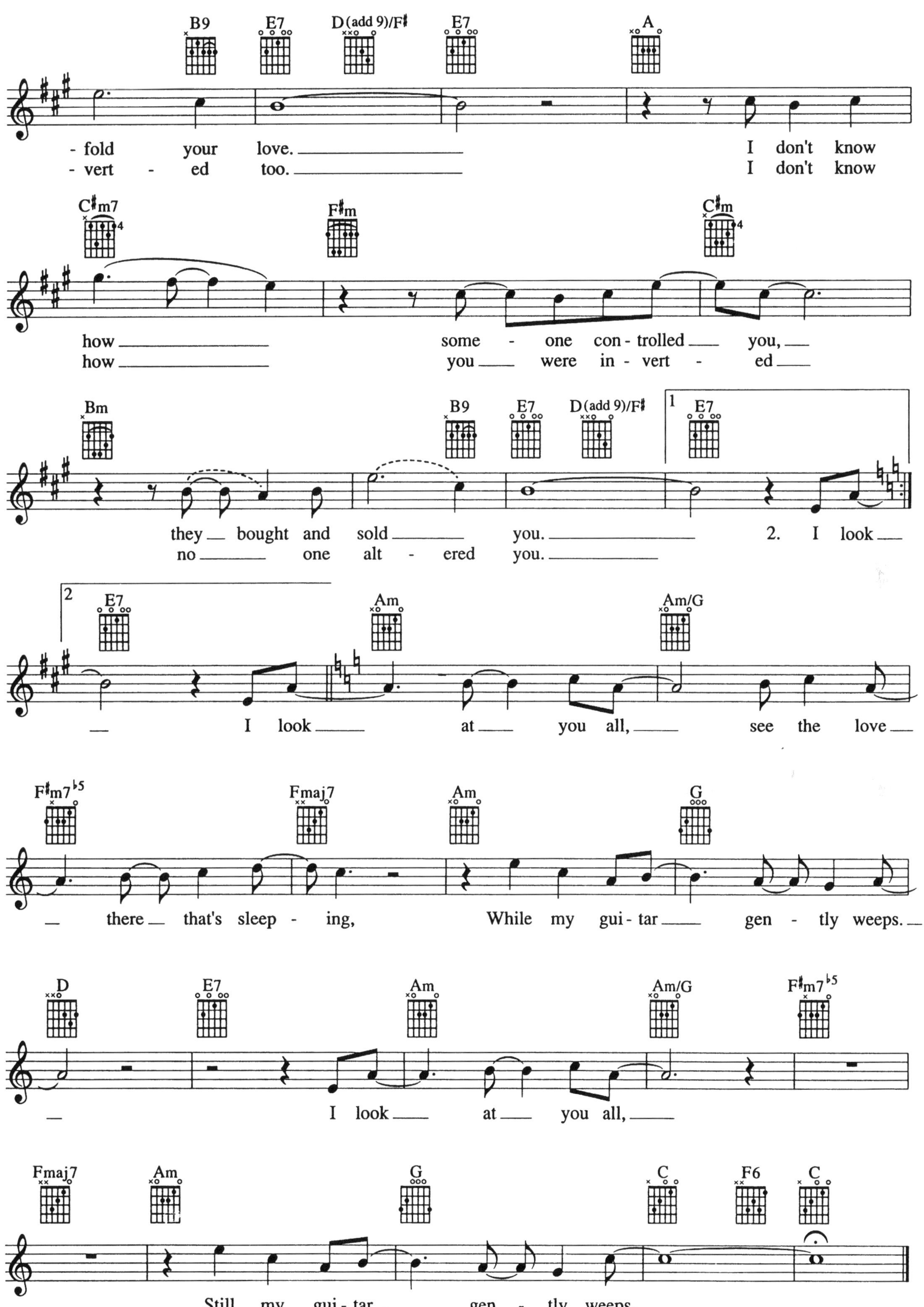
B9 E7 D(add 9)/F♯ E7 A
-fold your love. I don't know
-vert - ed too. I don't know
C♯m7 F♯m C♯m
how some - one con-trolled you,
how you were in - vert - ed
Bm B9 E7 D(add 9)/F♯ E7
they bought and sold you. 2. I look
no one alt - ered you.
E7 Am Am/G
I look at you all, see the love
F♯m7♭5 Fmaj7 Am G
there that's sleep - ing, While my gui-tar gen - tly weeps.
D E7 Am Am/G F♯m7♭5
I look at you all,
Fmaj7 Am G C F6 C
Still my gui-tar gen - tly weeps.

Why Don't We Do It In The Road?

Words & Music by John Lennon & Paul McCartney.

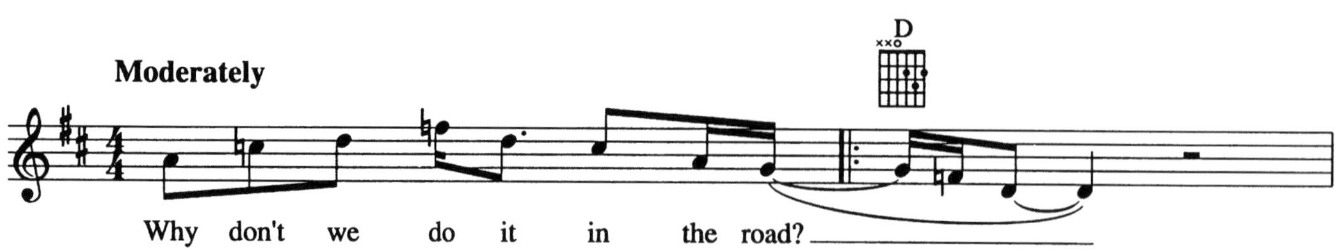
Moderately
D
Why don't we do it in the road?

Why don't we do it in the road?
D7sus
D7
G
Why don't we do it in the road?
G7
D7
Why don't we do it in the road?

A7
1
G7
D7
No-one will be watch - ing us; Why don't we do it in the road?

2
G7
Tacet
Why don't we do it in the road? — — don't we do it in the road? ——

D7
Tacet
D
— Oh, —— Why — don't we do it —— in the road?

Why don't we do it in — the road? ——

D7
G7
Why don't we do it, do — it in the road? ——

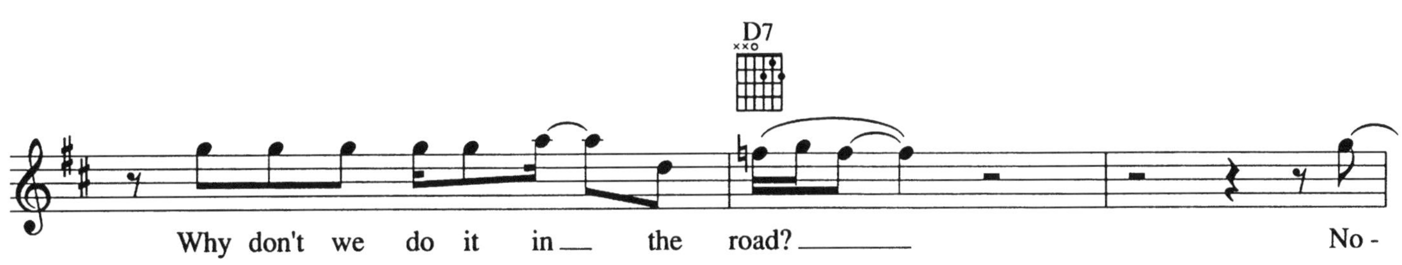
D7
Why don't we do it in — the road? —— No -

A7
G7
Tacet
D7
- one will be watch-ing us; — Why don't we do it in the road?

Yer Blues.

Words & Music by John Lennon & Paul McCartney.

Moderate jazz waltz tempo
C7
1. Yes, I'm lone - ly, wan - na die.
(2) morn - ing, wan - na die.
F7
Yes, I'm lone - ly, wan - na
In the eve - ning, wan - na
C7
E♭
die.
die.
If I ain't dead al - read - y.
G F Em E♭m Dm
Tacet
C
Ooh, girl, you know the reas - on why.
F C
1 G7
2 G7
2. In the
1. My

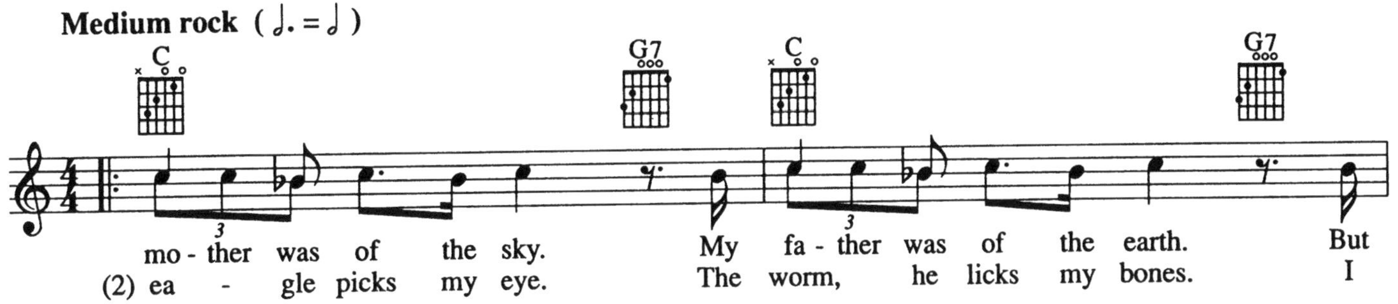
Medium rock
C
G7
C
G7
mo - ther was of the sky. My fa - ther was of the earth. But
(2) ea - gle picks my eye. The worm, he licks my bones. I

C
Tacet
Tempo 1
C7
I am of the u - ni - verse and you know what it's worth.
feel so su - i - ci - dal just like Dy - lan's Mis - ter Jones.
I'm

F
C7
lone - ly, wan - na die.

E♭
If I ain't dead al - read - y,

G
F
Em
E♭m
Dm
Tacet
C
ooh girl, you know the rea - son why.

F
C
1 G7
2 G7
(2) The
The

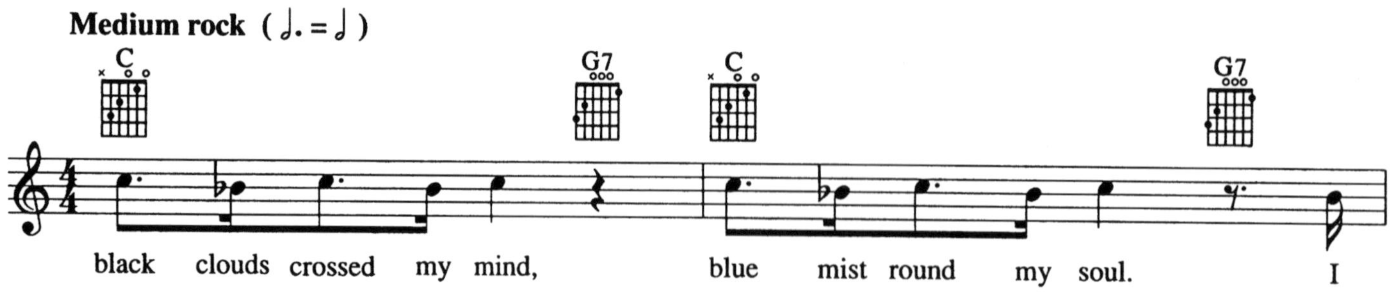
Medium rock (𝅗𝅥. = 𝅗𝅥)
C
G7
C
G7
black clouds crossed my mind, blue mist round my soul. I

C
feel so su - i - ci - dal ev - en hate my rock and roll. Wan - na

F7
C7
die. Yeah, wan - na die.

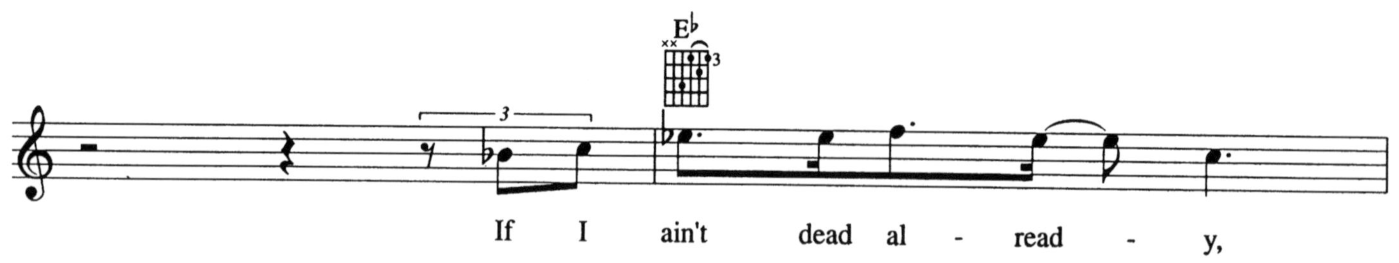
E♭
If I ain't dead al - read - y,

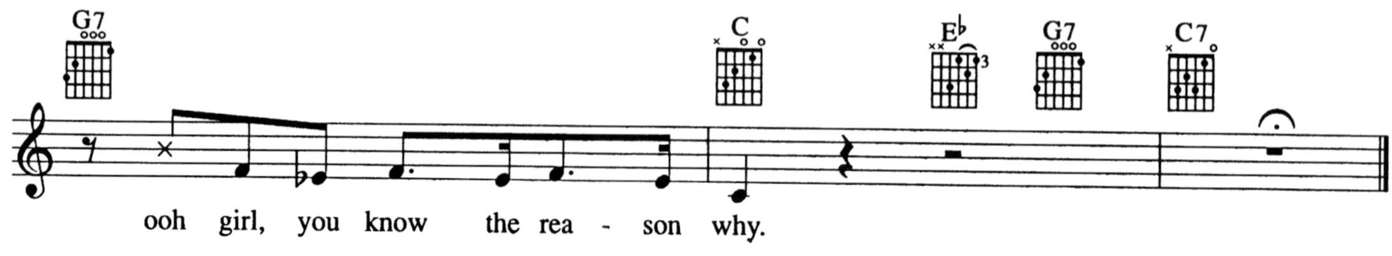
G7
C
E♭
G7
C7
ooh girl, you know the rea - son why.

Because.

Words & Music by John Lennon & Paul McCartney.

Moderately Slow
D♭ C♯° Cm
Ah 1. Be - cause the world is round, it turns me
cause the wind is high, it blows my
cause the sky is blue, it makes me
Dm7♭5 G7/D A♭ Cm A♭9 A♭13
To Coda
on; Be - cause the world is round.
mind; Be - cause the wind is high.
cry; Be - cause the sky is blue.
D♭ C♯° C♯°
Tacet
Tacet
Ah 2. Be - Love is old, love is
F G7
D.S. al Coda
new; love is all, love is you. 3. Be -
Coda
D♭ C♯° Cm
Ah
Dm7♭5 G7/D A♭
Ah
Cm A♭9 A♭13 D♭ D♭°
Oo Ah.

Carry That Weight.

Words & Music by John Lennon & Paul McCartney.

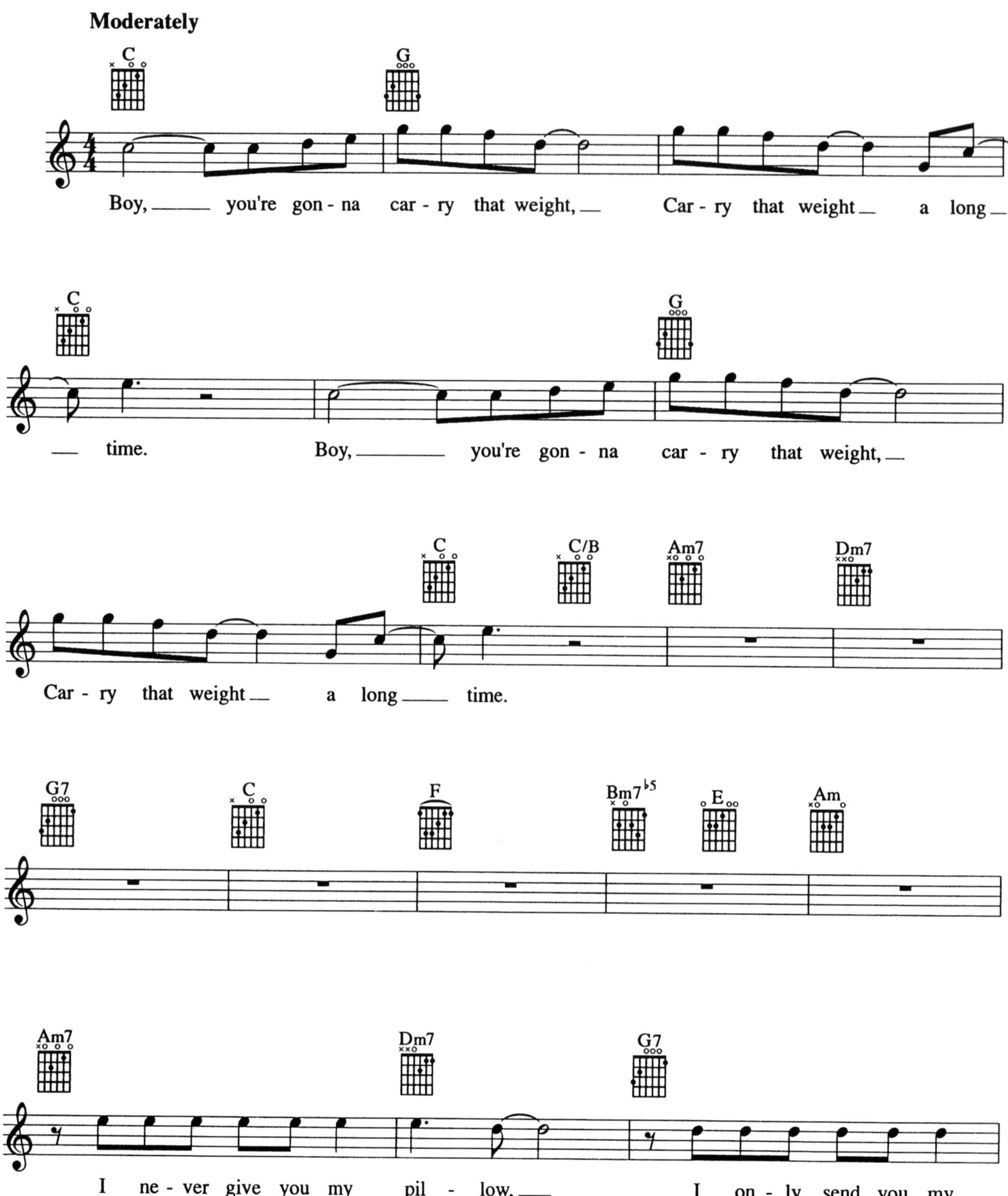
Moderately
C
G
Boy, you're gon - na car - ry that weight, Car - ry that weight a long
C
G
time. Boy, you're gon - na car - ry that weight,
C
C/B
Am7
Dm7
Car - ry that weight a long time.
G7
C
F
Bm7♭5
E
Am
Am7
Dm7
G7
I ne - ver give you my pil - low, I on - ly send you my

C
Fmaj7
Bm7♭5
E7
in - vi - ta - tions. And in the mid - dle of the cel - e - bra - tions, I

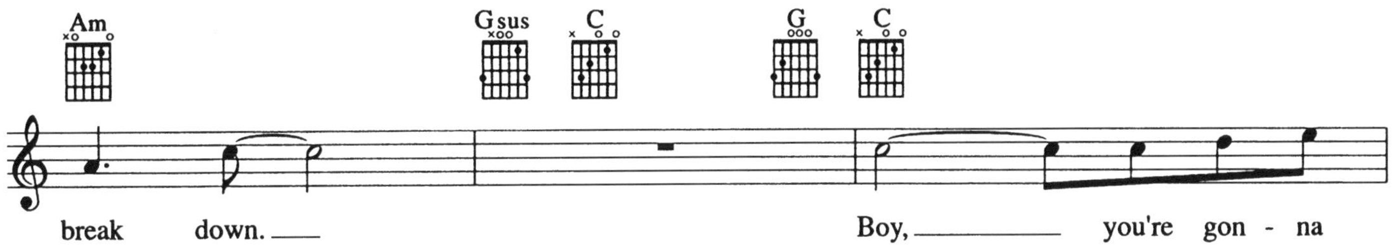
Am
Gsus
C
G
C
break down. Boy, you're gon - na

G
C
car - ry that weight, Car - ry that weight a long time.

C
G
Boy, you're gon - na car - ry that weight, Car - ry that weight a long

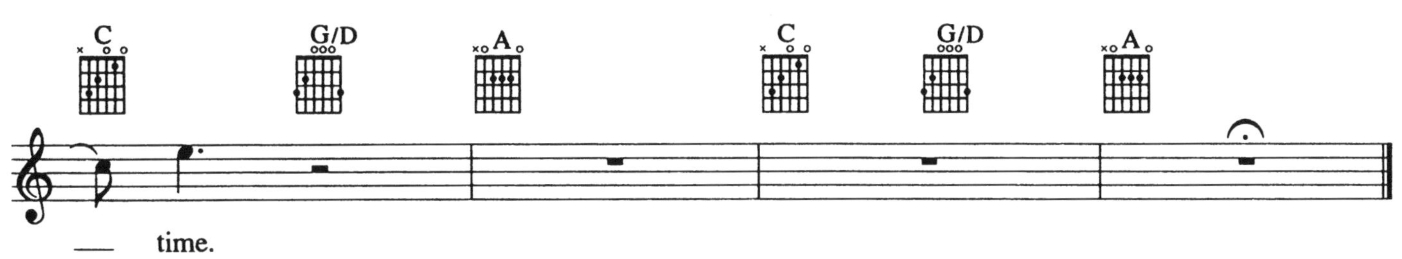
C
G/D
A
C
G/D
A
time.

Come Together.

WORDS & MUSIC BY JOHN LENNON & PAUL McCARTNEY.

Moderately slow, with double tempo feel

Dm7
1. Here come old flat - top, He come groov - ing up slow - ly, He got

A
Joo Joo eye - ball, He one ho - ly roll - er, He got hair down

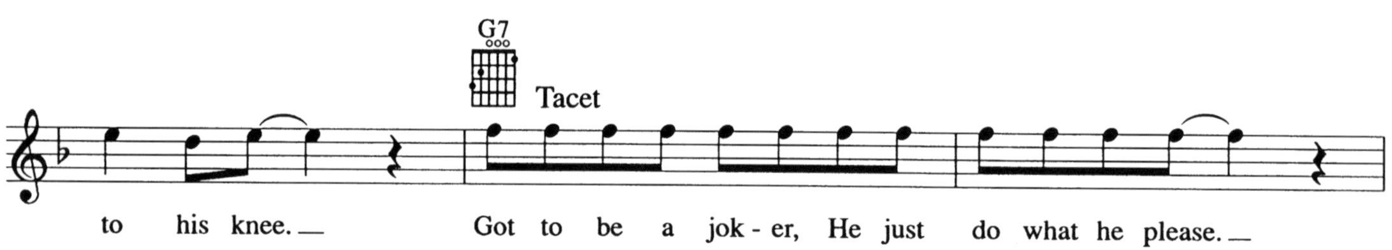
G7
Tacet
to his knee. Got to be a jok - er, He just do what he please.

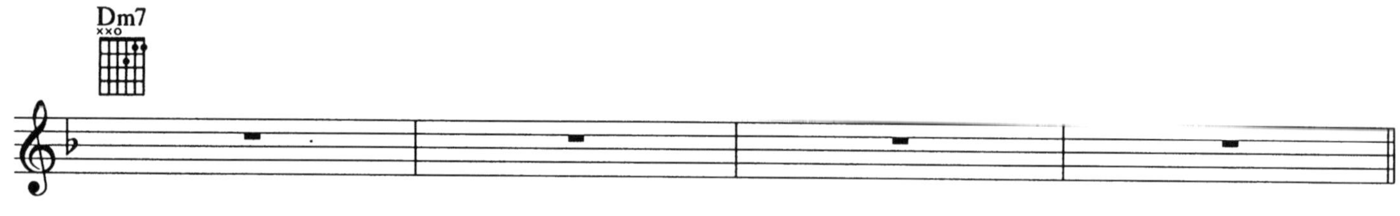
Dm7

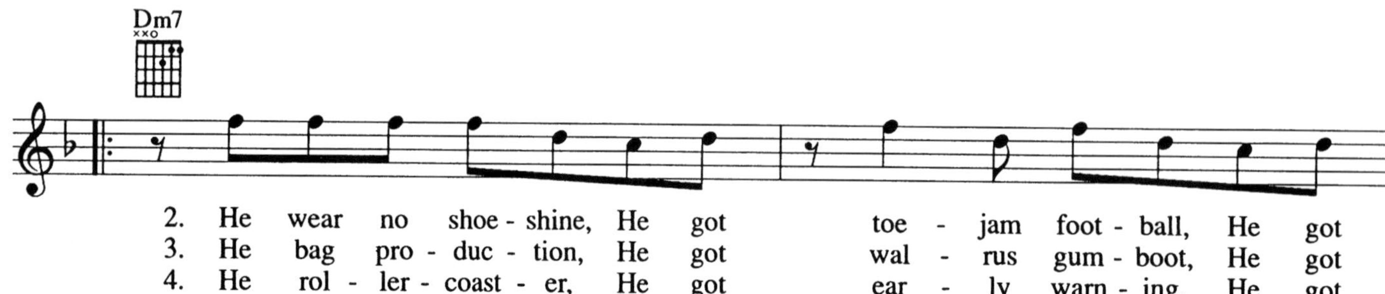
Dm7
2. He wear no shoe - shine, He got toe - jam foot - ball, He got
3. He bag pro - duc - tion, He got wal - rus gum - boot, He got
4. He rol - ler - coast - er, He got ear - ly warn - ing, He got

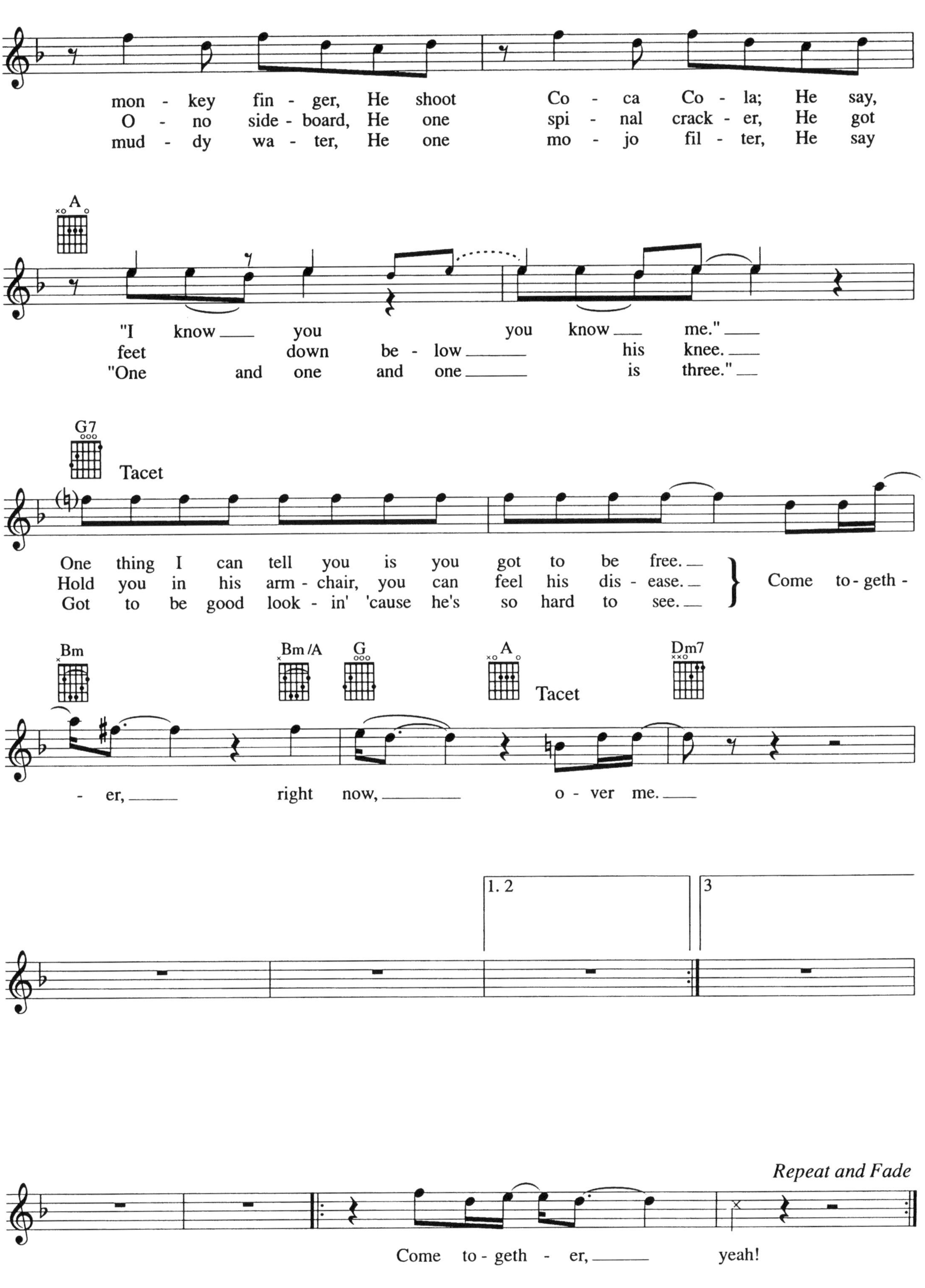

mon - key fin - ger, He shoot Co - ca Co - la; He say,
O - no side - board, He one spi - nal crack - er, He got
mud - dy wa - ter, He one mo - jo fil - ter, He say

A

"I know ___ you you know ___ me." ___
feet down be - low ___ his knee. ___
"One and one and one ___ is three." ___

G7
Tacet

One thing I can tell you is you got to be free. ___
Hold you in his arm - chair, you can feel his dis - ease. ___
Got to be good look - in' 'cause he's so hard to see. ___
} Come to - geth -

Bm Bm/A G A Dm7
Tacet

- er, ___ right now, ___ o - ver me. ___

1. 2 3

Repeat and Fade
Come to - geth - er, ___ yeah!

Don't Let Me Down.

Words & Music by John Lennon & Paul McCartney.

Slowly
Fm
Fm7
B♭11
E♭
Don't let me down,
Don't let me down.
Fm
Fm7
B♭11
Don't let me down,
Don't let me
A♭/E♭
E♭
Tacet
down.
No - bod - y ev - er loved me like she
And from the first time that she real - ly
Fm7
Fm/B♭
E♭
E♭sus
does, Oo she does, yes, she does.
done me, Oo she done me, she done me good.
E♭
Tacet
Fm
And if some - bod - y loved me like she do me, Oo she
I guess no - bod - y ev - er real - ly done me, Oo she

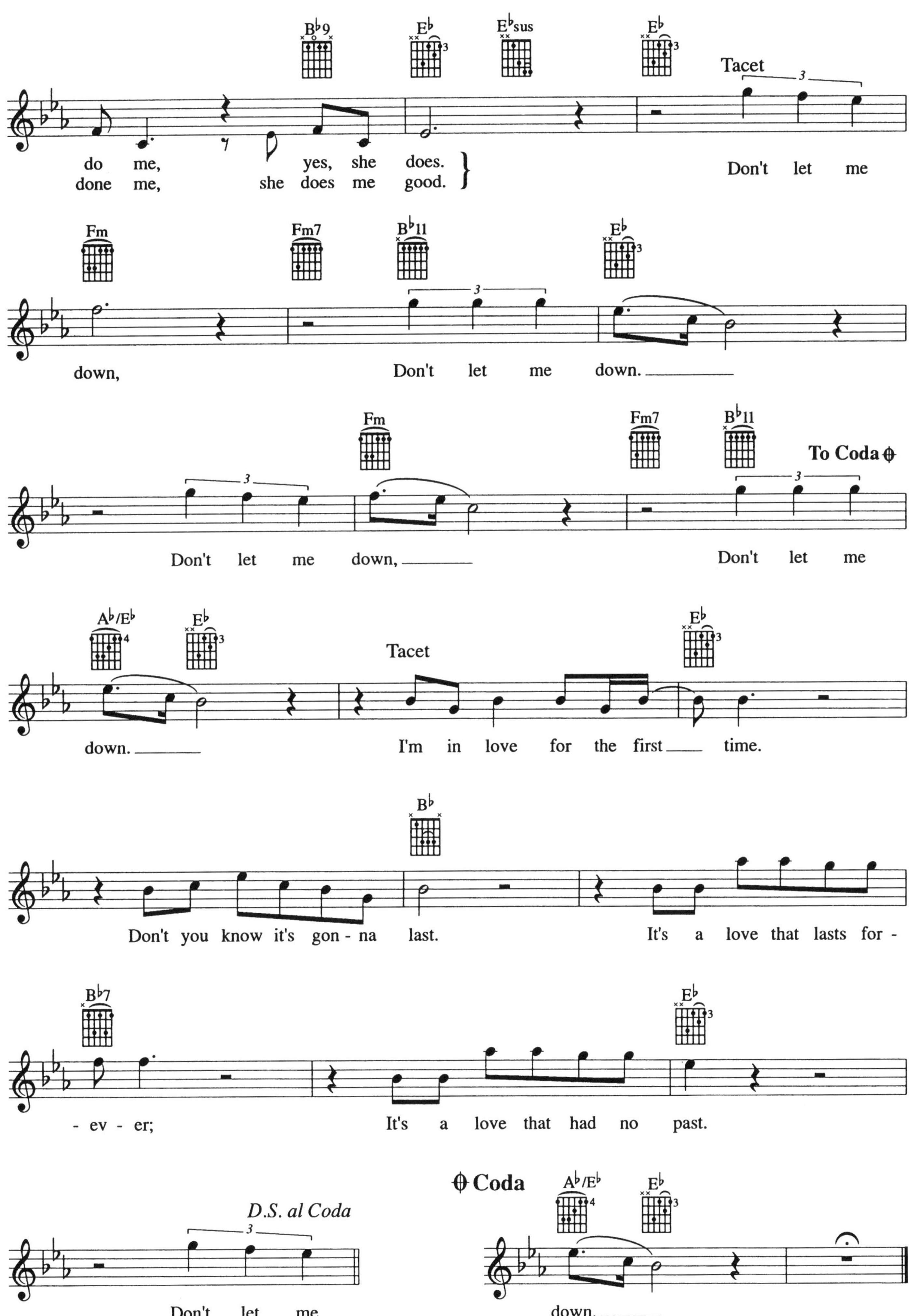

B♭9
E♭
E♭sus
E♭
Tacet
do me, yes, she does.
done me, she does me good.
Don't let me
Fm
Fm7
B♭11
E♭
down, Don't let me down.
Fm
Fm7
B♭11
To Coda
Don't let me down, Don't let me
A♭/E♭
E♭
Tacet
E♭
down. I'm in love for the first time.
B♭
Don't you know it's gon - na last. It's a love that lasts for -
B♭7
E♭
- ev - er; It's a love that had no past.
D.S. al Coda
Don't let me
Coda
A♭/E♭
E♭
down.

Get Back.

Words & Music by John Lennon & Paul McCartney.

Moderately
A
D/A
A7
D
D7
1. Jo Jo was a man who thought he was a lon - er, but he knew it could - n't last. Jo Jo left his home in Tuc - son, Ar - i - zo - na, for some Cal - i - for - nia grass.
2. Sweet Lor - et - ta Mar - tin thought she was a wom - an, but she was an - oth - er man. All the girls a - round her say she's got it com - ing, but she gets it while she can.
Get back! Get back! Get back to where you once be - longed. Get back! Get back! Get back to where you once be - longed.
1
(Get back, Jo Jo)
2
Tacet

Give Peace A Chance.

Words & Music by John Lennon & Paul McCartney.

Moderately
C
Ev - 'ry - bod - y's talk - ing a - bout 1. Bag - is - m, Shag - is - m,
2. Min - is - ters, Sin - is - ters,
3. Rev - o - lu - tion, Ev - o - lu - tion,
4. John and Yo - ko, Tim - my Lea - ry,
Drag - is - m, Mad - is - m, Rag - is - m, Tag - is - m,
Ban - is - ters and Can - is - ters, Bish - ops and Fish - ops,
Mas - ti - ca - tion, Fla - gel - la - tion, Reg - u - la - tions, In - te - gra - tions,
Rose - ma - ry, Tom - my Smoth - ers, Bob - by Dy - lan, Tom - my Coo - per,
This - is - m, That - is - m, is - m, is - m, is - m.
Rab - bits and Pop - eyes, Bye - bye Bye - byes.
Med - i - ta - tions, U - nited Na - tions Con - grat - u - la - tions.
De - rek Tay - lor, Nor - man Mail - er, All - en Gins - berg, Ha - re Krish - na,
G7
Ha - re, Ha - re Krish - na. All we are say - ing is
F Em G7 C G7
give peace a chance. All we are say -
F Em G7 C
1.2.3
4
- ing is give peace a chance.

Golden Slumbers.

Words & Music by John Lennon & Paul McCartney.

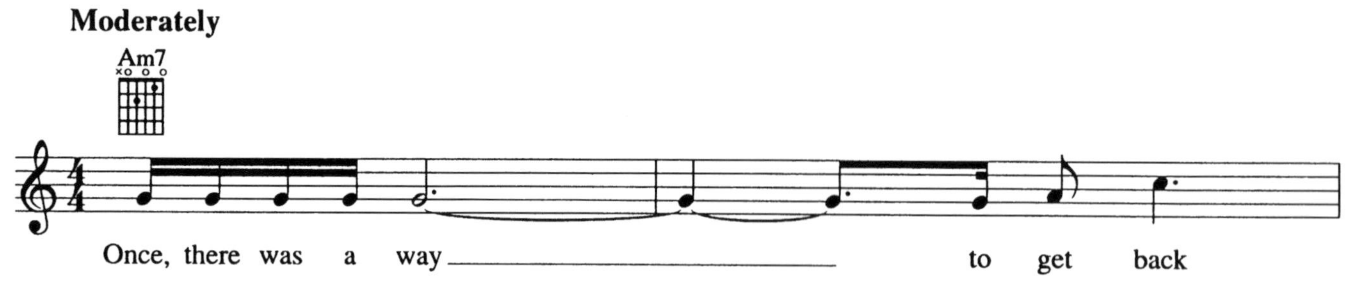
Moderately
Am7
Once, there was a way to get back

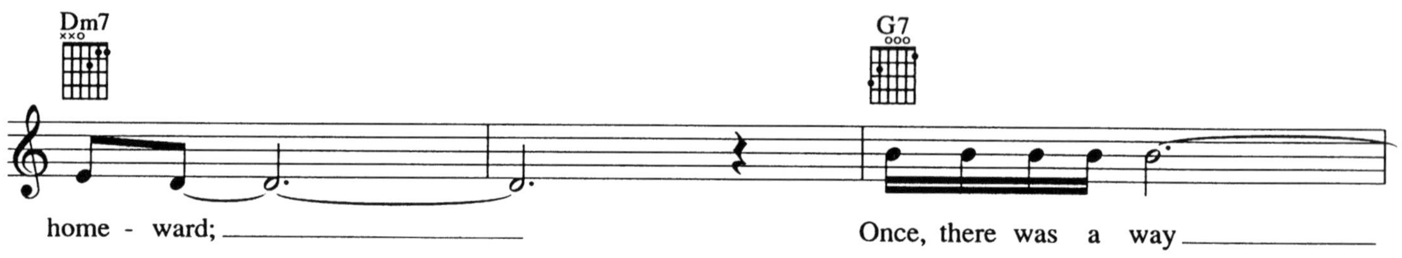
Dm7
G7
home - ward; Once, there was a way

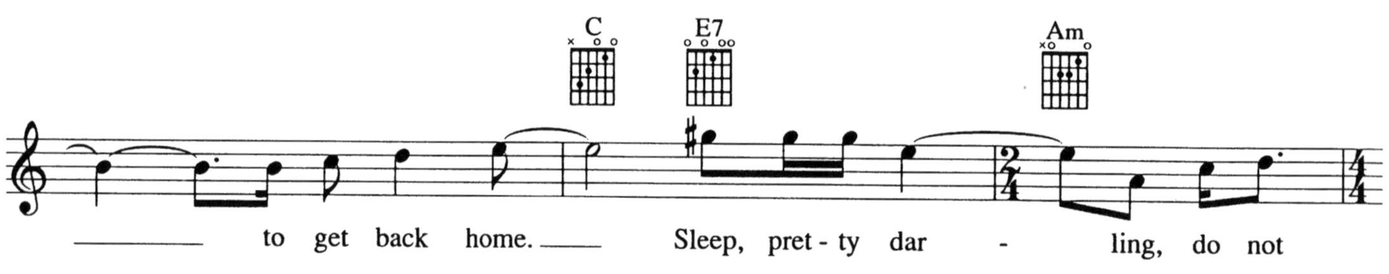
C
E7
Am
to get back home. Sleep, pret - ty dar - ling, do not

Dm9
G7
C
cry, And I will sing a lul - la - by.

Fmaj7
C
Gold - en slum - bers fill your eyes.

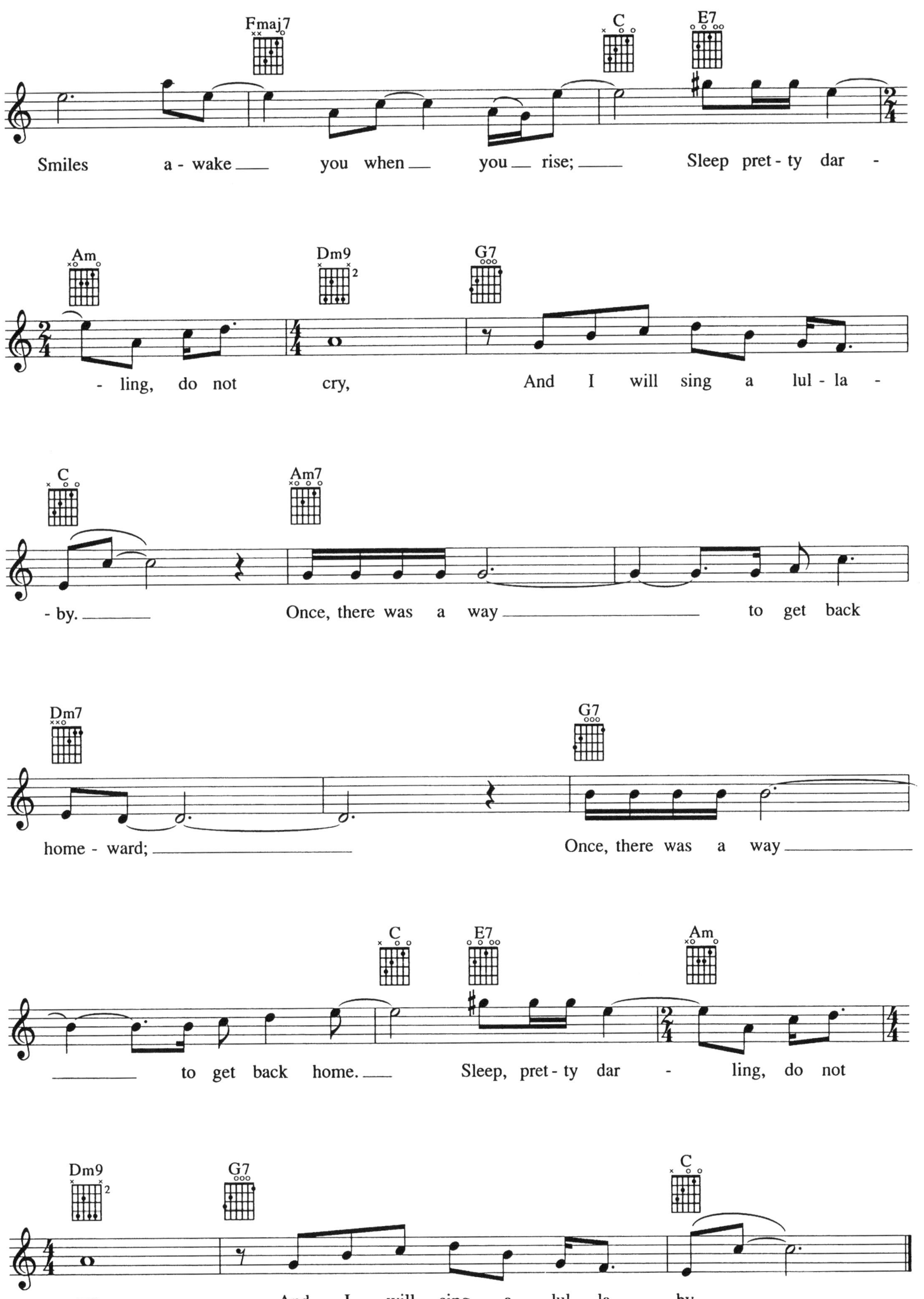
Fmaj7 C E7
Smiles a - wake you when you rise; Sleep pret - ty dar -
Am Dm9 G7
- ling, do not cry, And I will sing a lul - la -
C Am7
- by. Once, there was a way to get back
Dm7 G7
home - ward; Once, there was a way
C E7 Am
to get back home. Sleep, pret - ty dar - ling, do not
Dm9 G7 C
cry, And I will sing a lul - la - by.

Goodbye.

Words & Music by John Lennon & Paul McCartney.

Moderately bright
G Bm Em
1. Please don't wake me un - til late; To - mor - row comes and
2. Songs that lin - gered on my lips ex - cite me now and
3. Far a - way, my lov - er sings a lone - ly song and
C Am7 D7 G D7 G
I will not be late. Late to - day, when it be -
lin - ger on my mind. Leave your flow - ers at my
calls me to his side. When a song of lone - ly
Bm Em C D7 G Am7
- comes to - mor - row. I will leave to go a - way.
door, I'll leave them for the one who waits be - hind.
love in - vites me on, I must go to his side.
D7
Good - bye, good - bye, good - bye,
1.2
3
G
good - bye, my love, good - bye.
love, good - bye.

Her Majesty.

Words & Music by John Lennon & Paul McCartney.

Fairly Bright
F
Her Maj - es - ty's a pret - ty nice girl, But she
G7 C7 F
does - n't have a lot to say.
Her Maj - es - ty's a
G7 C7
pret - ty nice girl, But she chang - es from day to day.
Dm
I wan - na tell her that I love her a lot, but I
F7 B♭ B♭m
got - ta get a bel - ly full of wine.
Her Maj - es - ty's a
F D7 Gm7 C7
pret - ty nice girl, Some day I'm gon - na make her mine,
F D7 Gm7 C7 F
oh yeah, Some day I'm gon - na make her mine.

Here Comes The Sun.

Words & Music by George Harrison.

Moderately
A
Dmaj7
Here comes the sun, doo da doo doo, Here comes the sun,
B7/D♯
A
D
A/C♯
Bm7
E7
and I say "It's all right."
D
1. Lit - tle dar - ling, it's been a long, cold, lone - ly win - ter;
2. Lit - tle dar - ling, the smiles re - turn - ing to their fac - es;
3. Lit - tle dar - ling, I feel that ice is slow - ly melt - ing;
Lit - tle dar - ling, it feels like years since it's been here.
Lit - tle dar - ling, it seems like years since it's been here.
Lit - tle dar - ling, it seems like years since it's been clear.
Dmaj 9
Here comes the sun, Here comes the sun,
B7
To Coda
and I say "It's all right."

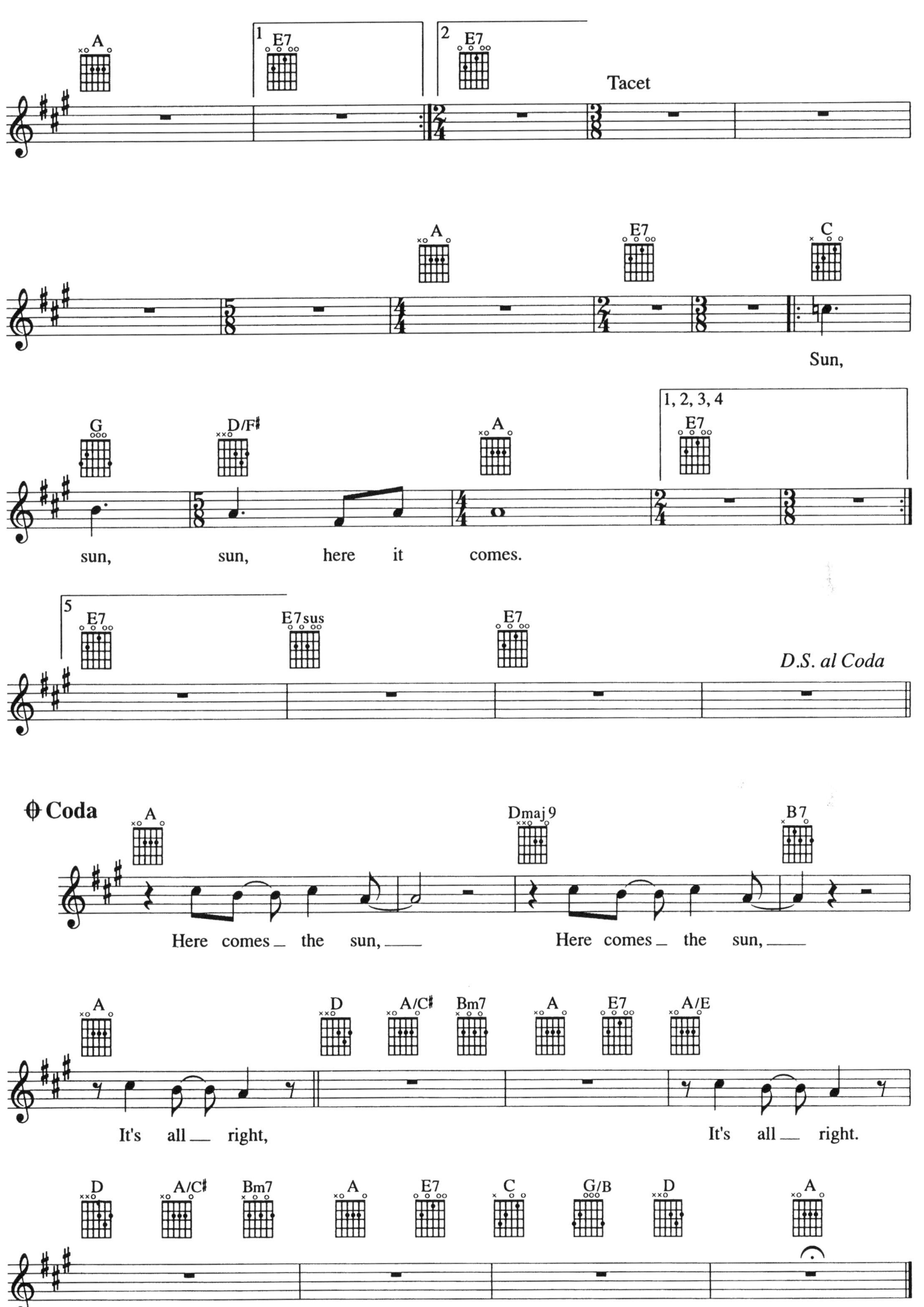
A
E7
Tacet
C
Sun,
G
D/F♯
sun, sun, here it comes.
1, 2, 3, 4
E7sus
D.S. al Coda
Coda
Dmaj 9
B7
Here comes the sun,
Here comes the sun,
D
A/C♯
Bm7
A/E
It's all right,
It's all right.
G/B

I Want You.

Words & Music by John Lennon & Paul McCartney.

Fast Tempo
Am
I want (1.2.4) you; I want you so bad.
(3) (Instrumental)

I want you; I want you so

Dm7
F
G
G♯+
Am
bad, it's driv - ing me mad, it's driv - ing me mad.

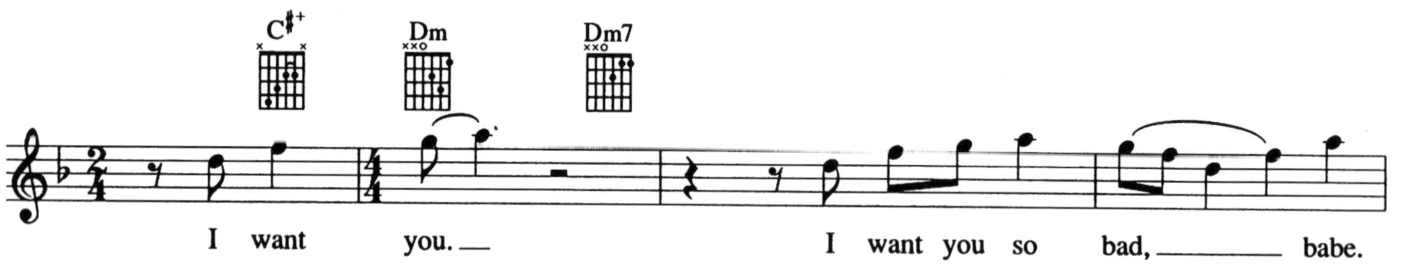
C♯+
Dm
Dm7
I want you. I want you so bad, babe.

Dm
Dm7
I want you. I want you so

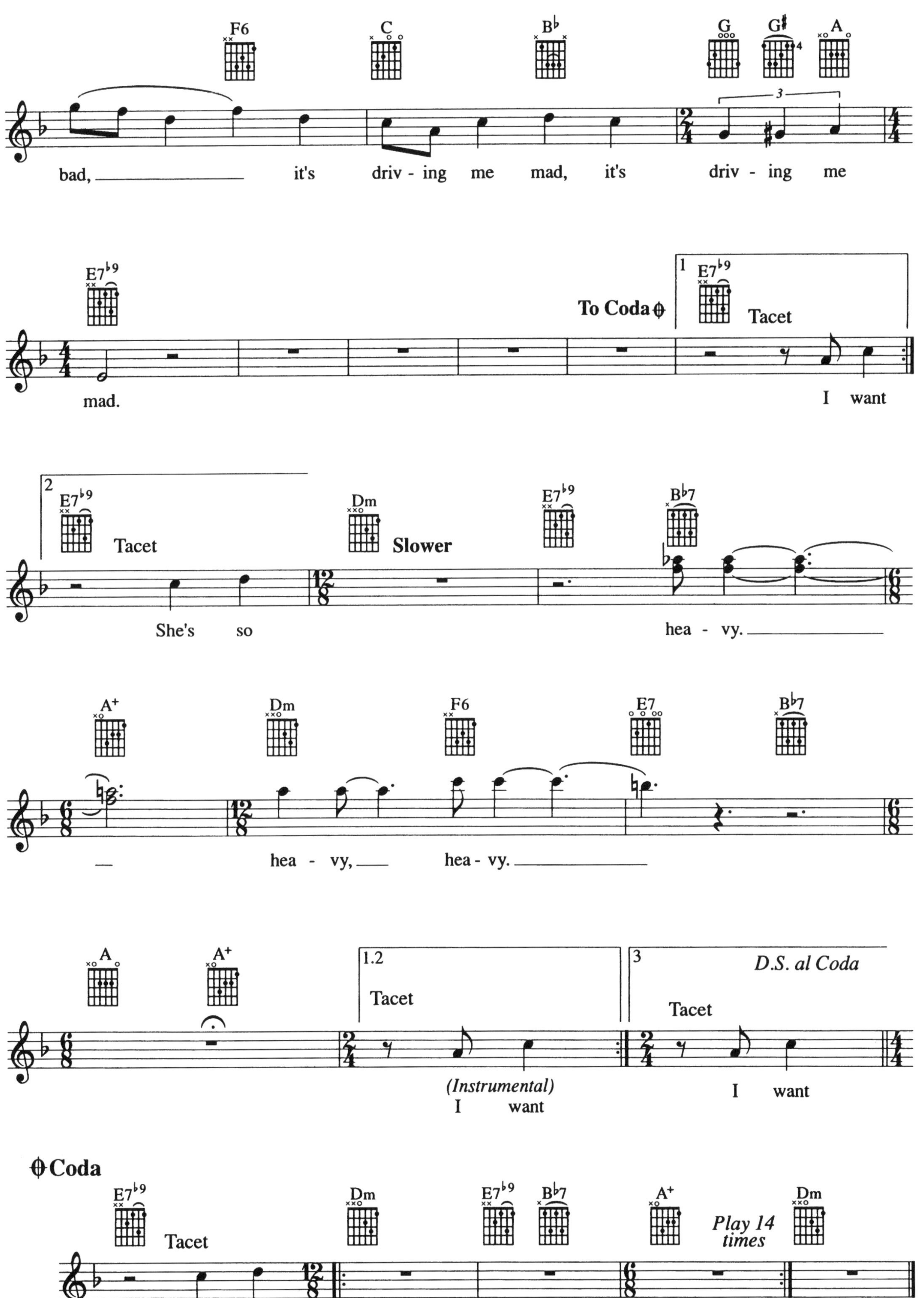

F6
C
B♭
G
G♯
A
bad, it's driv - ing me mad, it's driv - ing me
E7♭9
To Coda
1
E7♭9
Tacet
mad.
I want
2
E7♭9
Tacet
Dm
Slower
E7♭9
B♭7
She's so
hea - vy.
A+
Dm
F6
E7
B♭7
hea - vy, hea - vy.
A
A+
1.2
Tacet
(Instrumental)
I want
3
D.S. al Coda
Tacet
I want
Coda
E7♭9
Tacet
Dm
E7♭9
B♭7
A+
Play 14 times
Dm
She's so

Maxwell's Silver Hammer.

Words & Music by John Lennon & Paul McCartney.

Moderately (♫ played as ♩♪)
D B7 Em A7 D A D B7 Em A7 D A E7
1. Joan was quiz - zi - cal, stud - ied pat - a - phys - i - cal sci - ence in the home. Late nights all a - lone with a test - tube, oh, oh, oh, oh.
2. Back in school a - gain, Max - well plays the fool a - gain, Teach - er gets an - noyed. Wish - ing to a - void an un - pleas - ant sce - e - e - ene.
3. P. C. Thir - ty one said "we've caught a dir - ty one," Max - well stands a - lone. Paint - ing tes - ti - mo - ni - al pic - tures, oh, oh, oh, oh.
Max - well Ed - i - son, ma - jor - ing in med - i - cine, calls her on the phone; "Can I take you out to the pic - tures, Jo - o - o - an?" But as she's get - ting read - y to go, a
She tells Max to stay when the class has gone a - way. So he waits be - hind. Writ - ing fif - ty times "I must not be so - o - o - o." But when she turns her back on the boy, he
Rose and Val - er - ie scream - ing from the gal - ler - y say he must go free. The judge does not a - gree and he tells them so - o - o - o. But as the words are leav - ing his lips, a

A7
D
knock comes on the door. Bang! Bang! Max-well's sil-ver ham-mer came
creeps up from be-hind. Bang! Bang! Max-well's sil-ver ham-mer came
noise comes from be-hind Bang! Bang! Max-well's sil-ver ham-mer came
E7
A7
down up-on her head.
down up-on her head.
down up-on his head.
Clang! Clang! Max-well's sil-ver ham-mer made
1
Em A7 D F♯7 Bm D7 G G/B A7/C♯
sure that she was dead.
D A7/C♯ D
2.3
Em7 A D
sure that she was dead.
E A Em A
D
To Coda
F♯7/C♯ Bm D7/A G
D.C. al Coda
Coda
D F♯7/C♯ Bm D7/A G G7 A/C♯ D
Sil-ver ham-mer.

Mean Mr Mustard.

Words & Music by John Lennon & Paul McCartney.

Moderately
E♭ E♭sus E♭
1. Mean Mis - ter Mus - tard sleeps in the park, shaves in the dark, tryin' to save pa - per.
2. His sis - ter Pam works in a shop, she nev - er stops, she's a go get - ter.
B♭7 B♭ C♭ C D♭
Sleeps in a hole in the road,
Takes him out to look at the Queen,
D♭7 D♭ C C♭ B♭7
Sav - ing up to buy him some clothes,
on - ly place that he's ev - er been,
Keeps a ten bob note up his nose, Such a
Al - ways shouts out some - thing ob - scene, Such a
1 E♭ C♭ B♭7 E♭ C♭
mean old man, Such a mean old man.
B♭7 2 E♭ C♭ B♭7
dir - ty old man,
E♭ C♭ B♭7 E♭
dir - ty old man.

Octopus's Garden.

WORDS & MUSIC BY RINGO STARR.

Moderately Bright
E
B/D♯
C♯m
4
1. I'd like to be under the sea in an
2. We would be warm be - low the storm in our
A
B
B7
oct - o - pus - 's gar - den, in the shade.
lit - tle hide a - way be - neath the waves,
E
B/D♯
C♯m
4
He'd let us in knows where we've been
Rest - ing our head on the sea - bed
A
B
in his oct - o - pus - 's gar - den in the shade.
in an oct - o - pus - 's gar - den near a cave.
C♯m
4
I'd ask my friends to come and see
We would sing and dance a - round
A
B
an oct - o - pus - 's gar - den with me.
be - cause we know we can't be found.

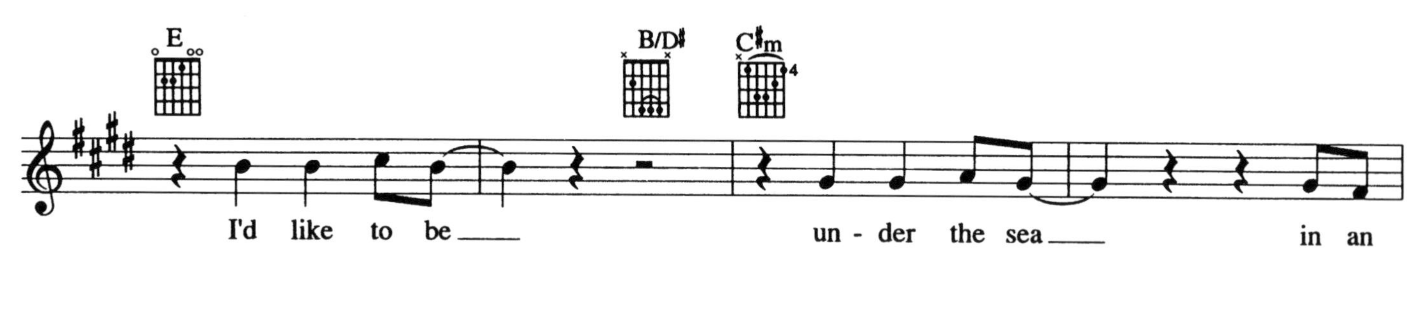
E
B/D♯
C♯m
I'd like to be under the sea in an

A
1 E
oct - o - pus - 's gar - den, in the shade.
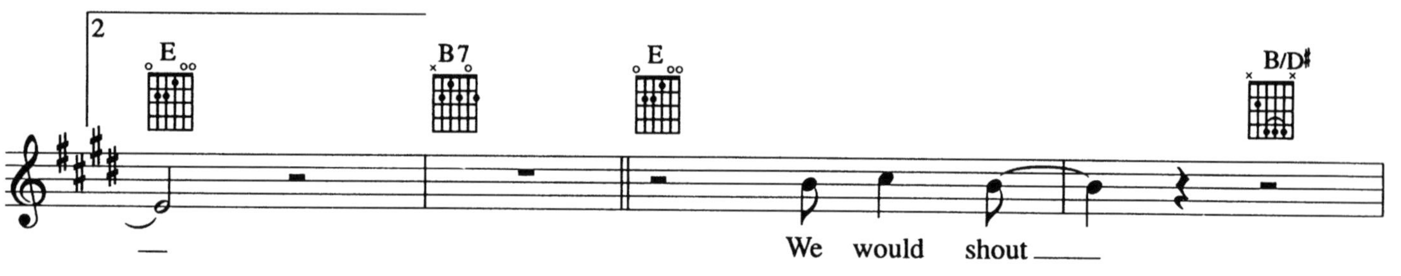
2 E
B7
E
B/D♯
We would shout
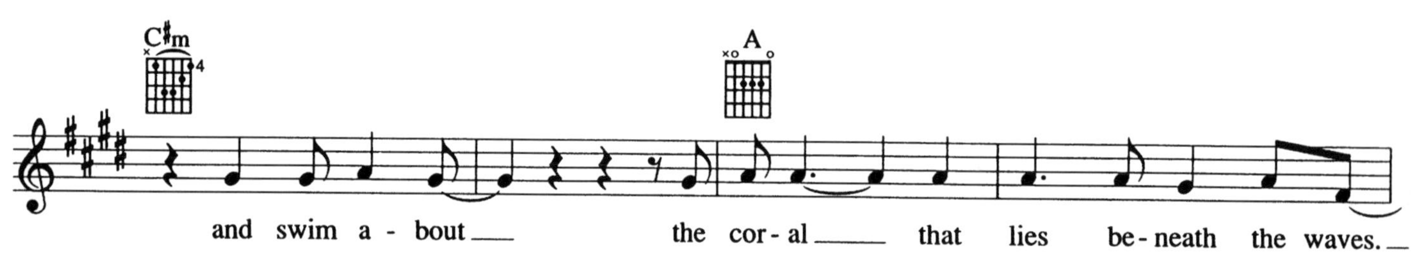
C♯m
A
and swim a - bout the cor - al that lies be - neath the waves.

B
A/C♯
B
E
B/D♯
Oh, what joy for

C♯m
A
ev - 'ry girl and boy know - ing they're hap - py and they're

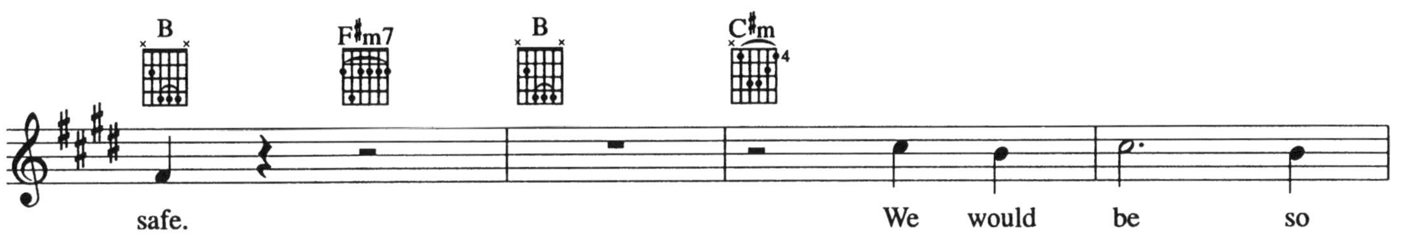
B
F#m7
B
C#m
safe. We would be so

A
hap - py, you and me; No one there to tell us what to do.

B
E
B/D#
C#m
I'd like to be un - der the sea

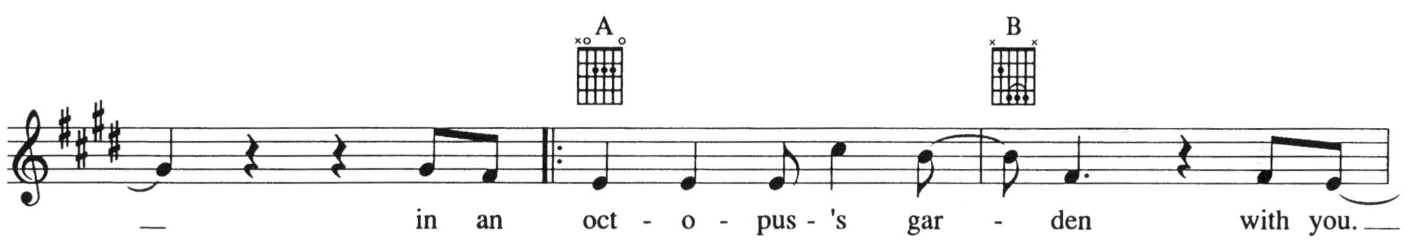
A
B
in an oct - o - pus - 's gar - den with you.

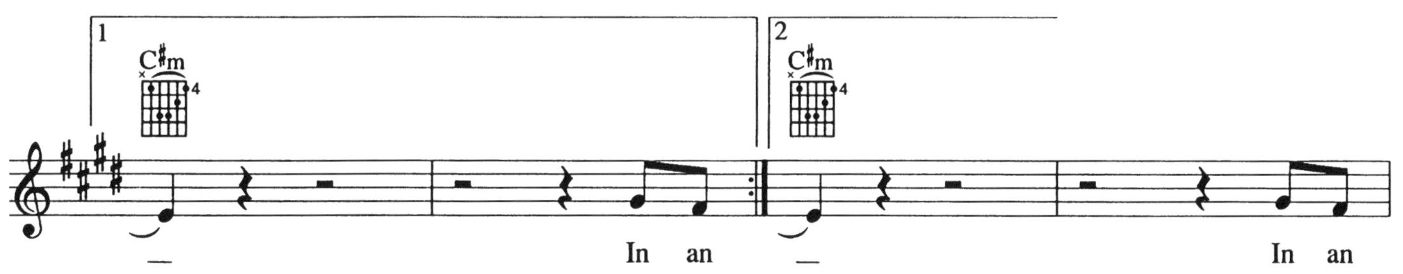
1
C#m
2
C#m
In an
In an

A
B
E
Tacet
E♭
E
oct - o - pus - 's gar - den with you.

Oh! Darling.

Words & Music by John Lennon & Paul McCartney.

Slowly
G+
C
G
Oh! Dar - ling, please be - lieve me,
Dar - ling, if you leave me,
Am
F
Dm7
G
I'll nev - er do you no harm. Be - lieve me when I tell you,
I'll nev - er make it a - lone. Be - lieve me when I beg you,
Dm7
G
C
F
1
C
G
I'll nev - er do you no harm. Oh!
Don't ev - er leave me a - lone.
2
C
C7
F
A♭7
When you told me you did - n't need me an - y - more, Well, you
C
know I near - ly broke down and cried. When you

D7
told me ___ you did - n't need me an - y - more, ___ Well, you

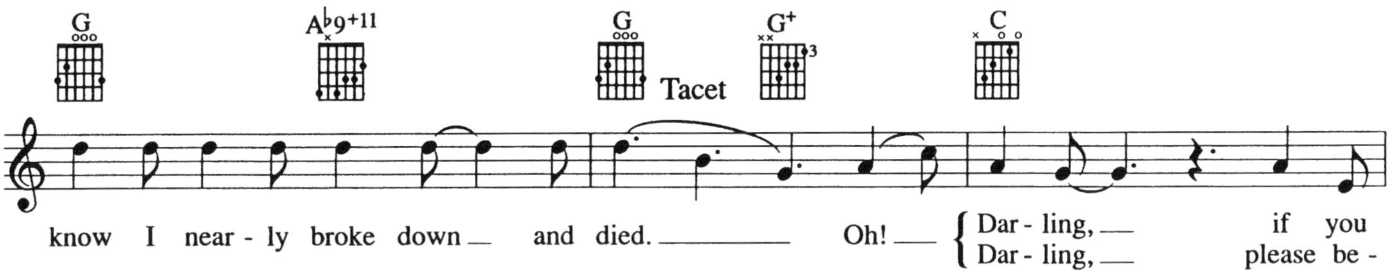
G
A♭9+11
G
Tacet
G+
C
know I near - ly broke down ___ and died. ___ Oh! ___
Dar - ling, ___ if you
Dar - ling, ___ please be -

G
Am
F
leave me, ___ I'll nev - er make it ___ a - lone. ___ Be -
- lieve me, ___ I'll nev - er let ___ you down. ___ Be -

Dm7
G
1
Dm7
G
C
F
- lieve me when I tell you, I'll nev - er do you ___ no harm. ___
- lieve me when I tell you,

C
C7
2
Dm7
G7
C
F
C
D♭7
C7
2. When you I'll nev - er do you ___ no harm.

Old Brown Shoe.

WORDS & MUSIC BY GEORGE HARRISON.

Bright Shuffle
C7
I want a love that's right, right is on - ly half of what's wrong.
(2) pick me up from where some try to drag me down.
(3) Love is yours; to miss that love is some - thing I'd hate.
Dm7
I want a short - haired girl who some - times wears it twice as long.
And when I see you smile re - plac - ing ev - 'ry thought - less frown.
I'll make an ear - ly start, I'm mak - ing sure that I'm not late.
Now
For
F
A♭
I'm step - pin' out this old brown shoe, Ba - by I'm in love with you.
Got me es - cap - ing from this zoo, Ba - by I'm in love with you.
your sweet top lip I'm in the queue, Ba - by I'm in love with you.
F
E7
I'm so glad you came here, it won't be the same now, I'm
I'm so glad you came here, it won't be the same now, when
I'm so glad you came here, it won't be the same now, when

Am
To Coda
1
C7
2
Am
tell - ing you.
I'm with you.
I'm with you.
2. Though you

G
If I grow up I'll be a sing - er, Wear - ing rings on

F7
G
ev - 'ry fin - ger, Not wor - ry - ing what they or you'll say.

F7
F♯°
I'll live and love and may - be some - day, Who knows, ba - by?

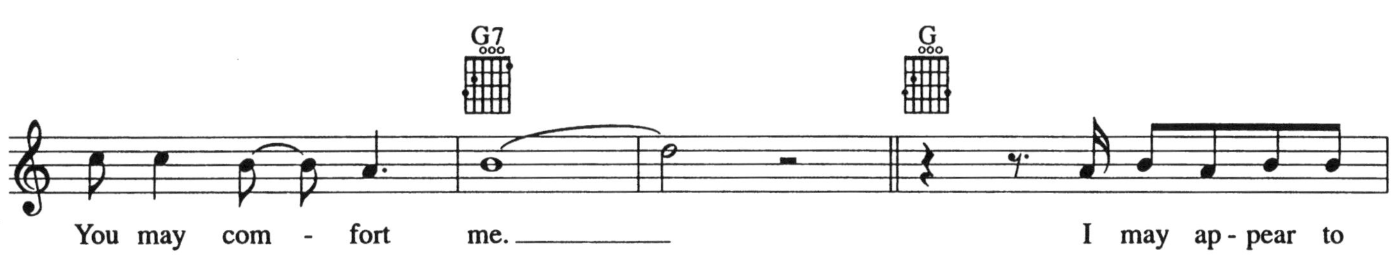
G7
G
You may com - fort me. I may ap - pear to

F7
be im - per - fect, My love is some - thing you can't re - ject.

G
I'm chang - ing fas - ter than the weath - er,

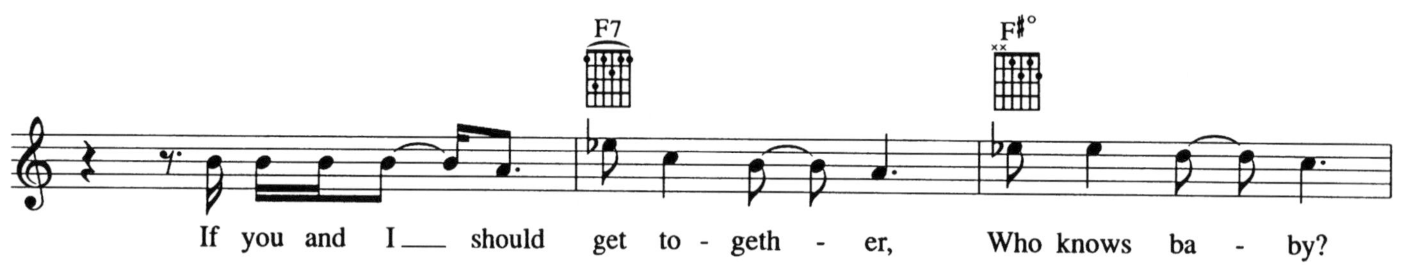
F7
F♯°
If you and I should get to - geth - er, Who knows ba - by?

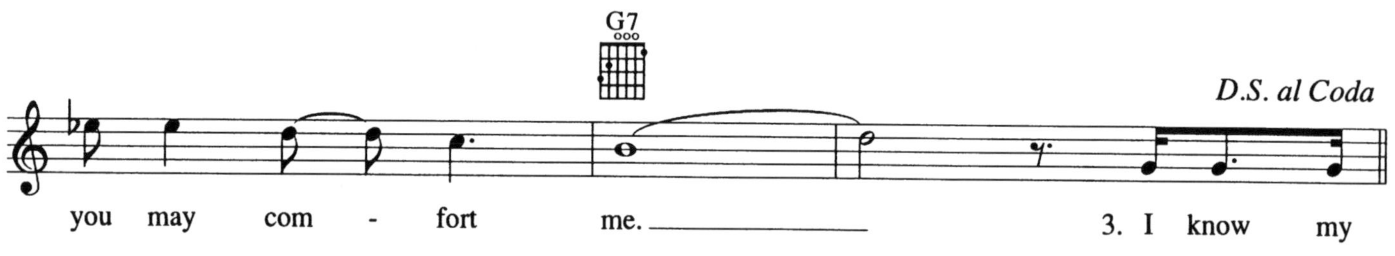
G7
D.S. al Coda
you may com - fort me. 3. I know my

Coda
Am
F
E7
I'm so glad you came here, it won't be the same now, when

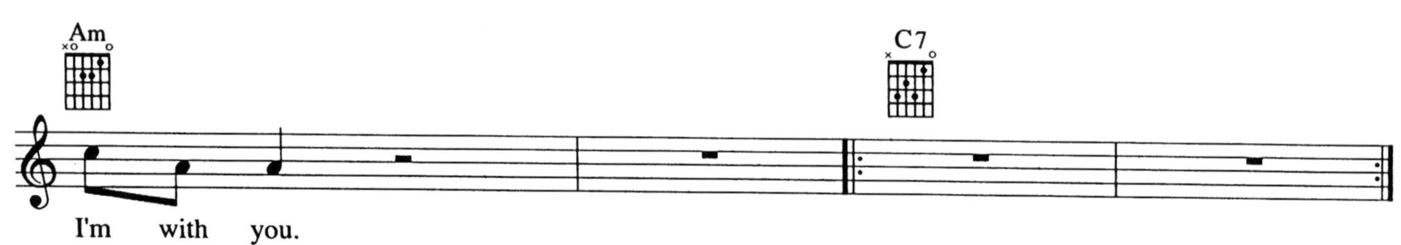
Am
C7
I'm with you.

Dig It.

Words & Music by John Lennon, Paul McCartney,
George Harrison & Richard Starkey.

Brightly, with a beat
B♭
F
C7
C9
C7sus
Like a Rolling Stone, Like a Rolling Stone, A-like a Rolling Stone,
Like the F. B. I. and the C. I. A. and the B. B. C.
B. B. King, and Doris Day.
Matt Busby. Dig it, Dig it. Dig it, Dig it.
Dig it, Dig it, Dig it, Dig it, Dig it, Dig it, Dig it, Dig it.
Repeat to Fade

Polythene Pam.

WORDS & MUSIC BY JOHN LENNON & PAUL McCARTNEY.

Bright 4
D A E
Well, you should see Pol - y - thene Pam. She's so good
D A E
look - ing, but she looks like a man. Well, you should
G B
see her in drag, dressed in her pol - y - thene bag, yes, you should
C D E C D E
see Pol - y - thene Pam. Yeah, yeah, yeah.
D/E A E D/E A E
Get a

D
A
E
dose of her in jack - boots and kilt,
She's kill - er

D
A
E
dill - er when she's dressed to the hilt.
She's the

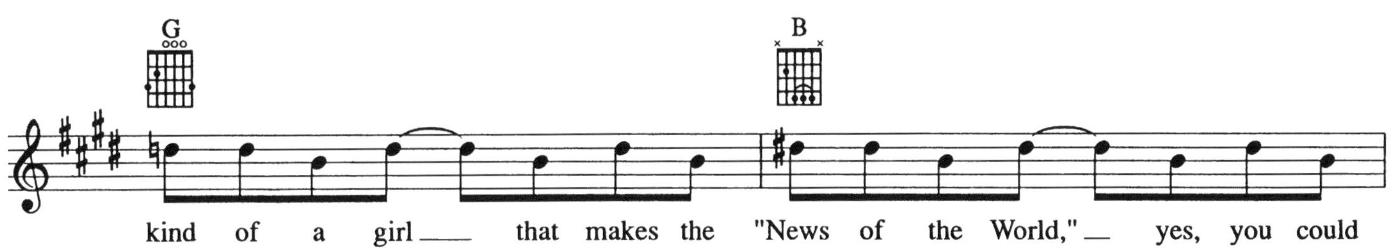
G
B
kind of a girl that makes the "News of the World," yes, you could

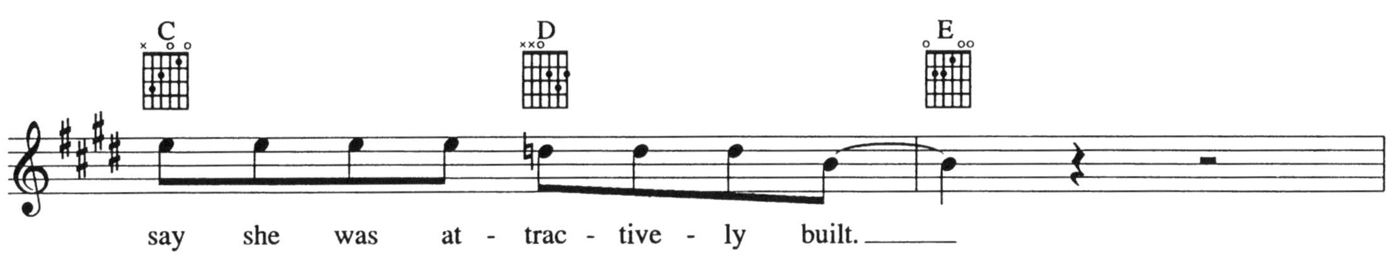
C
D
E
say she was at - trac - tive - ly built.

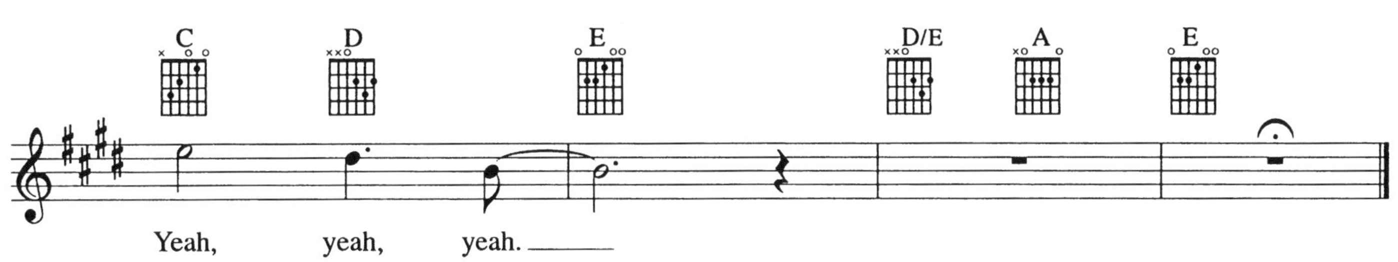
C
D
E
D/E
A
E
Yeah, yeah, yeah.

She Came In Through The Bathroom Window.

Words & Music by John Lennon & Paul McCartney.

Moderately slow 4
F
B♭
1. She came in through the bath - room win - dow,
(2) dan - cer,
(3) - part - ment,
F
Dm
B♭
pro - tec - ted by a sil - ver spoon.
she worked at fif - teen clubs a day.
and got my - self a stea - dy job.
F
Dm
B♭
But now she sucks her thumb and won - ders by the
And though she thought I knew the ans - wer, well, I
And though she tried her best to help me, she could
B♭7
F
banks of her own la - goon.
knew what I could not say.
steal, but she could not rob.
Did - n't a - ny - bo - dy tell

B♭m
F
B♭m
her?
Did - n't a - ny - bo - dy see?

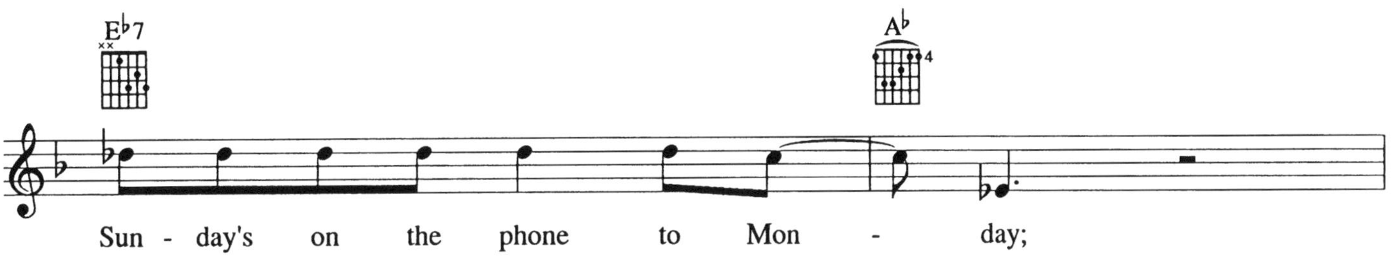
E♭7
A♭
4
Sun - day's on the phone to Mon - day;

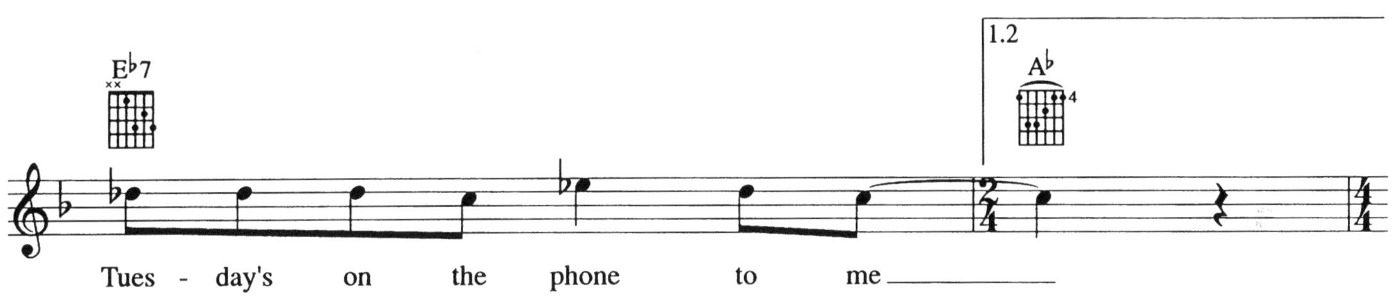
E♭7
1.2
A♭
4
Tues - day's on the phone to me

F
3
A♭
4
F
2. She said she'd al - ways been a
3. And so I quit the p'lice de -
oh yeah.

Something.

Words & Music by George Harrison.

Slowly
C
Cmaj7
1. Some - thing in the way she moves,
2. Some - where in her smile she knows,
3. Some - thing in the way she moves,
C7
F7
C/E
At - tracts me like no oth - er lov - er;
That I don't need no oth - er lov - er;
And all I have to do is think of her;
D7
G
Am7
G7
Some - thing in the way she woos me.
Some - thing in her style that shows me.
Some - thing in the way she shows me.
I
Am/G
E+
Am/G
D7
To Coda
don't want to leave her now, you know I be - lieve and how.
1
F
E♭
G7
2
F
E♭
G7
A
Double Tempo
You're ask - ing me

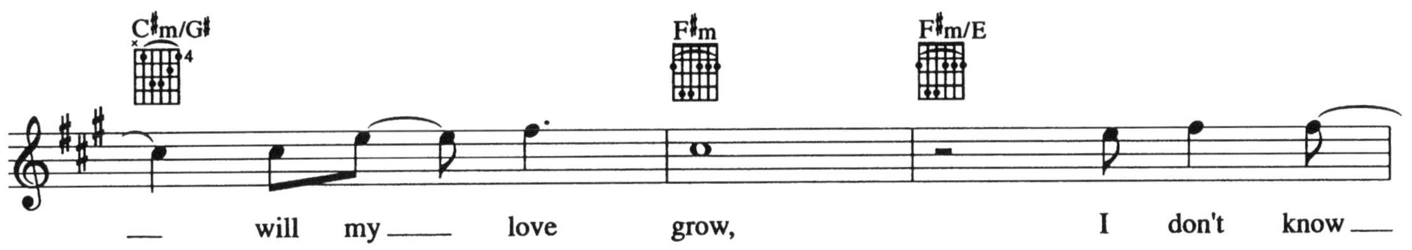
C♯m/G♯
F♯m
F♯m/E
will my love grow,
I don't know

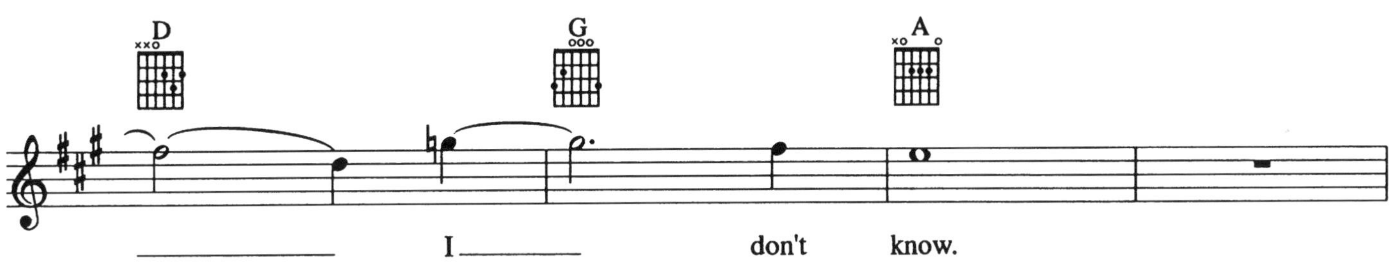
D
G
A
I don't know.

C♯m/G♯
F♯m
F♯m/E
You stick a - round now it may show,
I don't know,

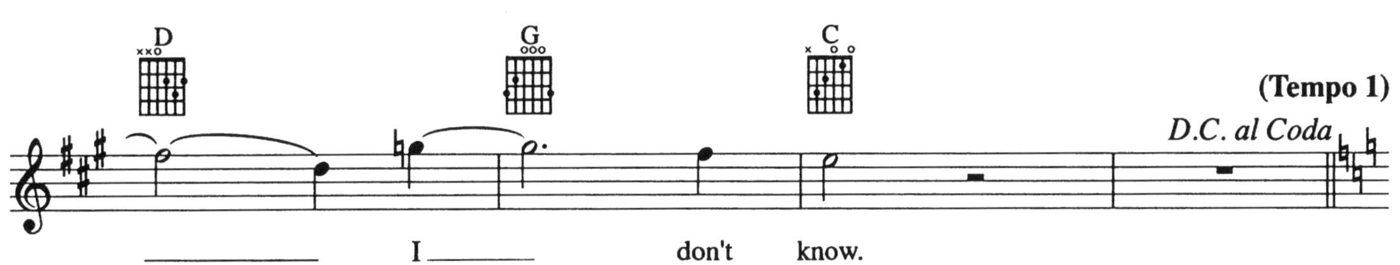
D
G
C
(Tempo 1)
D.C. al Coda
I don't know.

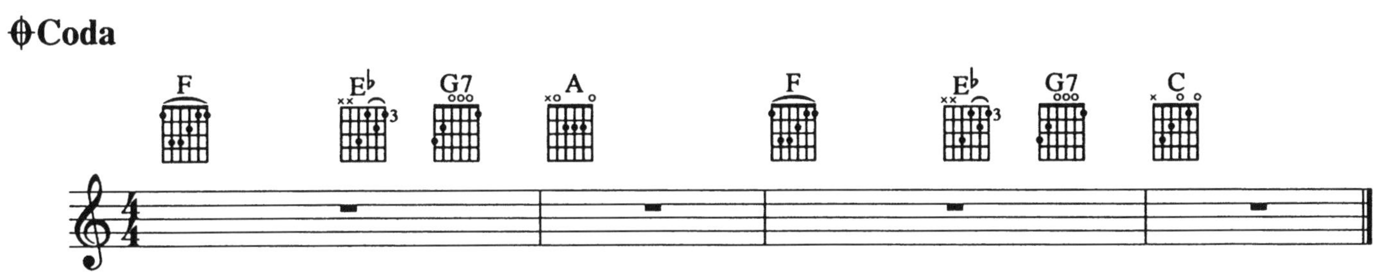
Coda
F
E♭
G7
A
F
E♭
G7
C

The End.

Words & Music by John Lennon & Paul McCartney.

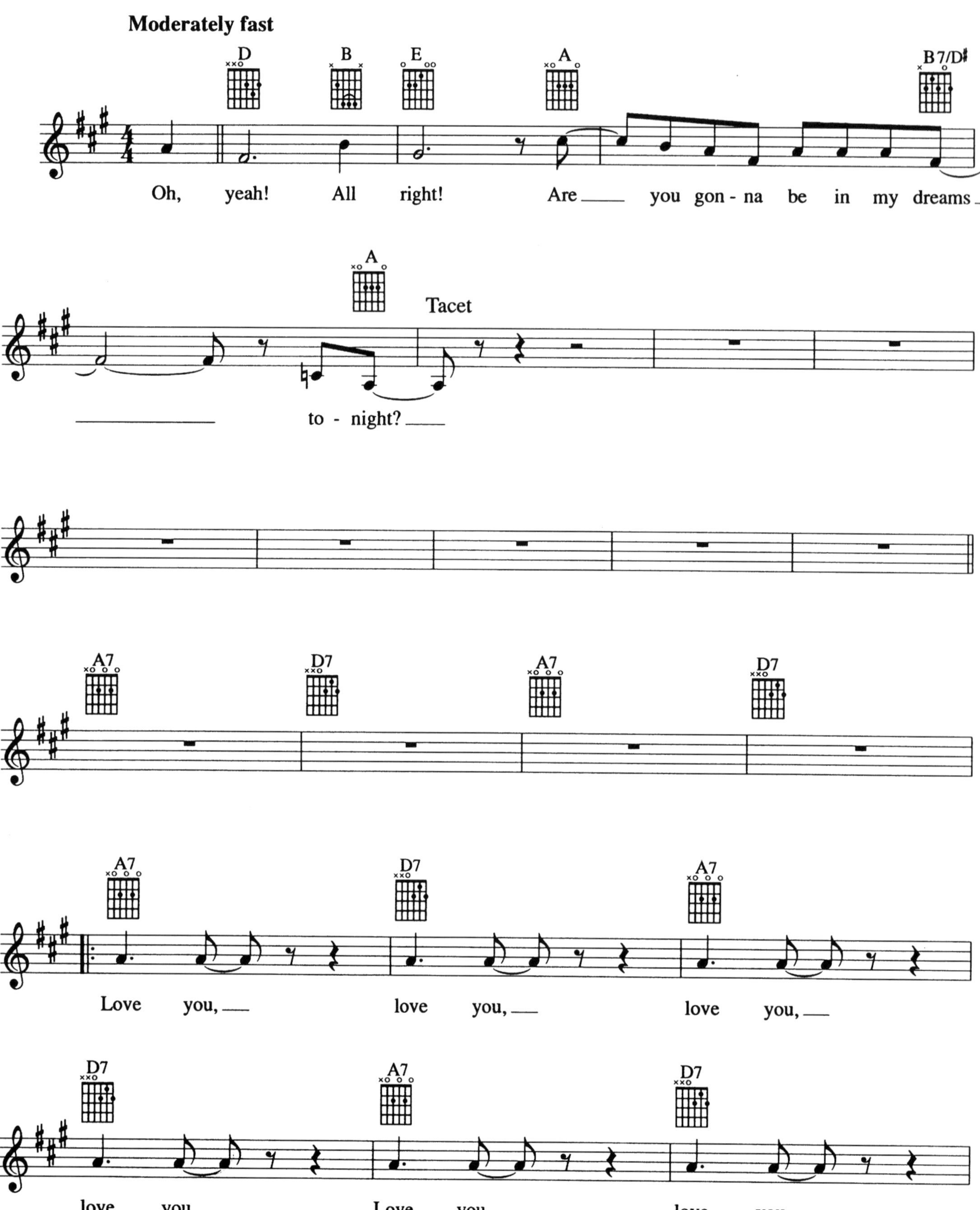
Moderately fast
D
B
E
A
B7/D♯
Oh, yeah! All right! Are you gon - na be in my dreams
A
Tacet
to - night?
A7
D7
A7
D7
A7
D7
A7
Love you, love you, love you,
D7
A7
D7
love you, Love you, love you,

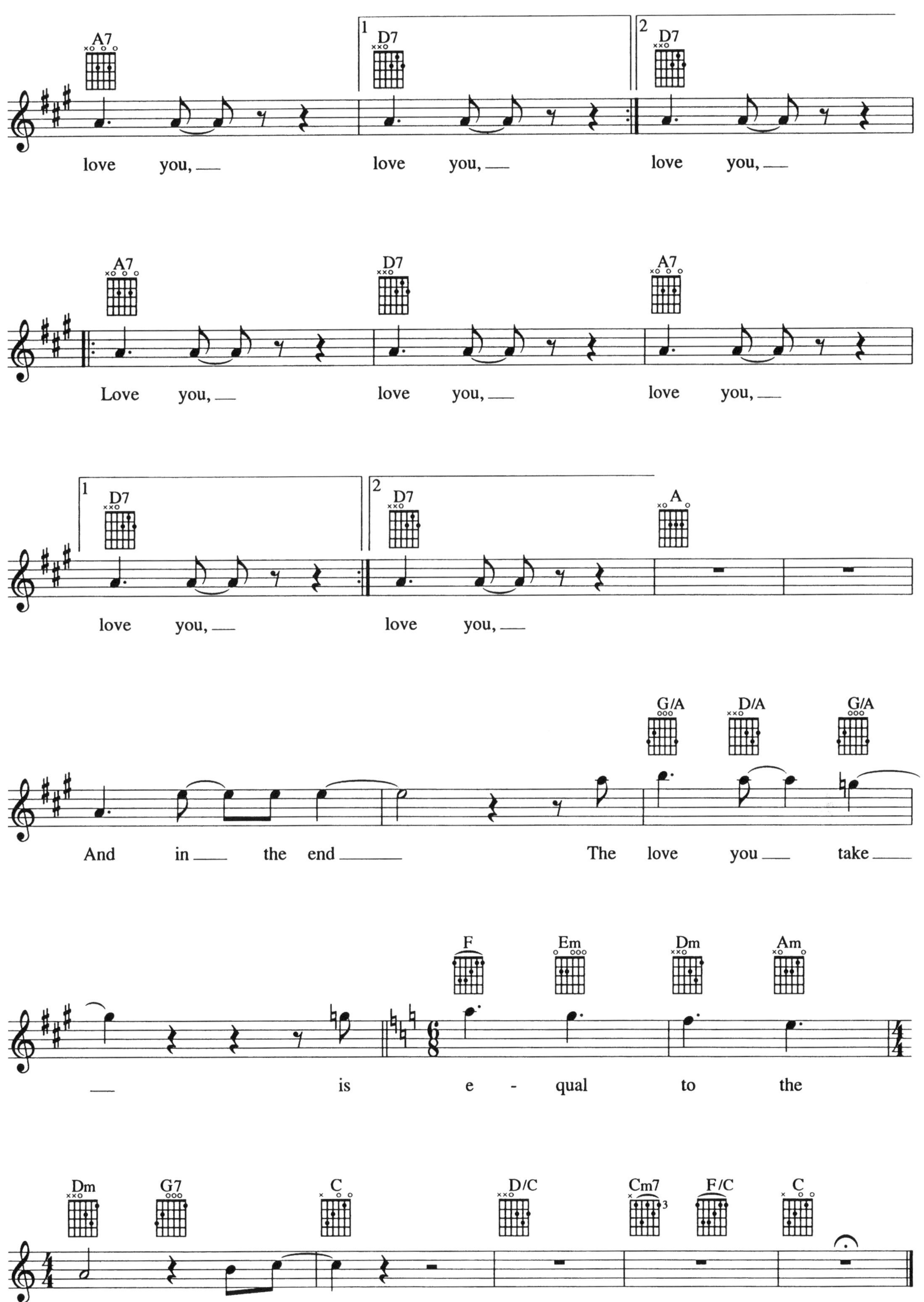
A7
1 D7
2 D7
love you,
love you,
love you,
A7
D7
A7
Love you,
love you,
love you,
1 D7
2 D7
A
love you,
love you,
G/A
D/A
G/A
And in the end
The love you take
F
Em
Dm
Am
is e - qual to the
Dm
G7
C
D/C
Cm7
F/C
C
love you make.

Two Of Us.

WORDS & MUSIC BY JOHN LENNON & PAUL McCARTNEY.

Fairly bright tempo
G
1. Two of us, rid - ing no - where, spend - ing some - one's hard earned pay.
2. Two of us, send - ing post - cards, writ - ing let - ters on my wall.
3.4. Two of us, wear - ing rain - coats, stand - ing so - lo in the sun.
C
Bm
Am
You and me, Sun - day driv - ing, not ar - riv - ing on our way back home.
You and me, burn - ing match - es, lift - ing latch - es on our way back home.
You and me, chas - ing pa - per, get - ting no - where on our way back home.
D7
We're on our way home, we're on our way

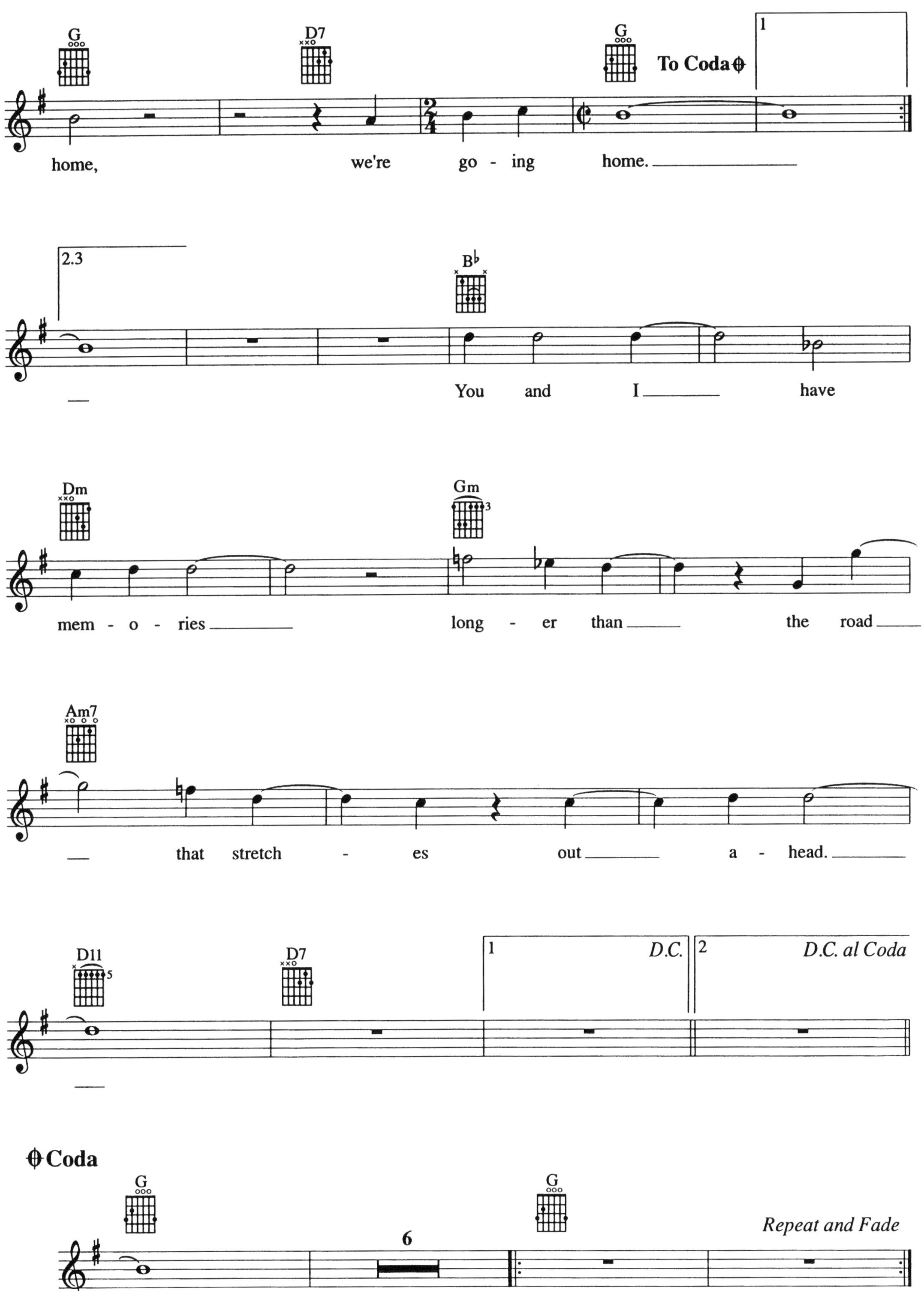
G
D7
G
To Coda
1
home, we're go - ing home.
2.3
B♭
You and I have
Dm
Gm
mem - o - ries long - er than the road
Am7
that stretch - es out a - head.
D11
D7
1 D.C.
2 D.C. al Coda
Coda
G
6
G
Repeat and Fade

You Never Give Me Your Money.

Words & Music by John Lennon & Paul McCartney.

Slowly
Gm7 Cm F7
1. You nev - er give me your mon - ey, you on - ly give me your
2. I nev - er give you my num - ber, I on - ly give you my
B♭ E♭maj7 Am7♭5 D7
fun - ny pa - per; And in the mid - dle of ne - go - ti - a - tions you
sit - u - a - tion; And in the mid - dle of in - ves - ti - ga - tion I
Gm 1 2 B♭ F7 Double tempo (♩=𝅗𝅥) B♭
break down. Out of col - lege,
break down. An - y job - ber
D7 Gm B♭7
mon - ey spent, see no fu - ture, pay no rent.
got the sack, Mon - day morn - ing, turn - ing back.
E♭ F7 B♭
All the mon - ey's gone, no - where to go.
Yel - low lor - ry slow, no - where to go.
1 2 A♭ tempo 1
But oh, that mag - ic feel - ing,

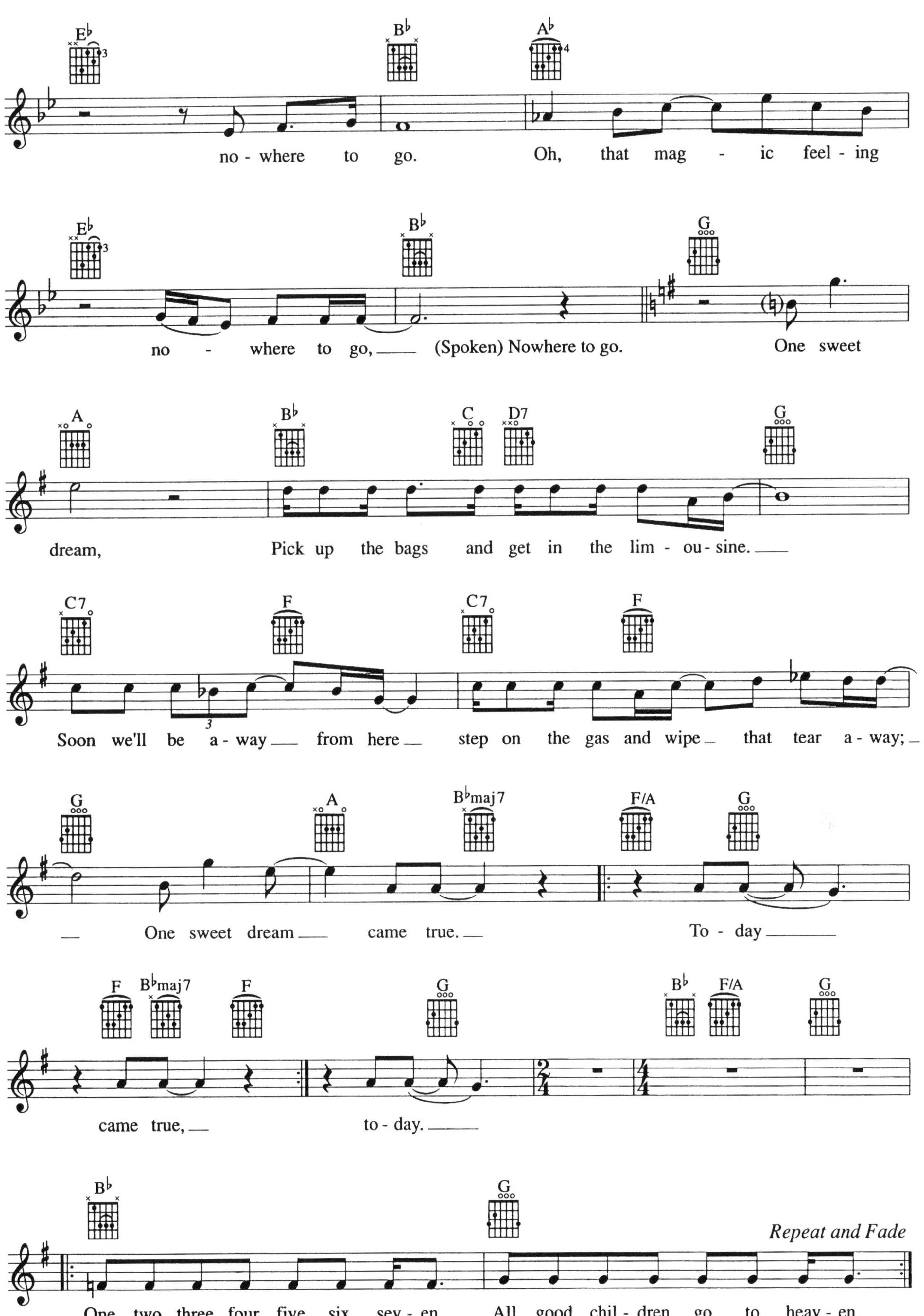
E♭ B♭ A♭
no - where to go. Oh, that mag - ic feel - ing
E♭ B♭ G
no - where to go, (Spoken) Nowhere to go. One sweet
A B♭ C D7 G
dream, Pick up the bags and get in the lim - ou - sine.
C7 F C7 F
Soon we'll be a - way from here step on the gas and wipe that tear a - way;
G A B♭maj7 F/A G
One sweet dream came true. To - day
F B♭maj7 F G B♭ F/A G
came true, to - day.
B♭ G
Repeat and Fade
One, two, three, four, five, six, sev - en, All good chil - dren go to heav - en.

Dig A Pony.

WORDS & MUSIC BY JOHN LENNON & PAUL McCARTNEY.

Moderately
G C/G G/B D9 G C/G G
I hi hi hi hi.
1. Dig a
2. Pick a
3. Feel the
Em Am
po - ny. Well, you can cel - e - brate an - y - thing you
moon dog. Well, you can rad - i - ate ev - 'ry - thing you
wind blow. Well, you can in - di - cate ev - 'ry - thing you
F7 Am F7
want, Yes, you can cel - e - brate an - y - thing you want.
are, Yes, you can rad - i - ate ev - 'ry - thing you are.
see, Yes, you can in - di - cate an - y - thing you see.
D7 D11 D7 G C/G G Am G C
Oh,
Oh, now
Oh, now
I hi hi hi hi.
G Em
(1) Do a road hog.
(2) Roll a stone - y.
(3) Cold and lone - ly.
Well, you can
Well, you can
Well, you can

Am
F7
pen - e - trate ___ an - y place you go.
im - i - tate ___ ev - 'ry - one you know.
syn - di - cate ___ an - y boat you row.
Yes,
Yes,
Yeah,
Am
F7
D7
you can pen - e - trate ___ an - y place you go.
you can im - i - tate ___ ev - 'ry - one you know.
you can syn - di - cate ___ an - y boat you row.
I told you so. ___
F
C
G
F
All I want is you.
Ev - 'ry - thing has got to
C
G
G9
Slower
Tacet
be just like you want it to. ___
Be - cause ___
a tempo
To Coda
(3rd time)
G
C/G
G
Am/G
G
Em
Am
F7
Am
F7
D7
D.C. al Coda
Oh, ___ now,
Coda
F
C
G

Sun King.

Words & Music by John Lennon & Paul McCartney.

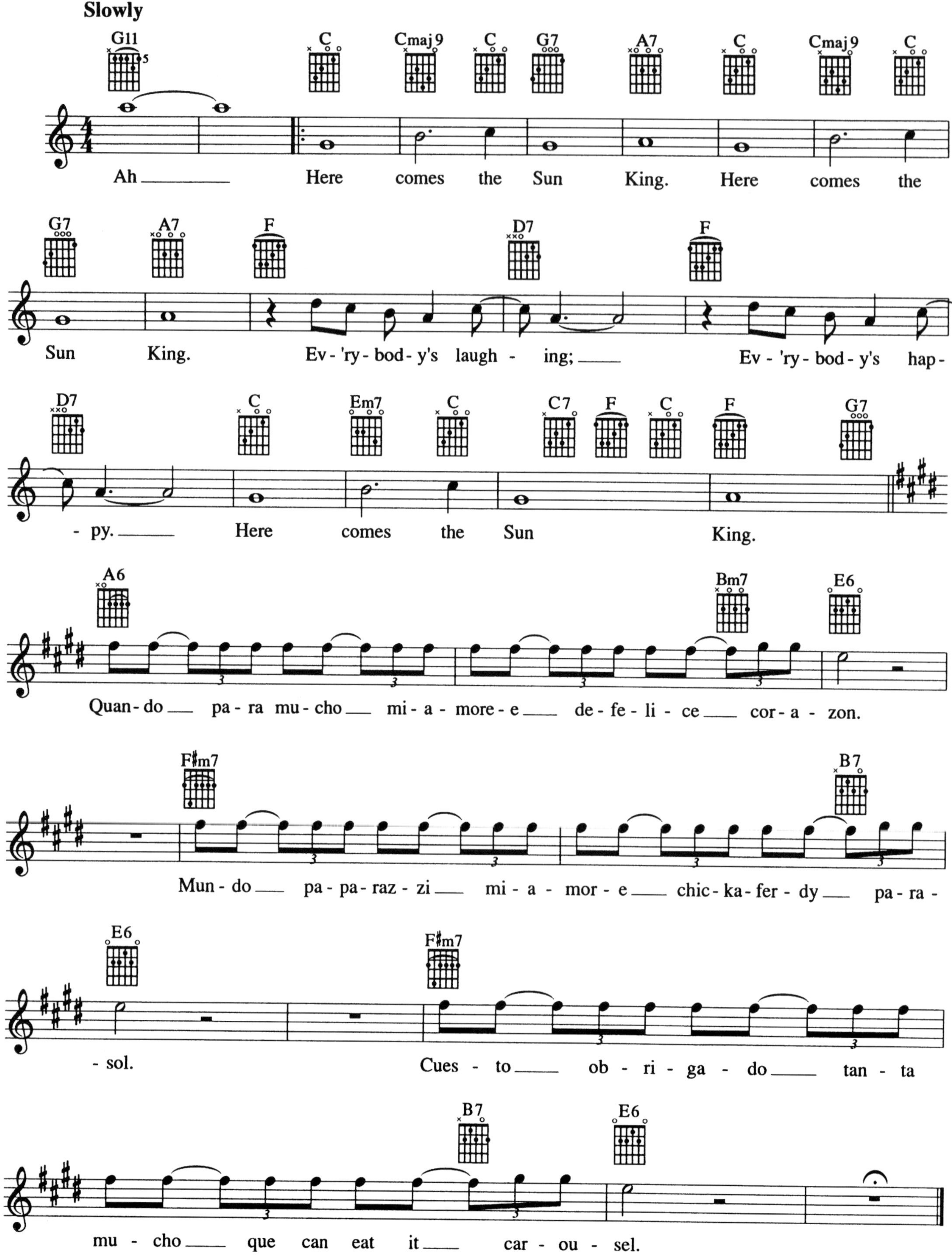
Slowly
G11 C Cmaj9 C G7 A7 C Cmaj9 C
Ah Here comes the Sun King. Here comes the
G7 A7 F D7 F
Sun King. Ev - 'ry - bod - y's laugh - ing; Ev - 'ry - bod - y's hap -
D7 C Em7 C C7 F C F G7
- py. Here comes the Sun King.
A6 Bm7 E6
Quan - do pa - ra mu - cho mi - a - more - e de - fe - li - ce cor - a - zon.
F♯m7 B7
Mun - do pa - pa - raz - zi mi - a - mor - e chic - ka - fer - dy pa - ra -
E6 F♯m7
- sol. Cues - to ob - ri - ga - do tan - ta
B7 E6
mu - cho que can eat it car - ou - sel.

For You Blue.

Words & Music by George Harrison.

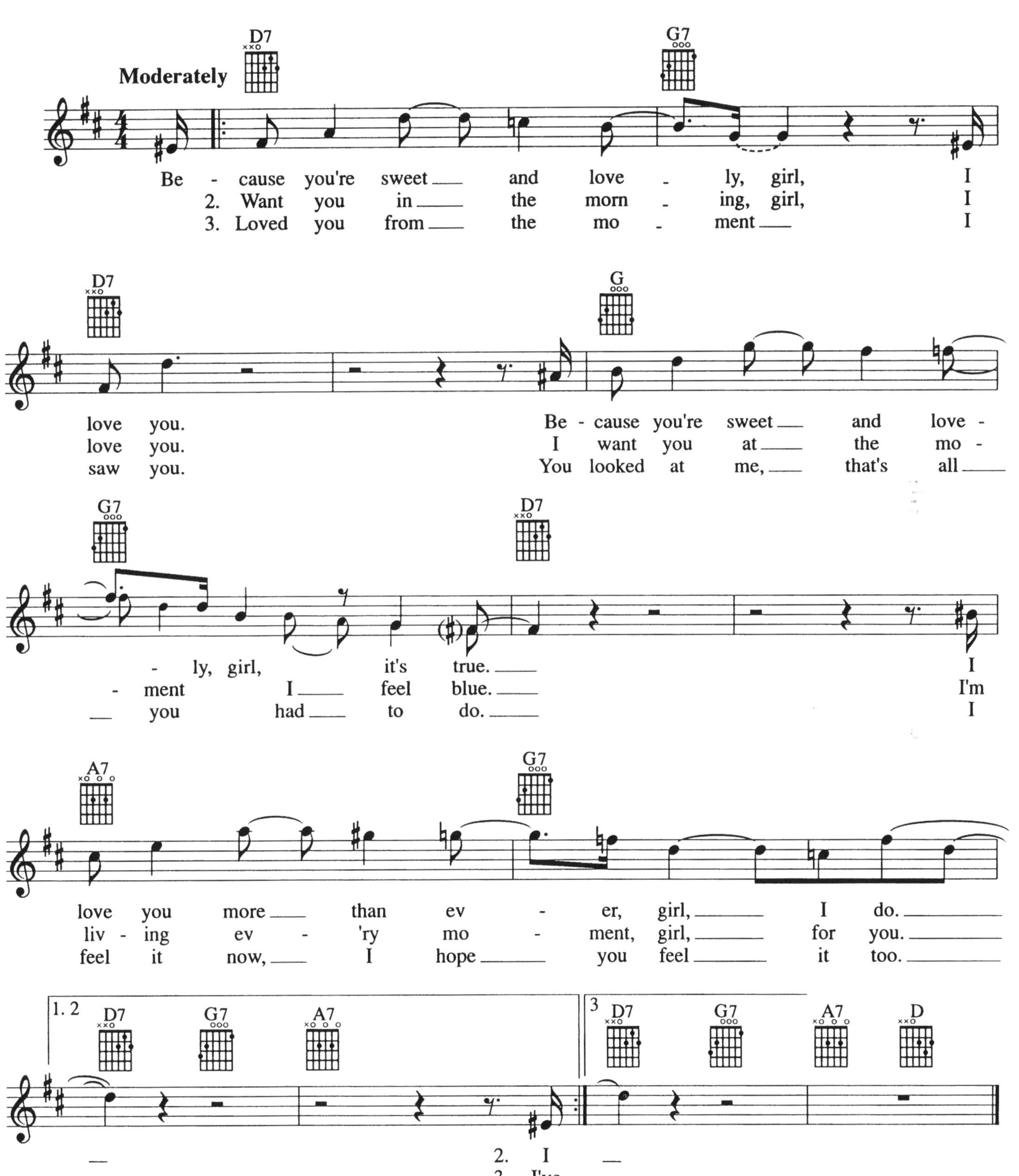
Moderately
D7
G7
Be - cause you're sweet and love - ly, girl, I
2. Want you in the morn - ing, girl, I
3. Loved you from the mo - ment I
D7
G
love you. Be - cause you're sweet and love -
love you. I want you at the mo -
saw you. You looked at me, that's all
G7
D7
- ly, girl, it's true. I
- ment I feel blue. I'm
you had to do. I
A7
G7
love you more than ev - er, girl, I do.
liv - ing ev - 'ry mo - ment, girl, for you.
feel it now, I hope you feel it too.
1. 2
D7
G7
A7
2. I
3. I've
3
D7
G7
A7
D

Hey Jude.

WORDS & MUSIC BY JOHN LENNON & PAUL McCARTNEY.

Slowly
F C C7 C7sus C7
1. Hey Jude, don't make it bad, Take a sad song and make it
4. Jude, don't make it bad, Take a sad song and make it
F B♭ F
To Coda
bet - ter. Re - mem - ber to let her in - to your heart, Then you can start
bet - ter. Re - mem - ber to let her un - der your skin, Then you be - gin
C7 F F
to make it bet - ter. Hey
2. Jude, don't be a -
3. Jude, don't let me
C C7 C7sus C7 F
- fraid. You were made to go out and get her. The
down. You have found her now go and get her. Re -
B♭ F
min - ute you let her un - der your skin, Then you be - gin
- mem - ber to let her in - to your heart, Then you can start
C7 F F7
to make it bet - ter. And an - y - time you feel the pain
to make it bet - ter. So let it out and let it in.

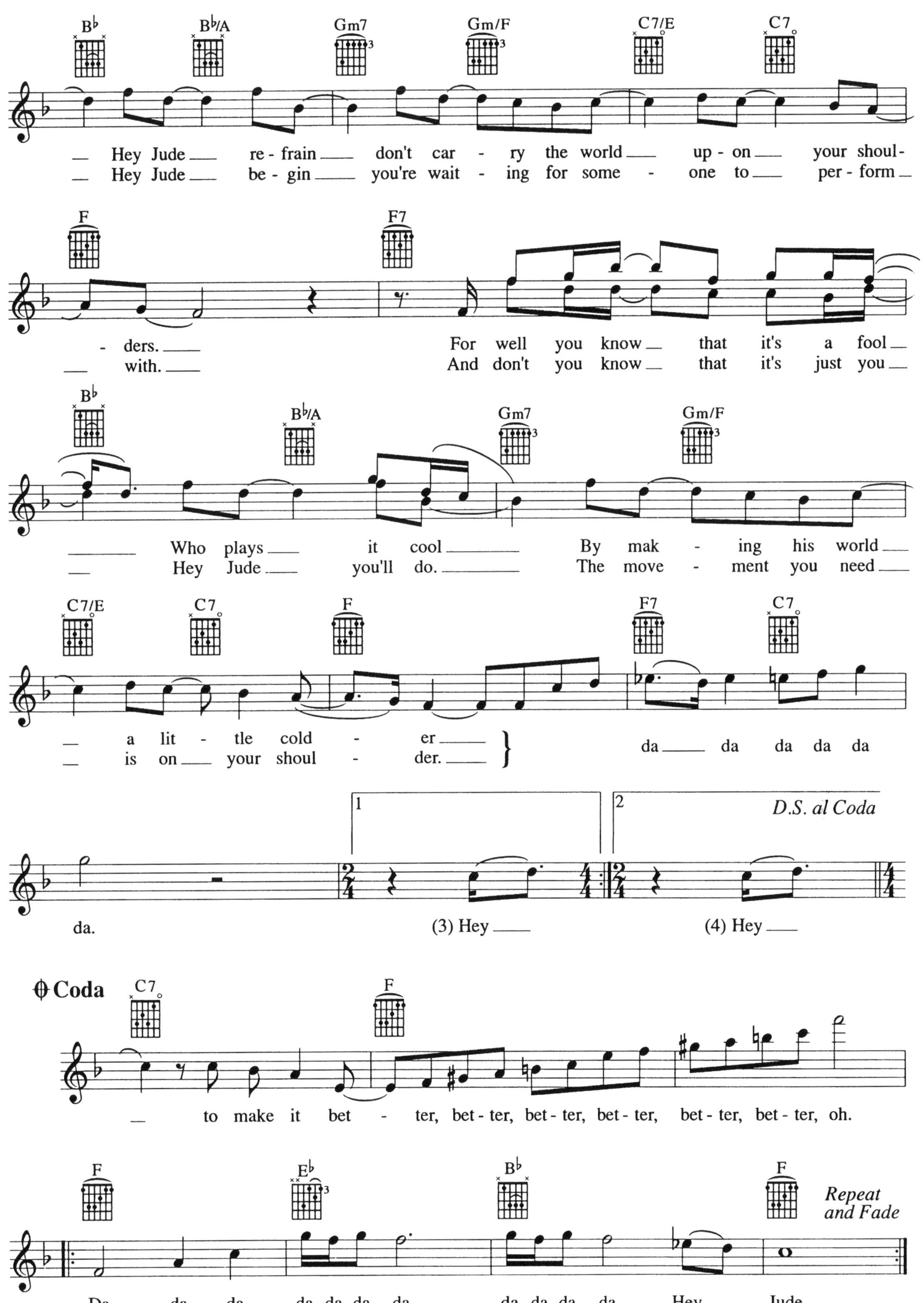
B♭ B♭/A Gm7 Gm/F C7/E C7
— Hey Jude — re - frain — don't car - ry the world — up - on — your shoul -
— Hey Jude — be - gin — you're wait - ing for some - one to — per - form —
F F7
- ders. — For well you know — that it's a fool —
— with. — And don't you know — that it's just you —
B♭ B♭/A Gm7 Gm/F
— Who plays — it cool — By mak - ing his world —
— Hey Jude — you'll do. — The move - ment you need —
C7/E C7 F F7 C7
— a lit - tle cold - er — da — da da da da
— is on — your shoul - der. —
1 2 D.S. al Coda
da. (3) Hey — (4) Hey —
Coda
C7 F
— to make it bet - ter, bet - ter, bet - ter, bet - ter, bet - ter, bet - ter, oh.
F E♭ B♭ F
Repeat and Fade
Da da da da da da da da da da da Hey — Jude.

I Me Mine.

Words & Music by George Harrison.

Bright Waltz
Am Am/C D
1.3. All through the day, I me mine,
2. All I can hear, I me mine,
G E7 Am
I me mine, I me mine.
I me mine, I me mine.
Am/C D G
All through the night I me mine, I me mine,
E - ven those tears, I me mine, I me mine,
E7 Am Dm Em
I me mine. Now they're fright - ened of leav - ing it,
I me mine. No - one's fright - ened of play - ing it,
Dm6 G7 G#o F/A E
ev - 'ry - one's weav - ing it, com - ing on strong all the time.
ev - 'ry - one's say - ing it, flow - ing more free - ly than wine.

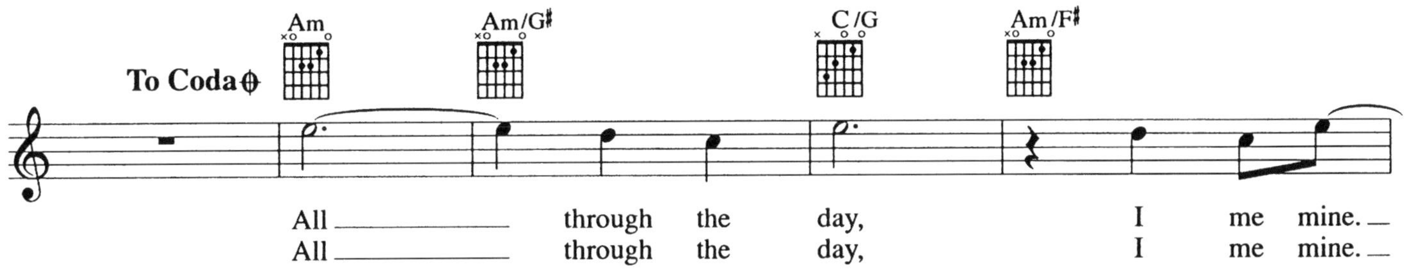
To Coda
Am
Am/G♯
C/G
Am/F♯
All through the day, I me mine.
All through the day, I me mine.

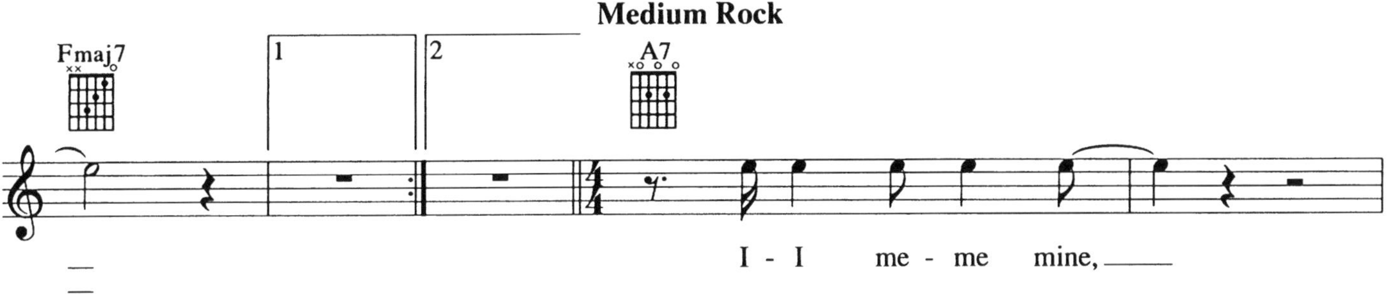
Medium Rock
Fmaj7
1
2
A7
I - I me - me mine,

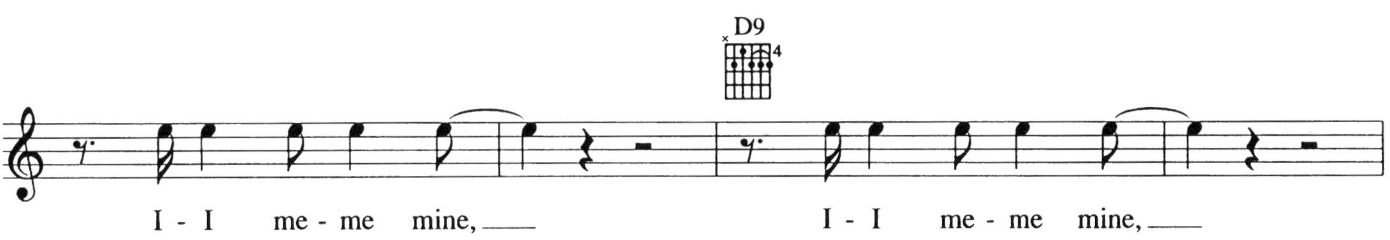
D9
I - I me - me mine,
I - I me - me mine,

A7
D.C. al Coda
Coda
Am
Am/G♯
I - I me - me mine.
All through your

C/G
Am/F♯
Fmaj7
life, I me mine.

I've Got A Feeling.

Words & Music by John Lennon & Paul McCartney.

Moderately
G
C/G
1. I've got a feel - ing, a feel - ing deep in - side
2. Oh, please be - lieve me, I'd hate to miss the train,
3. I've got a feel - ing, that keeps me on my toes,
oh yeah, oh, yeah. (Spoken) That's right
oh yeah, yeah, oh, yeah.
oh yeah, oh, yeah.
I've got a feel - ing, a feel - ing I can't hide,
And if you leave me I won't be late a - gain,
I've got a feel - ing, I think that ev - 'ry - bod - y knows,
oh, no, no, oh, no,
oh, no, oh, no,
oh, yeah, oh, yeah,

C/G
G7
D
F
Oh, no.
Oh, no,
Oh, yeah.
Yeah,
yeah,

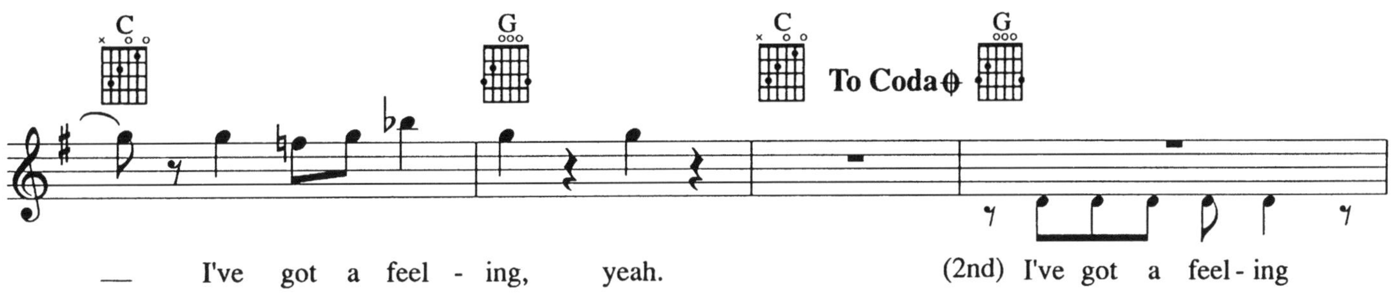
C
G
C
To Coda
G
I've got a feel - ing, yeah.
(2nd) I've got a feel - ing

1
C
2
C
D7
Yeah,
All these years I've been wan - der - in' a - round;

F7
C
Won - der - in' how come no - bod - y told me
All I have been look - in' for was

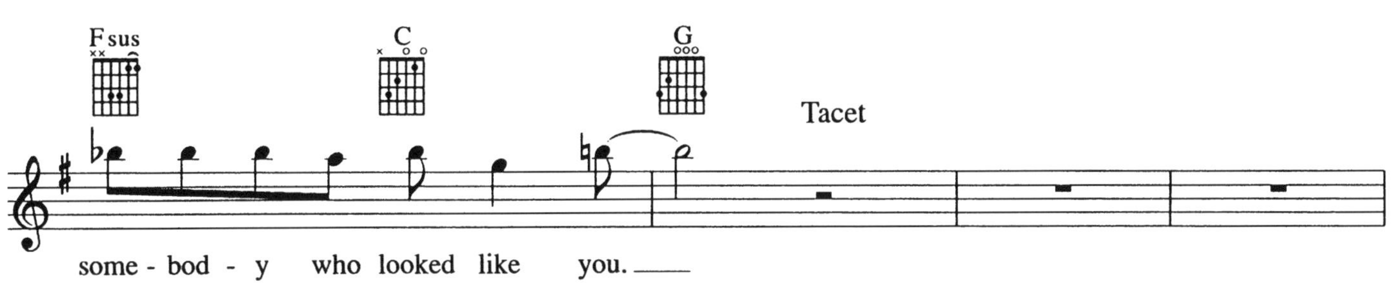
Fsus
C
G
Tacet
some - bod - y who looked like you.

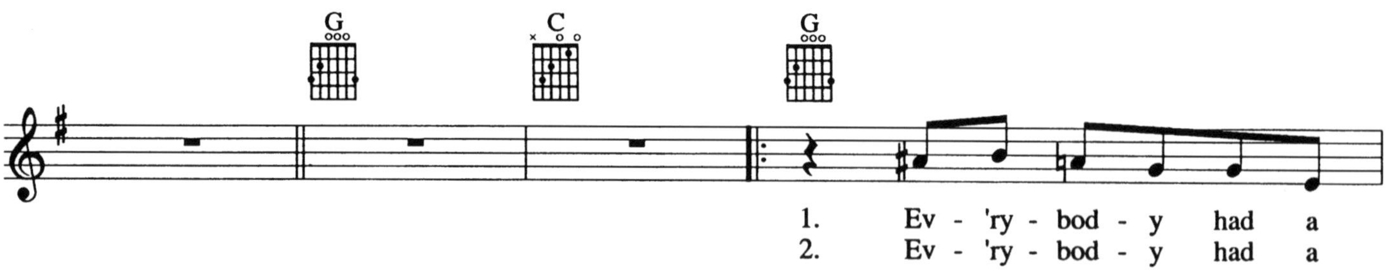
G
C
G
1. Ev - 'ry - bod - y had a
2. Ev - 'ry - bod - y had a

C
G
C
hard year, Ev - 'ry - bod - y had a good time,
good year, Ev - 'ry - bod - y let their hair down,

G
C
G
Ev - 'ry - bod - y had a wet dream, Ev - 'ry - bod - y saw the
Ev - 'ry - bod - y pulled their socks up, Ev - 'ry - bod - y put their

C
1
G
C
sun shine, Oh, yeah (oh, yeah,) oh, yeah, oh yeah.
foot down, Oh, yeah

G
C
2
G7
F♯7/G
F7/G
G

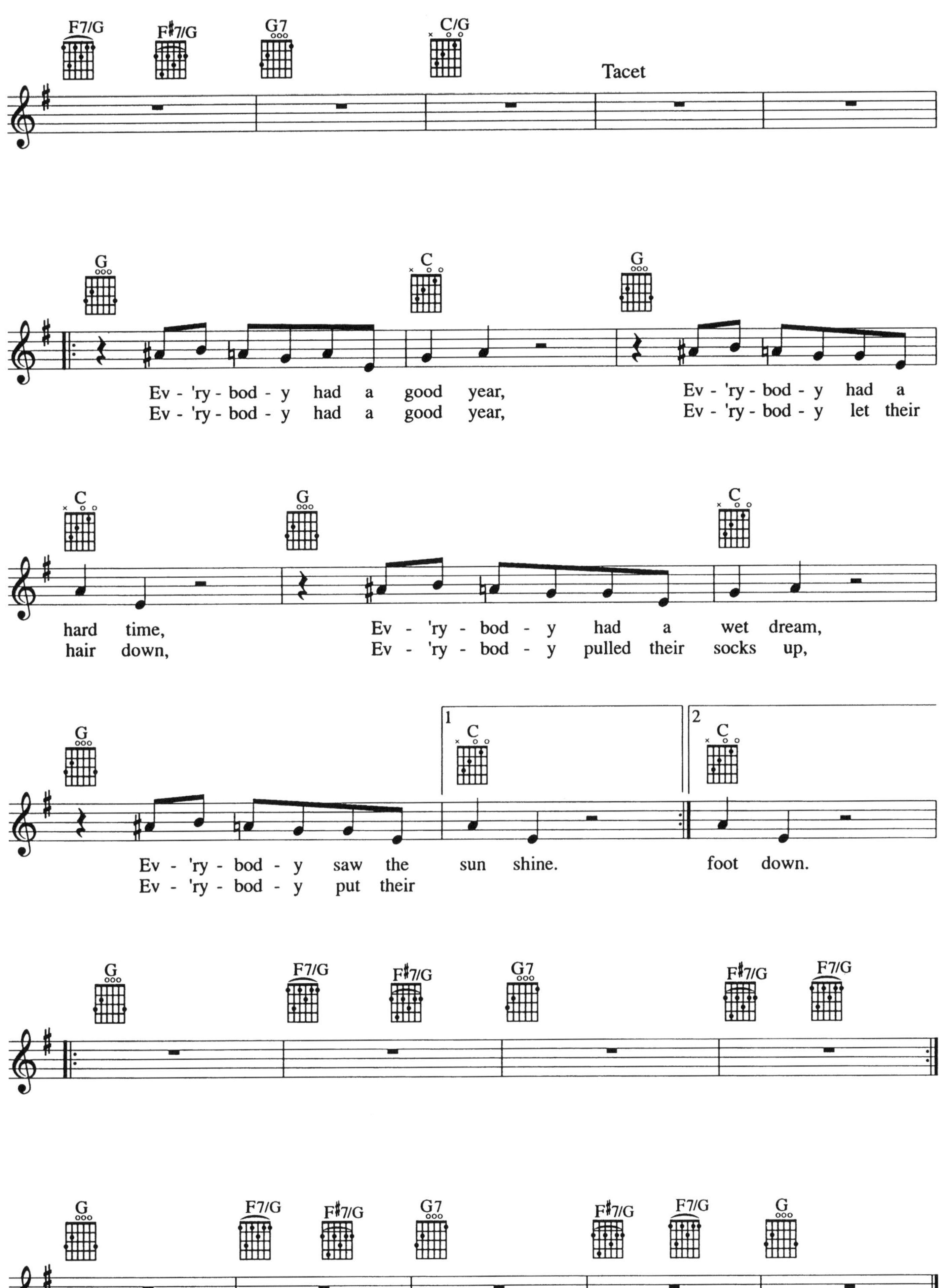
F7/G
F♯7/G
G7
C/G
Tacet
G
C
Ev - 'ry - bod - y had a good year,
Ev - 'ry - bod - y had a good year,
Ev - 'ry - bod - y had a
Ev - 'ry - bod - y let their
hard time,
hair down,
Ev - 'ry - bod - y had a wet dream,
Ev - 'ry - bod - y pulled their socks up,
Ev - 'ry - bod - y saw the sun shine.
Ev - 'ry - bod - y put their
foot down.
1
2

Let It Be.

Words & Music by John Lennon & Paul McCartney.

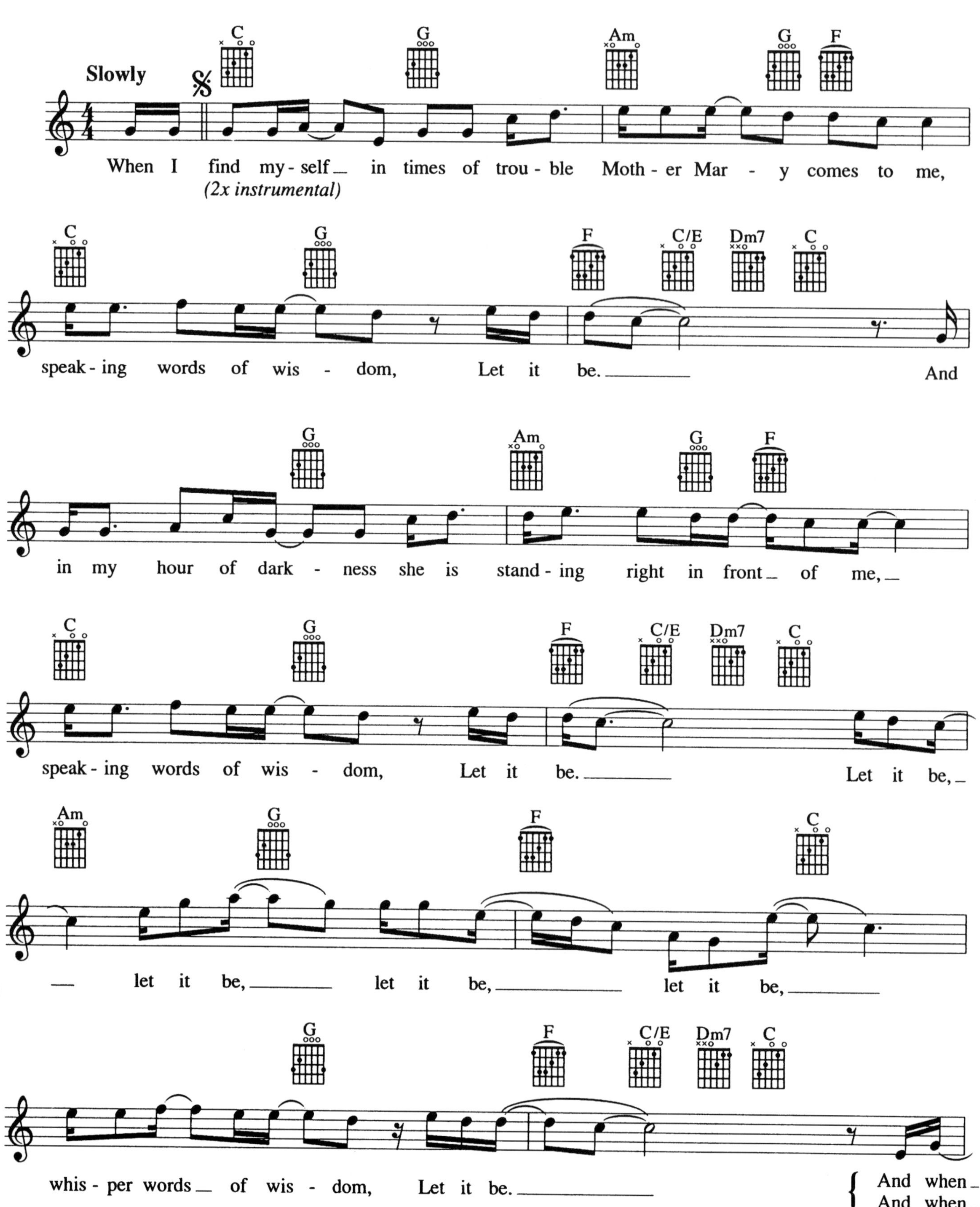
Slowly
C G Am G F
When I find my-self in times of trou-ble Moth-er Mar-y comes to me,
(2x instrumental)
C G F C/E Dm7 C
speak-ing words of wis-dom, Let it be. And
G Am G F
in my hour of dark-ness she is stand-ing right in front of me,
C G F C/E Dm7 C
speak-ing words of wis-dom, Let it be. Let it be,
Am G F C
let it be, let it be, let it be,
G F C/E Dm7 C
whis-per words of wis-dom, Let it be.
And when
And when

G
Am
G
F
— the bro - ken heart - ed peo - ple liv - ing in — the world a - gree
— the night — is cloud - y there is still a light — that shines on me
C
G
F
C/E
Dm7
C
There will be an an - swer. Let it be. — For
Shine un - til to - mor - row. Let it be. — I
G
Am
G
F
though they may be part - ed, there is still a chance that they — will see —
wake up to the sound — of mu - sic Moth - er Mar - y comes — to me —
C
G
F
C/E
Dm7
C
There will be an an - swer, Let it be. —
Speak - ing words of wis - dom, Let it be. —
Let it be, —
Am
G
F
C
— let it be, — let it be, — let it be, —
G
F
C/E
Dm7
C
G
There will be — an an - swer, Let it be. — Let it be, —

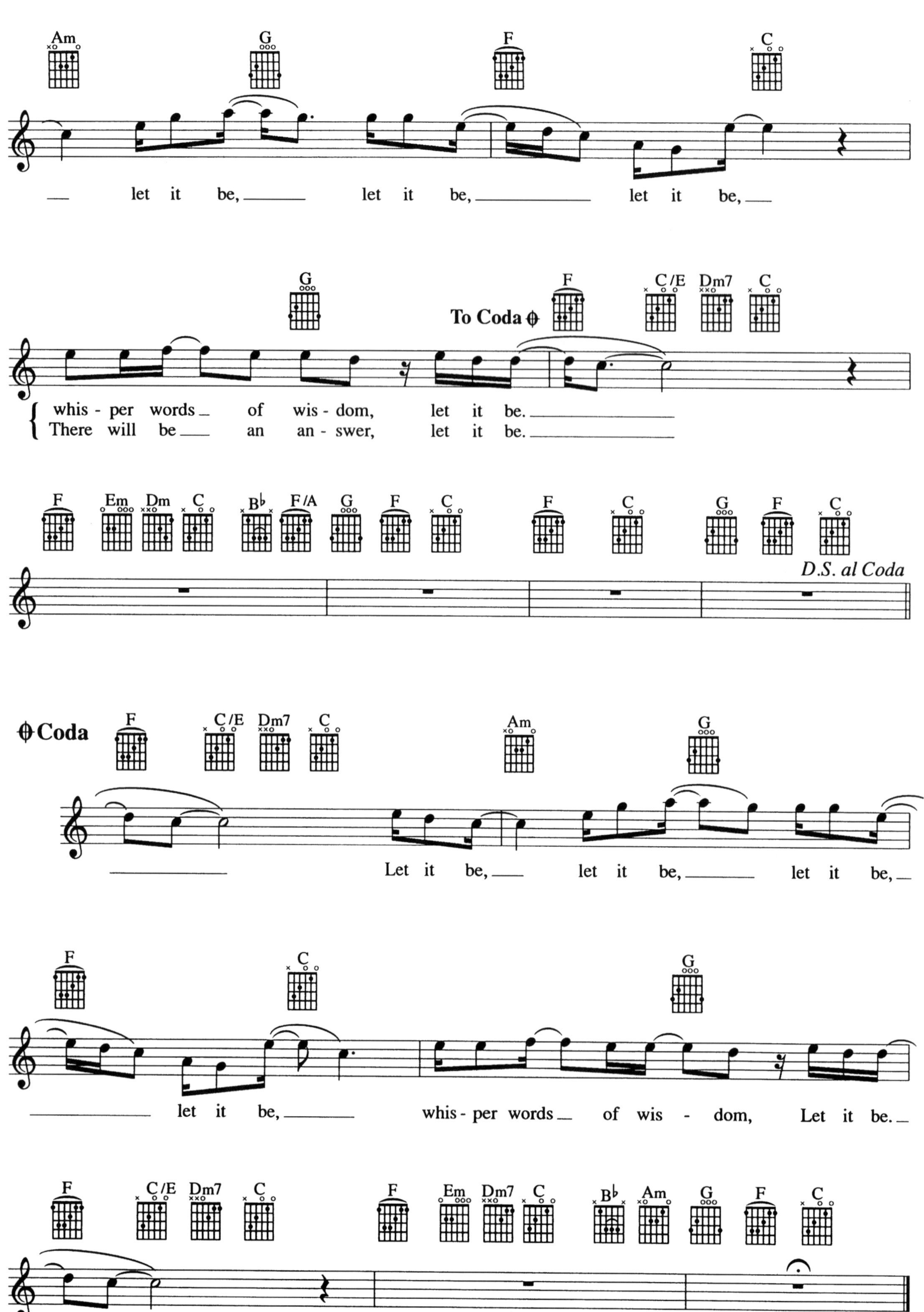
Am G F C
let it be, let it be, let it be,
G To Coda F C/E Dm7 C
whis - per words of wis - dom, let it be.
There will be an an - swer, let it be.
F Em Dm C B♭ F/A G F C F C G F C
D.S. al Coda
Coda F C/E Dm7 C Am G
Let it be, let it be, let it be,
F C G
let it be, whis - per words of wis - dom, Let it be.
F C/E Dm7 C F Em Dm7 C B♭ Am G F C

All You Need Is Love.

Words & Music by John Lennon & Paul McCartney.

Moderately

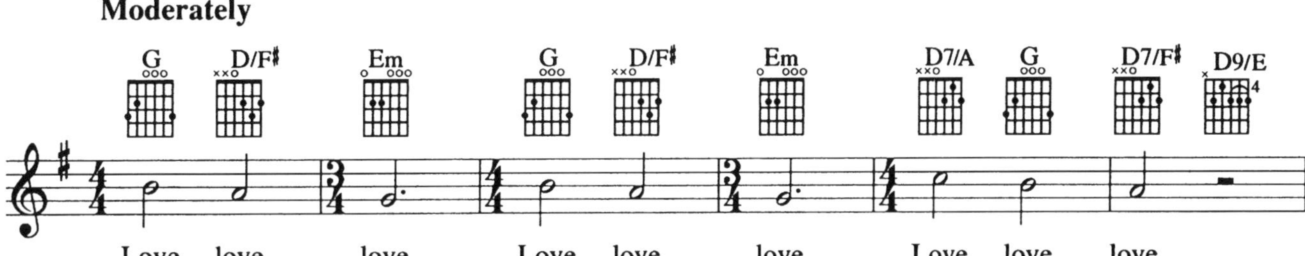
G
D/F♯
Em
G
D/F♯
Em
D7/A
G
D7/F♯
D9/E
Love love love. Love love love. Love love love.

D7
D7/C
D7/B
G
D/F♯
1. There's no-thing you can do that can't be done.
2. There's no-thing you can make that can't be made.
3. There's no-thing you can know that is-n't known.

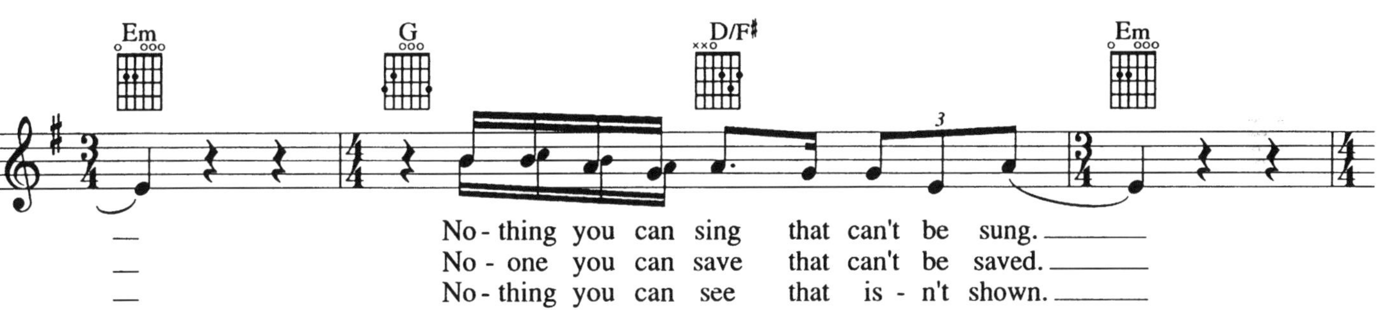
Em
G
D/F♯
Em
No-thing you can sing that can't be sung.
No-one you can save that can't be saved.
No-thing you can see that is-n't shown.

D7/A
G
D/F♯
D7/E
No-thing you can say but you can learn how to play the game.
No-thing you can do but you can learn how to be you in time.
No-where you can be that is-n't where you're meant to be.
It's

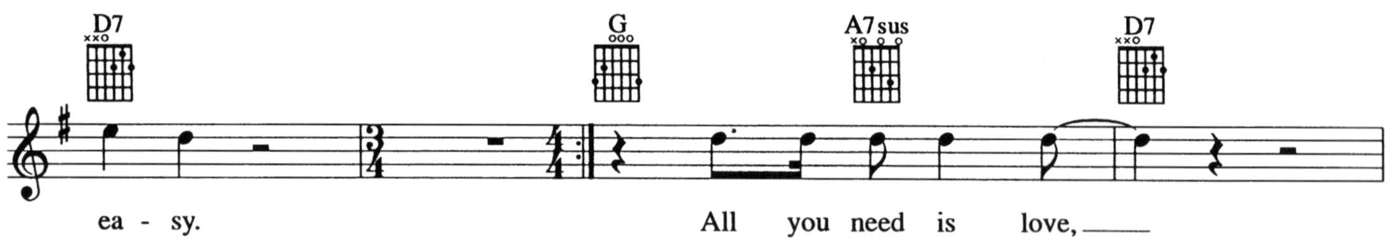
D7
G
A7sus
D7
ea - sy.
All you need is love,

G
A7sus
D7
G
B7
Em
G/D
All you need is love;
All you need is love,
love.

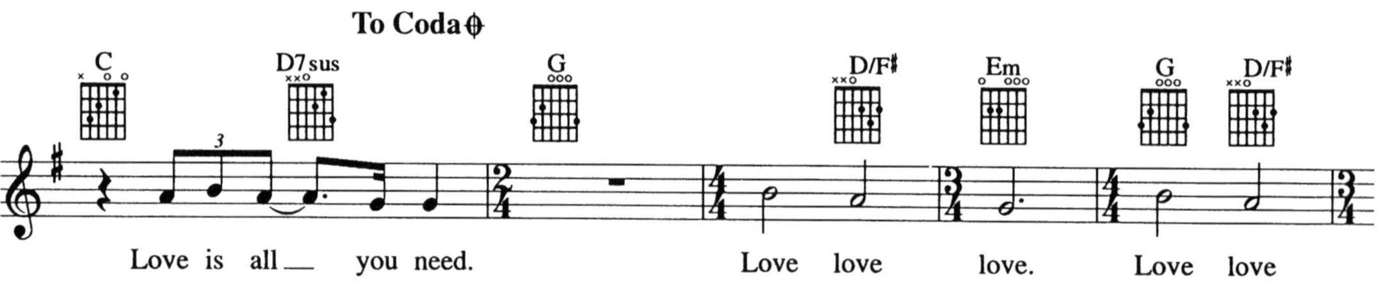
To Coda
C
D7sus
G
D/F♯
Em
G
D/F♯
3
Love is all you need.
Love love
love.
Love love

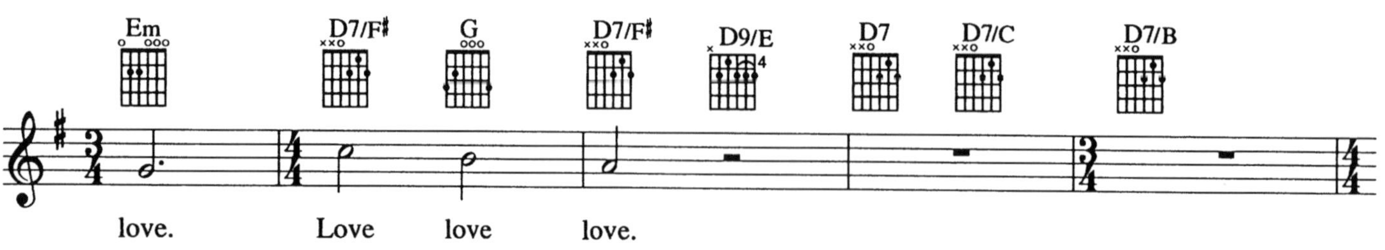
Em
D7/F♯
G
D7/F♯
D9/E
D7
D7/C
D7/B
love.
Love love
love.

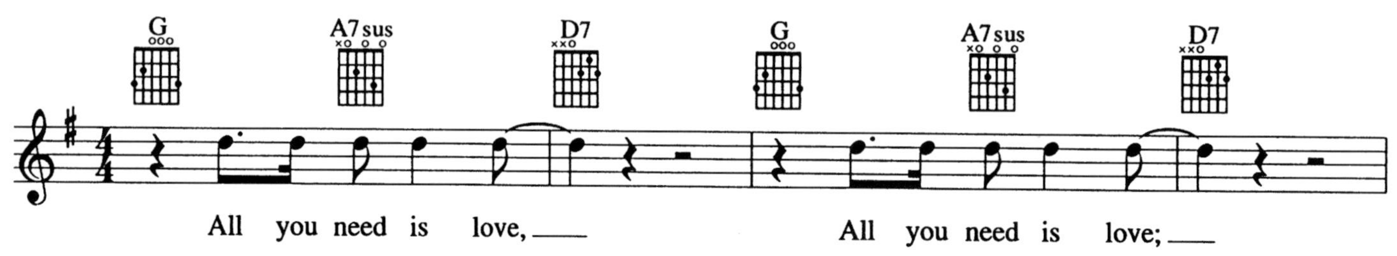
G
A7sus
D7
G
A7sus
D7
All you need is love,
All you need is love;

G
B7
Em
G/D
C
D7sus
All you need is love, love. Love is all you need.

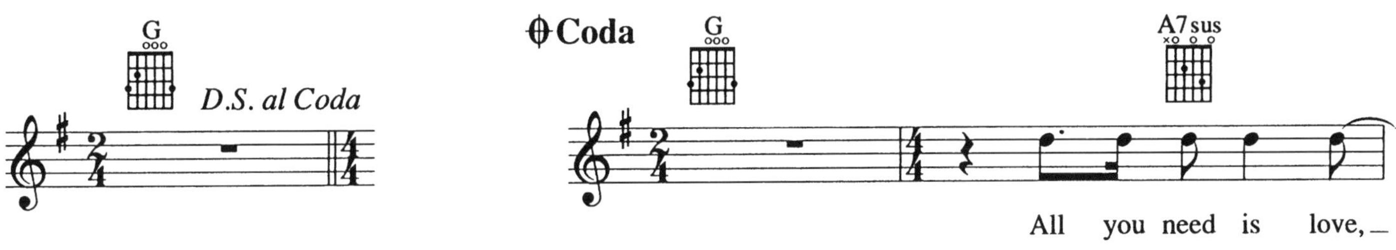
G
D.S. al Coda
Coda
G
A7sus
All you need is love,

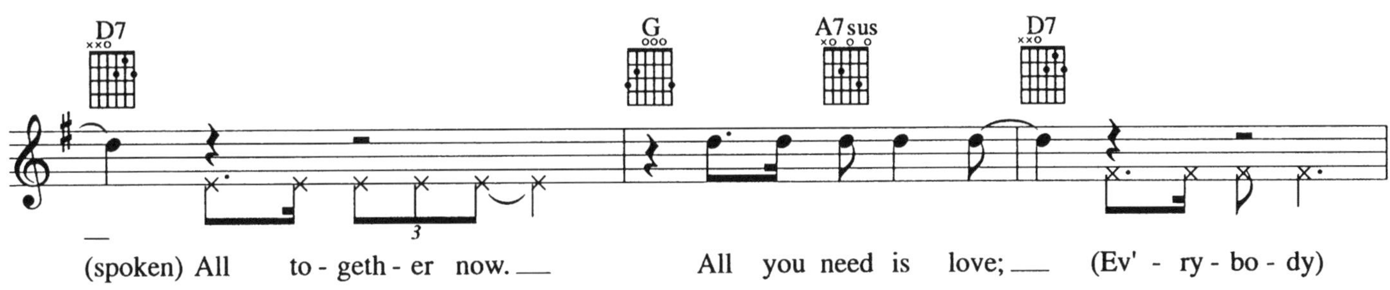
D7
G
A7sus
D7
(spoken) All to - geth - er now. All you need is love; (Ev' - ry - bo - dy)

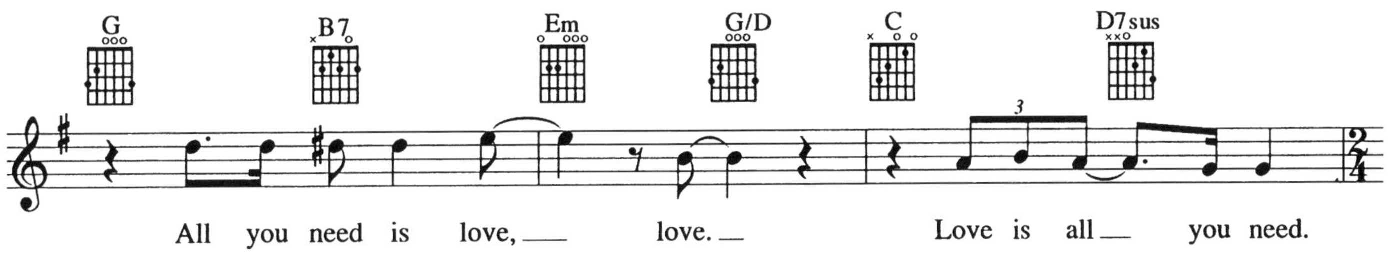
G
B7
Em
G/D
C
D7sus
All you need is love, love. Love is all you need.

G
D7
G
D11
D7
Love is all you need Love is all
(Love is all you need)

One After 909.

Words & Music by John Lennon & Paul McCartney.

Bright rock tempo
C
My ba - by said she's trav - 'llin' on the one af - ter Nine - o - Nine.
(2) begged her not to go, and I begged her on my bend - ed knees.
(3) She said she's trav - 'llin' on the one af - ter Nine - o - Nine.
C7
C
I said "Move o - ver, hon - ey, I'm
"You're on - ly fool - in' round, you're
I said "Move o - ver, hon - ey, I'm
C7
trav - el - lin' on that line."
on - ly fool - in' round with me."
trav - el - lin' on that line."
I said
C7
Tacet
C7
Tacet
F7
"Move ov - er." once,
"Move ov - er." twice,
"Come on, ba - by, don't be
C
To Coda
G7
G+
cold as ice!"
She said she's trav - 'llin' on the one af - ter Nine - o - Nine.

C7
1
2
F7
2. I
I've got my bag,
C7
D7
Run to the sta - tion. Rail - man says, "you got the
G7
F7
C7
wrong lo - ca - tion." I've got my bag, Run right home;
D7
G7
Then I find ___ I've got the num - ber wrong.
G7+
D.S. al Coda
(3) Well,
Coda
G7
C7
one af - ter Nine - o, She said she's trav - 'llin' on the
G7
C7
one af - ter Nine - o, She said she's trav - 'llin' on the
G7
C7
F
A♭7
C
C7
one af - ter Nine - o - Nine. ___

The Ballad Of John And Yoko.

Words & Music by John Lennon & Paul McCartney.

Rock Tempo
E♭
1. Stand - ing in the dock at South - amp - ton,
2. Final - ly made the plane in - to Pa - ris,
3. Pa - ris to the Am - ster - dam Hil - ton,
4. Made a light - ning trip to Vi - en - na,
5. Caught the ear - ly plane back to Lon - don,
trying to get to Hol - land or France. The
hon - ey - moon - ing down by the Seine. Pe - ter
talk - ing in our beds for a week. The
eat - ing choc' - late cake in a bag. The
fif - ty a - corns tied in a sack. The
E♭7
man in the mac said "You've got to go back;" you know they
Brown called to say "you can make it O. K; you can get
news - peo - ple said, "Say, what're you do - ing in bed?" I said, "We're
news - pa - pers said, "She's gone to his head; They
men from the press said "We wish you suc - cess It's
did - n't ev - en give us a chance.
mar - ried in Gib - ral - tar near Spain.
on - ly trying to get us some peace."
look just like two Gu - rus in drag."
good to have the both of you back."
Christ! you know it ain't eas -
A♭
E♭
- y, you know how hard it can be;
B♭7
To Coda
The way things are go - ing they're gon - na cru - ci - fy

E♭
1, 4
2
3
me.
3. Drove from
A♭
Sav-ing up your mon-ey for a rain - y day,
giv-ing all your clothes to char-i-
- ty.
Last night the wife said, "Oh boy, when you're dead you
B♭7
D.C. (with repeat)
al Coda
don't take noth-ing with you but your soul."
Think!
Coda
E♭
B♭7
me.
The way things are go - ing
they're gon - na cru - ci - fy
E♭
me.
B♭
E♭
E♭6

The Long And Winding Road.

WORDS & MUSIC BY JOHN LENNON & PAUL McCARTNEY.

Slowly

Cm Gm A♭/B♭

The long and wind - ing road ___ that ___ leads ___
wild and wind - y night ___ that the rain

E♭ E♭/D♭ A♭ E♭/G

— to your door ___ will nev - er dis - ap -
— washed a - way ___ has left a pool of

Cm7 Fm7 B♭7 E♭7sus E♭7

- pear. I've seen that road be - fore. ___
tears. Cry - ing for the day. ___

A♭ E♭/G Cm Cm7 Fm7 B♭7

It al - ways leads ___ me here. Lead me to your ___
Why leave me stand - ing here? Let me know the ___

1 E♭ 2 E♭ E♭/B♭ A♭

door. The way Man - y times ___ I've been a - lone ___ and

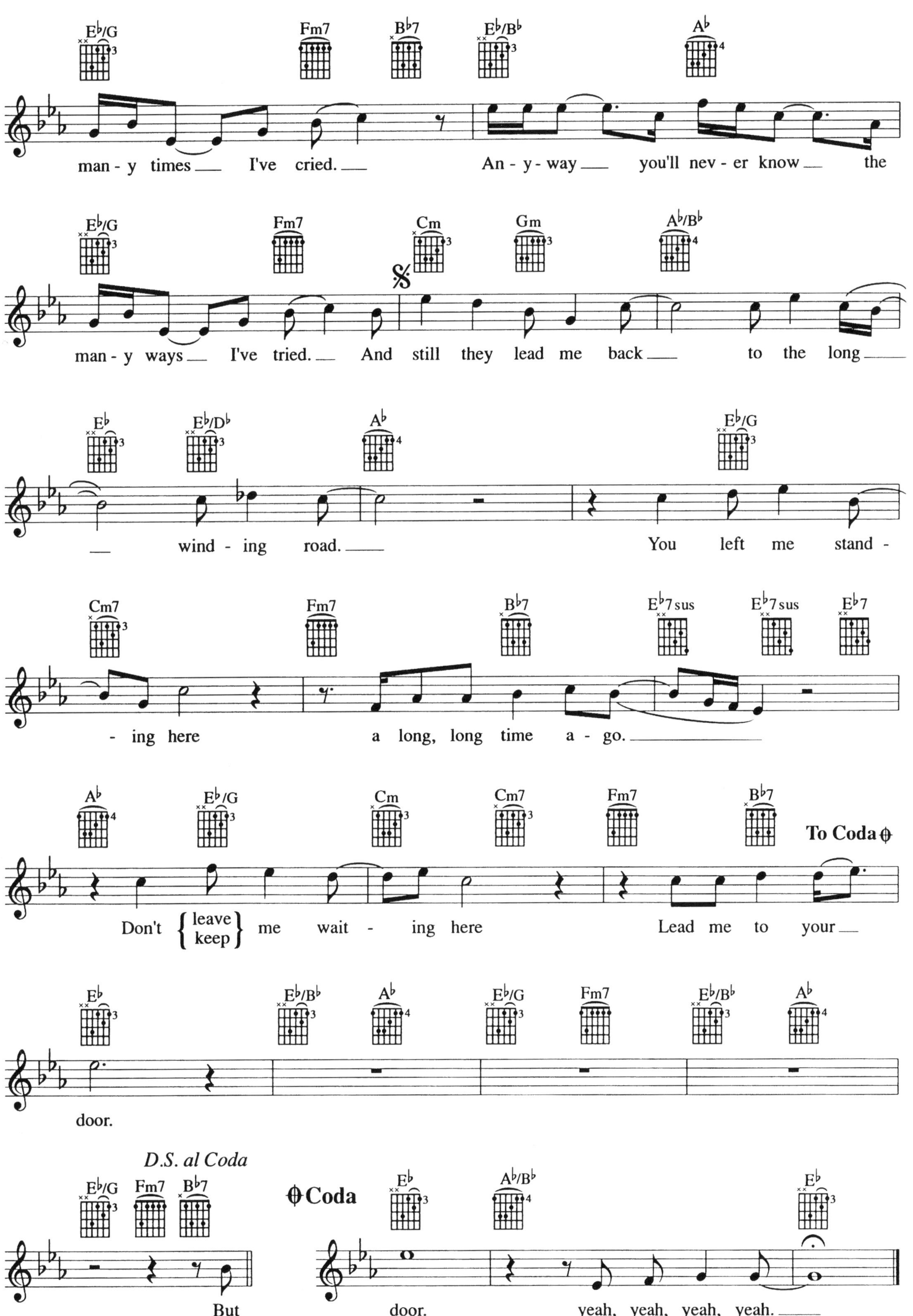
E♭/G Fm7 B♭7 E♭/B♭ A♭
man - y times I've cried. An - y - way you'll nev - er know the
E♭/G Fm7 Cm Gm A♭/B♭
man - y ways I've tried. And still they lead me back to the long
E♭ E♭/D♭ A♭ E♭/G
wind - ing road. You left me stand -
Cm7 Fm7 B♭7 E♭7sus E♭7sus E♭7
- ing here a long, long time a - go.
A♭ E♭/G Cm Cm7 Fm7 B♭7
To Coda
Don't leave keep me wait - ing here Lead me to your
E♭ E♭/B♭ A♭ E♭/G Fm7 E♭/B♭ A♭
door.
D.S. al Coda
E♭/G Fm7 B♭7
But
Coda
E♭ A♭/B♭ E♭
door. yeah, yeah, yeah, yeah.

You Know My Name (Look Up The Number).

Words & Music by John Lennon & Paul McCartney.

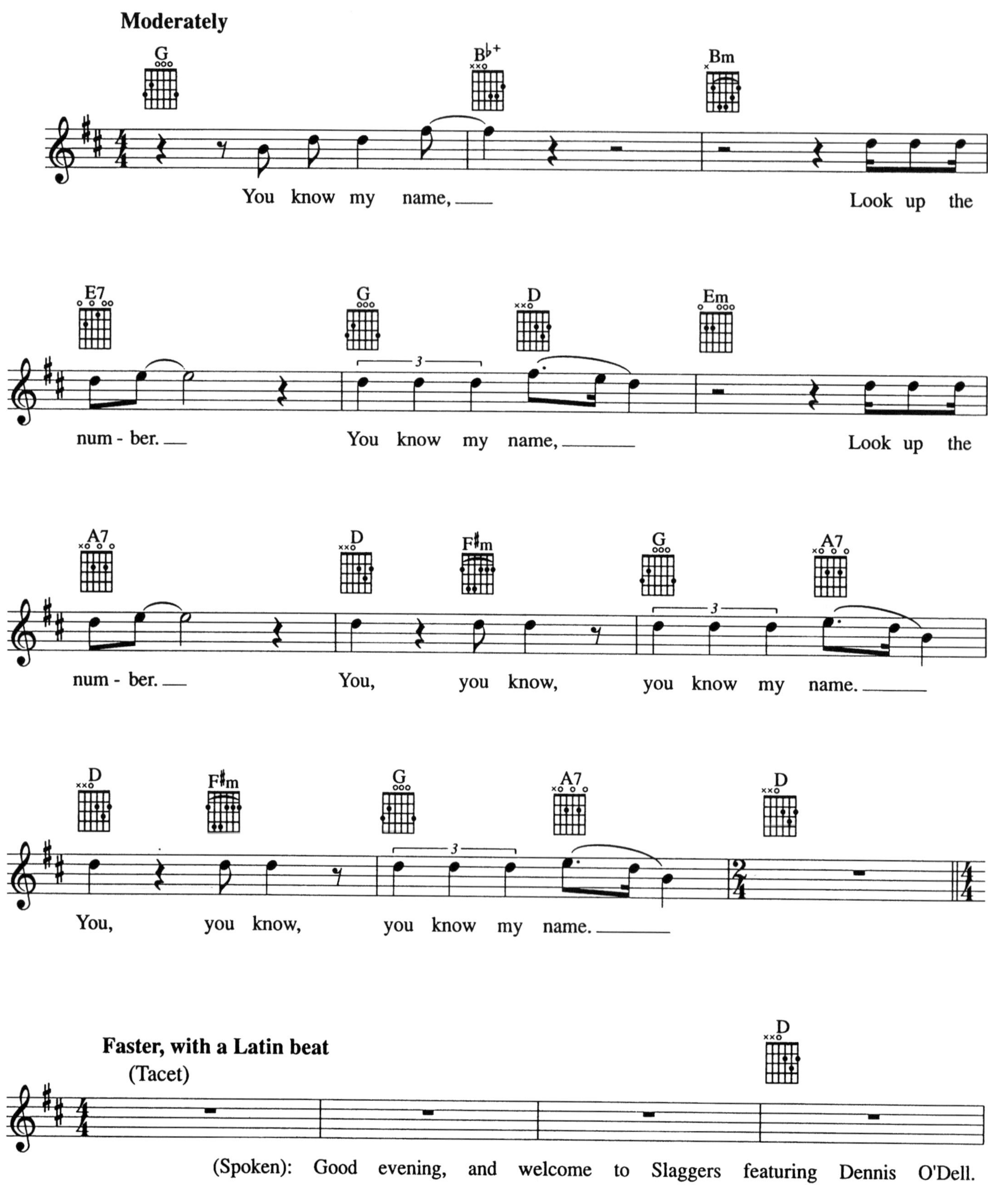
Moderately
G
B♭+
Bm
You know my name,
Look up the
E7
G
D
Em
num - ber.
You know my name,
Look up the
A7
D
F♯m
G
A7
num - ber.
You, you know, you know my name.
D
F♯m
G
A7
D
You, you know, you know my name.
Faster, with a Latin beat
(Tacet)
D
(Spoken): Good evening, and welcome to Slaggers featuring Dennis O'Dell.

Repeat 3 times, using effeminate voices on 2nd & 3rd repeats
A7
D
A7
G
Come on, Ringo,
Let's hear it for Dennis.
Good evening.
(Sing) You know my name,

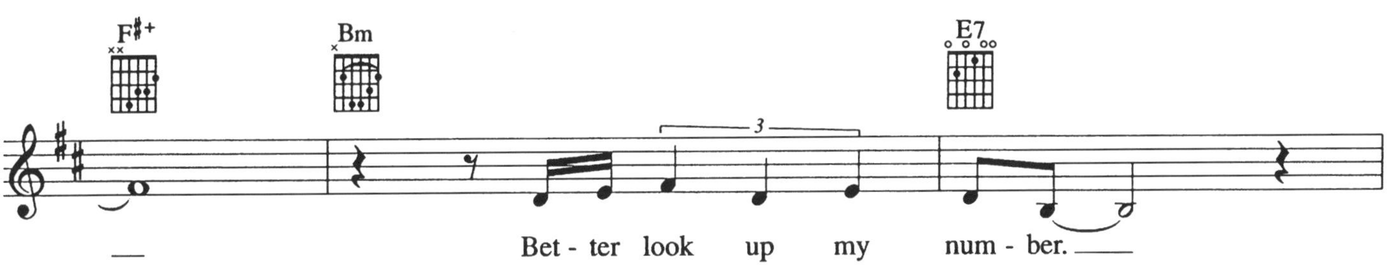
F#+
Bm
E7
3
Bet - ter look up my num - ber.

G
D
Em
A7
3
You know my name,
(That's right) Look up my num - ber.

D
G
A
D
You, you know, you know my name. you, you know,

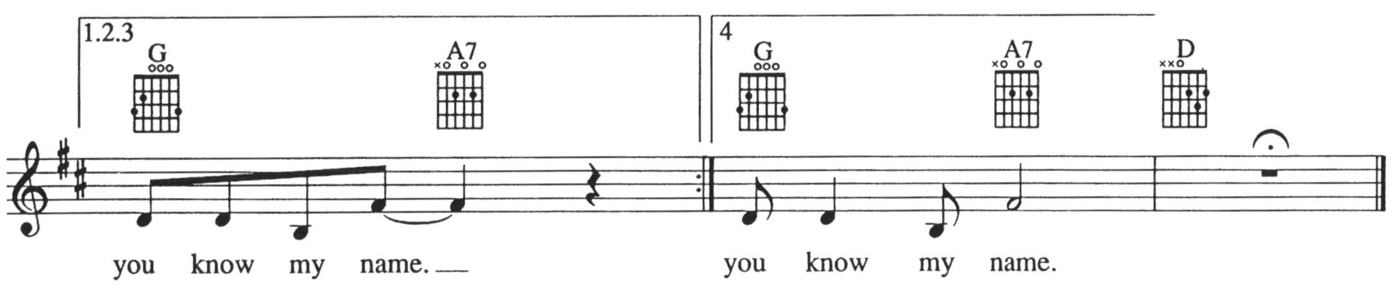
1.2.3
G
A7
4
G
A7
D
you know my name.
you know my name.

Maggie Mae.

ARRANGED BY JOHN LENNON, PAUL McCARTNEY, GEORGE HARRISON & RICHARD STARKEY.

Steady 2 beat
G C
Oh, dir - ty Mag - gie Mae they have
G
tak - en her a - way and she'll nev - er walk down Lisle Street an - y -
D G
- mow - er. Oh, the judge he guilt - y found her of
C D7
rob - bing the home - ward bound - er; that dir - ty, no good
G C
rob - bin' Mag - gie Mae It's the part of Liv - er - pool
G
she re - turned me to Two pounds ten a week,
C G/B D
that was my pay.

6/10 (174536)